ENGLISH LITERATURE:
Four Representative Types

Peter Waranoff

ACADEMIC CHAIRMAN
NEW YORK CITY SCHOOL SYSTEM

Norman Adler

NEW YORK CITY SCHOOL SYSTEM

GLOBE BOOK COMPANY, New York 10010

... CONTENTS

... INTRODUCTION

In Shakespeare's *Hamlet*, the title character defines the purpose
of a play as "to hold, as 'twere, the mirror up to nature." The
definition might apply with equal force to other types of literature. For all types present reflections of life. Whether the materials are of the imagination, as with the novel and the play, or
are bound in varying degrees to literal fact, as with biography
and commentary, literature shows us life in its possibilities as
well as in actuality.

This volume contains four representative types of English
literature: the novel, drama, biography, and personal narrative.
Each mirrors a different view of life in a manner made possible
by its type.

There is no limit to the kinds of things that might be said
in each type. Depending on the bias of the author, the view may
be tragic, satiric, heroic, or lightly humorous, and the subject
may be anything at all. What is important is that the reader be
quickened into a more intense awareness of a part of existence
than he had before.

The books in this volume do just that: they quicken our
awareness by holding their individual "mirrors up to nature."
The tragic mirror happens to be incorporated in the novel, the
satiric in the play, the heroic in the biography, and the lightly
humorous in the personal commentary. If other titles had been
chosen, each view might have been expressed in another literary
type. So rich and varied is the storehouse of English literature
that each type provides an abundance of its own.

The Novel

The English novel is often said to date back to 1740. This is
the year an imaginative printer named Samuel Richardson pub-

lished a series of model letters for study and imitation by young ladies. In those days before telephone and easy transportation, letter-writing was as much a part of a well-bred young lady's education as good manners. Richardson's special contribution was to tell a continuing story from one letter to the next. So intriguing were his incidents and characterizations that soon the letters of *Pamela*, as both the heroine and the volume were called, were read more for their story than for the writing skills they presumed to teach.

The popularity of *Pamela* inspired imitations, and even a parody. An early work of Henry Fielding is *Joseph Andrews*, a humorous re-telling of Richardson's story with a male hero. One of Fielding's contributions was to abandon the letter form for various other styles. In *Tom Jones*, his greatest novel, he used straight descriptive narrative, the interpolated essay, omniscient revelations of what his characters are thinking—indeed, whatever at any point might suit his story's purpose.

Fielding demonstrated in *Tom Jones* that freedom of style can be matched by even greater freedom of subject matter and tone. His hero is a roguish young man whose wild adventures in eighteenth-century England, in both town and country, provide an enormously entertaining picture of that time. In the course of the book many different notes are sounded: there are joy, pathos, comedy both gentle and ribald, and reflection alternating with rollicking action. Fielding indeed proved that the author of a novel may move in space and time, outside and inside his characters, and from mood to mood as he can in no other literary form.

Yet, a novel is more than a long succession of fictitious episodes with a degree of variety. To be truly a novel, a story must have a plot, a more or less logical building of incident toward some particular end. The main characters, at least, should evidence development. At the conclusion they should be changed persons, having surmounted or succumbed in significant ways to the trials of the plot. By these standards, most critics would hesitate to classify as authentic novels such lengthy pre-Richardson narratives as Bunyan's *A Pilgrim's Progress*, Defoe's *Robinson Crusoe*, and Swift's *Gulliver's Travels*.

The English novel, thus beginning in the middle of the eighteenth century, developed through the years into the most popular of all literary forms. Its outstanding creators have had enormous audiences. Following Richardson and Fielding in the eighteenth century, Tobias Smollett and Laurence Sterne had avid followings. In the nineteenth century, the names of Jane Austen, Sir Walter Scott, Charles Dickens, William Makepeace Thackeray, George Eliot, and Thomas Hardy all ranked high. In the transition between the nineteenth and the twentieth centuries, there were Rudyard Kipling, Joseph Conrad, H. G. Wells, and Arnold Bennett; and in the twentieth century, James Joyce, D. H. Lawrence, W. Somerset Maugham, E. M. Forster, Joyce Cary, Evelyn Waugh, Aldous Huxley, George Orwell, C. P. Snow, and many others stand out.

The Mayor of Casterbridge by Thomas Hardy, the novel selection in this volume, is one of the great tragic novels in English literature. A product of the latter part of the nineteenth century, when the novel was already a mature craft, it is a finished work of art. Its theme is universal: a man of strong character, but with a fatal fault, struggles manfully with his destiny. He may be defeated in the end, but, through his struggle, he achieves a kind of greatness. The other characters, both major and minor, are skillfully drawn; the incidents are unusual and intriguing, and a vivid sense of time and place informs the background. Altogether, *The Mayor of Casterbridge* is a fine representative of its type.

The Play

"The play's the thing wherein I'll catch the conscience of the King," cries Hamlet. Not only do plays "mirror" our existence, but they also appeal to our conscience. Perhaps not all—some merely entertain, providing a few hours' escape from the cares of the world—but the most memorable plays, and those most in the current of the English tradition, stir our moral sense.

The first English plays developed in late medieval times and were called *mystery* and *miracle* plays, after the Bible stories they re-created. Although presented in the open air in city streets on movable wagons serving as stages, they were edifying religious spectacles. Equally instructive in Christian values were the later *morality* plays. These were allegories of man's temptation and fall, and his redemption through faith and good works. The most famous morality play is *Everyman*, wherein the hero is battleground for the struggle between the personified virtues and vices for man's soul.

The coming of age of English drama took place in the late sixteenth and early seventeenth centuries. Although the theater then was largely secular, concerned with romantic love, ambition, historical adventure, and other worldly themes, it was not lacking in moral ballast. Its outstanding practitioner was William Shakespeare, whose most admired plays, *Hamlet, Othello, King Lear, Macbeth, Twelfth Night*, and *The Tempest*, are all set in a universe of right versus wrong. Shakespeare's characters, for all their poetic qualities and primitive grandeur, are enhanced by their moral concerns. Even the magnificent blank-verse language has added impact for its ethical reverberations.

Two other great playwrights of this period are Christopher Marlowe, whose poetic *Doctor Faustus* is a non-Christian morality play on the Faust legend, and Ben Jonson, whose satiric comedies chastise human nature and lampoon the follies of his own era.

The plays of the Restoration and post-Restoration periods (roughly the late seventeenth and early eighteenth centuries), while "naughty" by Puritan standards, pay lip service to the virtues as they mock the vices. William Congreve, George Farquhar, William Wycherley, and, later, Richard Brinsley Sheridan, present witty pictures of a wicked age, and, though the wickedness provides most of the laughs, conscience is invariably appeased at the end.

The middle of the eighteenth to the middle of the nineteenth centuries was a rather poor period for playwrights. Evidently, Restoration license had gone too far and theater managers scurried to put on harmless sentimental comedies, grandiose but conventional tragedies, and watered-down Shakespeare. The best to come out of this period are Oliver Goldsmith's proper comedy

She Stoops to Conquer, and John Dryden's re-telling of the Antony and Cleopatra story, without Shakespeare's candor, in the all-too-formal *All For Love.*

It was not until the end of the nineteenth century that liveliness and creativity came back to the theater. For pure verbal wit and mastery of epigram, the plays of Oscar Wilde are highly amusing. And while the morals may be seemingly tacked onto the proceedings, they are there nevertheless. However, it was Wilde's contemporary and, by virtue of long life, the contemporary of all playwrights of the first half of the twentieth century as well, George Bernard Shaw, who genuinely married wit to moral earnestness in writing the finest English plays since Shakespeare. Although John Galsworthy, Sir James Barrie, Noel Coward, Terence Rattigan, and John Osborne are all estimable playwrights of our epoch, they are dwarfed by the figure of the great Shaw.

It is Shaw's brilliant comedy *Pygmalion* that is the play selection in this volume. In this play, Shaw holds up his characteristic mirror of satire to deliver a social and human preachment. Through the amusing story of the cockney flower girl transformed by lessons in speech and manners into a fine lady, Shaw pierces the flimsiness and artificiality of class distinctions. He also subjects to gentle ridicule the arrogance of the male ego that sees its handiwork as more important than the human ends it should properly serve. These, and other appeals to our "conscience," are all conveyed in one of the most charming and humorous tales ever to appear in dramatic literature.

The Biography

Full-scale English biographies did not appear until the end of the eighteenth century with the publication of James Boswell's *Life of Samuel Johnson.* But interest in the lives of great and prominent men existed long before then, as evidenced by the popularity of the sixteenth-century translation of Plutarch's *Lives* by Thomas North. The century that followed saw the publication of a *Sketch of Thomas More* by his son-in-law,

William Roper. Not long afterward appeared *Brief Lives* by Izaak Walton, *Life of Mrs. Godolphin* by John Evelyn, and *Worthies of England* by Thomas Fuller. Although by modern standards not more than brief sketches, all of these works testify to the strong early interest in biographical writing.

It is interesting to speculate on the source of this interest. From what in human nature did it spring? Perhaps the answer lies in so simple a thing as man's curiosity about his fellow man. We all want to know what the next fellow does and says, what is done and said to him, and, if possible, what he is thinking about at the time. If we can discover why everything happens the way it does, so much the better. The impulse is not unrelated to the almost universal craving for gossip.

But gossip is usually concerned with the trivial, and good biography never is. The person written about in a biography should be of some significance. He may or may not be well known, but he should be a person well worth knowing. His experiences may affect the lives of nations, or they may be of direct consequence only to himself and a few other people. But they should have value, and the value should be perceived and appreciated by the reader.

James Boswell's *Life of Samuel Johnson*, the first massive, well-documented English biography, has as its subject a man of considerable significance. Johnson was not only a great pioneer lexicographer, but a writer, brilliant conversationalist, and, by the force of his strongly uttered opinions, a literary dictator who was admired and feared by his contemporaries. In the biography, Boswell reveals the full humanity of the man, noting his personal idiosyncrasies and foibles as well as his accomplishments. As a close friend who was present when many of the recorded incidents occurred, he transcribed the very words and tones of Johnson's conversations. The result is a work of rich entertainment and scholarship, unmatched in the history of English biography.

Johnson himself wrote a number of biographies, none either as ambitious or as successful as the one written about him. Perhaps the best is *The Life of Richard Savage*, a sympathetic account of the wretched life of a hack writer.

The next century witnessed a vogue for the lengthy, re-searched biography introduced by Boswell. Two typical ex-amples from this period are Robert Southey's *Life of Lord Nelson* and Elizabeth Gaskell's *Life of Charlotte Brontë*. As the century wore on, the dominant spirit in most English biographies became more and more adulatory. In reaction to this, Lytton Strachey, in the early twentieth century, wrote a biography of *Queen Victoria* and sketches of other *Eminent Victorians* that brought a refreshing skepticism to the genre. In Strachey's wake, and borrowing some of his light, have followed many other outstanding biographers, including Philip Guedalla, Harold Nicolson, Peter Quennel, C. Woodham Smith, A. L. Rowse, and Robert Payne.

Robert Payne's *The Gold of Troy*, the biography selection in this volume, is an absorbing modern account of a nineteenth-century life. Heinrich Schliemann, the archeologist and ex-plorer of the sites of ancient Troy and Mycenae, is seen as a heroic figure. He is a man who took chances and accomplished much. Yet Payne, the product of a skeptical age, sees all of Schliemann's faults and lets us see them too. The impression he creates is of a rough force of nature asserting itself through a strange and colorful life. The tale of the man is paralleled by the legends that Schliemann vivified through his work. All of this Robert Payne brings out with consummate skill, blending the man, his work, and the significance of both, in masterly fashion.

The Personal Commentary

Personal commentary may take many forms—diaries, letters, essays, confessions, memoirs, and so on. It is perhaps the most natural of literary types, as it directly expresses an individual's response to experience. We read it not for an objective treatment of a topic, but rather for its reflection through the tastes, crochets and prejudices of an observing personality. It is not the truth we seek so much as better acquaintance with the teller and his special world.

Thomas Dekker's *The Gull's Hornbook* is a good early seventeenth-century example of English personal commentary. The author, a contemporary playwright of Shakespeare's, was very much annoyed by the behavior of many young gallants of his time. These "gulls," or fools, as he called them, spent their days in idleness and affectation. Wherever they went they not only made laughingstocks of themselves but also caused discomfort, if not worse, to others. Of particular annoyance to Dekker was their deportment in the theater, where, seated on the stage, they would harass the actors, distract the audience, and openly insult the author. Perhaps as a form of revenge Dekker wrote his "hornbook," or primer, describing the daily routines of these young men. At the same time, he provided us with a lively account of the London he personally knew. The account is given piquancy by the flavor of the author's biases and banes.

Numerous other fine works of personal commentary adorn English literature. Among diaries there is the famous one by the late seventeenth-century man of affairs, Samuel Pepys, who was so concerned that his jottings be kept secret from his wife and servants that he wrote them in cipher. Fortunately for our knowledge of Pepys' times and our acquaintance with the author's entertaining mind, in 1825 they were discovered and decoded. In our own time, another remarkable set of diaries written two centuries ago was discovered and published, those of James Boswell, the biographer of Johnson. *The London Journal*, telling of Boswell's experiences as a young man in London, is particularly worth reading.

Among letter-writers, two eighteenth-century figures stand out, Jonathan Swift and Lord Chesterfield. Swift wrote the *Journal to Stella*, the title given to letters of ardent friendship toward his former pupil, in which he commented revealingly on details of his daily existence. Chesterfield wrote letters to his son offering both advice on the making of a gentleman and opinions on the leading ideas of his time.

The growth of periodicals in the eighteenth century provided scope for the narrative essay, the chatty commentary on manners that often reflected the highly personal preferences and peeves of their authors. The so-called *Roger de Coverley Papers*, written by Joseph Addison and Richard Steele for the readers of *The Spectator*, contain many good examples of the essay form of personal commentary. Other outstanding practitioners of this form, writing in later times, are Charles Lamb and Max Beerbohm.

Periodicals also provided an audience for the confessional form of personal commentary. Perhaps the most famous of the English confessionals is the early nineteenth-century *Confessions of an English Opium-Eater* by Thomas de Quincey. Related to the confessional is the personal memoir, of which Robert Louis Stevenson's accounts of his *Inland Voyage* and *Travels With a Donkey* are excellent examples.

It is difficult to classify with exactness the kind of personal commentary the selection for this volume, P. G. Wodehouse's *America, I Like You*, constitutes. It is part confessional, part memoir, and part collection of essays on a variety of subjects, mainly touching on the author's American experiences. The confessional part has to do with Wodehouse's acknowledgment of his own limitations and frailties. This does not inhibit him from a good-natured enjoyment of the shortcomings of others, nor from presenting a perceptively humorous memoir of life in the United States. Although employing the same light-hearted style to be found in his novels, Wodehouse in *America, I Like You* speaks to us directly as Wodehouse—that is, as directly as Wodehouse might ever speak, which includes indirection, exaggeration, and various quirks all his own.

For what it is, a personal commentary on manners rather than morals by a man more bent on entertaining than instructing, *America, I Like You* is a delight to read. As a dessert course to the other somewhat more substantial works in this volume, it should leave a pleasant, lingering taste.

THE MAYOR
OF CASTERBRIDGE
A Story of a Man of Character
Thomas Hardy

A NOVEL

THOMAS HARDY

The Author and the Novel

Although one of the greatest of English novelists, Thomas Hardy devoted less than a third of his eighty-eight years to the writing of novels. Born in 1840 into a middle-class family whose livelihood was the building trade, he first pursued a career in architecture, as a restorer of churches. But even then, in his spare time he read widely, studied Latin and Greek literature in the originals, and dabbled in the writing of poetry and fiction.

During this period Hardy published his first novel, partly at his own expense. It was not well received, but he went on writing and with the clear success of his third novel, *Far From the Madding Crowd*, he abandoned architecture for the full-time career of author. In the two and a half decades that followed, through the late 1890's, he produced a number of truly distinguished novels, as well as many poems and short stories. The novels include such works as *The Return of the Native, Jude the Obscure, Tess of the D'Urbervilles,* and *The Mayor of Casterbridge,* which is reprinted in this volume. All of these won high praise, as well as the flattering attention of controversy. They also enjoyed good sales. Then suddenly, at the peak of his creative powers, Hardy stopped writing novels.

Why he did so has long been a puzzle. Perhaps he was upset by the increasing number of attacks against him for dealing with themes too unconventional for his time. Perhaps he felt he had

2

said everything he wanted to say in the novel form. Or, as some critics believe, perhaps the project that had fascinated him almost all of his adult life simply claimed his full attention—the writing of an epic poetic play on the Napoleonic Wars. The result of this interest was the publication over a period of eight years of a three-volume work, *The Dynasts,* regarded by Hardy as his greatest creative effort. During and after the work on *The Dynasts* he continued to write fine short poems—but no more novels.

Of Hardy's novels, *The Mayor of Casterbridge* is one of the most artistically satisfying. It contains striking incidents and well-drawn characters; yet all are subordinated to a single powerful impression, like the fusion of elements in the cathedrals that Hardy the architect so much admired. This impression is of the folly and dignity of man. It has its source in the main character, Michael Henchard.

Henchard is first seen as an unemployed farm laborer, with wife and infant daughter, stopping at a county fair. There, in one of the most bizarre opening episodes in all fiction, the drunken Henchard sells his wife and daughter at auction to a sailor. The next day when he is sober, he is contrite, but the damage is done—his wife and child are gone. He vows then not to touch liquor for twenty-one years.

The incident is but a prologue. We advance eighteen years and see Henchard as a successful grain merchant and leading citizen of the market town of Casterbridge. He has kept his vows, has worked hard and has prospered. At the height of his career, on his inauguration as town mayor, the events of the past begin to catch up with him and, mixed with new entanglements, subject him to the severest strains. How this energetic man, compounded of conflicting elements of honesty and self-delusion, rashness and violent affections, comes to deal with some of life's severest trials is the main matter of the book.

Hardy permits us to see Henchard vividly against his environment. It is the same environment that we find in most of Hardy's novels, a rural section of southern England that the author calls Wessex. The time is the middle of the nineteenth century, before the rapid industrial and agricultural changes of Hardy's lifetime transformed the countryside. Casterbridge, the market town, is described as though it were a natural part of the land. The people there are unsophisticated and only remotely aware of the world outside. Their lives, which are directly dependent on growing things, are strongly bound by the weather and other vagaries of nature. Their customs and traditions, partaking of superstition and folk ritual, are of an older time. Theirs is an ancient, self-contained universe, an appropriate setting for a drama of human passions. And Henchard—as merchant, public figure, and human being—is an integral and important part of this universe.

The influence of Hardy's early classical reading is clearly evident. Henchard's ordeal conveys something of the awesome feeling of Greek tragedy. There is an echo of Sophocles' *Oedipus Rex*, the drama of a great hero's sufferings for a rash act committed in his past. Like Oedipus, Henchard is a formidable man, and what happens to him really matters. If his destiny follows from his own character and from circumstance in almost equal parts, so, Hardy and Sophocles seem to agree, does it with all of us.

By the time we have finished reading *The Mayor of Casterbridge*, we have known a man and his special sense of life. If, finally, we choose to judge the man, it is with the compassion born of understanding that only the highest art can give.

ONE EVENING of late summer, before the nineteenth century had reached one-third of its span, a young man and woman, the latter carrying a child, were approaching the large village of Weydon-Priors, in Upper Wessex, on foot. They were plainly but not ill clad, though the thick hoar of dust which had accumulated on their shoes and garments from an obviously long journey lent a disadvantageous shabbiness to their appearance just now.

The man was of fine figure, swarthy, and stern in aspect; and he showed in profile a facial angle so slightly inclined as to be almost perpendicular. He wore a short jacket of brown corduroy, newer than the remainder of his suit, which was a fustian[1] waistcoat with white horn buttons, breeches of the same, tanned leggings, and a straw hat overlaid with black glazed canvas. At his back he carried by a looped strap a rush basket, from which protruded at one end the crutch of a hay knife, a wimble[2] for hay bonds being also visible in the aperture. His measured, springless walk was the walk of the skilled countryman as distinct from the desultory shamble of the general laborer; while in the turn and plant of each foot there was, further, a dogged and cynical indifference personal to himself, showing its presence even in the regularly interchanging fustian folds, now in the left leg, now in the right, as he paced along.

What was really peculiar, however, in this couple's progress, and would have attracted the attention of any casual observer otherwise disposed to overlook them, was the perfect silence

1. *Fustian:* rough cloth.
2. *Wimble:* hole-borer.

they preserved. They walked side by side in such a way as to suggest afar off the low, easy, confidential chat of people full of reciprocity: but on closer view it could be discerned that the man was reading, or pretending to read, a ballad sheet which he kept before his eyes with some difficulty by the hand that was passed through the basket strap. Whether this apparent cause were the real cause, or whether it were an assumed one to escape an intercourse that would have been irksome to him, nobody but himself could have said precisely; but his taciturnity was unbroken, and the woman enjoyed no society whatever from his presence. Virtually she walked the highway alone, save for the child she bore. Sometimes the man's elbow almost touched her shoulder, for she kept as close to his side as was possible without actual contact; but she seemed to have no idea of taking his arm, nor he of offering it; and far from exhibiting surprise at his ignoring silence she appeared to receive it as a natural thing. If any word at all were uttered by the little group, it was an occasional whisper of the woman to the child—a tiny girl in short clothes and blue boots of knitted yarn—and the murmured babble of the child in reply.

The chief—almost the only—attraction of the young woman's face was its mobility. When she looked down sideways to the girl she became pretty, and even handsome, particularly that in the action her features caught slantwise the rays of the strongly colored sun, which made transparencies of her eyelids and nostrils and set fire on her lips. When she plodded on in the shade of the hedge, silently thinking, she had the hard, half-apathetic expression of one who deems anything possible at the hands of Time and Chance except, perhaps, fair play. The first phase was the work of Nature, the second probably of civilization.

That the man and woman were husband and wife, and the parents of the girl in arms, there could be little doubt. No other than such relationship would have accounted for the atmosphere of stale familiarity which the trio carried along with them like a nimbus as they moved down the road.

The wife mostly kept her eyes fixed ahead, though with little interest—the scene for that matter being one that might have been matched at almost any spot in any county in England at this time of the year; a road neither straight nor crooked, neither level nor hilly, bordered by hedges, trees, and other vegetation, which had entered the blackened-green stage of color that the doomed leaves pass through on their way to dingy, and yellow, and red. The grassy margin of the bank, and the nearest hedgerow boughs, were powdered by the dust that had been stirred over them by hasty vehicles, the same dust as it lay on the road deadening their footfalls like a carpet; and this, with the aforesaid total absence of conversation, allowed every extraneous sound to be heard.

For a long time there was none, beyond the voice of a weak bird singing a trite old evening song that might doubtless have been heard on the hill at the same hour, and with the self-same trills, quavers, and breves, at any sunset of that season for centuries untold. But as they approached the village sundry distant shouts and rattles reached their ears from some elevated spot in that direction, as yet screened from view by foliage. When the outlying houses of Weydon-Priors could just be descried, the family group was met by a turnip-hoer with his hoe on his shoulder, and his dinner bag suspended from it. The reader promptly glanced up.

"Any trade doing here?" he asked phlegmatically, designating the village in his van by a wave of the broadsheet. And thinking the laborer did not understand him, he added, "Anything in the hay-trussing[3] line?"

The turnip-hoer had already begun shaking his head. "Why, save the man, what wisdom's in him that 'a should come to Weydon for a job of that sort this time o' year?"

3. *Hay-trussing:* bundling hay.

"Then is there any house to let—a little small new cottage just a builded, or such like?" asked the other.

The pessimist still maintained a negative. "Pulling down is more the nater of Weydon. There were five houses cleared away last year, and three this; and the volk nowhere to go— no, not so much as a thatched hurdle; that's the way o' Weydon-Priors."

The hay-trusser, which he obviously was, nodded with some superciliousness. Looking toward the village, he continued, "There is something going on here, however, is there not?"

"Ay. 'Tis Fair Day. Though what you hear now is little more than the clatter and scurry of getting away the money o' children and fools, for the real business is done earlier than this. I've been working within sound o't all day, but I didn't go up—not I. 'Twas no business of mine."

The trusser and his family proceeded on their way, and soon entered the fair field, which showed standing places and pens where many hundreds of horses and sheep had been exhibited and sold in the forenoon but were now in great part taken away. At present, as their informant had observed, but little real business remained on hand, the chief being the sale by auction of a few inferior animals, that could not otherwise be disposed of, and had been absolutely refused by the better class of traders, who came and went early. Yet the crowd was denser now than during the morning hours, the frivolous contingent of visitors, including journeymen out for a holiday, a stray soldier or two come on furlough, village shopkeepers, and the like, having latterly flocked in; persons whose activities found a congenial field among the peep shows, toy stands, waxworks, inspired monsters, disinterested medical men who traveled for the public good, thimble-riggers, knickknack vendors, and readers of Fate.

Neither of our pedestrians had much heart for these things, and they looked around for a refreshment tent among the many which dotted the down. Two, which stood nearest to them in the ochreous haze of expiring sunlight, seemed almost equally inviting. One was formed of new, milk-hued canvas, and bore red flags on its summit; it announced "Good Home-brewed Beer, Ale, and Cider." The other was less new; a little iron stovepipe came out of it at the back, and in front appeared the placard, "Good Furmity[4] Sold Hear." The man mentally weighed the two inscriptions, and inclined to the former tent.

"No—no—the other one," said the woman. "I always like furmity; and so does Elizabeth-Jane; and so will you. It is nourishing after a long hard day."

"I've never tasted it," said the man. However, he gave way to her representations, and they entered the furmity booth forthwith.

A rather numerous company appeared within, seated at the long narrow tables that ran down the tent on each side. At the upper end stood a stove, containing a charcoal fire, over which hung a large three-legged crock, sufficiently polished round the rim to show that it was made of bell metal. A haggish creature of about fifty presided, in a white apron, which, as it threw an air of respectability over her as far as it extended, was made so wide as to reach nearly round her waist. She slowly stirred the contents of the pot. The dull scrape of her large spoon was audible throughout the tent as she thus kept from burning the mixture of corn in the grain, flour, milk, raisins, currants, and what not, that composed the antiquated slop in which she dealt. Vessels holding the separate ingredients stood on a white-clothed table of boards and trestles close by.

The young man and woman ordered a basin each of the mixture, steaming hot, and sat down to consume it at leisure. This was very well so far, for furmity, as the woman had said,

4. *Furmity*: usually spelled *frumenty*; wheat in boiled milk with sugar.

was nourishing, and as proper a food as could be obtained within the four seas; though, to those not accustomed to it, the grains of wheat swollen as large as lemon pips, which floated on its surface, might have a deterrent effect at first.

But there was more in that tent than met the cursory glance; and the man, with the instinct of a perverse character, scented it quickly. After a mincing attack on his bowl, he watched the hag's proceedings from the corner of his eye, and saw the game she played. He winked to her, and passed up his basin in reply to her nod; when she took a bottle from under the table, slyly measured out a quantity of its contents, and tipped the same into the man's furmity. The liquor poured in was rum. The man as slyly sent back money in payment.

He found the concoction, thus strongly laced, much more to his satisfaction than it had been in its natural state. His wife had observed the proceeding with much uneasiness; but he persuaded her to have hers laced also, and she agreed to a milder allowance after some misgiving.

The man finished his basin, and called for another, the rum being signaled for in yet stronger proportion. The effect of it was soon apparent in his manner, and his wife but too sadly perceived that in strenuously steering off the rocks of the licensed liquor tent she had only got into maelstrom depths here amongst the smugglers.

The child began to prattle impatiently, and the wife more than once said to her husband, "Michael, how about our lodging? You know we may have trouble in getting it if we don't go soon."

But he turned a deaf ear to those bird-like chirpings. He talked loud to the company. The child's black eyes, after slow, round, ruminating gazes at the candles when they were lighted, fell together; then they opened, then shut again, and she slept.

At the end of the first basin the man had risen to serenity; at the second he was jovial; at the third, argumentative, at the fourth, the qualities signified by the shape of his face, the occasional clench of his mouth, and the fiery spark of his dark eye, began to tell in his conduct; he was overbearing—even brilliantly quarrelsome.

The conversation took a high turn, as it often does on such occasions. The ruin of good men by bad wives, and, more particularly, the frustration of many a promising youth's high aims and hopes and the extinction of his energies by an early imprudent marriage, was the theme.

"I did for myself that way thoroughly," said the trusser, with a contemplative bitterness that was well-nigh resentful. "I married at eighteen, like the fool that I was; and this is the consequence o't." He pointed at himself and family with a wave of the hand intended to bring out the penuriousness of the exhibition.

The young woman his wife, who seemed accustomed to such remarks, acted as if she did not hear them, and continued her intermittent private words on tender trifles to the sleeping and waking child, who was just big enough to be placed for a moment on the bench beside her when she wished to ease her arms. The man continued—

"I haven't more than fifteen shillings in the world, and yet I am a good experienced hand in my line. I'd challenge England to beat me in the fodder business; and if I were a free man again I'd be worth a thousand pound before I'd done o't. But a fellow never knows these little things till all chance of acting upon 'em is past."

The auctioneer selling the old horses in the field outside could be heard saying, "Now this is the last lot—now who'll take the last lot for a song? Shall I say forty shillings? 'Tis a very promising brood mare, a trifle over five years old, and nothing the matter with the hoss at all, except that she's a little holler in the back and had her left eye knocked out by the kick of another, her own sister, coming along the road."

"For my part I don't see why men who have got wives and don't want 'em, shouldn't get rid of 'em as these gypsy fellows do their old horses," said the man in the tent. "Why shouldn't they put 'em up and sell 'em by auction to men who are in need of such articles? Hey? Why, begad, I'd sell mine this minute if anybody would buy her!"

"There's them that would do that," some of the guests replied, looking at the woman, who was by no means ill-favored.

"True," said a smoking gentleman, whose coat had the fine polish about the collar, elbows, seams, and shoulder blades that long-continued friction with grimy surfaces will produce, and which is usually more desired on furniture than on clothes. From his appearance he had possibly been in former time groom or coachman to some neighboring county family. "I've had my breedings in as good circles, I may say, as any man," he added, "and I know true cultivation, or nobody do; and I can declare she's got it—in the bone, mind ye, I say—as much as any female in the fair—though it may want a little bringing out." Then, crossing his legs, he resumed his pipe with a nicely adjusted gaze at a point in the air.

The fuddled young husband stared for a few seconds at this unexpected praise of his wife, half in doubt of the wisdom of his own attitude toward the possessor of such qualities. But he speedily lapsed into his former conviction, and said harshly—

"Well, then, now is your chance; I am open to an offer for this gem o' creation."

She turned to her husband and murmured, "Michael, you have talked this nonsense in public places before. A joke is a joke, but you may make it once too often, mind!"

"I know I've said it before; I meant it. All I want is a buyer."

At the moment a swallow, one among the last of the season, which had by chance found its way through an opening into the upper part of the tent, flew to and fro in quick curves above their heads, causing all eyes to follow it absently. In watching the bird till it made its escape the assembled company neglected to respond to the workman's offer, and the subject dropped.

But a quarter of an hour later the man, who had gone on lacing his furmity more and more heavily, though he was either so strong-minded or such an intrepid toper that he still appeared fairly sober, recurred to the old strain, as in a musical fantasy the instrument fetches up the original theme. "Here—I am waiting to know about this offer of mine. The woman is no good to me. Who'll have her?"

The company had by this time decidedly degenerated, and the renewed inquiry was received with a laugh of appreciation. The woman whispered; she was imploring and anxious: "Come, come, it is getting dark, and this nonsense won't do. If you don't come along, I shall go without you. Come!"

She waited and waited; yet he did not move. In ten minutes the man broke in upon the desultory conversation of the furmity drinkers with, "I asked this question, and nobody answered to 't. Will any Jack Rag or Tom Straw among ye buy my goods?"

The woman's manner changed, and her face assumed the grim shape and color of which mention has been made.

"Mike, Mike," said she; "this is getting serious. O!—too serious!"

"Will anybody buy her?" said the man.

"I wish somebody would," said she firmly. "Her present owner is not at all to her liking!"

"Nor you to mine," said he. "So we are agreed about that. Gentlemen, you hear? It's an agreement to part. She shall take the girl if she wants to, and go her ways. I'll take my tools, and go my ways. 'Tis simple as Scripture history. Now then, stand up, Susan, and show yourself."

"Don't, my chiel," whispered a buxom stay-lace dealer in voluminous petticoats, who sat near the woman; "yer good man don't know what he's saying."

The woman, however, did stand up. "Now, who's auctioneer?" cried the hay-trusser.

"I be," promptly answered a short man, with a nose resembling a copper knob, a damp voice, and eyes like button-holes. "Who'll make an offer for this lady?"

The woman looked on the ground, as if she maintained her position by a supreme effort of will.

"Five shillings," said some one, at which there was a laugh.

"No insults," said the husband. "Who'll say a guinea?"[5]

Nobody answered; and the female dealer in stay-laces inter-posed.

"Behave yerself moral, good man, for Heaven's love! Ah, what a cruelty is the poor soul married to! Bed and board is dear at some figures, 'pon my 'vation 'tis!"

"Set it higher, auctioneer," said the trusser.

"Two guineas!" said the auctioneer; and no one replied.

"If they don't take her for that, in ten seconds they'll have to give more," said the husband. "Very well. Now, auctioneer, add another."

"Three guineas—going for three guineas!" said the rheumy man.

"No bid?" said the husband. "Good Lord, why she's cost me fifty times the money, if a penny. Go on."

"Four guineas!" cried the auctioneer.

"I'll tell ye what—I won't sell her for less than five," said the husband, bringing down his fist so that the basins danced. "I'll sell her for five guineas to any man that will pay me the money, and treat her well; and he shall have her for ever, and never hear aught o' me. But she shan't go for less. Now then five guineas—and she's yours. Susan, you agree?"

She bowed her head with absolute indifference.

"Five guineas," said the auctioneer, "or she'll be withdrawn. Do anybody give it? The last time. Yes or no?"

"Yes," said a loud voice from the doorway.

All eyes were turned. Standing in the triangular opening which formed the door of the tent was a sailor, who, unob-served by the rest, had arrived there within the last two or three minutes. A dead silence followed his affirmation.

5. *Guinea:* a pound and a shilling, now the equivalent of about $2.95.

"You say you do?" asked the husband, staring at him.

"I say so," replied the sailor.

"Saying is one thing, and paying is another. Where's the money?"

The sailor hesitated a moment, looked anew at the woman, came in, unfolded five crisp pieces of paper, and threw them down upon the tablecloth. They were Bank-of-England notes for five pounds. Upon the face of this he chinked down the shillings severally—one, two, three, four, five.

The sight of real money in full amount, in answer to a challenge for the same till then deemed slightly hypothetical, had a great effect upon the spectators. Their eyes became riveted upon the faces of the chief actors, and then upon the notes as they lay, weighted by the shillings, on the table.

Up to this moment it could not positively have been asserted that the man, in spite of his tantalizing declaration, was really in earnest. The spectators had indeed taken the proceedings throughout as a piece of mirthful irony carried to extremes; and had assumed that, being out of work, he was, as a consequence, out of temper with the world, and society, and his nearest kin. But with the demand and response of real cash the jovial frivolity of the scene departed. A lurid color seemed to fill the tent, and change the aspect of all therein. The mirth wrinkles left the listeners' faces, and they waited with parting lips.

"Now," said the woman, breaking the silence, so that her low dry voice sounded quite loud, "before you go further, Michael, listen to me. If you touch that money, I and this girl go with the man. Mind, it is a joke no longer."

"A joke? Of course it is not a joke!" shouted her husband, his resentment rising at her suggestion. "I take the money: the sailor takes you. That's plain enough. It has been done elsewhere—and why not here?"

" 'Tis quite on the understanding that the young woman is willing," said the sailor blandly. "I wouldn't hurt her feelings for the world."

"Faith, nor I," said her husband. "But she is willing, provided she can have the child. She said so only the other day when I talked o't!"

"That you swear?" said the sailor to her.

"I do," said she, after glancing at her husband's face and seeing no repentance there.

"Very well, she shall have the child, and the bargain's complete," said the trusser. He took the sailor's notes and deliberately folded them, and put them with the shillings in a high remote pocket, with an air of finality.

The sailor looked at the woman and smiled. "Come along!" he said kindly. "The little one too—the more the merrier!" She paused for an instant, with a close glance at him. Then dropping her eyes again, and saying nothing, she took up the child and followed him as he made towards the door. On reaching it, she turned, and pulling off her wedding ring, flung it across the booth in the hay-trusser's face.

"Mike," she said, "I've lived with thee a couple of years and had nothing but temper! Now I'm no more to 'ee; I'll try my luck elsewhere. 'Twill be better for me and Elizabeth-Jane, both. So good-by!"

Seizing the sailor's arm with her right hand, and mounting the little girl on her left, she went out of the tent sobbing bitterly.

A stolid look of concern filled the husband's face, as if, after all, he had not quite anticipated this ending; and some of the guests laughed.

"Is she gone?" he said.

"Faith, ay; she's gone clane enough," said some rustics near the door.

He rose and walked to the entrance with the careful tread of one conscious of his alcoholic load. Some others followed, and they stood looking into the twilight. The difference between the peacefulness of inferior nature and the willful hostilities of mankind was very apparent at this place. In contrast with the harshness of the act just ended within the tent was the sight of several horses crossing their necks and rubbing each other lovingly as they waited in patience to be harnessed for the homeward journey. Outside the fair, in the valleys and woods, all was quiet. The sun had recently set, and the west heaven was hung with rosy cloud, which seemed permanent, yet slowly changed. To watch it was like looking at some grand feat of stagery from a darkened auditorium. In presence of this scene after the other there was a natural instinct to abjure man as the blot on an otherwise kindly universe; till it was remembered that all terrestrial conditions were intermittent, and that mankind might some night be innocently sleeping when these quiet objects were raging loud.

"Where do the sailor live?" asked a spectator, when they had vainly gazed around.

"God knows that," replied the man who had seen high life. "He's without doubt a stranger here."

"He came in about five minutes ago," said the furmity woman, joining the rest with her hands on her hips. "And then 'a stepped back, and then 'a looked in again. I'm not a penny the better for him."

"Serves the husband well be-right," said the stay-lace vendor. "A comely respectable body like her—what can a man want more? I glory in the woman's sperrit. I'd ha' done it myself—od send if I wouldn't, if a husband had behaved so to me! I'd go, and 'a might call, and call, till his keacorn was raw; but I'd never come back—no, not till the great trumpet, would I!"

"Well, the woman will be better off," said another of a more deliberative turn. "For seafaring natures be very good shelter for shorn lambs, and the man do seem to have plenty of money, which is what she's not been used to lately, by all showings."

"Mark me—I'll not go after her!" said the trusser, returning doggedly to his seat. "Let her go! If she's up to such vagaries she must suffer for 'em. She'd no business to take the maid—'tis my maid; and if it were the doing again she shouldn't have her!''

Perhaps from some little sense of having countenanced an indefensible proceeding, perhaps because it was late, the customers thinned away from the tent shortly after this episode. The man stretched his elbows forward on the table, leant his face upon his arms, and soon began to snore. The furmity seller decided to close for the night, and after seeing the rum bottles, milk, corn, raisins, etc., that remained on hand, loaded into the cart, came to where the man reclined. She shook him, but could not wake him. As the tent was not to be struck that night, the fair continuing for two or three days, she decided to let the sleeper, who was obviously no tramp, stay where he was, and his basket with him. Extinguishing the last candle, and lowering the flap of the tent, she left it, and drove away.

. . . CHAPTER 2

THE MORNING sun was streaming through the crevices of the canvas when the man awoke. A warm glow pervaded the whole atmosphere of the marquee, and a single big blue fly buzzed musically round and round it. Besides the buzz of the fly there was not a sound. He looked about—at the benches —at the table supported by trestles—at his basket of tools—at the stove where the furmity had been boiled—at the empty basins—at some shed grains of wheat—at the corks which dotted the grassy floor. Among the odds and ends he discerned a little shining object, and picked it up. It was his wife's ring.

A confused picture of the events of the previous evening seemed to come back to him, and he thrust his hand into his breast pocket. A rustling revealed the sailor's bank notes thrust carelessly in.

This second verification of his dim memories was enough; he knew now they were not dreams. He remained seated, looking on the ground for some time. "I must get out of this as soon as I can," he said deliberately at last, with the air of one who could not catch his thoughts without pronouncing them. "She's gone—to be sure she is—gone with that sailor who bought her, and little Elizabeth-Jane. We walked here, and I had the furmity, and rum in it—and sold her. Yes, that's what happened, and here am I. Now, what am I to do—am I sober enough to walk, I wonder?" He stood up, found that he was in fairly good condition for progress, unencumbered. Next he shouldered his tool basket and found he could carry it. Then lifting the tent door he emerged into the open air.

Here the man looked around with gloomy curiosity. The freshness of the September morning inspired and braced him as he stood. He and his family had been weary when they arrived the night before, and they had observed but little of the place; so that he now beheld it as a new thing. It exhibited itself as the top of an open down, bounded on one extreme by a plantation, and approached by a winding road. At the bottom stood the village which lent its name to the upland and the annual fair that was held thereon. The spot stretched downward into valleys, and onward to other uplands, dotted with barrows, and trenched with the remains of prehistoric forts. The whole scene lay under the rays of a newly risen sun, which had not as yet dried a single blade of the heavily dewed grass, whereon the shadows of the yellow and red vans were projected far away, those thrown by the felloe of each wheel being elongated in shape to the orbit of a comet. All the gypsies and showmen who had remained on the ground lay snug within their carts and tents, or wrapped in horsecloths under them, and were silent and still as death, with the exception of an occasional snore that revealed their presence. But the Seven Sleepers had a dog; and dogs of the mysterious breeds that vagrants own, that are as much like cats as dogs and as much like foxes as cats, also lay about here.

A little one started up under one of the carts, barked as a matter of principle, and quickly lay down again. He was the only positive spectator of the hay-trusser's exit from the Weydon Fair field.

This seemed to accord with his desire. He went on in silent thought, unheeding the yellowhammers which flitted about the hedges with straws in their bills, the crowns of the mushrooms, and the tinkling of local sheep bells, whose wearer had had the good fortune not to be included in the fair. When he reached a lane, a good mile from the scene of the previous evening, the man pitched his basket and leant upon a gate. A difficult problem or two occupied his mind.

"Did I tell my name to anybody last night, or didn't I tell my name?" he said to himself; and at last concluded that he did not. His general demeanor was enough to show how he was surprised and nettled that his wife had taken him so literally—as much could be seen in his face, and in the way he nibbled a straw which he pulled from the hedge. He knew that she must have been somewhat excited to do this; moreover, she must have believed that there was some sort of binding force in the transaction. On this latter point he felt almost certain, knowing her freedom from levity of character, and the extreme simplicity of her intellect. There may, too, have been enough recklessness and resentment beneath her ordinary placidity to make her stifle any momentary doubts. On a previous occasion when he had declared during a fuddle that he would dispose of her as he had done, she had replied that she would not hear him say that many times more before it happened, in the resigned tones of a fatalist. . . . "Yet she knows I am not in my senses when I do that!" he exclaimed. "Well, I must walk about till I find her. . . . Seize her, why didn't she know better than bring me into this disgrace!" he roared out. "She wasn't queer if I was. 'Tis like Susan to show such idiotic simplicity. Meek—that meekness has done me more harm than the bitterest temper!"

When he was calmer he turned to his original conviction that he must somehow find her and his little Elizabeth-Jane, and put up with the shame as best he could. It was of his own making, and he ought to bear it. But first he resolved to register an oath, a greater oath than he had ever sworn before: and to do it properly he required a fit place and imagery; for there was something fetishistic in this man's beliefs.

He shouldered his basket and moved on, casting his eyes inquisitively round upon the landscape as he walked, and at the distance of three or four miles perceived the roofs of a village and the tower of a church. He instantly made toward the latter object. The village was quite still, it being that motionless hour of rustic daily life which fills the interval between the departure of the field laborers to their work, and the rising of their wives and daughters to prepare the breakfast for their return. Hence he reached the church without observation, and the door being only latched he entered. The hay-trusser deposited his basket by the font, went up the nave till he reached the altar rails, and opening the gate entered the sacrarium, where he seemed to feel a sense of the strangeness for a moment; then he knelt upon the footpace. Dropping his head upon the clamped book which lay on the communion table, he said aloud—

"I, Michael Henchard, on this morning of the sixteenth of September, do take an oath before God here in this solemn place that I will avoid all strong liquors for the space of twenty-one years to come, being a year for every year that I have lived. And this I swear upon the book before me; and may I be strook dumb, blind, and helpless, if I break this my oath!"

When he had said it and kissed the big book, the hay-trusser arose, and seemed relieved at having made a start in a new direction. While standing in the porch a moment he saw a thick jet of wood smoke suddenly start up from the red chimney of a cottage near, and knew that the occupant had just lit her fire. He went round to the door, and the housewife agreed to prepare him some breakfast for a trifling payment, which was done. Then he started on the search for his wife and child.

The perplexing nature of the undertaking became apparent soon enough. Though he examined and inquired, and walked hither and thither day after day, no such characters as those he described had anywhere been seen since the evening of the fair. To add to the difficulty he could gain no sound of the sailor's name. As money was short with him he decided, after some hesitation, to spend the sailor's money in the prosecution of this search; but it was equally in vain. The truth was that a certain shyness of revealing his conduct prevented Michael Henchard from following up the investigation with the loud hue-and-cry such a pursuit demanded to render it effectual; and it was probably for this reason that he obtained no clue, though everything was done by him that did not involve an explanation of the circumstances under which he had lost her.

Weeks counted up to months, and still he searched on, maintaining himself by small jobs of work in the intervals. By this time he had arrived at a seaport, and there he derived intelligence that persons answering somewhat to his description had emigrated a little time before. Then he said he would search no longer, and that he would go and settle in the district which he had had for some time in his mind. Next day he started, journeying southwestward, and did not pause, except for nights' lodgings, till he reached the town of Casterbridge, in a far distant part of Wessex.

. . . **CHAPTER 3**

THE HIGHROAD into the village of Weydon-Priors was again carpeted with dust. The trees had put on as of yore their aspect of dingy green, and where the Henchard family of three had once walked along, two persons not unconnected with that family walked now.

The scene in its broad aspect had so much of its previous character, even to the voices and rattle from the neighboring village down, that it might for that matter have been the afternoon following the previously recorded episode. Change was only to be observed in details; but here it was obvious that a long procession of years had passed by. One of the two who walked the road was she who had figured as the young wife of Henchard on the previous occasion; now her face had lost much of its rotundity; her skin had undergone a textural change; and though her hair had not lost its color it was considerably thinner than heretofore. She was dressed in the mourning clothes of a widow. Her companion, also in black, appeared as a well-formed young woman about eighteen, completely possessed of that ephemeral precious essence youth, which is itself beauty, irrespective of complexion or contour.

A glance was sufficient to inform the eye that this was Susan Henchard's grown-up daughter. While life's middle summer had set its hardening mark on the mother's face, her former spring-like specialities were transferred so dexterously by Time to the second figure, her child, that the absence of certain facts within her mother's knowledge from the girl's mind would have seemed for the moment, to one reflecting on those facts, to be a curious imperfection in Nature's powers of continuity.

They walked with joined hands, and it could be perceived that this was the act of simple affection. The daughter carried in her outer hand a withy basket of old-fashioned make; the mother a blue bundle, which contrasted oddly with her black stuff gown.

Reaching the outskirts of the village they pursued the same track as formerly, and ascended to the fair. Here, too, it was evident that the years had told. Certain mechanical improvements might have been noticed in the roundabouts and high-fliers, machines for testing rustic strength and weight, and in the erections devoted to shooting for nuts. But the real business of the fair had considerably dwindled. The new periodical great markets of neighboring towns were beginning to interfere seriously with the trade carried on here for centuries. The pens for sheep, the tie ropes for horses, were about half as long as they had been. The stalls of tailors, hosiers, coopers, linen drapers, and other such trades had almost disappeared, and the vehicles were far less numerous. The mother and daughter threaded the crowd for some little distance, and then stood still.

"Why did we hinder our time by coming in here? I thought you wished to get onward?" said the maiden.

"Yes, my dear Elizabeth-Jane," explained the other. "But I had a fancy for looking up here."

"Why?"

"It was here I first met with Newson—on such a day as this."

"First met with Father here? Yes, you have told me so before. And now he's drowned and gone from us." As she spoke the girl drew a card from her pocket and looked at it with a sigh. It was edged with black, and inscribed within a design resembling a mural tablet were the words, "In affectionate memory of Richard Newson, mariner, who was unfortunately lost at sea, in the month of November 184—, aged forty-one years."

"And it was here," continued her mother, with more hesitation, "that I last saw the relation we are going to look for—Mr. Michael Henchard."

"What is his exact kin to us, Mother? I have never clearly had it told me."

"He is, or was—for he may be dead—a connection by marriage," said her mother deliberately.

"That's exactly what you have said a score of times before!" replied the young woman, looking about her inattentively. "He's not a near relation, I suppose?"

"Not by any means."

"He was a hay-trusser, wasn't he, when you last heard of him?"

"He was."

"I suppose he never knew me?" the girl innocently continued.

Mrs. Henchard paused for a moment, and answered uneasily, "Of course not, Elizabeth-Jane. But come this way." She moved on to another part of the field.

"It is not much use inquiring here for anybody, I should think," the daughter observed, as she gazed round about. "People at fairs change like the leaves of trees; and I daresay you are the only one here today who was here all those years ago."

"I am not so sure of that," said Mrs. Newson, as she now called herself, keenly eyeing something under a green bank a little way off. "See there."

The daughter looked in the direction signified. The object pointed out was a tripod of sticks stuck into the earth from which hung a three-legged crock, kept hot by a smoldering wood fire beneath. Over the pot stooped an old woman, haggard, wrinkled, and almost in rags. She stirred the contents of the pot with a large spoon, and occasionally croaked in a broken voice, "Good furmity sold here!"

It was indeed the former mistress of the furmity tent—once thriving, cleanly, white-aproned, and chinking with money —now tentless, dirty, owning no tables or benches, and having scarce any customers except two small boys, who came up and asked for "A ha'p'orth, please—good measure," which she served in a couple of chipped yellow basins of commonest clay.

"She was here at that time," resumed Mrs. Newson, making a step as if to draw nearer.

"Don't speak to her—it isn't respectable!" urged the other.

"I will just say a word—you, Elizabeth-Jane, can stay here."

The girl was not loth, and turned to some stalls of colored prints while her mother went forward. The old woman begged for the latter's custom as soon as she saw her, and responded to Mrs. Henchard-Newson's request for a pennyworth with more alacrity than she had shown in selling sixpennyworths in her younger days. When the *soi-disant*[1] widow had taken the basin of thin poor slop that stood for the rich concoction of the former time, the hag opened a little basket behind the fire, and looking up slyly, whispered, "Just a thought o' rum in it?—smuggled, you know—say two penn'orth—'twill make it slip down like a cordial!"

Her customer smiled bitterly at this survival of the old trick, and shook her head with a meaning the old woman was far from translating. She pretended to eat a little of the furmity with the leaden spoon offered, and as she did so said blandly to the hag, "You've seen better days?"

"Ah, ma'am—well ye may say it!" responded the old woman, opening the sluices of her heart forthwith. "I've stood in this fairground, maid, wife, and widow, these nine-and-thirty year, and in that time have known what it was to do business with the richest stomachs in the land! Ma'am, you'd hardly believe that I was once the owner of a great pavilion tent that was the attraction of the fair. Nobody could come, nobody could go, without having a dish of Mrs. Goodenough's furmity. I knew the clergy's taste, the dandy gent's taste; I knew the town's taste, the country's taste. I even knowed the taste of the coarse shameless females. But Lord's my life—the world's no memory; straightforward dealings don't bring profit—'tis the sly and the underhand that get on in these times!"

Mrs. Newson glanced round—her daughter was still bending over the distant stalls. "Can you call to mind," she said cautiously to the old woman, "the sale of a wife by her husband in your tent eighteen years ago today?"

1. *Soi-disant:* Self-styled.

The hag reflected, and half shook her head. "If it had been a big thing I should have minded it in a moment," she said. "I can mind every serious fight o' married parties, every murder, every manslaughter, even every pocket-picking—leastwise large ones—that 't has been my lot to witness. But a selling? Was it done quiet-like?"

"Well, yes. I think so."

The furmity woman half shook her head again. "And yet," she said, "I do. At any rate I can mind a man doing something o' the sort—a man in a cord jacket, with a basket of tools; but, Lord bless ye, we don't gi'e it headroom, we don't, such as that. The only reason why I can mind the man is that he came back here to the next year's fair, and told me quite private-like that if a woman ever asked for him I was to say he had gone to —where?—Casterbridge—yes—to Casterbridge, said he. But, Lord's my life, I shouldn't ha' thought of it again."

Mrs. Newson would have rewarded the old woman as far as her small means afforded had she not discreetly borne in mind that it was by that unscrupulous person's liquor her husband had been degraded. She briefly thanked her informant, and rejoined Elizabeth, who greeted her with, "Mother, do let's go on—it was hardly respectable for you to buy refreshments there. I see none but the lowest do."

"I have learned what I wanted, however," said her mother quietly. "The last time our relative visited this fair he said he was living at Casterbridge. It is a long, long way from here, and it was many years ago that he said it; but there I think we'll go."

With this they descended out of the fair, and went onward to the village, where they obtained a night's lodging.

. . . **CHAPTER 4**

HENCHARD's wife acted for the best, but she had involved herself in difficulties. A hundred times she had been upon the point of telling her daughter Elizabeth-Jane the true story of her life, the tragical crisis of which had been the transaction at Weydon Fair, when she was not much older than the girl now beside her. But she had refrained. An innocent maiden had thus grown up in the belief that the relations between the genial sailor and her mother were the ordinary ones that they had always appeared to be. The risk of endangering a child's strong affection by disturbing ideas which had grown with her growth was to Mrs. Henchard too fearful a thing to contemplate. It had seemed, indeed, folly to think of making Elizabeth-Jane wise.

But Susan Henchard's fear of losing her dearly loved daughter's heart by a revelation had little to do with any sense of wrongdoing on her own part. Her simplicity—the original ground of Henchard's contempt for her—had allowed her to live on in the conviction that Newson had acquired a morally real and justifiable right to her by his purchase—though the exact bearings and legal limits of that right were vague. It may seem strange to sophisticated minds that a sane young matron could believe in the seriousness of such a transfer; and were there not numerous other instances of the same belief the thing might scarcely be credited. But she was by no means the first or last peasant woman who had religiously adhered to her purchaser, as too many rural records show.

The history of Susan Henchard's adventures in the interim can be told in two or three sentences. Absolutely helpless she had been taken off to Canada, where they had lived several years without any great worldly success, though she worked as hard as any woman could to keep their cottage cheerful and well-provided. When Elizabeth-Jane was about twelve years old the three returned to England, and settled at Falmouth, where Newson made a living for a few years as boatman and general handy shoreman.

He then engaged in the Newfoundland trade, and it was during this period that Susan had an awakening. A friend to

whom she confided her history ridiculed her grave acceptance
of her position; and all was over with her peace of mind. When
Newson came home at the end of one winter he saw that the
delusion he had so carefully sustained had vanished for ever.

There was then a time of sadness, in which she told him
her doubts if she could live with him longer. Newson left
home again on the Newfoundland trade when the season came
round. The vague news of his loss at sea a little later on solved
a problem which had become torture to her meek conscience.
She saw him no more.

Of Henchard they heard nothing. To the liege subjects of
Labor, the England of those days was a continent, and a mile
a geographical degree.

Elizabeth-Jane developed into womanliness. One day, a
month or so after receiving intelligence of Newson's death
off the Bank of Newfoundland, when the girl was about
eighteen, she was sitting on a willow chair in the cottage they
still occupied, working twine nets for the fishermen. Her
mother was in a back corner of the same room, engaged in the
same labor; and dropping the heavy wood needle she was
filling she surveyed her daughter thoughtfully. The sun shone
in at the door upon the young woman's head and hair, which
was worn loose, so that the rays streamed into its depths as
into a hazel copse. Her face, though somewhat wan and incomplete, possessed the raw materials of beauty in a promising
degree. There was an under-handsomeness in it, struggling
to reveal itself through the provisional curves of immaturity,
and the casual disfigurements that resulted from the straitened circumstances of their lives. She was handsome in the
bone, hardly as yet handsome in the flesh. She possibly might
never be fully handsome, unless the carking[1] accidents of her
daily existence could be evaded before the mobile parts of
her countenance had settled to their final mold.

The sight of the girl made her mother sad—not vaguely, but

1. *Carking:* troubling.

by logical inference. They both were still in that strait waist-coat of poverty from which she had tried so many times to be delivered for the girl's sake. The woman had long per-ceived how zealously and constantly the young mind of her companion was struggling for enlargement; and yet now, in her eighteenth year, it still remained but little unfolded. The desire—sober and repressed—of Elizabeth-Jane's heart was in-deed to see, to hear, and to understand. How could she be-come a woman of wider knowledge, higher repute—"better," as she termed it—this was her constant inquiry of her mother. She sought further into things than other girls in her position ever did, and her mother groaned as she felt she could not aid in the search.

The sailor, drowned or no, was probably now lost to them; and Susan's staunch, religious adherence to him as her husband in principle, till her views had been disturbed by enlighten-ment, was demanded no more. She asked herself whether the present moment, now that she was a free woman again, were not as opportune a one as she would find in a world where everything had been so inopportune, for making a desperate effort to advance Elizabeth. To pocket her pride and search for the first husband seemed, wisely or not, the best initiatory step. He had possibly drunk himself into his tomb. But he might, on the other hand, have had too much sense to do so; for in her time with him he had been given to bouts only, and was not a habitual drunkard.

At any rate, the propriety of returning to him, if he lived, was unquestionable. The awkwardness of searching for him lay in enlightening Elizabeth, a proceeding which her mother could not endure to contemplate. She finally resolved to un-dertake the search without confiding to the girl her former relations with Henchard, leaving it to him if they found him to take what steps he might choose to that end. This will account for their conversation at the fair and the half-in-formed state in which Elizabeth was led onward.

In this attitude they proceeded on their journey, trusting solely to the dim light afforded of Henchard's whereabouts by the furmity woman. The strictest economy was indispensable. Sometimes they might have been seen on foot, sometimes on farmers' wagons, sometimes in carriers' vans; and thus they drew near to Casterbridge. Elizabeth-Jane discovered to her alarm that her mother's health was not what it once had been, and there was ever and anon in her talk that renunciatory tone which showed that, but for the girl, she would not be very sorry to quit a life she was growing thoroughly weary of.

It was on a Friday evening, near the middle of September, and just before dusk, that they reached the summit of a hill within a mile of the place they sought. There were high-banked hedges to the coach road here, and they mounted upon the green turf within, and sat down. The spot commanded a full view of the town and its environs.

"What an old-fashioned place it seems to be!" said Elizabeth-Jane, while her silent mother mused on other things than topography. "It is huddled all together; and it is shut in by a square wall of trees, like a plot of garden ground by a box-edging."

Its squareness was, indeed, the characteristic which most struck the eye in this antiquated borough, the borough of Casterbridge—at that time, recent as it was, untouched by the faintest sprinkle of modernism. It was compact as a box of dominoes. It had no suburbs—in the ordinary sense. Country and town met at a mathematical line.

To birds of the more soaring kind Casterbridge must have appeared on this fine evening as a mosaic-work of subdued reds, browns, grays, and crystals, held together by a rectangular frame of deep green. To the level eye of humanity it stood as an indistinct mass behind a dense stockade of limes and chestnuts, set in the midst of miles of rotund down and concave field. The mass became gradually dissected by the vision into towers, gables, chimneys, and casements, the highest glazings shining bleared and bloodshot with the coppery fire they caught from the belt of sunlit cloud in the west.

From the center of each side of this tree-bound square ran avenues east and west, and south into the wide expanse of cornland and coomb to the distance of a mile or so. It was by one of these avenues that the pedestrians were about to enter. Before they had risen to proceed two men passed outside the hedge, engaged in argumentative conversation.

"Why, surely," said Elizabeth, as they receded, "those men mentioned the name of Henchard in their talk—the name of our relative?"

"I thought so too," said Mrs. Newson.

"That seems a hint to us that he is still here."

"Yes."

"Shall I run after them, and ask them about him——"

"No, no, no! Not for the world just yet. He may be in the workhouse, or in the stocks, for all we know."

"Dear me—why should you think that, mother?"

" 'Twas just something to say—that's all! But we must make private inquiries."

Having sufficiently rested they proceeded on their way at evenfall. The dense trees of the avenue rendered the road dark as a tunnel, though the open land on each side was still under a faint daylight; in other words, they passed down a midnight between two gloamings. The features of the town had a keen interest for Elizabeth's mother, now that the human side came to the fore. As soon as they had wandered about they could see that the stockade of gnarled trees which framed in Casterbridge was itself an avenue, standing on a low green bank or escarpment, with a ditch yet visible without. Within the avenue and bank was a wall more or less discontinuous, and within the wall were packed the abodes of the burghers.

Though the two women did not know it these external features were but the ancient defenses of the town, planted as a promenade.

High Street, Casterbridge.

The lamplights now glimmered through the engirdling trees, conveying a sense of great snugness and comfort inside, and rendering at the same time the unlighted country without strangely solitary and vacant in aspect, considering its nearness to life. The difference between burgh and champaign[2] was increased, too, by sounds which now reached them above others—the notes of a brass band. The travelers returned into the High Street, where there were timber houses with over-

2. *Burgh and champaign:* town and country.

hanging stories, whose small-paned lattices were screened by
dimity curtains on a drawing string, and under whose barge
boards old cobwebs waved in the breeze. There were houses
of brick nogging, which derived their chief support from
those adjoining. There were slate roofs patched with tiles, and
tile roofs patched with slate, with occasionally a roof of
thatch.[3]

The agricultural and pastoral character of the people upon
whom the town depended for its existence was shown by the
class of objects displayed in the shop windows. Scythes, reap
hooks, sheep shears, bill hooks, spades, mattocks, and hoes at
the iron-monger's; beehives, butter firkins, churns, milking
stools and pails, hay rakes, field flagons, and seed lips at the
cooper's; cart ropes and plough harness at the saddler's; carts,
wheelbarrows, and mill gear at the wheelwright's and ma-
chinist's; horse embrocations at the chemist's; at the glover's
and leather-cutter's, hedging gloves, thatchers' kneecaps,
ploughmen's leggings, villagers' pattens and clogs.

They came to a grizzled church, whose massive square
tower rose unbroken into the darkening sky, the lower parts
being illuminated by the nearest lamps sufficiently to show
how completely the mortar from the joints of the stonework
had been nibbled out by time and weather, which had planted
in the crevices thus made little tufts of stone crop and grass
almost as far up as the very battlements. From this tower the
clock struck eight, and thereupon a bell began to toll with a
peremptory clang. The curfew was still rung in Casterbridge,
and it was utilized by the inhabitants as a signal for shutting
their shops. No sooner did the deep notes of the bell throb
between the housefronts than a clatter of shutters arose
through the whole length of the High Street. In a few minutes
business at Casterbridge was ended for the day.

Other clocks struck eight from time to time—one gloomily

3. Most of these old houses have now been pulled down (1912). (Hardy's
note.)

from the jail, another from the gable of an almshouse, with a preparative creak of machinery, more audible than the note of the bell; a row of tall, varnished case clocks from the interior of a clock-maker's shop joined in one after another just as the shutters were enclosing them, like a row of actors delivering their final speeches before the fall of the curtain; then chimes were heard stammering out the Sicilian Mariners' Hymn;[4] so that chronologists of the advanced school were appreciably on their way to the next hour before the whole business of the old one was satisfactorily wound up.

In an open space before the church walked a woman with her gown sleeves rolled up so high that the edge of her under-linen was visible, and her skirt tucked up through her pocket hole. She carried a loaf under her arm from which she was pulling pieces of bread and handing them to some other women who walked with her; which pieces they nibbled critically. The sight reminded Mrs. Henchard-Newson and her daughter that they had an appetite; and they inquired of the woman for the nearest baker's.

"Ye may as well look for manna-food as good bread in Casterbridge just now," she said, after directing them. "They can blare their trumpets and trump their drums, and have their roaring dinners"—waving her hand toward a point further along the street, where the brass band could be seen standing in front of an illuminated building—"but we must needs be put-to for want of a wholesome crust. There's less good bread than good beer in Casterbridge now."

"And less good beer than swipes," said a man with his hands in his pockets.

"How does it happen there's no good bread?" asked Mrs. Henchard.

"Oh, 'tis the corn[5] factor—he's the man that our millers and

---

4. These chimes, like those of other country churches, have been silenced for many years. (Hardy's note.)

5. *Corn:* Corn and wheat are used synonymously in England.

bakers all deal wi', and he has sold 'em growed wheat, which
they didn't know was growed, so they *say*, till the dough ran
all over the ovens like quicksilver; so that the loaves be as
flat as toads, and like suet pudden inside. I've been a wife, and
I've been a mother, and I never see such unprincipled bread
in Casterbridge as this before.—But you must be a real stranger
here not to know what's made all the poor volks' insides plim
like blowed bladders this week?"

"I am," said Elizabeth's mother shyly.

Not wishing to be observed further till she knew more of
her future in this place, she withdrew with her daughter from
the speaker's side. Getting a couple of biscuits at the shop
indicated as a temporary substitute for a meal, they next bent
their steps instinctively to where the music was playing.

. . . **CHAPTER 5**

A FEW score yards brought them to the spot where the town
band was now shaking the window panes with the strains of
"The Roast Beef of Old England."

The building before whose doors they had pitched their
music stands was the chief hotel in Casterbridge—namely, the
King's Arms. A spacious bow window projected into the
street over the main portico, and from the open sashes came
the babble of voices, the jingle of glasses, and the drawing of
corks. The blinds, moreover, being left unclosed, the whole
interior of this room could be surveyed from the top of a
flight of stone steps to the road-wagon office opposite, for
which reason a knot of idlers had gathered there.

"We might, perhaps, after all, make a few inquiries about
—our relation Mr. Henchard," whispered Mrs. Newson who,
since her entry into Casterbridge, had seemed strangely weak
and agitated. "And this, I think, would be a good place for
trying it—just to ask, you know, how he stands in the town

—if he is here, as I think he must be. You, Elizabeth-Jane, had better be the one to do it. I'm too worn out to do anything— pull down your fall first."

She sat down upon the lowest step, and Elizabeth-Jane obeyed her directions and stood among the idlers.

"What's going on tonight?" asked the girl, after singling out an old man and standing by him long enough to acquire a neighborly right of converse.

"Well, ye must be a stranger sure," said the old man, without taking his eyes from the window. "Why, 'tis a great public dinner of the gentle people and such like leading volk—wi' the Mayor in the chair. As we plainer fellows bain't invited, they leave the winder shutters open that we may get jist a sense o't out here. If you mount the steps you can see 'em. That's Mr. Henchard, the Mayor, at the end of the table, a facing ye; and that's the Council men right and left. . . . Ah, lots of them when they begun life were no more than I be now!"

"Henchard!" said Elizabeth-Jane, surprised, but by no means suspecting the whole force of the revelation. She ascended to the top of the steps.

Her mother, though her head was bowed, had already caught from the inn window tones that strangely riveted her attention, before the old man's words, "Mr. Henchard, the Mayor," reached her ears. She arose, and stepped up to her daughter's side as soon as she could do so without showing exceptional eagerness.

The interior of the hotel dining room was spread out before her, with its tables, and glass, and plate, and inmates. Facing the window, in the chair of dignity, sat a man about forty years of age; of heavy frame, large features, and commanding voice; his general build being rather coarse than compact. He had a rich complexion, which verged on swarthiness, a flashing black eye, and dark, bushy brows and hair. When he indulged in an occasional loud laugh at some remark among the guests, his large mouth parted so far back as to show to the rays of the chandelier a full score or more of the two-and-thirty sound white teeth that he obviously still could boast of.

That laugh was not encouraging to strangers; and hence it may have been well that it was rarely heard. Many theories might have been built upon it. It fell in well with conjectures of a temperament which would have no pity for weakness, but would be ready to yield ungrudging admiration to greatness and strength. Its producer's personal goodness, if he had any, would be of a very fitful cast—an occasional almost oppressive generosity rather than a mild and constant kindness.

Susan Henchard's husband—in law, at least—sat before them, matured in shape, stiffened in line, exaggerated in traits; disciplined, thought-marked—in a word, older. Elizabeth, encumbered with no recollections as her mother was, regarded him with nothing more than the keen curiosity and interest which the discovery of such unexpected social standing in the long-sought relative naturally begot. He was dressed in an old-fashioned suit, an expanse of frilled shirt showing on his broad breast; jeweled studs, and a heavy gold chain. Three glasses stood at his right hand; but, to his wife's surprise, the two for wine were empty, while the third, a tumbler, was half full of water.

When last she had seen him he was sitting in a corduroy jacket, fustian waistcoat and breeches, and tanned leather leggings, with a basin of hot furmity before him. Time, the magician, had wrought much here. Watching him, and thus thinking of past days, she became so moved that she shrank back against the jamb of the wagon-office doorway to which the steps gave access, the shadow from it conveniently hiding her features. She forgot her daughter till a touch from Elizabeth-Jane aroused her. "Have you seen him, Mother?" whispered the girl.

"Yes, yes," answered her companion hastily. "I have seen him, and it is enough for me! Now I only want to go—pass away—die."

"Why—O what?" She drew closer, and whispered in her mother's ear, "Does he seem to you not likely to befriend us? I thought he looked a generous man. What a gentleman he is, isn't he? And how his diamond studs shine! How strange that you should have said he might be in the stocks, or in the workhouse, or dead! Did ever anything go more by contraries! Why do you feel so afraid of him? I am not at all; I'll call upon him—he can but say he don't own such remote kin."

"I don't know at all—I can't tell what to set about. I feel so down."

"Don't be that, Mother, now we have got here and all! Rest there where you be a little while—I will look on and find out more about him."

"I don't think I can ever meet Mr. Henchard. He is not how I thought he would be—he overpowers me! I don't wish to see him any more."

"But wait a little time and consider."

Elizabeth-Jane had never been so much interested in anything in her life as in their present position, partly from the natural elation she felt at discovering herself akin to a coach; and she gazed again at the scene. The younger guests were talking and eating with animation; their elders were searching for tidbits, and sniffing and grunting over their plates like sows nuzzling for acorns. Three drinks seemed to be sacred to the company—port, sherry, and rum; outside which old-established trinity few or no palates ranged.

A row of ancient rummers with ground figures on their sides, and each primed with a spoon, was now placed down the table, and these were promptly filled with grog at such high temperatures as to raise serious considerations for the articles exposed to its vapors. But Elizabeth-Jane noticed that, though this filling went on with great promptness up and down the table, nobody filled the Mayor's glass, who still drank large quantities of water from the tumbler behind the clump of crystal vessels intended for wine and spirits.

"They don't fill Mr. Henchard's wineglasses," she ventured to say to her elbow acquaintance, the old man.

"Ah, no; don't ye know him to be the celebrated abstaining worthy of that name? He scorns all tempting liquors; never touches nothing. O yes, he've strong qualities that way. I have heard tell that he sware a gospel oath in bygone times, and has abode by it ever since. So they don't press him, knowing it would be unbecoming in the face of that; for yer gospel oath is a serious thing."

Another elderly man, hearing this discourse, now joined in by inquiring, "How much longer have he got to suffer from it, Solomon Longways?"

"Another two year, they say. I don't know the why and the wherefore of his fixing such a time, for 'a never has told anybody. But 'tis exactly two calendar years longer, they say. A powerful mind to hold out so long!"

"True. . . . But there's great strength in hope. Knowing that in four-and-twenty months' time ye'll be out of your bondage, and able to make up for all you've suffered, by partaking without stint—why, it keeps a man up, no doubt."

"No doubt, Christopher Coney, no doubt. And 'a must need such reflections—a lonely widow man," said Longways.

"When did he lose his wife?" asked Elizabeth.

"I never knowed her. 'Twas afore he came to Casterbridge," Solomon Longways replied with terminative emphasis, as if the fact of his ignorance of Mrs. Henchard were sufficient to deprive her history of all interest. "But I know that 'a's a banded teetotaler, and that if any of his men be ever so little overtook by a drop he's down upon 'em as stern as the Lord."

"Has he many men, then?" said Elizabeth-Jane.

"Many! Why, my good maid, he's the powerfulest member of the Town Council, and quite a principal man in the country round besides. Never a big dealing in wheat, barley, oats, hay, roots, and such-like but Henchard's got a hand in

it. Ay, and he'll go into other things too; and that's where he
makes his mistake. He worked his way up from nothing when
'a came here; and now he's a pillar of the town. Not but what
he's been shaken a little to-year about this bad corn he has
supplied in his contracts. I've seen the sun rise over Durnover
Moor these nine-and-sixty year, and though Mr. Henchard
has never cussed me unfairly ever since I've worked for'n,
seeing I be but a little small man, I must say that I have never
before tasted such rough bread as has been made from Henchard's wheat lately. 'Tis that growed out that ye could a'most
call it malt, and there's a list at bottom o' the loaf as thick as
the sole of one's shoe."

The band now struck up another melody, and by the time
it was ended the dinner was over, and speeches began to be
made. The evening being calm, and the windows still open,
these orations could be distinctly heard. Henchard's voice
arose above the rest; he was telling a story of his hay-dealing
experiences, in which he had outwitted a sharper who had
been bent upon outwitting him.

"Ha-ha-ha!" responded his audience at the upshot of the
story; and hilarity was general till a new voice arose with,
"This is all very well; but how about the bad bread?"

It came from the lower end of the table, where there sat
a group of minor tradesmen who, although part of the company, appeared to be a little below the social level of the
others; and who seemed to nourish a certain independence of
opinion and carry on discussions not quite in harmony with
those at the head; just as the west end of a church is sometimes persistently found to sing out of time and tune with the
leading spirits in the chancel.

This interruption about the bad bread afforded infinite satisfaction to the loungers outside, several of whom were in the
mood which finds its pleasures in others' discomfiture; and
hence they echoed pretty freely, "Hey! How about the bad

bread, Mr. Mayor?" Moreover, feeling none of the restraints
of those who shared the feast, they could afford to add, "You
rather ought to tell the story o' that, sir!"

The interruption was sufficient to compel the Mayor to
notice it.

"Well, I admit that the wheat turned out badly," he said.
"But I was taken in in buying it as much as the bakers who
bought it o' me."

"And the poor folk who had to eat it whether or no," said
the inharmonious man outside the window.

Henchard's face darkened. There was temper under the thin
bland surface—the temper which, artificially intensified, had
banished a wife nearly a score of years before.

"You must make allowances for the accidents of a large
business," he said. "You must bear in mind that the weather
just at the harvest of that corn was worse than we have known
it for years. However, I have mended my arrangements on account o't. Since I have found my business too large to be well
looked after by myself alone, I have advertised for a thorough
good man as manager of the corn department. When I've got
him you will find these mistakes will no longer occur—matters
will be better looked into."

"But what are you going to do to repay us for the past?"
inquired the man who had before spoken, and who seemed to
be a baker or miller. "Will you replace the grown flour we've
still got by sound grain?"

Henchard's face had become still more stern at these inter-
ruptions, and he drank from his tumbler of water as if to calm
himself or gain time. Instead of vouchsafing a direct reply, he
stiffly observed—

"If anybody will tell me how to turn grown wheat into
wholesome wheat I'll take it back with pleasure. But it can't
be done."

Henchard was not to be drawn again. Having said this, he
sat down.

CHAPTER 6

Now the group outside the window had within the last few minutes been reinforced by new arrivals, some of them respectable shopkeepers and their assistants, who had come out for a whiff of air after putting up the shutters for the night; some of them of a lower class. Distinct from either there appeared a stranger—a young man of remarkably pleasant aspect —who carried in his hand a carpetbag of the smart floral pattern prevalent in such articles at that time.

He was ruddy and of a fair countenance, bright-eyed, and slight in build. He might possibly have passed by without stopping at all, or at most for half a minute to glance in at the scene, had not his advent coincided with the discussion on corn and bread; in which event this history had never been enacted. But the subject seemed to arrest him, and he whispered some inquiries of the other bystanders, and remained listening.

When he heard Henchard's closing words, "It can't be done," he smiled impulsively, drew out his pocketbook and wrote down a few words by the aid of the light in the window. He tore out the leaf, folded and directed it, and seemed about to throw it in through the open sash upon the dining table; but, on second thoughts, edged himself through the loiterers, till he reached the door of the hotel, where one of the waiters who had been serving inside was now idly leaning against the doorpost.

"Give this to the Mayor at once," he said, handing in his hasty note.

Elizabeth-Jane had seen his movements and heard the words, which attracted her both by their subject and by their accent —a strange one for those parts. It was quaint and northerly.

The waiter took the note, while the young stranger continued——

"And can ye tell me of a respectable hotel that's a little more moderate than this?"

The waiter glanced indifferently up and down the street.

"They say the Three Mariners, just below here, is a very good place," he languidly answered; "but I have never stayed there myself."

The Scotchman, as he seemed to be, thanked him, and strolled on in the direction of the Three Mariners aforesaid, apparently more concerned about the question of an inn than about the fate of his note, now that the momentary impulse of writing it was over. While he was disappearing slowly down the street the waiter left the door, and Elizabeth-Jane saw with some interest the note brought into the dining room and handed to the Mayor.

Henchard looked at it carelessly, unfolded it with one hand, and glanced it through. Thereupon it was curious to note an unexpected effect. The nettled, clouded aspect which had held possession of his face since the subject of his corn dealings had been broached, changed itself into one of arrested attention. He read the note slowly, and fell into thought, not moody, but fitfully intense, as that of a man who has been captured by an idea.

By this time toasts and speeches had given place to songs, the wheat subject being quite forgotten. Men were putting their heads together in twos and threes, telling good stories, with pantomimic laughter which reached convulsive grimace. Some were beginning to look as if they did not know how they had come there, what they had come for, or how they were going to get home again; and provisionally sat on with a dazed smile. Square-built men showed a tendency to become hunchbacks; men with a dignified presence lost it in a curious obliquity of figure, in which their features grew disarranged and one-sided; whilst the heads of a few who had dined with extreme thoroughness were somehow sinking into their shoulders, the corners of their mouth and eyes being bent upwards by the subsidence. Only Henchard did not conform to these flexuous changes; he remained stately and vertical, silently thinking.

The clock struck nine. Elizabeth-Jane turned to her companion. "The evening is drawing on, Mother," she said. "What do you propose to do?"

She was surprised to find how irresolute her mother had become. "We must get a place to lie down in," she murmured. "I have seen—Mr. Henchard; and that's all I wanted to do."

"That's enough for tonight, at any rate," Elizabeth-Jane replied soothingly. "We can think tomorrow what is best to do about him. The question now is—is it not?—how shall we find a lodging?"

As her mother did not reply Elizabeth-Jane's mind reverted to the words of the waiter, that the Three Mariners was an inn of moderate charges. A recommendation good for one person was probably good for another. "Let's go where the young man has gone to," she said. "He is respectable. What do you say?"

Her mother assented, and down the street they went.

In the meantime the Mayor's thoughtfulness, engendered by the note as stated, continued to hold him in abstraction; till, whispering to his neighbor to take his place, he found opportunity to leave the chair. This was just after the departure of his wife and Elizabeth.

Outside the door of the assembly room he saw the waiter, and beckoning to him asked who brought the note which had been handed in a quarter of an hour before.

"A young man, sir—a sort of traveler. He was a Scotchman seemingly."

"Did he say how he had got it?"

"He wrote it himself, sir, as he stood outside the window."

"Oh—wrote it himself. . . . Is the young man in the hotel?"

"No, sir. He went to the Three Mariners, I believe."

The Mayor walked up and down the vestibule of the hotel with his hands under his coat tails, as if he were merely seeking a cooler atmosphere than that of the room he had quitted. But there could be no doubt that he was in reality still possessed to the full by the new idea, whatever that might be. At length he went back to the door of the dining room, paused, and found that the songs, toasts, and conversation were proceeding quite satisfactorily without his presence. The Corporation, private residents, and major and minor tradesmen had, in fact, gone in for comforting beverages to such an extent that they had quite forgotten, not only the Mayor, but all those vast political, religious, and social differences which they felt necessary to maintain in the daytime, and which separated them like iron grills. Seeing this the Mayor took his hat, and when the waiter had helped him on with a thin Holland overcoat, went out and stood under the portico.

Very few persons were now in the street; and his eyes, by a sort of attraction, turned and dwelt upon a spot about a hundred yards further down. It was the house to which the writer of the note had gone—the Three Mariners—whose two prominent Elizabethan gables, bow window, and passage light could be seen from where he stood. Having kept his eyes on it for a while he strolled in that direction.

This ancient house of accommodation for man and beast, now, unfortunately, pulled down, was built of mellow sandstone, with mullioned windows of the same material, markedly out of perpendicular from the settlement of foundations. The bay window projecting into the street, whose interior was so popular among the frequenters of the inn, was closed with shutters, in each of which appeared a heart-shaped aperture, somewhat more attenuated in the right and left ventricles than is seen in Nature. Inside these illuminated holes, at a distance of about three inches, were ranged at this hour, as every passer knew, the ruddy polls of Billy Wills the glazier, Smart the shoemaker, Buzzford the general dealer, and others of a secondary set of worthies, of a grade somewhat below that of the diners at the King's Arms, each with his yard of clay.

A four-centered Tudor arch was over the entrance, and

over the arch the signboard, now visible in the rays of an opposite lamp. Hereon the Mariners, who had been represented
by the artist as persons of two dimensions only—in other
words, flat as a shadow—were standing in a row in paralyzed
attitudes. Being on the sunny side of the street the three
comrades had suffered largely from warping, splitting, fading,
and shrinkage, so that they were but a half-invisible film upon
the reality of the grain, and knots, and nails, which composed
the signboard. As a matter of fact, this state of things was not
so much owing to Stannidge the landlord's neglect, as from
the lack of a painter in Casterbridge who would undertake to
reproduce the features of men so traditional.

A long, narrow, dimly-lit passage gave access to the inn,
within which passage the horses going to their stalls at the
back, and the coming and departing human guests, rubbed
shoulders indiscriminately, the latter running no slight risk of
having their toes trodden upon by the animals. The good
stabling and the good ale of the Mariners, though somewhat
difficult to reach on account of there being but this narrow
way to both, were nevertheless perseveringly sought out by
the sagacious old heads who knew what was what in Casterbridge.

Henchard stood without the inn for a few instants; then
lowering the dignity of his presence as much as possible by
buttoning the brown Holland coat over his shirt front, and
in other ways toning himself down to his ordinary everyday
appearance, he entered the inn door.

. . . **CHAPTER 7**

Elizabeth-Jane and her mother had arrived some twenty
minutes earlier. Outside the house they had stood and considered whether even this homely place, though recommended
as moderate, might not be too serious in its prices for their light

pockets. Finally, however, they had found courage to enter, and duly met Stannidge the landlord; a silent man, who drew and carried frothing measures to this room and to that, shoulder to shoulder with his waiting maids—a stately slowness, however, entering into his ministrations by contrast with theirs, as became one whose service was somewhat optional. It would have been altogether optional but for the orders of the landlady, a person who sat in the bar, corporeally motionless, but with a flitting eye and quick ear, with which she observed and heard through the open door and hatchway the pressing needs of customers whom her husband overlooked though close at hand. Elizabeth and her mother were passively accepted as sojourners, and shown to a small bedroom under one of the gables, where they sat down.

The principle of the inn seemed to be to compensate for the antique awkwardness, crookedness, and obscurity of the passages, floors, and windows, by quantities of clean linen spread about everywhere, and this had a dazzling effect upon the travelers.

" 'Tis too good for us—we can't meet it!" said the elder woman, looking round the apartment with misgiving as soon as they were left alone.

"I fear it is, too," said Elizabeth. "But we must be respectable."

"We must pay our way even before we must be respectable," replied her mother. "Mr. Henchard is too high for us to make ourselves known to him, I much fear; so we've only our own pockets to depend on."

"I know what I'll do," said Elizabeth-Jane after an interval of waiting, during which their needs seemed quite forgotten under the press of business below. And leaving the room, she descended the stairs and penetrated to the bar.

If there was one good thing more than another which characterized this single-hearted girl it was a willingness to sacrifice her personal comfort and dignity to the common weal.

"As you seem busy here tonight, and mother's not well off, might I take out part of our accommodation by helping?" she asked of the landlady.

The latter, who remained as fixed in the armchair as if she had been melted into it when in a liquid state, and could not now be unstuck, looked the girl up and down inquiringly, with her hands on the chair arms. Such arrangements as the one Elizabeth proposed were not uncommon in country villages; but, though Casterbridge was old-fashioned, the custom was well-nigh obsolete here. The mistress of the house, however, was an easy woman to strangers, and she made no objection. Thereupon Elizabeth, being instructed by nods and motions from the taciturn landlord as to where she could find the different things, trotted up and down stairs with materials for her own and her parent's meal.

While she was doing this the wood partition in the center of the house thrilled to its center with the tugging of a bell-pull upstairs. A bell below tinkled a note that was feebler in sound than the twanging of wires and cranks that had produced it.

"'Tis the Scotch gentleman," said the landlady omnisciently; and turning her eyes to Elizabeth, "Now then, can you go and see if his supper is on the tray? If it is you can take it up to him. The front room over this."

Elizabeth-Jane, though hungry, willingly postponed serving herself awhile, and applied to the cook in the kitchen, whence she brought forth the tray of supper viands, and proceeded with it upstairs to the apartment indicated. The accommodation of the Three Mariners was far from spacious, despite the fair area of ground it covered. The room demanded by intrusive beams and rafters, partitions, passages, staircases, disused ovens, settles, and four-posters, left comparatively small quarters for human beings. Moreover, this being at a time before home-brewing was abandoned by the smaller victualers, and a house in which the twelve-bushel strength was still religiously adhered to by the landlord in his ale, the quality of the liquor was the chief attraction of the premises, so that everything had to make way for utensils and operations in connection therewith. Thus Elizabeth found that the Scotchman was located in a room quite close to the small one that had been allotted to herself and her mother.

When she entered nobody was present but the younger man himself—the same whom she had seen lingering without the windows of the King's Arms Hotel. He was now idly reading a copy of the local paper, and was hardly conscious of her entry, so that she looked at him quite coolly, and saw how his forehead shone where the light caught it, and how nicely his hair was cut, and the sort of velvet pile or down that was on the skin at the back of his neck, and how his cheek was so truly curved as to be part of a globe, and how clearly drawn were the lids and lashes which hid his bent eyes.

She set down the tray, spread his supper, and went away without a word. On her arrival below the landlady, who was as kind as she was fat and lazy, saw that Elizabeth-Jane was rather tired, though in her earnestness to be useful she was waiving her own needs altogether. Mrs. Stannidge thereupon said with a considerate peremptoriness that she and her mother had better take their own suppers if they meant to have any.

Elizabeth fetched their simple provisions, as she had fetched the Scotchman's, and went up to the little chamber where she had left her mother, noiselessly pushing open the door with the edge of the tray. To her surprise her mother, instead of being reclined on the bed where she had left her, was in an erect position, with lips parted. At Elizabeth's entry she lifted her finger.

The meaning of this was soon apparent. The room allotted to the two women had at one time served as a dressing room to the Scotchman's chamber, as was evidenced by signs of a door of communication between them—now screwed up and pasted over with the wall-paper. But, as is frequently the case with hotels of far higher pretensions than the Three Mariners, every word spoken in either of these rooms was distinctly audible in the other. Such sounds came through now.

Thus silently conjured Elizabeth deposited the tray, and her mother whispered as she drew near, " 'Tis he."

"Who?" said the girl.

"The Mayor."

The tremors in Susan Henchard's tone might have led any person but one so perfectly unsuspicious of the truth as the girl was, to surmise some closer connection than the admitted simple kinship as a means of accounting for them.

Two men were indeed talking in the adjoining chamber, the young Scotchman and Henchard, who, having entered the inn while Elizabeth-Jane was in the kitchen waiting for the supper, had been deferentially conducted upstairs by host Stannidge himself. The girl noiselessly laid out their little meal, and beckoned to her mother to join her, which Mrs. Henchard mechanically did, her attention being fixed on the conversation through the door.

"I merely strolled in on my way home to ask you a question about something that has excited my curiosity," said the Mayor, with careless geniality. "But I see you have not finished supper."

"Ay, but I will be done in a little! Ye needn't go, sir. Take a seat. I've almost done, and it makes no difference at all."

Henchard seemed to take the seat offered, and in a moment he resumed: "Well, first I should ask, did you write this?" A rustling of paper followed.

"Yes, I did," said the Scotchman.

"Then," said Henchard," I am under the impression that we have met by accident while waiting for the morning to keep an appointment with each other? My name is Henchard; ha'n't you replied to an advertisement for a corn-factor's manager that I put into the paper—ha'n't you come here to see me about it?"

"No," said the Scotchman, with some surprise.

"Surely you are the man," went on Henchard insistingly, "who arranged to come and see me? Joshua, Joshua, Jipp—Jopp—what was his name?"

"You're wrong!" said the young man. "My name is Donald Farfrae. It is true I am in the corren trade—but I have replied to no advairrtisment, and arranged to see no one. I am on my way to Bristol—from there to the other side of the warrld, to try my fortune in the great wheat-growing districts of the West! I have some inventions useful to the trade, and there is no scope for developing them heere."

"To America—well, well," said Henchard, in a tone of disappointment, so strong as to make itself felt like a damp atmosphere. "And yet I could have sworn you were the man."

The Scotchman murmured another negative, and there was a silence, till Henchard resumed: "Then I am truly and sincerely obliged to you for the few words you wrote on that paper."

"It was nothing, sir."

"Well, it has a great importance for me just now. This row about my grown wheat, which I declare to Heaven I didn't know to be bad till the people came complaining, has put me to my wits' end. I've some hundreds of quarters of it on hand; and if your renovating process will make it wholesome, why, you can see what a quag 'twould get me out of. I saw in a moment there might be truth in it. But I should like to have it proved; and of course you don't care to tell the steps of the process sufficiently for me to do that, without my paying ye well for't first."

The young man reflected a moment or two. "I don't know that I have any objection," he said. "I'm going to another country, and curing bad corn is not the line I'll take up there. Yes, I'll tell ye the whole of it—you'll make more out of it heere than I will in a foreign country. Just look heere a minute, sir. I can show ye by a sample in my carpetbag."

The click of a lock followed, and there was a sifting and rustling; then a discussion about so many ounces to the bushel, and drying, and refrigerating, and so on.

"These few grains will be sufficient to show ye with," came in the young fellow's voice; and after a pause, during which some operation seemed to be intently watched by them both, he exclaimed, "There, now, do you taste that."

"It's complete!—quite restored, or—well—nearly."

"Quite enough restored to make good seconds out of it," said the Scotchman. "To fetch it back entirely is impossible; Nature won't stand so much as that, but heere you go a great way toward it. Well, sir, that's the process; I don't value it, for it can be but of little use in countries where the weather is more settled than in ours; and I'll be only too glad if it's of service to you."

"But hearken to me," pleaded Henchard. "My business, you know, is in corn and in hay; but I was brought up as a hay-trusser simply, and hay is what I understand best, though I now do more in corn than in the other. If you'll accept the place, you shall manage the corn branch entirely, and receive a commission in addition to salary."

"You're liberal—very liberal; but no, no—I cannet!" the young man still replied, with some distress in his accents.

"So be it!" said Henchard conclusively. "Now—to change the subject—one good turn deserves another; don't stay to finish that miserable supper. Come to my house; I can find something better for 'ee than cold ham and ale."

Donald Farfrae was grateful—said he feared he must decline—that he wished to leave early next day.

"Very well," said Henchard quickly, "please yourself. But I tell you, young man, if this holds good for the bulk, as it has done for the sample, you have saved my credit, stranger though you be. What shall I pay you for this knowledge?"

"Nothing at all, nothing at all. It may not prove necessary to ye to use it often, and I don't value it at all. I thought I might just as well let ye know, as you were in a difficulty, and they were harrd upon ye."

Henchard paused. "I shan't soon forget this," he said. "And from a stranger! . . . I couldn't believe you were not the man I had engaged! Says I to myself 'He knows who I am, and recommends himself by this stroke.' And yet it turns out, after all, that you are not the man who answered my advertisement, but a stranger!"

"Ay, ay; that's so," said the young man.

Henchard again suspended his words, and then his voice came thoughtfully: "Your forehead, Farefrae, is something like my poor brother's—now dead and gone; and the nose, too, isn't unlike his. You must be, what—five foot nine, I reckon? I am six foot one and a half out of my shoes. But what of that? In my business, 'tis true that strength and bustle build up a firm. But judgment and knowledge are what keep it established. Unluckily, I am bad at science, Farfrae; bad at figures —a rule o' thumb sort of man. You are just the reverse—I can see that. I have been looking for such as you these two year, and yet you are not for me. Well, before I go, let me ask this: Though you are not the young man I thought you were, what's the difference? Can't ye stay just the same? Have you really made up your mind about this American notion? I won't mince matters. I feel you would be invaluable to me —that needn't be said—and if you will bide and be my manager, I will make it worth your while."

"My plans are fixed," said the young man, in negative tones. "I have formed a scheme, and so we need na say any more about it. But will you not drink with me, sir? I find this Casterbridge ale warreming to the stomach."

"No, no; I fain would, but I can't," said Henchard gravely, the scraping of his chair informing the listeners that he was rising to leave. "When I was a young man I went in for that sort of thing too strong—far too strong—and was well-nigh ruined by it! I did a deed on account of it which I shall be ashamed of to my dying day. It made such an impression on me that I swore, there and then, that I'd drink nothing stronger than tea for as many years as I was old that day. I have kept my oath; and though, Farfrae, I am sometimes that dry in the dog days that I could drink a quarter-barrel to the pitching, I think o' my oath, and touch no strong drink at all."

"I'll no' press ye, sir—I'll no' press ye. I respect your vow."

"Well, I shall get a manager somewhere, no doubt," said Henchard, with strong feeling in his tones. "But it will be long before I see one that would suit me so well!"

The young man appeared much moved by Henchard's warm convictions of his value. He was silent till they reached the door. "I wish I could stay—sincerely I would like to," he replied. "But no—it cannet be! It cannet! I want to see the warrld."

. . . CHAPTER 8

THUS they parted; and Elizabeth-Jane and her mother remained each in her thoughts over their meal, the mother's face being strangely bright since Henchard's avowal of shame for a past action. The quivering of the partition to its core presently denoted that Donald Farfrae had again rung his bell, no doubt to have his supper removed; for humming a tune, and walking up and down, he seemed to be attracted by the lively bursts of conversation and melody from the general company below. He sauntered out upon the landing, and descended the staircase.

When Elizabeth-Jane had carried down his supper tray, and also that used by her mother and herself, she found the bustle of serving to be at its height below, as it always was at this hour. The young woman shrank from having anything to do with the ground-floor serving, and crept silently about observing the scene—so new to her, fresh from the seclusion of a seaside cottage. In the general sitting room, which was large, she remarked the two or three dozen strong-backed chairs that stood round against the wall, each fitted with its genial occupant; the sanded floor; the black settle which, projecting endwise from the wall within the door, permitted Elizabeth to be a spectator of all that went on without herself being particularly seen.

The young Scotchman had just joined the guests. These, in addition to the respectable master-tradesmen occupying the seats of privilege in the bow window and its neighborhood, included an inferior set at the unlighted end, whose seats were benches against the wall, and who drank from cups instead of from glasses. Among the latter she noticed some of those personages who had stood outside the windows of the King's Arms.

Behind their backs was a small window, with a wheel ventilator in one of the panes, which would suddenly start off spinning with a jingling sound, as suddenly stop, and as suddenly start again.

While thus furtively making her survey the opening words of a song greeted her ears from the front of the settle, in a melody and accent of peculiar charm. There had been some singing before she came down; and now the Scotchman had made himself so soon at home that, at the request of some of the master-tradesmen, he, too, was favoring the room with a ditty.

Elizabeth-Jane was fond of music; she could not help pausing to listen; and the longer she listened the more she was enraptured. She had never heard any singing like this; and it was evident that the majority of the audience had not heard such frequently, for they were attentive to a much greater degree than usual. They neither whispered, nor drank, nor dipped their pipestems in their ale to moisten them, nor pushed the mug to their neighbors. The singer himself grew emotional, till she could imagine a tear in his eye as the words went on:—

"It's hame, and it's hame, hame fain would I be,

O hame, hame, hame to my ain countree!
There's an eye that ever weeps, and a fair face will be fain,
As I pass through Annan Water with my bonnie bands again;
When the flower is in the bud, and the leaf upon the tree,
The lark shall sing me hame to my ain countree!"

There was a burst of applause, and a deep silence which was even more eloquent than the applause. It was of such a kind that the snapping of a pipestem too long for him by old Solomon Longways, who was one of those gathered at the shady end of the room, seemed a harsh and irreverent act. Then the ventilator in the window pane spasmodically started off for a new spin, and the pathos of Donald's song was temporarily effaced.

" 'Twas not amiss—not at all amiss!" muttered Christopher Coney, who was also present. And removing his pipe a finger's breadth from his lips, he said aloud, "Draw on with the next verse, young gentleman, please."

"Yes. Let's have it again, stranger," said the glazier, a stout, bucket-headed man, with a white apron rolled up round his waist. "Folks don't lift up their hearts like that in this part of the world." And turning aside, he said in undertones, "Who is the young man?—Scotch, d'ye say?"

"Yes, straight from the mountains of Scotland, I believe," replied Coney.

Young Farfrae repeated the last verse. It was plain that nothing so pathetic had been heard at the Three Mariners for a considerable time. The difference of accent, the excitability of the singer, the intense local feeling, and the seriousness with which he worked himself up to a climax, surprised this set of worthies, who were only too prone to shut up their emotions with caustic words.

"Danged if our country down here is worth singing about like that!" continued the glazier, as the Scotchman again melodized with a dying fall, "My ain countree!" "When you take away from among us the fools and the rogues, and the

lammigers, and the wanton hussies, and the slatterns, and
such like, there's cust few left to ornament a song with in
Casterbridge, or the country round."

"True," said Buzzford, the dealer, looking at the grain of
the table. "Casterbridge is a old, hoary place o' wickedness,
by all account. 'Tis recorded in history that we rebelled
against the King one or two hundred years ago, in the time
of the Romans, and that lots of us was hanged on Gallows
Hill, and quartered, and our different jints sent about the
country like butcher's meat; and for my part I can well believe it."

"What did ye come away from yer own country for,
young maister, if ye be so wownded about it?" inquired
Christopher Coney, from the background, with the tone of
a man who preferred the original subject. "Faith, it wasn't
worth your while on our account, for, as Maister Billy Wills
says, we be bruckle folk here—the best o' us hardly honest
sometimes, what with hard winters, and so many mouths to
fill, and God a'mighty sending his little taties so terrible small
to fill 'em with. We don't think about flowers and fair faces,
not we—except in the shape o' cauliflowers and pigs' chaps."

"But, no!" said Donald Farfrae, gazing round into their
faces with earnest concern; "the best of ye hardly honest—
not that surely? None of ye has been stealing what didn't
belong to him?"

"Lord! no, no!" said Solomon Longways, smiling grimly.
"That's only his random way o' speaking. 'A was always such
a man of under-thoughts." (And reprovingly toward Christopher): "Don't ye be so over-familiar with a gentleman that
ye know nothing of—and that's traveled a'most from the
North Pole."

Christopher Coney was silenced, and as he could get no
public sympathy, he mumbled his feelings to himself: "Be
dazed, if I loved my country half as well as the young feller
do, I'd live by claning my neighbor's pigsties afore I'd go

away! For my part I've no more love for my country than I have for Botany Bay!"[1]

"Come," said Longways; "let the young man draw onward with his ballet, or we shall be here all night."

"Soul of my body, then we'll have another!" said the general dealer.

"Can you turn a strain to the ladies, sir?" inquired a fat woman with a figured purple apron, the waist string of which was overhung so far by her sides as to be invisible.

"Let him breathe—let him breathe, Mother Cuxsom. He hain't got his second wind yet," said the master glazier.

"O yes, but I have!" exclaimed the young man; and he at once rendered "O Nannie" with faultless modulations, and another or two of the like sentiment, winding up at their earnest request with "Auld Lang Syne."

By this time he had completely taken possession of the hearts of the Three Mariners' inmates, including even old Coney. Notwithstanding an occasional odd gravity which awoke their sense of the ludicrous for the moment, they began to view him through a golden haze which the tone of his mind seemed to raise around him. Casterbridge had sentiment—Casterbridge had romance; but this stranger's sentiment was of differing quality. Or rather, perhaps, the difference was mainly superficial; he was to them like the poet of a new school who takes his contemporaries by storm; who is not really new, but is the first to articulate what all his listeners have felt, though but dumbly till then.

The silent landlord came and leaned over the settle while the young man sang; and even Mrs. Stannidge managed to unstick herself from the framework of her chair in the bar and get as far as the doorpost, which movement she accomplished by rolling herself round, as a cask is trundled on the chine by a drayman without losing much of its perpendicular.

"And are you going to bide in Casterbridge, sir?" she asked.

1. *Botany Bay:* penal colony in the Pacific.

"Ah—no!" said the Scotchman, with melancholy fatality in his voice, "I'm only passing thirrough! I am on my way to Bristol, and on frae there to foreign parts."

"We be truly sorry to hear it," said Solomon Longways. "We can ill afford to lose tuneful windpipes like yours when they fall among us. And verily, to mak' acquaintance with a man a-come from so far, from the land o' perpetual snow, as we may say, where wolves and wild boars and other dangerous animalcules be as common as blackbirds hereabout— why, 'tis a thing we can't do every day; and there's good sound information for bide-at-homes like we when such a man opens his mouth."

"Nay, but ye mistake my country," said the young man, looking round upon them with tragic fixity, till his eye lighted up and his cheek kindled with a sudden enthusiasm to right their errors. "There are not perpetual snow and wolves at all in it!—except snow in winter, and—well—a little in summer just sometimes, and a 'gaberlunzie' or two stalking about here and there, if ye may call them dangerous. Eh, but you should take a summer jarreny to Edinboro', and Arthur's Seat, and all round there, and then go on to the lochs, and all the Highland scenery—in May and June—and you would never say 'tis the land of wolves and perpetual snow!"

"Of course not—it stands to reason," said Buzzford. " 'Tis barren ignorance that leads to such words. He's a simple homespun man, that never was fit for good company—think nothing of him, sir."

"And do ye carry your flock bed, and your quilt, and your crock, and your bit of chiney? or do ye go in bare bones, as I may say?" inquired Christopher Coney.

"I've sent on my luggage—though it isn't much; for the voyage is long." Donald's eyes dropped into a remote gaze as he added: "But I said to myself, 'Never a one of the prizes of life will I come by unless I undertake it!' and I decided to go."

A general sense of regret, in which Elizabeth-Jane shared

not least, made itself apparent in the company. As she looked at Farfrae from the back of the settle she decided that his statements showed him to be no less thoughtful than his fascinating melodies revealed him to be cordial and impassioned. She admired the serious light in which he looked at serious things. He had seen no jest in ambiguities and roguery, as the Casterbridge toss-pots had done; and rightly not—there was none. She disliked those wretched humors of Christopher Coney and his tribe; and he did not appreciate them. He seemed to feel exactly as she felt about life and its surroundings—that they were a tragical rather than a comical thing; that though one could be gay on occasion, moments of gaiety were interludes, and no part of the actual drama. It was extraordinary how similar their views were.

Though it was still early the young Scotchman expressed his wish to retire, whereupon the landlady whispered to Elizabeth to run upstairs and turn down his bed. She took a candlestick and proceeded on her mission, which was the act of a few moments only. When, candle in hand, she reached the top of the stairs on her way down again, Mr. Farfrae was at the foot coming up. She could not very well retreat; they met and passed in the turn of the staircase.

She must have appeared interesting in some way—notwithstanding her plain dress—or rather, possibly, in consequence of it, for she was a girl characterized by earnestness and soberness of mien, with which simple drapery accorded well. Her face flushed, too, at the slight awkwardness of the meeting, and she passed him with her eyes bent on the candle flame that she carried just below her nose. Thus it happened that when confronting her he smiled; and then, with the manner of a temporarily light-hearted man, who has started himself on a flight of song whose momentum he cannot readily check, he softly tuned an old ditty that she seemed to suggest—

> "As I came in by my bower door,
>   As day was waxin' wearie,

Oh wha came tripping down the stair
But bonnie Peg my dearie."

Elizabeth-Jane, rather disconcerted, hastened on; and the
Scotchman's voice died away, humming more of the same
within the closed door of his room.

Here the scene and sentiment ended for the present. When,
soon after, the girl rejoined her mother, the latter was still
in thought—on quite another matter than a young man's song.

"We've made a mistake," she whispered (that the Scotchman might not overhear). "On no account ought ye to have
helped serve here tonight. Not because of ourselves, but for
the sake of *him*. If he should befriend us, and take us up, and
then find out what you did when staying here, 'twould grieve
and wound his natural pride as Mayor of the town."

Elizabeth, who would perhaps have been more alarmed at
this than her mother had she known the real relationship, was
not much disturbed about it as things stood. Her "he" was
another man than her poor mother's. "For myself," she said,
"I didn't at all mind waiting a little upon him. He's so respectable, and educated—far above the rest of 'em in the inn.
They thought him very simple not to know their grim broad
way of talking about themselves here. But of course he didn't
know—he was too refined in his mind to know such things!"
Thus she earnestly pleaded.

Meanwhile, the "he" of her mother was not so far away as
even they thought. After leaving the Three Mariners he had
sauntered up and down the empty High Street, passing and
repassing the inn in his promenade. When the Scotchman
sang his voice had reached Henchard's ears through the heart-
shaped holes in the window shutters, and had led him to pause
outside them a long while.

"To be sure, to be sure, how that fellow does draw me!"
he had said to himself. "I suppose 'tis because I'm so lonely.
I'd have given him a third share in the business to have
stayed!"

CHAPTER 9

WHEN Elizabeth-Jane opened the hinged casement next morning the mellow air brought in the feel of imminent autumn almost as distinctly as if she had been in the remotest hamlet. Casterbridge was the complement of the rural life around; not its urban opposite. Bees and butterflies in the cornfields at the top of the town, who desired to get to the meads at the bottom, took no circuitous course, but flew straight down High Street without any apparent consciousness that they were traversing strange latitudes. And in autumn airy spheres of thistledown floated into the same street, lodged upon the shop fronts, blew into drains; and innumerable tawny and yellow leaves skimmed along the pavement, and stole through people's doorways into their passages with a hesitating scratch on the floor, like the skirts of timid visitors.

Hearing voices, one of which was close at hand, she withdrew her head and glanced from behind the window curtains. Mr. Henchard—now habited no longer as a great personage, but as a thriving man of business—was pausing on his way up the middle of the street, and the Scotchman was looking from the window adjoining her own. Henchard, it appeared, had gone a little way past the inn before he had noticed his acquaintance of the previous evening. He came back a few steps, Donald Farfrae opening the window further.

"And you are off soon, I suppose?" said Henchard upwards.

"Yes—almost this moment, sir," said the other. "Maybe I'll walk on till the coach makes up on me."

"Which way?"

"The way ye are going."

"Then shall we walk together to the top o' town?"

"If ye'll wait a minute," said the Scotchman.

In a few minutes the latter emerged, bag in hand. Henchard looked at the bag as at an enemy. It showed there was no mistake about the young man's departure. "Ah, my lad," he said, "you should have been a wise man, and have stayed with me."

"Yes, yes—it might have been wiser," said Donald, looking microscopically at the houses that were furthest off. "It is only telling ye the truth when I say my plans are vague."

They had by this time passed on from the precincts of the inn, and Elizabeth-Jane heard no more. She saw that they continued in conversation, Henchard turning to the other occasionally, and emphasizing some remark with a gesture. Thus they passed the King's Arms Hotel, the Market House, St. Peter's churchyard wall, ascending to the upper end of the long street till they were small as two grains of corn; when they bent suddenly to the right into the Bristol Road, and were out of view.

"He was a good man—and he's gone," she said to herself. "I was nothing to him, and there was no reason why he should have wished me good-by."

The simple thought, with its latent sense of slight, had molded itself out of the following little fact: when the Scotchman came out at the door he had by accident glanced up at her; and then he had looked away again without nodding, or smiling, or saying a word.

"You are still thinking, mother," she said, when she turned inwards.

"Yes; I am thinking of Mr. Henchard's sudden liking for that young man. He was always so. Now, surely, if he takes so warmly to people who are not related to him at all, may he not take as warmly to his own kin?"

While they debated this question a procession of five large wagons went past, laden with hay up to the bedroom windows. They came in from the country, and the steaming horses had probably been traveling a great part of the night. To the shaft of each hung a little board, on which was painted in white letters, "Henchard, Corn Factor and Hay Merchant."

The spectacle renewed his wife's conviction that, for her daughter's sake, she should strain a point to rejoin him.

The discussion was continued during breakfast, and the end of it was that Mrs. Henchard decided, for good or for ill, to send Elizabeth-Jane with a message to Henchard, to the effect that his relative Susan, a sailor's widow, was in town; leaving it to him to say whether or not he would recognize her. What had brought her to this determination were chiefly two things. He had been described as a lonely widower; and he had expressed shame for a past transaction of his life. There was promise in both.

"If he says no," she enjoined, as Elizabeth-Jane stood, bonnet on, ready to depart; "if he thinks it does not become the good position he has reached to in the town, to own—to let us call on him as—his distant kinsfolk, say, 'Then, sir, we would rather not intrude; we will leave Casterbridge as quietly as we have come, and go back to our own country.' . . . I almost feel that I would rather he did say so, as I have not seen him for so many years, and we are so—little allied to him!"

"And if he say yes?" inquired the more sanguine one.

"In that case," answered Mrs. Henchard cautiously, "ask him to write me a note, saying when and how he will see us —or *me*."

Elizabeth-Jane went a few steps towards the landing. "And tell him," continued her mother, "that I fully know I have no claim upon him—that I am glad to find he is thriving; that I hope his life may be long and happy—there, go." Thus with a half-hearted willingness, a smothered reluctance, did the poor forgiving woman start her unconscious daughter on this errand.

It was about ten o'clock, and market day, when Elizabeth paced up the High Street, in no great hurry; for to herself her position was only that of a poor relation deputed to hunt up a rich one. The front doors of the private houses were mostly left open at this warm autumn time, no thought of umbrella stealers disturbing the minds of the placid burgesses. Hence, through the long, straight entrance passages thus unclosed could be seen, as through tunnels, the mossy gardens at the back, glowing with nasturtiums, fuchsias, scarlet geraniums, "bloody warriors," snap-dragons, and dahlias, this floral blaze being backed by crusted gray stonework remaining from a yet remoter Casterbridge than the venerable one visible in the street. The old-fashioned fronts of these houses, which had older than old-fashioned backs, rose sheer from the pavement, into which the bow windows protruded like bastions, necessitating a pleasing *chassez-déchassez*[1] movement to the time-pressed pedestrian at every few yards. He was bound also to evolve other Terpsichorean[2] figures in respect of doorsteps, scrapers, cellar hatches, church buttresses, and the over-hanging angles of walls which, originally unobtrusive, had become bowlegged and knock-kneed.

In addition to these fixed obstacles which spoke so cheerfully of individual unrestraint as to boundaries, movables occupied the path and roadway to a perplexing extent. First the vans of the carriers in and out of Casterbridge, who hailed from Mellstock, Weatherbury, the Hintocks, Sherton-Abbas, Kingsbere, Overcombe, and many other towns and villages round. Their owners were numerous enough to be regarded as a tribe, and had almost distinctiveness enough to be regarded as a race. Their vans had just arrived, and were drawn up on each side of the street in close file, so as to form at places a wall between the pavement and the roadway. Moreover, every shop pitched out half its contents upon trestles and boxes on the curb, extending the display each week a little further and further into the roadway, despite the expostulations of the two feeble old constables, until there remained but a tortuous defile for carriages down the center of the street, which af-

---

1. *Chassez-déchassez:* out and back (French).
2. *Terpsichorean:* dancing.

forded fine opportunities for skill with the reins. Over the pavement on the sunny side of the way hung shopblinds so constructed as to give the passenger's hat a smart buffet off his head, as from the unseen hands of Cranstoun's Goblin Page, celebrated in romantic lore.

Horses for sale were tied in rows, their forelegs on the pavement, their hind legs in the street, in which position they occasionally nipped little boys by the shoulder who were passing to school. And any inviting recess in front of a house that had been modestly kept back from the general line was utilized by pig dealers as a pen for their stock.[3]

The yeomen, farmers, dairymen, and townsfolk, who came to transact business in these ancient streets, spoke in other ways than by articulation. Not to hear the words of your interlocutor in metropolitan centers is to know nothing of his meaning. Here the face, the arms, the hat, the stick, the body throughout spoke equally with the tongue. To express satisfaction the Casterbridge market man added to his utterance a broadening of the cheeks, a crevicing of the eyes, a throwing back of the shoulders, which was intelligible from the other end of the street. If he wondered, though all Henchard's carts and wagons were rattling past him, you knew it from perceiving the inside of his crimson mouth, and a target-like circling of his eyes. Deliberation caused sundry attacks on the moss of adjoining walls with the end of his stick, a change of his hat from the horizontal to the less so; a sense of tediousness announced itself in a lowering of the person by spreading the knees to a lozenge-shaped aperture and contorting the arms. Chicanery, subterfuge, had hardly a place in the streets of this honest borough to all appearance; and it was said that the lawyers in the courthouse hard by occasionally threw in strong arguments for the other side out of pure generosity

3. The reader will scarcely need to be reminded that time and progress have obliterated from the town that suggested these descriptions many or most of the old-fashioned features here enumerated. (Hardy's note.)

(though apparently by mischance) when advancing their own.

Thus Casterbridge was in most respects but the pole, focus, or nerve knot of the surrounding country life; differing from the many manufacturing towns which are as foreign bodies set down, like boulders on a plain, in a green world with which they have nothing in common. Casterbridge lived by agriculture at one remove further from the fountainhead than the adjoining villages—no more. The townsfolk understood every fluctuation in the rustic's condition, for it affected their receipts as much as the laborer's; they entered into the troubles and joys which moved the aristocratic families ten miles round —for the same reason. And even at the dinner parties of the professional families the subjects of discussion were corn, cattle disease, sowing and reaping, fencing and planting; while politics were viewed by them less from their own standpoint of burgesses with rights and privileges than from the standpoint of their county neighbors.

All the venerable contrivances and confusions which delighted the eye by their quaintness, and in a measure reasonableness, in this rare old market town, were metropolitan novelties to the unpracticed eyes of Elizabeth-Jane, fresh from netting fish seines in a seaside cottage. Very little inquiry was necessary to guide her footsteps. Henchard's house was one of the best, faced with dull red and gray old brick. The front door was open, and, as in other houses, she could see through the passage to the end of the garden—nearly a quarter of a mile off.

Mr. Henchard was not in the house, but in the store yard. She was conducted into the mossy garden, and through a door in the wall, which was studded with rusty nails speaking of generations of fruit trees that had been trained there. The door opened upon the yard, and here she was left to find him as she could. It was a place flanked by hay barns, into which tons of fodder, all in trusses, were being packed from the wagons she had seen pass the inn that morning. On other sides of the yard were wooden granaries on stone staddles, to which access was given by Flemish ladders, and a storehouse several floors high. Wherever the doors of these places were open, a closely packed throng of bursting wheat sacks could be seen standing inside, with the air of awaiting a famine that would not come.

She wandered about this place, uncomfortably conscious of the impending interview, till she was quite weary of searching; she ventured to inquire of a boy in what quarter Mr. Henchard could be found. He directed her to an office which she had not seen before, and knocking at the door she was answered by a cry of "Come in."

Elizabeth turned the handle; and there stood before her, bending over some sample bags on a table, not the corn merchant, but the young Scotchman Mr. Farfrae—in the act of pouring some grains of wheat from one hand to the other. His hat hung on a peg behind him, and the roses of his carpet-bag glowed from the corner of the room.

Having toned her feelings and arranged words on her lips for Mr. Henchard, and for him alone, she was for the moment confounded.

"Yes, what is it?" said the Scotchman, like a man who permanently ruled there.

She said she wanted to see Mr. Henchard.

"Ah, yes; will you wait a minute? He's engaged just now," said the young man, apparently not recognizing her as the girl at the inn. He handed her a chair, bade her sit down, and turned to his sample bags again. While Elizabeth-Jane sits waiting in great amaze at the young man's presence we may briefly explain how he came there.

When the two new acquaintances had passed out of sight that morning towards the Bath and Bristol road they went on silently, except for a few commonplaces, till they had gone down an avenue on the town walls called the Chalk Walk, leading to an angle where the North and West escarpments met. From this high corner of the square earthworks a vast

extent of country could be seen. A footpath ran steeply down
the green slope, conducting from the shady promenade on
the walls to a road at the bottom of the scarp. It was by this
path the Scotchman had to descend.

"Well, here's success to 'ee," said Henchard, holding out
his right hand and leaning with his left upon the wicket which
protected the descent. In the act there was the inelegance of
one whose feelings are nipped and wishes defeated. "I shall
often think of this time, and of how you came at the very
moment to throw a light upon my difficulty."

Still holding the young man's hand he paused, and then
added deliberately: "Now I am not the man to let a cause be
lost for want of a word. And before ye are gone for ever I'll
speak. Once more, will ye stay? There it is, flat and plain. You
can see that it isn't all selfishness that makes me press 'ee; for
my business is not quite so scientific as to require an intellect
entirely out of the common. Others would do for the place
without doubt. Some selfishness perhaps there is, but there is
more; it isn't for me to repeat what. Come bide with me—and
name your own terms. I'll agree to 'em willingly and 'ithout
a word of gainsaying; for, hang it, Farfrae, I like thee well!"

The young man's hand remained steady in Henchard's for
a moment or two. He looked over the fertile country that
stretched beneath them, then backward along the shaded walk
reaching to the top of the town. His face flushed.

"I never expected this—I did not!" he said. "It's Providence!
Should any one go against it? No; I'll not go to America; I'll
stay and be your man!"

His hand, which had lain lifeless in Henchard's, returned
the latter's grasp.

"Done," said Henchard.

"Done," said Donald Farfrae.

The face of Mr. Henchard beamed forth a satisfaction that
was almost fierce in its strength. "Now you are my friend!"
he exclaimed. "Come back to my house; let's clinch it at once
by clear terms, so as to be comfortable in our minds." Farfrae

caught up his bag and retraced the North-West Avenue in Henchard's company as he had come. Henchard was all confidence now.

"I am the most distant fellow in the world when I don't care for a man," he said. "But when a man takes my fancy he takes it strong. Now I am sure you can eat another breakfast? You couldn't have eaten much so early, even if they had anything at that place to gi'e thee, which they hadn't; so come to my house and we will have a solid, staunch tuck-in, and settle terms in black-and-white if you like; though my word's my bond. I can always make a good meal in the morning. I've got a splendid cold pigeon pie going just now. You can have some home-brewed if you want to, you know."

"It is too airly in the morning for that," said Farfrae with a smile.

"Well, of course, I didn't know. I don't drink it because of my oath; but I am obliged to brew for my work people."

Thus talking they returned, and entered Henchard's premises by the back way or traffic entrance. Here the matter was settled over the breakfast, at which Henchard heaped the young Scotchman's plate to a prodigal fullness. He would not rest satisfied till Farfrae had written for his luggage from Bristol, and dispatched the letter to the post office. When it was done this man of strong impulses declared that his new friend should take up his abode in his house—at least till some suitable lodgings could be found.

He then took Farfrae round and showed him the place, and the stores of grain, and other stock; and finally entered the offices where the younger of them has already been discovered by Elizabeth.

. . . CHAPTER 10

WHILE she still sat under the Scotchman's eyes a man came up to the door, reaching it as Henchard opened the door of the inner office to admit Elizabeth. The newcomer stepped for-

ward like the quicker cripple at Bethesda,[1] and entered in her
stead. She could hear his words to Henchard: "Joshua Jopp,
sir—by appointment—the new manager."

"The new manager!—he's in his office," said Henchard
bluntly.

"In his office!" said the man with a stultified air.

"I mentioned Thursday," said Henchard; "and as you did
not keep your appointment, I have engaged another manager.
At first I thought he must be you. Do you think I can wait
when business is in question?"

"You said Thursday or Saturday, sir," said the newcomer,
pulling out a letter.

"Well, you are too late," said the corn factor. "I can say
no more."

"You as good as engaged me," murmured the man.

"Subject to an interview," said Henchard. "I am sorry for
you—very sorry indeed. But it can't be helped."

There was no more to be said, and the man came out, encountering Elizabeth-Jane in his passage. She could see that
his mouth twitched with anger, and that bitter disappointment
was written in his face everywhere.

Elizabeth-Jane now entered, and stood before the master of
the premises. His dark pupils—which always seemed to have
a red spark of light in them, though this could hardly be a
physical fact—turned indifferently round under his dark brows
until they rested on her figure. "Now then, what is it, my
young woman?" he said blandly.

"Can I speak to you—not on business, sir?" said she.

"Yes—I suppose." He looked at her more thoughtfully.

"I am sent to tell you, sir," she innocently went on, that a
distant relative of yours by marriage, Susan Newson, a sailor's
widow, is in the town; and to ask whether you would wish to
see her."

1. *Bethesda:* pool in Jerusalem where the crippled were healed (*John*
5:2-4).

The rich *rouge-et-noir*[2] of his countenance underwent a slight change. "Oh—Susan is—still alive?" he asked with difficulty.

"Yes, sir."

"Are you her daughter?"

"Yes, sir—her only daughter."

"What—do you call yourself—your Christian name?"

"Elizabeth-Jane, sir."

"Newson?"

"Elizabeth-Jane Newson."

This at once suggested to Henchard that the transaction of his early married life at Weydon Fair was unrecorded in the family history. It was more than he could have expected. His wife had behaved kindly to him in return for his unkindness, and had never proclaimed her wrong to her child or to the world.

"I am—a good deal interested in your news," he said. "And as this is not a matter of business, but pleasure, suppose we go indoors."

It was with a gentle delicacy of manner, surprising to Elizabeth, that he showed her out of the office and through the outer room, where Donald Farfrae was overhauling bins and samples with the inquiring inspection of a beginner in charge. Henchard preceded her through the door in the wall to the suddenly changed scene of the garden and flowers, and onward into the house. The dining room to which he introduced her still exhibited the remnants of the lavish breakfast laid for Farfrae. It was furnished to profusion with heavy mahogany furniture of the deepest red-Spanish hues. Pembroke tables, with leaves hanging so low that they well-nigh touched the floor, stood against the walls on legs and feet shaped like those of an elephant, and on one lay three huge folio volumes—a Family Bible, a "Josephus,"[3] and a "Whole

2. *Rouge-et-noir:* red and black (French).
3. *Josephus:* ancient historian (37-95).

Duty of Man." In the chimney corner was a fire grate with a fluted semicircular back, having urns and festoons cast in relief thereon; and the chairs were of the kind which, since that day, has cast luster upon the names of Chippendale and Sheraton, though, in point of fact, their patterns may have been such as those illustrious carpenters never saw or heard of.

"Sit down—Elizabeth-Jane—sit down," he said, with a shake in his voice as he uttered her name; and sitting down himself he allowed his hands to hang between his knees, while he looked upon the carpet. "Your mother, then, is quite well?"

"She is rather worn out, sir, with traveling."

"A sailor's widow—when did he die?"

"Father was lost last spring."

Henchard winced at the word "father," thus applied. "Do you and she come from abroad—America or Australia?" he asked.

"No. We have been in England some years. I was twelve when we came here from Canada."

"Ah; exactly." By such conversation he discovered the circumstances which had enveloped his wife and her child in such total obscurity that he had long ago believed them to be in their graves. These things being clear, he returned to the present. "And where is your mother staying?"

"At the Three Mariners."

"And you are her daughter Elizabeth-Jane?" repeated Henchard. He arose, came close to her, and glanced in her face. "I think," he said, suddenly turning away with a wet eye, "you shall take a note from me to your mother. I should like to see her. . . . She is not left very well off by her late husband?" His eye fell on Elizabeth's clothes, which, though a respectable suit of black, and her very best, were decidedly old-fashioned even to Casterbridge eyes.

"Not very well," she said, glad that he had divined this without her being obliged to express it.

He sat down at the table and wrote a few lines; next taking from his pocketbook a five-pound note, which he put in the envelope with the letter, adding to it, as by an afterthought, five shillings. Sealing the whole up carefully, he directed it to "Mrs. Newson, Three Mariners Inn," and handed the packet to Elizabeth.

"Deliver it to her personally, please," said Henchard. "Well, I am glad to see you here, Elizabeth-Jane—very glad. We must have a long talk together—but not just now."

He took her hand at parting, and held it so warmly that she, who had known so little friendship, was much affected, and tears rose to her aerial-gray eyes. The instant that she was gone Henchard's state showed itself more distinctly; having shut the door he sat in his dining room stiffly erect, gazing at the opposite wall as if he read his history there.

"Begad!" he suddenly exclaimed, jumping up. "I didn't think of that. Perhaps these are imposters—and Susan and the child dead after all!"

However, a something in Elizabeth-Jane soon assured him that, as regarded her, at least, there could be little doubt. And a few hours would settle the question of her mother's identity; for he had arranged in his note to see her that evening.

"It never rains but it pours!" said Henchard. His keenly excited interest in his new friend the Scotchman was now eclipsed by this event; and Donald Farfrae saw so little of him during the rest of the day that he wondered at the suddenness of his employer's moods.

In the meantime Elizabeth had reached the inn. Her mother, instead of taking the note with the curiosity of a poor woman expecting assistance, was much moved at sight of it. She did not read it at once, asking Elizabeth to describe her reception, and the very words Mr. Henchard used. Elizabeth's back was turned when her mother opened the letter. It ran thus:—

"Meet me at eight o'clock this evening, if you can, at the Ring on the Budmouth Road. The place is easy to find. I can say no more now. The news upsets me almost. The girl seems to be in ignorance. Keep her so till I have seen you.   M.H."

He said nothing about the enclosure of five guineas. The amount was significant; it may tacitly have said to her that he bought her back again. She waited restlessly for the close of the day, telling Elizabeth-Jane that she was invited to see Mr. Henchard; that she would go alone. But she said nothing to show that the place of meeting was not at his house, nor did she hand the note to Elizabeth.

. . . CHAPTER II

THE RING at Casterbridge was merely the local name of one of the finest Roman amphitheaters, if not the very finest, remaining in Britain.

Casterbridge announced old Rome in every street, alley, and precinct. It looked Roman, bespoke the art of Rome, concealed dead men of Rome. It was impossible to dig more than a foot or two deep about the town fields and gardens without coming upon some tall soldier or other of the Empire, who had lain there in his silent unobstrusive rest for a space of fifteen hundred years. He was mostly found lying on his side, in an oval scoop in the chalk, like a chicken in its shell; his knees drawn up to his chest; sometimes with the remains of his spear against his arm; a fibula or brooch of bronze on his breast or forehead; an urn at his knees, a jar at his throat, a bottle at his mouth; and mystified conjecture pouring down upon him from the eyes of Casterbridge street boys and men, who had turned a moment to gaze at the familiar spectacle as they passed by.

Imaginative inhabitants, who would have felt an unpleasantness at the discovery of a comparatively modern skeleton in their gardens, were quite unmoved by these hoary shapes. They had lived so long ago, their time was so unlike the present, their hopes and motives were so widely removed from ours, that between them and the living there seemed to stretch a gulf too wide for even a spirit to pass.

The amphitheater was a huge circular enclosure, with a notch at opposite extremities of its diameter north and south. From its sloping internal form it might have been called the spittoon of the Jötuns.[1] It was to Casterbridge what the ruined Coliseum is to modern Rome, and was nearly of the same magnitude. The dusk of evening was the proper hour at which a true impression of this suggestive place could be received. Standing in the middle of the arena at that time there by degrees became apparent its real vastness, which a cursory view from the summit at noonday was apt to obscure. Melancholy, impressive, lonely, yet accessible from every part of the town, the historic circle was the frequent spot for appointments of a furtive kind. Intrigues were arranged there; tentative meetings were there experimented after divisions and feuds. But one kind of appointment—in itself the most common of any—seldom had place in the amphitheater: that of happy lovers.

Why, seeing that it was pre-eminently an airy, accessible, and sequestered spot for interviews, the cheerfulest form of those occurrences never took kindly to the soil of the ruin, would be a curious inquiry. Perhaps it was because its associations had about them something sinister. Its history proved that. Apart from the sanguinary nature of the games originally played therein, such incidents attached to its past as these: that for scores of years the town gallows had stood at one corner; that in 1705 a woman who had murdered her husband was half-strangled and then burned there in the presence of ten thousand spectators. Tradition reports that at a certain stage of the burning her heart burst and leapt out of her body, to the terror of them all, and that not one of those ten thousand people ever cared particularly for hot roast after that. In addition to these old tragedies, pugilistic encounters almost to the death had come off down to recent dates in that secluded arena, entirely invisible to the outside world save by

1. *Jötuns:* mythical race of giants.

climbing to the top of the enclosure, which few townspeople in the daily round of their lives ever took the trouble to do. So that, though close to the turnpike road, crimes might be perpetuated there unseen at midday.

Some boys had latterly tried to impart gaiety to the ruin by using the central arena as a cricket[2] ground. But the game usually languished for the aforesaid reason—the dismal privacy which the earthen circle enforced, shutting out every appreciative passer's vision, every commendatory remark from outsiders—everything, except the sky; and to play at games in such circumstances was like acting to an empty house. Possibly, too, the boys were timid, for some old people said that at certain moments in the summer time, in broad daylight, persons sitting with a book or dozing in the arena had, on lifting their eyes, beheld the slopes lined with a gazing legion of Hadrian's[3] soldiery as if watching the gladiatorial combat; and had heard the roar of their excited voices; that the scene would remain but a moment, like a lightning flash, and then disappear.

It was related that there still remained under the south entrance excavated cells for the reception of the wild animals and athletes who took part in the games. The arena was still smooth and circular, as if used for its original purpose not so very long ago. The sloping pathways by which spectators had ascended to their seats were pathways yet. But the whole was grown over with grass, which now, at the end of summer, was bearded with withered bents that formed waves under the brush of the wind, returning to the attentive ear Æolian[4] modulations, and detaining for moments the flying globes of thistledown.

Henchard had chosen this spot as being the safest from observation which he could think of for meeting his long-lost

2. *Cricket:* British game.
3. *Hadrian:* Roman emperor (76-138).
4. *Aeolian:* music made by the wind.

wife, and at the same time as one easily to be found by a stranger after nightfall. As Mayor of the town, with a reputation to keep up, he could not invite her to come to his house till some definite course had been decided on.

Just before eight he approached the deserted earthwork, and entered the débris of the former dens. In a few moments he could discern a female figure creeping in by the great north gap, or public gateway. They met in the middle of the arena. Neither spoke just at first—there was no necessity for speech —and the poor woman leant against Henchard, who supported her in his arms.

"I don't drink," he said in a low, halting, apologetic voice. "You hear, Susan?—I don't drink now—I haven't since that night." Those were his first words.

He felt her bow her head in acknowledgment that she understood. After a minute or two he again began:

"If I had known you were living, Susan! But there was every reason to suppose you and the child were dead and gone. I took every possible step to find you—traveled—advertised. My opinion at last was that you had started for some colony with that man, and had been drowned on your voyage out. Why did you keep silent like this?"

"O Michael! because of him—what other reason could there be? I thought I owed him faithfulness to the end of one of our lives—foolishly I believed there was something solemn and binding in the bargain; I thought that even in honor I dared not desert him when he had paid so much for me in good faith. I meet you now only as his widow—I consider myself that, and that I have no claim upon you. Had he not died I should never have come—never! Of that you may be sure."

"Ts-s-s! How could you be so simple?"

"I don't know. Yet it would have been very wicked—if I had not thought like that!" said Susan, almost crying.

"Yes—yes—so it would. It is only that which makes me feel 'ee an innocent woman. But—to lead me into this!"

"What, Michael?" she asked, alarmed.

"Why, this difficulty about our living together again, and Elizabeth-Jane. She cannot be told all—she would so despise us both that—I could not bear it!"

"That was why she was brought up in ignorance of you. I could not bear it either."

"Well—we must talk of a plan for keeping her in her present belief, and getting matters straight in spite of it. You have heard I am in a large way of business here—that I am Mayor of the town, and churchwarden, and I don't know what all?"

"Yes," she murmured.

"These things, as well as the dread of the girl discovering our disgrace, makes it necessary to act with extreme caution. So that I don't see how you two can return openly to my house as the wife and daughter I once treated badly, and banished from me; and there's the rub o't."

"We'll go away at once. I only came to see——"

"No, no, Susan; you are not to go—you mistake me!" he said, with kindly severity. "I have thought of this plan: that you and Elizabeth take a cottage in the town as the widow Mrs. Newson and her daughter; that I meet you, court you, and marry you, Elizabeth-Jane coming to my house as my stepdaughter. The thing is so natural and easy that it is half done in thinking o't. This would leave my shady, headstrong, disgraceful life as a young man absolutely unopened; the secret would be yours and mine only; and I should have the pleasure of seeing my own child under my roof, as well as my wife."

"I am quite in your hands, Michael," she said meekly. "I came here for the sake of Elizabeth; for myself, if you tell me to leave again tomorrow morning, and never come near you more, I am content to go."

"Now, now; we don't want to hear that," said Henchard gently. "Of course you won't leave again. Think over the plan I have proposed for a few hours; and if you can't hit upon a better one we'll adopt it. I have to be away for a day or two on business, unfortunately; but during that time you can get lodgings—the only ones in the town fit for you are those over the china shop in High Street—and you can also look for a cottage."

"If the lodgings are in High Street they are dear, I suppose?"

"Never mind—you *must* start genteel if our plan is to be carried out. Look to me for money. Have you enough till I come back?"

"Quite," said she.

"And are you comfortable at the inn?"

"Oh yes."

"And the girl is quite safe from learning the shame of her case and ours?—that's what makes me most anxious of all."

"You would be surprised to find how unlikely she is to dream of the truth. How could she ever suppose such a thing?"

"True!"

"I like the idea of repeating our marriage," said Mrs. Henchard, after a pause. "It seems the only right course, after all this. Now I think I must go back to Elizabeth-Jane, and tell her that our kinsman, Mr. Henchard, kindly wishes us to stay in the town."

"Very well—arrange that yourself. I'll go some way with you."

"No, no. Don't run any risk!" said his wife anxiously. "I can find my way back—it is not late. Please let me go alone."

"Right," said Henchard. "But just one word. Do you forgive me, Susan?"

She murmured something; but seemed to find it difficult to frame her answer.

"Never mind—all in good time," said he. "Judge me by my future works—good-by."

He retreated, and stood at the upper side of the Amphitheater while his wife passed out through the lower way, and descended under the trees to the town. Then Henchard himself went homeward, going so fast that by the time he reached his door he was almost upon the heels of the unconscious woman from whom he had just parted. He watched her up the street, and turned into his house.

. . . CHAPTER 12

ON ENTERING his own door after watching his wife out of sight, the Mayor walked on through the tunnel-shaped passage into the garden, and thence by the back door toward the stores and granaries. A light shone from the office window, and there being no blind to screen the interior Henchard could see Donald Farfrae still seated where he had left him, initiating himself into the managerial work of the house by overhauling the books. Henchard entered, merely observing, "Don't let me interrupt you, if ye will stay so late."

He stood behind Farfrae's chair, watching his dexterity in clearing up the numerical fogs which had been allowed to grow so thick in Henchard's books as almost to baffle even the Scotchman's perspicacity. The corn factor's mien was half admiring, and yet it was not without a dash of pity for the tastes of anyone who could care to give his mind to such finnikin[1] details. Henchard himself was mentally and physically unfit for grubbing subtleties from soiled paper; he had in a modern sense received the education of Achilles,[2] and found penmanship a tantalizing art.

"You shall do no more tonight," he said at length, spreading his great hand over the paper. "There's time enough tomorrow. Come indoors with me and have some supper. Now you shall! I am determined on't." He shut the account books with friendly force.

Donald had wished to get to his lodgings; but he already saw that his friend and employer was a man who knew no modera-

1. *Finnikin:* over-precise.
2. *Achilles:* legendary Greek warrior.

tion in his requests and impulses, and he yielded gracefully. He liked Henchard's warmth, even if it inconvenienced him; the great difference in their characters adding to the liking.

They locked up the office, and the young man followed his companion through the private little door which, admitting directly into Henchard's garden, permitted a passage from the utilitarian to the beautiful at one step. The garden was silent, dewy, and full of perfume. It extended a long way back from the house, first as lawn and flower beds, then as fruit garden, where the long-tied espaliers, as old as the old house itself, had grown so stout, and cramped, and gnarled that they had pulled their stakes out of the ground and stood distorted and writhing in vegetable agony, like leafy Laocoöns.[3] The flowers which smelt so sweetly were not discernible; and they passed through them into the house.

The hospitalities of the morning were repeated, and when they were over Henchard said, "Pull your chair round to the fireplace, my dear fellow, and let's make a blaze—there's nothing I hate like a black grate, even in September." He applied a light to the laid-in fuel, and a cheerful radiance spread around.

"It is odd," said Henchard," that two men should meet as we have done on a purely business ground, and that at the end of the first day I should wish to speak to 'ee on a family matter. But, damn it all, I am a lonely man, Farfrae: I have nobody else to speak to; and why shouldn't I tell it to 'ee?"

"I'll be glad to hear it, if I can be of service," said Donald, allowing his eyes to travel over the intricate wood carvings of the chimney piece, representing garlanded lyres, shields, and quivers, on either side of a draped ox-skull, and flanked by heads of Apollo and Diana[4] in low relief.

"I've not been always what I am now," continued Hen-

3. *Laocoöns:* statuary of Trojan priest and his sons being destroyed by serpents.
4. *Apollo . . . Diana:* Roman god and goddess.

chard, his firm deep voice being ever so little shaken. He was plainly under that strange influence which sometimes prompts men to confide to the new-found friend what they will not tell to the old. "I began life as a working hay-trusser, and when I was eighteen I married on the strength o' my calling. Would you think me a married man?"

"I heard in the town that you were a widower."

"Ah, yes—you would naturally have heard that. Well, I lost my wife nineteen years ago or so—by my own fault. . . . This is how it came about. One summer evening I was traveling for employment, and she was walking at my side, carrying the baby, our only child. We came to a booth in a country fair. I was a drinking man at that time."

Henchard paused a moment, threw himself back so that his elbow rested on the table, his forehead being shaded by his hand, which, however, did not hide the marks of introspective inflexibility on his features as he narrated in fullest detail the incidents of the transaction with the sailor. The tinge of indifference which had at first been visible in the Scotchman now disappeared.

Henchard went on to describe his attempts to find his wife; the oath he swore; the solitary life he led during the years which followed. "I have kept my oath for nineteen years," he went on; "I have risen to what you see me now."

"Ay!"

"Well—no wife could I hear of in all that time; and being by nature something of a woman-hater, I have found it no hardship to keep mostly at a distance from the sex. No wife could I hear of, I say, till this very day. And now—she has come back."

"Come back, has she!"

"This morning—this very morning. And what's to be done?"

"Can ye no' take her and live with her, and make some amends?"

"That's what I've planned and proposed. But, Farfrae," said

Henchard gloomily, "by doing right with Susan I wrong another innocent woman."

"Ye don't say that?"

"In the nature of things, Farfrae, it is almost impossible that a man of my sort should have the good fortune to tide through twenty years o' life without making more blunders than one. It has been my custom for many years to run across to Jersey in the way of business, particularly in the potato and root season. I do a large trade wi' them in that line. Well, one autumn when stopping there I fell quite ill, and in my illness I sank into one of those gloomy fits I sometimes suffer from, on account o' the loneliness of my domestic life, when the world seems to have the blackness of hell, and, like Job,[5] I could curse the day that gave me birth."

"Ah, now, I never feel like it," said Farfrae.

"Then pray to God that you never may, young man. While in this state I was taken pity on by a woman—a young lady I should call her, for she was of good family, well bred, and well educated—the daughter of some harum-scarum military officer who had got into difficulties, and had his pay sequestrated. He was dead now, and her mother too, and she was as lonely as I. This young creature was staying at the boarding house where I happened to have my lodging; and when I was pulled down she took upon herself to nurse me. From that she got to have a foolish liking for me. Heaven knows why, for I wasn't worth it. But being together in the same house, and her feelings warm, we got naturally intimate. I won't go into particulars of what our relations were. It is enough to say that we honestly meant to marry. There arose a scandal, which did me no harm, but was of course ruin to her. Though, Farfrae, between you and me, as man and man, I solemnly declare that philandering with womankind has neither been my vice nor my virtue. She was terribly careless

5. *Job:* Biblical figure.

of appearances, and I was perhaps more, because o' my dreary state; and it was through this that the scandal arose. At last I was well, and came away. When I was gone she suffered much on my account, and didn't forget to tell me so in letters one after another; till, latterly, I felt I owed her something, and thought that, as I had not heard of Susan for so long, I would make this other one the only return I could make, and ask her if she would run the risk of Susan being alive (very slight as I believed) and marry me, such as I was. She jumped for joy, and we should no doubt soon have been married—but, behold, Susan appears!"

Donald showed his deep concern at a complication so far beyond the degree of his simple experiences.

"Now see what injury a man may cause around him! Even after that wrongdoing at the fair when I was young, if I had never been so selfish as to let this giddy girl devote herself to me over at Jersey, to the injury of her name, all might now be well. Yet, as it stands, I must bitterly disappoint one of these women; and it is the second. My first duty is to Susan—there's no doubt about that."

"They are both in a very melancholy position, and that's true!" murmured Donald.

"They are! For myself I don't care—'twill all end one way. But these two." Henchard paused in reverie. "I feel I should like to treat the second, no less than the first, as kindly as a man can in such a case."

"Ah, well, it cannet be helped!" said the other, with philosophic woefulness. "You mun write to the young lady, and in your letter you must put it plain and honest that it turns out she cannet be your wife, the first having come back; that ye cannet see her more; and that—ye wish her weel."

"That won't do. 'Od seize it, I must do a little more than that! I must—though she did always brag about her rich uncle or rich aunt, and her expectations from 'em—I must send a

useful sum of money to her, I suppose—just as a little recom-
pense, poor girl. . . . Now, will you help me in this, and draw
up an explanation to her of all I've told ye, breaking it as
gently as you can? I'm so bad at letters."

"And I will."

"Now, I haven't told you quite all yet. My wife Susan has
my daughter with her—the baby that was in her arms at the
fair; and this girl knows nothing of me beyond that I am some
sort of relation by marriage. She has grown up in the belief
that the sailor to whom I made over her mother, and who is
now dead, was her father, and her mother's husband. What
her mother has always felt, she and I together feel now—that
we can't proclaim our disgrace to the girl by letting her know
the truth. Now what would you do?—I want your advice."

"I think I'd run the risk, and tell her the truth. She'll forgive
ye both."

"Never!" said Henchard. "I am not going to let her know
the truth. Her mother and I be going to marry again; and it
will not only help us to keep our child's respect, but it will
be more proper. Susan looks upon herself as the sailor's widow,
and won't think o' living with me as formerly without another
religious ceremony—and she's right."

Farfrae thereupon said no more. The letter to the young
Jersey woman was carefully framed by him, and the interview ended, Henchard saying, as the Scotchman left, " I feel
it a great relief, Farfrae, to tell some friend o' this! You see
now that the Mayor of Casterbridge is not so thriving in his
mind as it seems he might be from the state of his pocket."

"I do. And I'm sorry for ye!" said Farfrae.

When he was gone Henchard copied the letter, and, enclosing a check, took it to the post office, from which he walked
back thoughtfully.

"Can it be that it will go off so easily!" he said. "Poor thing
—God knows! Now then, to make amends to Susan!"

CHAPTER 13

THE cottage which Michael Henchard hired for his wife Susan under her name of Newson—in pursuance of their plan —was in the upper or western part of the town near the Roman wall, and the avenue which overshadowed it. The evening sun seemed to shine more yellowly there than anywhere else this autumn—stretching its rays, as the hours grew later, under the lowest sycamore boughs, and steeping the ground floor of the dwelling, with its green shutters, in a substratum of radiance which the foliage screened from the upper parts. Beneath these sycamores on the town walls could be seen from the sitting room the tumuli and earth forts of the distant uplands; making it altogether a pleasant spot, with the usual touch of melancholy that a past-marked prospect lends.

As soon as the mother and daughter were comfortably installed, with a white-aproned servant and all complete, Henchard paid them a visit, and remained to tea. During the entertainment Elizabeth was carefully hoodwinked by the very general tone of the conversation that prevailed—a proceeding which seemed to afford some humor to Henchard, though his wife was not particularly happy in it. The visit was repeated again and again with business-like determination by the Mayor, who seemed to have schooled himself into a course of strict mechanical rightness toward this woman of prior claim, at any expense to the later one and to his own sentiments.

One afternoon the daughter was not indoors when Henchard came, and he said drily, "This is a very good opportunity for me to ask you to name the happy day, Susan."

The poor woman smiled faintly; she did not enjoy pleasantries on a situation into which she had entered solely for the sake of her girl's reputation. She liked them so little, indeed, that there was room for wonder why she had countenanced deception at all, and had not bravely let the girl know her history. But the flesh is weak; and the true explanation came in due course.

"O Michael!" she said, "I am afraid all this is taking up your time and giving trouble—when I did not expect any such thing!" And she looked at him and at his dress as a man of affluence, and at the furniture he had provided for the room —ornate and lavish to her eyes.

"Not at all," said Henchard, in rough benignity. "This is only a cottage—it costs me next to nothing. And as to taking up my time"—here his red and black visage kindled with satisfaction—"I've a splendid fellow to superintend my business now—a man whose like I've never been able to lay hands on before. I shall soon be able to leave everything to him, and have more time to call my own than I've had for these last twenty years."

Henchard's visits here grew so frequent and so regular that it soon became whispered, and then openly discussed in Casterbridge that the masterful, coercive Mayor of the town was captured and enervated by the genteel widow Mrs. Newson. His well-known haughty indifference to the society of womankind, his silent avoidance of converse with the sex, contributed a piquancy to what would otherwise have been an unromantic matter enough. That such a poor fragile woman should be his choice was inexplicable, except on the ground that the engagement was a family affair in which sentimental passion had no place; for it was known that they were related in some way. Mrs. Henchard was so pale that the boys called her "The Ghost." Sometimes Henchard overheard this epithet when they passed together along the Walks—as the avenues on the walls were named—at which his face would darken with an expression of destructiveness toward the speakers ominous to see; but he said nothing.

He pressed on the preparations for his union, or rather reunion, with this pale creature in a dogged, unflinching spirit which did credit to his conscientiousness. Nobody would have conceived from his outward demeanor that there was no amatory fire or pulse of romance acting as stimulant to the bustle going on in his gaunt, great house; nothing but three large resolves—one, to make amends to his neglected Susan; another, to provide a comfortable home for Elizabeth-Jane under his paternal eye; and a third, to castigate himself with the thorns which these restitutory acts brought in their train; among them the lowering of his dignity in public opinion by marrying so comparatively humble a woman.

Susan Henchard entered a carriage for the first time in her life when she stepped into the plain brougham which drew up at the door on the wedding day to take her and Elizabeth-Jane to church. It was a windless morning of warm November rain, which floated down like meal, and lay in a powdery form on the nap of hats and coats. Few people had gathered round the church door though they were well packed within. The Scotchman, who assisted as groomsman, was of course the only one present, beyond the chief actors, who knew the true situation of the contracting parties. He, however, was too inexperienced, too thoughtful, too judicial, too strongly conscious of the serious side of the business, to enter into the scene in its dramatic aspect. That required the special genius of Christopher Coney, Solomon Longways, Buzzford, and their fellows. But they knew nothing of the secret; though, as the time for coming out of church drew on, they gathered on the pavement adjoining, and expounded the subject according to their lights.

" 'Tis five-and-forty years since I had my settlement in this here town," said Coney; "but daze me if ever I see a man wait so long before to take so little! There's a chance even for thee after this, Nance Mockridge." The remark was addressed to a woman who stood behind his shoulder—the same who had exhibited Henchard's bad bread in public when Elizabeth and her mother entered Casterbridge.

"Be cust if I'd marry any such as he, or thee either," replied that lady. "As for thee, Christopher, we know what ye be, and the less said the better. And as for he—well, there—(lowering her voice) 'tis said 'a was a poor parish 'prentice—I wouldn't say it for all the world—but 'a was a poor parish 'prentice, that began life wi' no more belonging to 'en than a carrion crow."

"And now he's worth ever so much a minute," murmured Longways. "When a man is said to be worth so much a minute, he's a man to be considered!"

Turning, he saw a circular disc reticulated with creases, and recognized the smiling countenance of the fat woman who had asked for another song at the Three Mariners. "Well, Mother Cuxsom," he said, "how's this? Here's Mrs. Newson, a mere skellinton, has got another husband to keep her, while a woman of your tonnage have not."

"I have not. Nor another to beat me. . . . Ah, yes, Cuxsom's gone, and so shall leather breeches!"

"Yes; with the blessing of God leather breeches shall go."

" 'Tisn't worth my old while to think of another husband," continued Mrs. Cuxsom. "And yet I'll lay my life I'm as respectable born as she."

"True; your mother was a very good woman—I can mind her. She were rewarded by the Agricultural Society for having begot the greatest number of healthy children without parish assistance, and other virtuous marvels."

" 'Twas that that kept us so low upon ground—that great hungry family."

"Ay. Where the pigs be many the wash runs thin."

"And dostn't mind how mother would sing, Christopher?" continued Mrs. Cuxsom, kindling at the retrospection; "and how we went with her to the party at Mellstock, do ye mind? —at old Dame Ledlow's, farmer Shinar's aunt, do ye mind?— she we used to call Toadskin, because her face were so yaller and freckled, do ye mind?"

"I do, hee-hee, I do!" said Christopher Coney.

"And well do I—for I was getting up husband-high at that time—one-half girl, and t'other half woman, as one may say. And canst mind"—she prodded Solomon's shoulder with her finger tip, while her eyes twinkled between the crevices of their lids—"canst mind the sherry wine, and the zilver snuffers, and how Joan Dummett was took bad when we were coming home, and Jack Griggs was forced to carry her through the mud; and how 'a let her fall in Dairyman Sweetapple's cowbarton, and we had to clane her gown wi' grass—never such a mess as 'a were in?"

"Ay—that I do—hee-hee, such doggery as there was in them ancient days, to be sure! Ah, the miles I used to walk then; and now I can hardly step over a furrow!"

Their reminiscences were cut short by the appearance of the reunited pair—Henchard looking round upon the idlers with that ambiguous gaze of his, which at one moment seemed to mean satisfaction, and at another fiery disdain.

"Well—there's a difference between 'em, though he do call himself a teetotaler," said Nance Mockridge. "She'll wish her cake dough afore she's done of him. There's a bluebeardy look about 'en; and 'twill out in time."

"Stuff—he's well enough! Some folk want their luck buttered. If I had a choice as wide as the ocean sea I wouldn't wish for a better man. A poor twanking woman like her—'tis a godsend for her, and hardly a pair of jumps or night-rail to her name."

The plain little brougham drove off in the mist, and the idlers dispersed. "Well, we hardly know how to look at things in these times!" said Solomon. "There was a man dropped down dead yesterday, not so very many miles from here; and what wi' that, and this moist weather, 'tis scarce worth one's while to begin any work o' consequence today. I'm in such a low key with drinking nothing but small table ninepenny this last week or two that I shall call and warm up at the Mar'ners as I pass along."

"I don't know but that I may as well go with 'ee, Solomon," said Christopher; "I'm as clammy as a cocklesnail."

. . . CHAPTER 14

A MARTINMAS summer of Mrs. Henchard's life set in with her entry into her husband's large house and respectable social orbit; and it was as bright as such summers well can be. Lest she should pine for deeper affection than he could give he made a point of showing some semblance of it in external action. Among other things he had the iron railings, that had smiled sadly in dull rust for the last eighty years, painted a bright green, and the heavy-barred, small-paned Georgian sash windows enlivened with three coats of white. He was as kind to her as a man, mayor, and churchwarden could possibly be. The house was large, the rooms lofty, and the landings wide; and the two unassuming women scarcely made a perceptible addition to its contents.

To Elizabeth-Jane the time was a most triumphant one. The freedom she experienced, the indulgence with which she was treated, went beyond her expectations. The reposeful, easy, affluent life to which her mother's marriage had introduced her was, in truth, the beginning of a great change in Elizabeth. She found she could have nice personal possessions and ornaments for the asking, and, as the medieval saying puts it, "Take, have, and keep, are pleasant words." With peace of mind came development, and with development beauty. Knowledge—the result of great natural insight—she did not lack; learning, accomplishments—those, alas, she had not; but as the winter and spring passed by her thin face and figure filled out in rounder and softer curves; the lines and contractions upon her young brow went away; the muddiness of skin which she had looked upon as her lot by nature departed with a change to abundance of good things, and a bloom came upon her cheek. Perhaps, too, her gray, thoughtful eyes revealed

an arch gaiety sometimes; but this was infrequent; the sort of
wisdom which looked from their pupils did not readily keep
company with these lighter moods. Like all people who have
known rough times, light-heartedness seemed to her too irrational and inconsequent to be indulged in except as a reckless dram now and then; for she had been too early habituated
to anxious reasoning to drop the habit suddenly. She felt none
of those ups and downs of spirit which beset so many people
without cause; never—to paraphrase a recent poet—never a
gloom in Elizabeth-Jane's soul but she well knew how it came
there; and her present cheerfulness was fairly proportionate
to her solid guarantees for the same.

It might have been supposed that, given a girl rapidly becoming good-looking, comfortably circumstanced, and for
the first time in her life commanding ready money, she would
go and make a fool of herself by dress. But no. The reasonableness of almost everything that Elizabeth did was nowhere
more conspicuous than in this question of clothes. To keep in
the rear of opportunity in matters of indulgence is as valuable
a habit as to keep abreast of opportunity in matters of enterprise. This unsophisticated girl did it by an innate perceptive-
ness that was almost genius. Thus she refrained from bursting
out like a water flower that spring, and clothing herself in
puffings and knickknacks, as most of the Casterbridge girls
would have done in her circumstances. Her triumph was tempered by circumspection; she had still that fieldmouse fear of
the coulter of destiny despite fair promise, which is common
among the thoughtful who have suffered early from poverty
and oppression.

"I won't be too gay on my account," she would say to
herself. "It would be tempting Providence to hurl mother and
me down, and afflict us again as He used to do."

We now see her in a black silk bonnet, velvet mantle or
silk spencer, dark dress, and carrying a sunshade. In this latter
article she drew the line at fringe, and had it plain edged, with

a little ivory ring for keeping it closed. It was odd about the necessity for that sunshade. She discovered that with the clarification of her complexion and the birth of pink cheeks her skin had grown more sensitive to the sun's rays. She protected those cheeks forthwith, deeming spotlessness part of womanliness.

Henchard had become very fond of her, and she went out with him more frequently than with her mother now. Her appearance one day was so attractive that he looked at her critically.

"I happened to have the ribbon by me, so I made it up," she faltered, thinking him perhaps dissatisfied with some bright trimming she had donned for the first time.

"Ay—of course—to be sure," he replied in his leonine way. "Do as you like—or rather as your mother advises ye. 'Od send—I've nothing to say to't!"

Indoors she appeared with her hair divided by a parting that arched like a white rainbow from ear to ear. All in front of this line was covered with a thick encampment of curls; all behind was dressed smoothly, and drawn to a knob.

The three members of the family were sitting at breakfast one day, and Henchard was looking silently, as he often did, at this head of hair, which in color was brown—rather light than dark. "I thought Elizabeth-Jane's hair—didn't you tell me that Elizabeth-Jane's hair promised to be black when she was a baby?" he said to his wife.

She looked startled, jerked his foot warningly, and murmured, "Did I?"

As soon as Elizabeth was gone to her own room Henchard resumed. "Begad, I nearly forgot myself just now! What I meant was that the girl's hair certainly looked as if it would be darker, when she was a baby."

"It did; but they alter so," replied Susan.

"Their hair gets darker, I know—but I wasn't aware it lightened ever?"

"Oh yes." And the same uneasy expression came out on her face, to which the future held the key. It passed as Henchard went on:

"Well, so much the better. Now, Susan, I want to have her called Miss Henchard—not Miss Newson. Lots o' people do it already in carelessness—it is her legal name—so it may as well be made her usual name—I don't like t'other name at all for my own flesh and blood. I'll advertise it in the Casterbridge paper—that's the way they do it. She won't object."

"No. O no. But——"

"Well, then, I shall do it," said he, peremptorily. "Surely, if she's willing, you must wish it as much as I?"

"O yes—if she agrees let us do it by all means," she replied.

Then Mrs. Henchard acted somewhat inconsistently; it might have been called falsely, but that her manner was emotional and full of the earnestness of one who wishes to do right at great hazard. She went to Elizabeth-Jane, whom she found sewing in her own sitting room upstairs, and told her what had been proposed about her surname. "Can you agree —is it not a slight upon Newson—now he's dead and gone?"

Elizabeth reflected. "I'll think of it, mother," she answered.

When, later in the day, she saw Henchard, she adverted to the matter at once, in a way which showed that the line of feeling started by her mother had been persevered in. "Do you wish this change so very much, sir?" she asked.

"Wish it? Why, my blessed fathers, what an ado you women make about a trifle! I proposed it—that's all. Now, 'Lizabeth-Jane, just please yourself. Curse me if I care what you do. Now, you understand, don't 'ee go agreeing to it to please me."

Here the subject dropped, and nothing more was said, and nothing was done, and Elizabeth still passed as Miss Newson, and not by her legal name.

Meanwhile the great corn and hay traffic conducted by Henchard throve under the management of Donald Farfrae as it had never thriven before. It had formerly moved in jolts; now it went on oiled casters. The crude *vivâ voce*[1] system of Henchard, in which everything depended upon his memory, and bargains were made by the tongue alone, was swept away. Letters and ledgers took the place of "I'll do't," and "you shall hae't"; and, as in all such cases of advance, the rugged picturesqueness of the old method disappeared with its inconveniences.

The position of Elizabeth-Jane's room—rather high in the house, so that it commanded a view of the hay-stores and granaries across the garden—afforded her opportunity for accurate observation of what went on there. She saw that Donald and Mr. Henchard were inseparables. When walking together Henchard would lay his arm familiarly on his manager's shoulder, as if Farfrae were a younger brother, bearing so heavily that his slight figure bent under the weight. Occasionally she would hear a perfect cannonade of laughter from Henchard, arising from something Donald had said, the latter looking quite innocent and not laughing at all. In Henchard's somewhat lonely life he evidently found the young man as desirable for comradeship as he was useful for consultations. Donald's brightness of intellect maintained in the corn factor the admiration it had won at the first hour of their meeting. The poor opinion, and but ill-concealed, that he entertained of the slim Farfrae's physical girth, strength, and dash was more than counterbalanced by the immense respect he had for his brains.

Her quiet eye discerned that Henchard's tigerish affection for the younger man, his constant liking to have Farfrae near him, now and then resulted in a tendency to domineer, which, however, was checked in a moment when Donald exhibited marks of real offense. One day, looking down on their figures from on high, she heard the latter remark, as they stood in

1. *Vivâ voce:* aloud, unwritten.

the doorway between the garden and yard, that their habit of
walking and driving about together rather neutralized Farfrae's value as a second pair of eyes, which should be used in
places where the principal was not. " 'Od damn it, cried
Henchard, "what's all the world! I like a fellow to talk to.
Now come along and hae some supper, and don't take too
much thought about things, or ye'll drive me crazy."

When she walked with her mother, on the other hand, she
often beheld the Scotchman looking at them with a curious
interest. The fact that he had met her at the Three Mariners
was insufficient to account for it, since on the occasions on
which she had entered his room he had never raised his eyes.
Besides, it was at her mother more particularly than at herself
that he looked, to Elizabeth-Jane's half-conscious, simpleminded, perhaps pardonable, disappointment. Thus she could
not account for this interest by her own attractiveness, and
she decided that it might be apparent only—a way of turning
his eyes that Mr. Farfrae had.

She did not divine the ample explanation of his manner,
without personal vanity, that was afforded by the fact of
Donald being the depository of Henchard's confidence in
respect of his past treatment of the pale, chastened mother who
walked by her side. Her conjectures on that past never went
further than faint ones based on things casually heard and seen
—mere guesses that Henchard and her mother might have been
lovers in their younger days, who had quarreled and parted.

Casterbridge, as has been hinted, was a place deposited in
the block upon a cornfield. There was no suburb in the modern sense, or transitional intermixture of town and down. It
stood, with regard to the wide fertile land adjoining, clean-cut
and distinct, like a chessboard on a green tablecloth. The farmer's boy could sit under his barley mow and pitch a stone
into the office window of the town clerk; reapers at work
among the sheaves nodded to acquaintances standing on the
pavement corner; the red-robed judge, when he condemned

a sheep stealer, pronounced sentence to the tune of Baa, that floated in at the window from the remainder of the flock browsing hard by; and at executions the waiting crowd stood in a meadow immediately before the drop, out of which the cows had been temporarily driven to give the spectators room.

The corn grown on the upland side of the borough was garnered by farmers who lived in an eastern purlieu called Durnover. Here wheat ricks overhung the old Roman street, and thrust their eaves against the church tower; green-thatched barns, with doorways as high as the gates of Solomon's temple, opened directly upon the main thoroughfare. Barns indeed were so numerous as to alternate with every half-dozen houses along the way. Here lived burgesses who daily walked the fallow; shepherds in an intramural squeeze. A street of farmers' homesteads—a street ruled by a mayor and corporation, yet echoing with the thump of the flail, the flutter of the winnowing fan, and the purr of the milk into the pails—a street which had nothing urban in it whatever —this was the Durnover end of Casterbridge.

Henchard, as was natural, dealt largely with this nursery or bed of small farmers close at hand—and his wagons were often down that way. One day, when arrangements were in progress for getting home corn from one of the aforesaid farms, Elizabeth-Jane received a note by hand, asking her to oblige the writer by coming at once to a granary on Durnover Hill. As this was the granary whose contents Henchard was removing, she thought the request had something to do with his business, and proceeded thither as soon as she had put on her bonnet. The granary was just within the farmyard, and stood on stone staddles, high enough for persons to walk under. The gates were open, but nobody was within. However, she entered and waited. Presently she saw a figure approaching the gate—that of Donald Farfrae. He looked up at the church clock, and came in. By some unaccountable shyness, some wish not to meet him there alone, she quickly ascended the stepladder leading to the granary door, and entered it before he had seen her. Farfrae advanced, imagining himself in solitude; and a few drops of rain beginning to fall he moved and stood under the shelter where she had just been standing. Here he leaned against one of the staddles, and gave himself up to patience. He, too, was plainly expecting some one; could it be herself? If so, why? In a few minutes he looked at his watch, and then pulled out a note, a duplicate of the one she had herself received.

The situation began to be very awkward, and the longer she waited the more awkward it became. To emerge from a door just above his head and descend the ladder, and show she had been in hiding there, would look so very foolish that she still waited on. A winnowing machine stood close beside her, and to relieve her suspense she gently moved the handle; whereupon a cloud of wheat husks flew out into her face, and covered her clothes and bonnet, and stuck into the fur of her victorine. He must have heard the slight movement for he looked up, and then ascended the steps.

"Ah—it's Miss Newson," he said as soon as he could see into the granary. "I didn't know you were there. I have kept the appointment, and am at your service."

"O Mr. Farfrae," she faltered; "so have I. But I didn't know it was you who wished to see me, otherwise I——"

"I wished to see you? O no—at least, that is, I am afraid there may be a mistake."

"Didn't you ask me to come here? Didn't you write this?" Elizabeth held out her note.

"No. Indeed, at no hand would I have thought of it! And for you—didn't you ask me? This is not your writing?" And he held up his.

"By no means."

"And is that really so! Then it's somebody wanting to see us both. Perhaps we would do well to wait a little longer."

Acting on this consideration they lingered, Elizabeth-Jane's face being arranged to an expression of preternatural composure, and the young Scot, at every footstep in the street without, looking from under the granary to see if the passer were about to enter and declare himself their summoner. They watched individual drops of rain creeping down the thatch of the opposite rick—straw after straw—till they reached the bottom; but nobody came, and the granary roof began to drip.

"The person is not likely to be coming," said Farfrae. "It's a trick perhaps, and if so, it's a great pity to waste our time like this, and so much to be done."

" 'Tis a great liberty," said Elizabeth.

"It's true, Miss Newson. We'll hear news of this some day, depend on't, and who it was that did it. I wouldn't stand for it hindering myself; but you, Miss Newson——"

"Neither do I."

They lapsed again into silence. "You are anxious to get back to Scotland, I suppose, Mr. Farfrae?" she inquired.

"O no, Miss Newson. Why would I be?"

"I only supposed you might be from the song you sang at the Three Mariners—about Scotland and home, I mean—which you seemed to feel so deep down in your heart; so that we all felt for you."

"Ay—and I did sing there—I did—— But, Miss Newson"— and Donald's voice musically undulated between two semitones, as it always did when he became earnest—"it's well you feel a song for a few minutes, and your eyes they get quite tearful; but you finish it, and for all you felt you don't mind it or think of it again for a long while. O no, I don't want to go back! Yet I'll sing the song to you wi' pleasure whenever you like. I could sing it now, and not mind at all."

"Thank you, indeed. But I fear I must go—rain or no."

"Ay! Then, Miss Newson, ye had better say nothing about this hoax, and take no heed of it. And if the person should say anything to you, be civil to him or her, as if you did not mind it—so you'll take the clever person's laugh away." In speaking his eyes became fixed upon her dress, still sown with wheat husks. "There's husks and dust on you. Perhaps you don't know it?" he said, in tones of extreme delicacy. "And it's very bad to let rain come upon clothes when there's chaff on them. It washes in and spoils them. Let me help you—blowing is the best."

As Elizabeth neither assented nor dissented Donald Farfrae began blowing her back hair, and her side hair, and her neck, and the crown of her bonnet, and the fur of her victorine, Elizabeth saying, "O, thank you," at every puff. At last she was fairly clean, though Farfrae, having got over his first concern at the situation, seemed in no manner of hurry to be gone.

"Ah—now I'll go and get ye an umbrella," he said.

She declined the offer, stepped out and was gone. Farfrae walked slowly after, looking thoughtfully at her diminishing figure, and whistling in undertones, "As I Came Down Through Cannobie."

. . . CHAPTER 15

AT FIRST Miss Newson's budding beauty was not regarded with much interest by anybody in Casterbridge. Donald Farfrae's gaze, it is true, was now attracted by the Mayor's so-called stepdaughter, but he was only one. The truth is that she was a poor illustrative instance of the prophet Baruch's[1] sly definition: "The virgin that loveth to go gay."

When she walked abroad she seemed to be occupied with an inner chamber of ideas, and to have slight need for visible objects. She formed curious resolves on checking gay fancies in the matter of clothes, because it was inconsistent with her past life to blossom gaudily the moment she had become possessed of money. But nothing is more insidious than the evolution of wishes from mere fancies, and of wants from mere

1. *Baruch:* Biblical figure (book of *Jeremiah*).

wishes. Henchard gave Elizabeth-Jane a box of delicately tinted gloves one spring day. She wanted to wear them to show her appreciation of his kindness, but she had no bonnet that would harmonize. As an artistic indulgence she thought she would have such a bonnet. When she had a bonnet that would go with the gloves she had no dress that would go with the bonnet. It was now absolutely necessary to finish; she ordered the requisite article, and found that she had no sunshade to go with the dress. In for a penny, in for a pound; she bought the sunshade, and the whole structure was at last complete.

Everybody was attracted, and some said that her bygone simplicity was the art that conceals art, the "delicate imposition" of Rochefoucauld; she had produced an effect, a contrast, and it had been done on purpose. As a matter of fact this was not true, but it had its result; for as soon as Casterbridge thought her artful it thought her worth notice. "It is the first time in my life that I have been so much admired," she said to herself; "though perhaps it is by those whose admiration is not worth having."

But Donald Farfrae admired her, too; and altogether the time was an exciting one; sex had never before asserted itself in her so strongly, for in former days she had perhaps been too impersonally human to be distinctively feminine. After an unprecedented success one day she came indoors, went upstairs, and leaned upon her bed face downwards, quite forgetting the possible creasing and damage. "Good Heaven," she whispered, "can it be? Here am I setting up as the town beauty!"

When she had thought it over, her usual fear of exaggerating appearances engendered a deep sadness. "There is something wrong in all this," she mused. "If they only knew what an unfinished girl I am—that I can't talk Italian, or use globes, or show any of the accomplishments they learn at boarding schools, how they would despise me! Better sell all this finery and buy myself grammar books and dictionaries and a history of all the philosophies!"

She looked from the window and saw Henchard and Farfrae in the hay yard talking, with the impetuous cordiality on the Mayor's part, and genial modesty on the younger man's, that was now so generally observable in their intercourse. Friendship between man and man; what a rugged strength there was in it, as evinced by these two. And yet the seed that was to lift the foundation of this friendship was at that moment taking root in a chink of its structure.

It was about six o'clock; the men were dropping off homeward one by one. The last to leave was a round-shouldered, blinking young man of nineteen or twenty, whose mouth fell ajar on the slightest provocation, seemingly because there was no chin to support it. Henchard called aloud to him as he went out of the gate. "Here—Abel Whittle!"

Whittle turned, and ran back a few steps. "Yes, sir," he said, in breathless deprecation, as if he knew what was coming next.

"Once more—be in time tomorrow morning. You see what's to be done, and you hear what I say, and you know I'm not going to be trifled with any longer."

"Yes, sir." Then Abel Whittle left, and Henchard and Farfrae; and Elizabeth saw no more of them.

Now there was good reason for this command on Henchard's part. Poor Abel, as he was called, had an inveterate habit of over-sleeping himself and coming late to his work. His anxious will was to be among the earliest; but if his comrades omitted to pull the string that he always tied round his great toe and left hanging out of the window for that purpose, his will was as wind. He did not arrive in time.

As he was often second hand at the hay-weighing, or at the crane which lifted the sacks, or was one of those who had to accompany the wagons into the country to fetch away stacks that had been purchased, this affliction of Abel's was productive of much inconvenience. For two mornings in the present week he had kept the others waiting nearly an hour; hence Henchard's threat. It now remained to be seen what would happen tomorrow.

Six o'clock struck, and there was no Whittle. At half-past six Henchard entered the yard; the wagon was horsed that Abel was to accompany; and the other man had been waiting twenty minutes. Then Henchard swore, and Whittle coming up breathless at that instant, the corn factor turned on him and declared with an oath that this was the last time; that if he were behind once more, by God, he would come and drag him out o' bed.

"There is sommit wrong in my make, your worshipful!" said Abel, "especially in the inside, whereas my poor dumb brain gets as dead as a clot afore I've said my few scrags of prayers. Yes—it came on as a stripling, just afore I'd got man's wages, whereas I never enjoy my bed at all, for no sooner do I lie down than I be asleep, and afore I be awake I be up. I've fretted my gizzard green about it, maister, but what can I do? Now last night, afore I went to bed, I only had a scant-ling o' cheese and——"

"I don't want to hear it!" roared Henchard. "Tomorrow the wagons must start at four, and if you're not here, stand clear. I'll mortify thy flesh for thee!"

"But let me clear up my points, your worshipful——"

Henchard turned away.

"He asked me and he questioned me, and then 'a wouldn't hear my points!" said Abel, to the yard in general. "Now, I shall twitch like a moment-hand all night tonight for fear o' him!"

The journey to be taken by the wagons next day was a long one into Blackmoor Vale, and at four o'clock lanterns were moving about the yard. But Abel was missing. Before either of the other men could run to Abel's and warn him, Henchard appeared in the garden doorway. "Where's Abel

Whittle? Not come after all I've said? Now I'll carry out my word, by my blessed fathers—nothing else will do him any good! I'm going up that way."

Henchard went off, entered Abel's house, a little cottage in Back Street, the door of which was never locked because the inmates had nothing to lose. Reaching Whittle's bedside the corn factor shouted a bass note so vigorously that Abel started up instantly, and beholding Henchard standing over him, was galvanized into spasmodic movements which had not much relation to getting on his clothes.

"Out of bed, sir, and off to the granary, or you leave my employ today! 'Tis to teach ye a lesson. March on; never mind your breeches!"

The unhappy Whittle threw on his sleeve waistcoat, and managed to get into his boots at the bottom of the stairs, while Henchard thrust his hat over his head. Whittle then trotted on down Back Street, Henchard walking sternly behind.

Just at this time Farfrae, who had been to Henchard's house to look for him, came out of the back gate, and saw something white fluttering in the morning gloom, which he soon perceived to be the part of Abel's shirt that showed below his waistcoat.

"For maircy's sake, what object's this?" said Farfrae, following Abel into the yard, Henchard being some way in the rear by this time.

"Ye see, Mr. Farfrae," gibbered Abel with a resigned smile of terror, "he said he'd mortify my flesh if so be I didn't get up sooner, and now he's-a-doing on't! Ye see it can't be helped, Mr. Farfrae; things do happen queer sometimes! Yes I'll go to Blackmoor Vale half naked as I be, since he do command; but I shall kill myself afterwards; I can't outlive the disgrace; for the womenfolk will be looking out of their winders at my mortification all the way along, and laughing me to scorn as a man 'ithout breeches! You know how I feel such things, Maister Farfrae, and how forlorn thoughts get hold upon me. Yes—I shall do myself harm—I feel it coming on!"

"Get back home, and slip on your breeches, and come to wark like a man! If ye go not, you'll ha'e your death standing there!"

"I'm afraid I mustn't! Mr. Henchard said——"

"I don't care what Mr. Henchard said, nor anybody else! 'Tis simple foolishness to do this. Go and dress yourself instantly, Whittle."

"Hullo, hullo!" said Henchard, coming up behind. "Who's sending him back?"

All the men looked toward Farfrae.

"I am," said Donald. "I say this joke has been carried far enough."

"And I say it hasn't! Get up in the wagon, Whittle."

"Not if I am manager," said Farfrae. "He either goes home, or I march out of this yard for good."

Henchard looked at him with a face stern and red. But he paused for a moment, and their eyes met. Donald went up to him, for he saw in Henchard's look that he began to regret this.

"Come," said Donald quietly, "a man o' your position should ken better, sir! It is tyrannical and no worthy of you."

"'Tis not tyrannical!" murmured Henchard, like a sullen boy. "It is to make him remember!" He presently added, in a tone of one bitterly hurt: "Why did you speak to me before them like that, Farfrae? You might have stopped till we were alone. Ah—I know why! I've told ye the secret o' my life—fool that I was to do't—and you take advantage of me!"

"I had forgot it," said Farfrae simply.

Henchard looked on the ground, said nothing more, and turned away. During the day Farfrae learned from the men that Henchard had kept Abel's old mother in coals and snuff all the previous winter, which made him less antagonistic to the corn factor. But Henchard continued moody and silent, and when one of the men inquired of him if some oats should be hoisted to an upper floor or not, he said shortly, "Ask Mr. Farfrae. He's master here!"

Morally he was; there could be no doubt of it. Henchard, who had hitherto been the most admired man in his circle, was the most admired no longer. One day the daughters of a deceased farmer in Durnover wanted an opinion on the value of their haystack, and sent a messenger to ask Mr. Farfrae to oblige them with one. The messenger, who was a child, met in the yard not Farfrae, but Henchard.

"Very well," he said. "I'll come."

"But please will Mr. Farfrae come?" said the child.

"I am going that way. . . . Why Mr. Farfrae?" said Henchard, with the fixed look of thought. "Why do people always want Mr. Farfrae?"

"I suppose because they like him so—that's what they say."

"Oh—I see—that's what they say—hey? They like him because he's cleverer than Mr. Henchard, and because he knows more; and in short, Mr. Henchard can't hold a candle to him —hey?"

"Yes—that's just it, sir—some of it."

"Oh, there's more? Of course there's more! What besides? Come, here's sixpence for a fairing."

" 'And he's better-tempered, and Henchard's a fool to him,' they say. And when some of the women were a-walking home they said, 'He's a diment—he's a chap o' wax—he's the best— he's the horse for my money,' says they. And they said, 'He's the most understanding man o' them two by long chalks. I wish he was the master instead of Henchard,' they said."

"They'll talk any nonsense," Henchard replied with covered gloom. "Well, you can go now. And *I* am coming to value the hay, d'ye hear?—I." The boy departed, and Henchard murmured, "Wish he were master here, do they?"

He went toward Durnover. On his way he overtook Farfrae. They walked on together, Henchard looking mostly on the ground.

"You're no yoursel' the day?" Donald inquired.

"Yes, I am very well," said Henchard.

"But ye are a bit down—surely ye are down? Why, there's nothing to be angry about! 'Tis splendid stuff that we've got from Blackmoor Vale. By the by, the people in Durnover want their hay valued."

"Yes. I am going there."

"I'll go with ye."

As Henchard did not reply Donald practiced a piece of music *sotto voce*,[2] till, getting near the bereaved people's door, he stopped himself with——

"Ah, as their father is dead I won't go on with such as that. How could I forget?"

"Do you care so very much about hurting folks' feelings?" observed Henchard with a half sneer. "You do, I know—especially mine!"

"I am sorry if I have hurt yours, sir," replied Donald, standing still, with a second expression of the same sentiment in the regretfulness of his face. "Why should you say it—think it?"

The cloud lifted from Henchard's brow, and as Donald finished the corn merchant turned to him, regarding his breast rather than his face.

"I have been hearing things that vexed me," he said. " 'Twas that made me short in my manner—made me overlook what you really are. Now, I don't want to go in here about this hay—Farfrae, you can do it better than I. They sent for 'ee, too. I have to attend a meeting of the Town Council at eleven, and 'tis drawing on for't."

They parted thus in renewed friendship, Donald forbearing to ask Henchard for meanings that were not very plain to him. On Henchard's part there was now again repose; and yet, whenever he thought of Farfrae, it was with a dim dread; and he often regretted that he had told the young man his whole heart, and confided to him the secrets of his life.

2. *Sotto voce:* in a low voice.

. . . **CHAPTER 16**

ON THIS account Henchard's manner toward Farfrae insensibly became more reserved. He was courteous—too courteous —and Farfrae was quite surprised at the good breeding which now for the first time showed itself among the qualities of a man he had hitherto thought undisciplined, if warm and sincere. The corn factor seldom or never again put his arm upon the young man's shoulder so as to nearly weigh him down with the pressure of mechanized friendship. He left off coming to Donald's lodgings and shouting into the passage, "Hoy, Farfrae, boy, come and have some dinner with us! Don't sit here in solitary confinement!" But in the daily routine of their business there was little change.

Thus their lives rolled on till a day of public rejoicing was suggested to the country at large in celebration of a national event that had recently taken place.

For some time Casterbridge, by nature slow, made no response. Then one day Donald Farfrae broached the subject to Henchard by asking if he would have any objection to lend some rick cloths to himself and a few others, who contemplated getting up an entertainment of some sort on the day named, and required a shelter for the same, to which they might charge admission at the rate of so much a head.

"Have as many cloths as you like," Henchard replied.

When his manager had gone about the business Henchard was fired with emulation. It certainly had been very remiss of him, as Mayor, he thought, to call no meeting ere this, to discuss what should be done on this holiday. But Farfrae had been so cursed quick in his movements as to give old-fashioned people in authority no chance of the initiative. However, it was not too late; and on second thoughts he determined to take upon his own shoulders the responsibility of organizing some amusements, if the other councilmen would leave the matter in his hands. To this they quite readily agreed, the majority being fine old crusted characters who had a decided taste for living without worry.

So Henchard set about his preparations for a really brilliant thing—such as should be worthy of the venerable town. As for Farfrae's little affair, Henchard nearly forgot it; except once now and then when, on it coming into his mind, he said to himself, "Charge admission at so much a head—just like a Scotchman!—who is going to pay anything a head?" The diversions which the Mayor intended to provide were to be entirely free.

He had grown so dependent upon Donald that he could scarcely resist calling him in to consult. But by sheer self-coercion he refrained. No, he thought, Farfrae would be suggesting such improvements in his damned luminous way that in spite of himself he, Henchard, would sink to the position of second fiddle, and only scrape harmonies to his manager's talents.

Everybody applauded the Mayor's proposed entertainment, especially when it became known that he meant to pay for it all himself.

Close to the town was an elevated green spot surrounded by an ancient square earthwork—earthworks square, and not square, were as common as blackberries hereabouts—a spot whereon the Casterbridge people usually held any kind of merrymaking, meeting, or sheep fair that required more space than the streets would afford. On one side it sloped to the river Froom, and from any point a view was obtained of the country round for many miles. This pleasant upland was to be the scene of Henchard's exploit.

He advertised about the town, in long posters of a pink color, that games of all sorts would take place here; and set to work a little battalion of men under his own eye. They erected greasy poles for climbing, with smoked hams and local cheeses at the top. They placed hurdles in rows for jumping over; across the river they laid a slippery pole, with a live pig of the neighborhood tied at the other end, to become the property of the man who could walk over and get it. There were also provided wheelbarrows for racing, donkeys for the same, a stage for boxing, wrestling, and drawing blood generally; sacks for jumping in. Moreover, not forgetting his principles, Henchard provided a mammoth tea, of which everybody who lived in the borough was invited to partake without payment. The tables were laid parallel with the inner slope of the rampart, and awnings were stretched overhead.

Passing to and fro the Mayor beheld the unattractive exterior of Farfrae's erection in the West Walk, rick cloths of different sizes and colors being hung up to the arching trees without any regard to appearance. He was easy in his mind now, for his own preparations far transcended these.

The morning came. The sky, which had been remarkably clear down to within a day or two, was overcast, and the weather threatening, the wind having an unmistakable hint of water in it. Henchard wished he had not been quite so sure about the continuance of a fair season. But it was too late to modify or postpone, and the proceedings went on. At twelve o'clock the rain began to fall, small and steady, commencing and increasing so insensibly that it was difficult to state exactly when dry weather ended or wet established itself. In an hour the slight moisture resolved itself into a monotonous smiting of earth by heaven, in torrents to which no end could be prognosticated.

A number of people had heroically gathered in the field, but by three o'clock Henchard discerned that his project was doomed to end in failure. The hams at the top of the poles dripped watered smoke in the form of a brown liquor, the pig shivered in the wind, the grain of the deal tables showed through the sticking tablecloths, for the awning allowed the rain to drift under at its will, and to enclose the sides at this hour seemed a useless undertaking. The landscape over the river disappeared; the wind played on the tent cords in Æolian improvisations; and at length rose to such a pitch that the whole erection slanted to the ground, those who had taken shelter within it having to crawl out on their hands and knees.

But toward six the storm abated, and a drier breeze shook the moisture from the grass bents. It seemed possible to carry out the program after all. The awning was set up again; the band was called out from its shelter, and ordered to begin, and where the tables had stood a place was cleared for dancing.

"But where are the folk?" said Henchard, after the lapse of half-an-hour, during which time only two men and a woman had stood up to dance. "The shops are all shut. Why don't they come?"

"They are at Farfrae's affair in the West Walk," answered a councilman who stood in the field with the Mayor.

"A few, I suppose. But where are the body o' 'em?"

"All out of doors are there."

"Then the more fools they!"

Henchard walked away moodily. One or two young fellows gallantly came to climb the poles, to save the hams from being wasted; but as there were no spectators, and the whole scene presented the most melancholy appearance, Henchard gave orders that the proceedings were to be suspended, and the entertainment closed, the food to be distributed among the poor people of the town. In a short time nothing was left in the field but a few hurdles, the tents and the poles.

Henchard returned to his house, had tea with his wife and daughter, and then walked out. It was now dusk. He soon saw that the tendency of all promenaders was toward a particular spot in the Walks, and eventually proceeded thither himself. The notes of a stringed band came from the enclosure that Farfrae had erected—the pavilion as he called it—and when the Mayor reached it he perceived that a gigantic tent had been ingeniously constructed without poles or ropes. The densest point of the avenue of sycamores had been selected, where the boughs made a closely interlaced vault overhead; to these boughs the canvas had been hung, and a barrel roof was the result. The end toward the wind was enclosed, the other end was open. Henchard went round and saw the interior.

In form it was like the nave of a cathedral with one gable removed, but the scene within was anything but devotional. A reel or fling of some sort was in progress; and the usually sedate Farfrae was in the midst of the other dancers in the costume of a wild Highlander, flinging himself about and spinning to the tune. For a moment Henchard could not help laughing. Then he perceived the immense admiration for the Scotchman that revealed itself in the women's faces; and when this exhibition was over, and a new dance proposed, and Donald had disappeared for a time to return in his natural garments, he had an unlimited choice of partners, every girl being in a coming-on disposition toward one who so thoroughly understood the poetry of motion as he.

All the town crowded to the Walk, such a delightful idea of a ballroom never having occurred to the inhabitants before. Among the rest of the onlookers were Elizabeth and her mother—the former thoughtful yet much interested, her eyes beaming with a longing lingering light, as if Nature had been advised by Correggio[1] in their creation. The dancing progressed with unabated spirit, and Henchard walked and waited till his wife should be disposed to go home. He did not care to keep in the light, and when he went into the dark it was worse, for there he heard remarks of a kind which were becoming too frequent:

"Mr. Henchard's rejoicings couldn't say good morning to this," said one. "A man must be a headstrong stunpoll to think folk would go up to that bleak place today."

The other answered that people said it was not only in such

---

1. *Correggio:* famed Italian painter (1494-1534).

things as those that the Mayor was wanting. "Where would his business be if it were not for this young fellow? 'Twas verily Fortune sent him to Henchard. His accounts were like a bramblewood when Mr. Farfrae came. He used to reckon his sacks by chalk strokes all in a row like garden palings, measure his ricks by stretching with his arms, weigh his trusses by a lift, judge his hay by a chaw, and settle the price with a curse. But now this accomplished young man does it all by ciphering and mensuration. Then the wheat—that sometimes used to taste so strong o' mice when made into bread that people could fairly tell the breed—Farfrae has a plan for purifying, so that nobody would dream the smallest four-legged beast had walked over it once. O yes, everybody is full of him, and the care Mr. Henchard has to keep him, to be sure!" concluded this gentleman.

"But he won't do it for long, good-now," said the other.

"No!" said Henchard to himself behind the tree. "Or if he do, he'll be honeycombed clean out of all the character and standing that he's built up in these eighteen year!"

He went back to the dancing pavilion. Farfrae was footing a quaint little dance with Elizabeth-Jane—an old country thing, the only one she knew, and though he considerately toned down his movements to suit her demurer gait, the pattern of the shining little nails in the soles of his boots became familiar to the eyes of every bystander. The tune had enticed her into it; being a tune of a busy, vaulting, leaping sort—some low notes on the silver string of each fiddle, then a skipping on the small, like running up and down ladders—"Miss M'Loed of Ayr" was its name, so Mr. Farfrae had said, and that it was very popular in his own country.

It was soon over, and the girl looked at Henchard for approval; but he did not give it. He seemed not to see her. "Look here, Farfrae," he said, like one whose mind was elsewhere, "I'll go to Port Bredy Great Market tomorrow myself. You can stay and put things right in your clothes box, and recover strength to your knees after your vagaries." He planted on Donald an antagonistic glare that had begun as a smile.

Some other townsmen came up, and Donald drew aside. "What's this, Henchard," said Alderman Tubber, applying his thumb to the corn factor like a cheese taster. "An opposition randy to yours, eh? Jack's as good as his master, eh? Cut ye out quite, hasn't he?"

"You see, Mr. Henchard," said the lawyer, another good-natured friend, "where you made the mistake was in going so far afield. You should have taken a leaf out of his book, and have had your sports in a sheltered place like this. But you didn't think of it, you see; and he did, and that's where he's beat you."

"He'll be top-sawyer soon of you too, and carry all afore him," added jocular Mr. Tubber.

"No," said Henchard gloomily. "He won't be that, because he's shortly going to leave me." He looked toward Donald, who had again come near. "Mr. Farfrae's time as my manager is drawing to a close—isn't it, Farfrae?"

The young man, who could now read the lines and folds of Henchard's strongly-traced face as if they were clear verbal inscriptions, quietly assented; and when people deplored the fact, and asked why it was, he simply replied that Mr. Henchard no longer required his help.

Henchard went home, apparently satisfied. But in the morning, when his jealous temper had passed away, his heart sank within him at what he had said and done. He was the more disturbed when he found that this time Farfrae was determined to take him at his word.

. . . CHAPTER 17

ELIZABETH-JANE had perceived from Henchard's manner that in assenting to dance she had made a mistake of some kind. In her simplicity she did not know what it was till a hint from a nodding acquaintance enlightened her. As the Mayor's stepdaughter, she learned, she had not been quite in her place in treading a measure amid such a mixed throng as filled the dancing pavilion.

Thereupon her ears, cheeks, and chin glowed like live coals at the dawning of the idea that her tastes were not good enough for her position, and would bring her into disgrace.

This made her very miserable, and she looked about for her mother; but Mrs. Henchard, who had less idea of conventionality than Elizabeth herself, had gone away, leaving her daughter to return at her own pleasure. The latter moved on into the dark dense old avenues, or rather vaults of living woodwork, which ran along the town boundary, and stood reflecting.

A man followed in a few minutes, and her face being toward the shine from the tent he recognized her. It was Farfrae —just come from the dialogue with Henchard which had signified his dismissal.

"And it's you, Miss Newson?—and I've been looking for ye everywhere!" he said, overcoming a sadness imparted by the estrangement with the corn merchant. "May I walk on with you as far as your street corner?"

She thought there might be something wrong in this, but did not utter any objection. So together they went on, first down the West Walk, and then into the Bowling Walk, till Farfrae said, "It's like that I'm going to leave you soon."

She faltered, "Why?"

"Oh—as a mere matter of business—nothing more. But we'll not concern ourselves about it—it is for the best. I hoped to have another dance with you."

She said she could not dance—in any proper way.

"Nay, but you do! It's the feeling for it rather than the learning of steps that makes pleasant dancers. . . . I fear I offended your father by getting up this! And now, perhaps, I'll have to go to another part o' the warrld altogether!"

This seemed such a melancholy prospect that Elizabeth-Jane

breathed a sigh—letting it off in fragments that he might not hear her. But darkness makes people truthful, and the Scotchman went on impulsively—perhaps he had heard her after all:

"I wish I was richer, Miss Newson; and your stepfather had not been offended; I would ask you something in a short time —yes, I would ask you tonight. But that's not for me!"

What he would have asked her he did not say, and instead of encouraging him she remained incompetently silent. Thus afraid one of another they continued their promenade along the walls till they got near the bottom of the Bowling Walk; twenty steps further and the trees would end, and the street corner and lamps appear. In consciousness of this they stopped.

"I never found out who it was that sent us to Durnover granary on a fool's errand that day," said Donald, in his undulating tones. "Did ye ever know yourself, Miss Newson?"

"Never," said she.

"I wonder why they did it!"

"For fun, perhaps."

"Perhaps it was not for fun. It might have been that they thought they would like us to stay waiting there, talking to one another? Ay, well! I hope you Casterbridge folk will not forget me if I go."

"That I'm sure we won't!" she said earnestly. "I—wish you wouldn't go at all."

They had got into the lamplight. "Now, I'll think over that," said Donald Farfrae. "And I'll not come up to your door; but part from you here; lest it make your father more angry still."

They parted, Farfrae returning into the dark Bowling Walk, and Elizabeth-Jane going up the street. Without any consciousness of what she was doing she started running with all her might till she reached her father's door. "O dear me— what am I at?" she thought, as she pulled up breathless.

Indoors she fell to conjecturing the meaning of Farfrae's enigmatic words about not daring to ask her what he fain would. Elizabeth, that silent observing woman, had long noted how he was rising in favor among the townspeople; and knowing Henchard's nature now she had feared that Farfrae's days as manager were numbered; so that the announcement gave her little surprise. Would Mr. Farfrae stay in Casterbridge despite his words and her father's dismissal? His occult breathings to her might be solvable by his course in that respect.

The next day was windy—so windy that walking in the garden she picked up a portion of the draft of a letter on business in Donald Farfrae's writing, which had flown over the wall from the office. The useless scrap she took indoors, and began to copy the calligraphy, which she much admired. The letter began "Dear Sir," and presently writing on a loose slip "Elizabeth-Jane," she laid the latter over "Sir," making the phrase "Dear Elizabeth-Jane." When she saw the effect a quick red ran up her face and warmed her through, though nobody was there to see what she had done. She quickly tore up the slip, and threw it away. After this she grew cool and laughed at herself, walked about the room, and laughed again; not joyfully, but distressfully rather.

It was quickly known in Casterbridge that Farfrae and Henchard had decided to dispense with each other. Elizabeth-Jane's anxiety to know if Farfrae were going away from the town reached a pitch that disturbed her, for she could no longer conceal from herself the cause. At length the news reached her that he was not going to leave the place. A man following the same trade as Henchard, but on a very small scale, had sold his business to Farfrae, who was forthwith about to start as corn and hay merchant on his own account.

Her heart fluttered when she heard of this step of Donald's, proving that he meant to remain; and yet, would a man who cared one little bit for her have endangered his suit by setting up a business in opposition to Mr. Henchard's? Surely not; and it must have been a passing impulse only which had led him to address her softly.

To solve the problem whether her appearance on the evening of the dance were such as to inspire a fleeting love at first sight, she dressed herself up exactly as she had dressed then—the muslin, the spencer, the sandals, the parasol—and looked in the mirror. The picture glassed back was, in her opinion, precisely of such a kind as to inspire that fleeting regard, and no more—"just enough to make him silly, and not enough to keep him so," she said luminously; and Elizabeth thought, in a much lower key, that by this time he had discovered how plain and homely was the informing spirit of that pretty outside.

Hence, when she felt her heart going out to him, she would say to herself with a mock pleasantry that carried an ache with it, "No, no, Elizabeth-Jane—such dreams are not for you!" She tried to prevent herself from seeing him, and thinking of him; succeeding fairly well in the former attempt, in the latter not so completely.

Henchard, who had been hurt at finding that Farfrae did not mean to put up with his temper any longer, was incensed beyond measure when he learned what the young man had done as an alternative. It was in the town hall, after a council meeting, that he first became aware of Farfrae's *coup* for establishing himself independently in the town; and his voice might have been heard as far as the town pump expressing his feelings to his fellow councilmen. Those tones showed that, though under a long reign of self-control he had become Mayor and churchwarden and what not, there was still the same unruly volcanic stuff beneath the rind of Michael Henchard as when he had sold his wife at Weydon Fair.

"Well, he's a friend of mine, and I'm a friend of his—or if we are not, what are we? 'Od send, if I've not been his friend, who has, I should like to know? Didn't he come here without a sound shoe to his foot? Didn't I keep him here—help him to a living? Didn't I help him to money, or whatever he wanted? I stuck out for no terms—I said 'Name your own price.' I'd have shared my last crust with that young fellow at one time, I liked him so well. And now he's defied me! But damn him, I'll have a tussle with him now—at fair buying and selling, mind—at fair buying and selling! And if I can't overbid such a stripling as he, then I'm not wo'th a varden! We'll show that we know our business as well as one here and there!"

His friends of the Corporation did not specially respond. Henchard was less popular now than he had been when, nearly two years before, they had voted him to the chief magistracy on account of his amazing energy. While they had collectively profited by this quality of the corn factor's they had been made to wince individually on more than one occasion. So he went out of the hall and down the street alone.

Reaching home he seemed to recollect something with a sour satisfaction. He called Elizabeth-Jane. Seeing how he looked when she entered she appeared alarmed.

"Nothing to find fault with," he said, observing her concern. "Only I want to caution you, my dear. That man, Farfrae—it is about him. I've see him talking to you two or three times—he danced with 'ee at the rejoicings, and came home with 'ee. Now, now, no blame to you. But just hearken: Have you made him any foolish promise? Gone the least beyond sniff and snaff at all?"

"No. I promised him nothing."

"Good. All's well that end's well. I particularly wish you not to see him again."

"Very well, sir."

"You promise?"

She hesitated for a moment, and then said——

"Yes, if you much wish it."

"I do. He's an enemy to our house!"

When she had gone he sat down, and wrote in a heavy hand to Farfrae thus:——

Sir,—I make request that henceforth you and my stepdaughter be as strangers to each other. She on her part has promised to

welcome no more addresses from you; and I trust, therefore, you
will not attempt to force them on her.

M. HENCHARD.

One would almost have supposed Henchard to have had
policy to see that no better *modus vivendi*[1] could be arrived
at with Farfrae than by encouraging him to become his son-
in-law. But such a scheme for buying over a rival had nothing
to recommend it to the Mayor's headstrong faculties. With
all domestic *finesse* of that kind he was hopelessly at variance.
Loving a man or hating him, his diplomacy was as wrong-
headed as a buffalo's; and his wife had not ventured to suggest
the course which she, for many reasons, would have welcomed gladly.

Meanwhile Donald Farfrae had opened the gates of commerce on his own account at a spot on Durnover Hill—as far
as possible from Henchard's stores, and with every intention
of keeping clear of his former friend and employer's customers. There was, it seemed to the younger man, room for
both of them and to spare. The town was small, but the corn-
and-hay trade was proportionately large, and with his native
sagacity he saw opportunity for a share of it.

So determined was he to do nothing which should seem
like trade-antagonism to the Mayor that he refused his first
customers—a large farmer of good repute—because Henchard
and this man had dealt together within the preceding three
months.

"He was once my friend," said Farfrae, "and it's not for me
to take business from him. I am sorry to disappoint you, but
I cannot hurt the trade of a man who's been so kind to me."

In spite of this praiseworthy course the Scotchman's trade
increased. Whether it were that his northern energy was an
over-mastering force among the easy-going Wessex worthies,
or whether it was sheer luck, the fact remained that whatever
he touched he prospered in. Like Jacob in Padan-Aram,[2] he

1. *Modus vivendi:* way of living.
2. *Jacob in Padan-Aram:* reference to episode in the old Testament.

would no sooner humbly limit himself to ringstraked-and-spotted exceptions of trade than the ringstraked-and-spotted would multiply and prevail.

But most probably luck had little to do with it. Character is Fate, said Novalis,[3] and Farfrae's character was just the reverse of Henchard's, who might not inaptly be described as Faust[4] has been described—as a vehement gloomy being who had quitted the ways of vulgar men without light to guide him on a better way.

Farfrae duly received the request to discontinue attentions to Elizabeth-Jane. His acts of that kind had been so slight that the request was almost superfluous. Yet he had felt a considerable interest in her, and after some cogitation he decided that it would be as well to enact no Romeo[5] part just then—for the young girl's sake no less than his own. Thus the incipient attachment was stifled down.

A time came when, avoid collision with his former friend as he might, Farfrae was compelled, in sheer self-defense, to close with Henchard in mortal commercial combat. He could no longer parry the fierce attacks of the latter by simple avoidance. As soon as their war of prices began everybody was interested, and some few guessed the end. It was, in some degree, Northern insight matched against Southern doggedness—the dirk against the cudgel—and Henchard's weapon was one which, if it did not deal ruin at the first or second stroke, left him afterwards well-nigh at his antagonist's mercy.

Almost every Saturday they encountered each other amid the crowd of farmers which thronged about the marketplace in the weekly course of their business. Donald was always ready, and even anxious, to say a few friendly words; but the Mayor invariably gazed stormfully past him, like one who had endured and lost on his account, and could in no sense forgive

---

3. *Novalis:* pen name of Friedrich von Hardenberg, German writer (1772-1801).
4. *Faust:* legendary literary character.
5. *Romeo:* lover in Shakespeare's play.

the wrong; nor did Farfrae's snubbed manner of perplexity at all appease him. The large farmers, corn merchants, millers, auctioneers, and others had each an official stall in the corn-market room, with their names painted thereon; and when to the familiar series of "Henchard," "Everdene," "Shiner," "Darton," and so on, was added one inscribed "Farfrae," in staring new letters, Henchard was stung into bitterness; like Bellerophon,[6] he wandered away from the crowd, cankered in soul.

From that day Donald Farfrae's name was seldom mentioned in Henchard's house. If at breakfast or dinner Elizabeth-Jane's mother inadvertently alluded to her favorite's movements, the girl would implore her by a look to be silent; and her husband would say, "What—are you, too, my enemy?"

. . . **CHAPTER 18**

THERE came a shock which had been foreseen for some time by Elizabeth, as the box passenger[1] foresees the approaching jerk from some channel across the highway.

Her mother was ill—too unwell to leave her room. Henchard, who treated her kindly, except in moments of irritation, sent at once for the richest, busiest doctor, whom he supposed to be the best. Bedtime came, and they burnt a light all night. In a day or two she rallied.

Elizabeth, who had been staying up, did not appear at breakfast on the second morning, and Henchard sat down alone. He was startled to see a letter for him from Jersey in a writing he knew too well, and had expected least to behold again. He took it up in his hands and looked at it as at a picture, a vision, a vista of past enactments; and then he read it as an unimportant finale to conjecture.

The writer said that she at length perceived how impossible

---

6. *Bellerophon:* Greek mythical hero.

1. *Box passenger:* carriage passenger who sits up with the driver.

it would be for any further communications to proceed between them now that his remarriage had taken place. That such reunion had been the only straightforward course open to him she was bound to admit.

"On calm reflection, therefore," she went on, "I quite forgive you for landing me in such a dilemma, remembering that you concealed nothing before our ill-advised acquaintance; and that you really did set before me in your grim way the fact of there being a certain risk in intimacy with you, slight as it seemed to be after fifteen or sixteen years of silence on your wife's part. I thus look upon the whole as a misfortune of mine, and not a fault of yours.

"So that, Michael, I must ask you to overlook those letters with which I pestered you day after day in the heat of my feelings. They were written whilst I thought your conduct to me cruel; but now I know more particulars of the position you were in I see how inconsiderate my reproaches were.

"Now you will, I am sure, perceive that the one condition which will make any future happiness possible for me is that the past connection between our lives be kept secret outside this isle. Speak of it I know you will not; and I can trust you not to write of it. One safeguard more remains to be mentioned—that no writings of mine, or trifling articles belonging to me, should be left in your possession through neglect or forgetfulness. To this end may I request you to return to me any such you may have, particularly the letters written in the first abandonment of feeling.

"For the handsome sum you forwarded to me as a plaster to the wound I heartily thank you.

"I am now on my way to Bristol, to see my only relative. She is rich, and I hope will do something for me. I shall return through Casterbridge and Budmouth, where I shall take the packet boat. Can you meet me with the letters and other trifles? I shall be in the coach which changes horses at the Antelope Hotel at half-past five Wednesday evening; I shall be wearing a Paisley shawl with a red center, and thus may easily be found. I should prefer this plan of receiving them to having them sent.—I remain still, yours ever,

"LUCETTA."

Henchard breathed heavily. "Poor thing—better you had not known me! Upon my heart and soul, if ever I should be left in a position to carry out that marriage with thee, I *ought* to do it—I ought to do it, indeed!"

The contingency that he had in his mind was, of course, the death of Mrs. Henchard.

As requested, he sealed up Lucetta's letters, and put the parcel aside till the day she had appointed: this plan of returning them by hand being apparently a little *ruse* of the young lady for exchanging a word or two with him on past times. He would have preferred not to see her; but deeming that there could be no great harm in acquiescing thus far, he went at dusk and stood opposite the coach office.

The evening was chilly, and the coach was late. Henchard crossed over to it while the horses were being changed; but there was no Lucetta inside or out. Concluding that something had happened to modify her arrangements he gave the matter up and went home, not without a sense of relief.

Meanwhile Mrs. Henchard was weakening visibly. She could not go out of doors any more. One day, after much thinking which seemed to distress her, she said she wanted to write something. A desk was put upon her bed with pen and paper, and at her request she was left alone. She remained writing for a short time, folded her paper carefully, called Elizabeth-Jane to bring a taper and wax, and then, still refusing assistance, sealed up the sheet, directed it, and locked it in her desk. She had directed it in these words:—

"*Mr. Michael Henchard. Not to be opened till Elizabeth-Jane's wedding day.*"

The latter sat up with her mother to the utmost of her strength night after night. To learn to take the universe seriously there is no quicker way than to watch—to be a "waker," as the country people call it. Between the hours at which the last toss-pot[2] went by and the first sparrow shook

2. *Toss-pot:* drunkard.

himself, the silence in Casterbridge—barring the rare sound of the watchman—was broken in Elizabeth's ear only by the timepiece in the bedroom ticking frantically against the clock on the stairs; ticking harder and harder till it seemed to clang like a gong; and all this while the subtle-souled girl asking herself why she was born, why sitting in a room, and blinking at the candle; why things around her had taken the shape they wore in preference to every other possible shape. Why they stared at her so helplessly, as if waiting for the touch of some wand that should release them from terrestrial constraint; what that chaos called consciousness, which spun in her at this moment like a top, tended to, and began in. Her eyes fell together; she was awake, yet she was asleep.

A word from her mother roused her. Without preface, and as the continuation of a scene already progressing in her mind, Mrs. Henchard said: "You remember the note sent to you and Mr. Farfrae—asking you to meet some one in Durnover Barton—and that you thought it was a trick to make fools of you?"

"Yes."

"It was not to make fools of you—it was done to bring you together. 'Twas I did it."

"Why?" said Elizabeth, with a start.

"I—wanted you to marry Mr. Farfrae."

"O mother!" Elizabeth-Jane bent down her head so much that she looked quite into her own lap. But as her mother did not go on, she said, "What reason?"

"Well, I had a reason. 'Twill out one day. I wish it could have been in my time! But there— nothing is as you wish it! Henchard hates him."

"Perhaps they'll be friends again," murmured the girl.

"I don't know—I don't know." After this her mother was silent, and dozed; and she spoke on the subject no more.

Some little time later on Farfrae was passing Henchard's house on a Sunday morning, when he observed that the blinds were all down. He rang the bell so softly that it only sounded a single full note and a small one; and then he was informed that Mrs. Henchard was dead—just dead—that very hour.

At the town pump there were gathered when he passed a few old inhabitants, who came there for water whenever they had, as at present, spare time to fetch it, because it was purer from that original fount than from their own wells. Mrs. Cuxsom, who had been standing there for an indefinite time with her pitcher, was describing the incidents of Mrs. Henchard's death, as she had learned them from the nurse.

"And she was as white as marble stone," said Mrs. Cuxsom. "And likewise such a thoughtful woman, too—ah, poor soul —that a' minded every little thing that wanted tending. 'Yes,' says she, 'when I'm gone, and my last breath's blowed, look in the top drawer o' the chest in the back room by the window, and you'll find all my coffin clothes; a piece of flannel —that's to put under me, and the little piece is to put under my head; and my new stockings for my feet—they are folded alongside, and all my other things. And there's four ounce pennies, the heaviest I could find, a-tied up in bits of linen, for weights—two for my right eye and two for my left,' she said. 'And when you've used 'em, and my eyes don't open no more, bury the pennies, good souls, and don't ye go spending 'em, for I shouldn't like it. And open the windows as soon as I am carried out, and make it as cheerful as you can for Elizabeth-Jane.' "

"Ah, poor heart!"

"Well, and Martha did it, and buried the ounce pennies in the garden. But if ye'll believe words, that man, Christopher Coney, went and dug 'em up, and spent 'em at the Three Mariners. 'Faith,' he said, 'why should death rob life o' four-pence? Death's not of such good report that we should respect 'en to that extent,' says he."

"T'was a cannibal deed!" deprecated her listeners.

"Gad, then, I won't quite ha'e it," said Solomon Longways.

"I say it today, and 'tis a Sunday morning, and I wouldn't speak wrongfully for a zilver zixpence at such a time. I don't see noo harm in it. To respect the dead is sound doxology; and I wouldn't sell skellintons—leastwise respectable skellintons—to be varnished for 'natomies, except I were out o' work. But money is scarce, and throats get dry. Why *should* death rob life o' fourpence? I say there was no treason in it."

"Well, poor soul; she's helpless to hinder that or anything now," answered Mother Cuxsom. "And all her shining keys will be took from her, and her cupboards opened; and little things a' didn't wish seen, anybody will see; and her wishes and ways will all be as nothing!"

. . . **CHAPTER 19**

HENCHARD and Elizabeth sat conversing by the fire. It was three weeks after Mrs. Henchard's funeral; the candles were not lighted, and a restless, acrobatic flame, poised on a coal, called from the shady walls the smiles of all shapes that could respond—the old pier glass, with gilt columns and huge entablature, the picture-frames, sundry knobs and handles, and the brass rosette at the bottom of each riband bell pull on either side of the chimney piece.

"Elizabeth, do you think much of old times?" said Henchard.

"Yes, sir; often," said she.

"Who do you put in your pictures of 'em?"

"Mother and Father—nobody else hardly."

Henchard always looked like one bent on resisting pain when Elizabeth-Jane spoke of Richard Newson as "father." "Ah! I am out of all that, am I not?" he said. . . . "Was Newson a kind father?"

"Yes, sir; very."

Henchard's face settled into an expression of stolid loneliness which gradually modulated into something softer. "Suppose I had been your real father?" he said. "Would you have cared for me as much as you cared for Richard Newson?"

"I can't think it," she said quickly. "I can think of no other as my father, except my father."

Henchard's wife was dissevered from him by death; his friend and helper Farfrae by estrangement; Elizabeth-Jane by ignorance. It seemed to him that only one of them could possibly be recalled, and that was the girl. His mind began vibrating between the wish to reveal himself to her and the policy of leaving well alone, till he could no longer sit still. He walked up and down, and then he came and stood behind her chair, looking down upon the top of her head. He could no longer restrain his impulse. "What did your mother tell you about me—my history?" he asked.

"That you were related by marriage."

"She should have told more—before you knew me! Then my task would not have been such a hard one. . . . Elizabeth, it is I who am your father, and not Richard Newson. Shame alone prevented your wretched parents from owning this to you while both of 'em were alive."

The back of Elizabeth's head remained still, and her shoulders did not denote even the movements of breathing. Henchard went on: "I'd rather have your scorn, your fear, anything than your ignorance; 'tis that I hate! Your mother and I were man and wife when we were young. What you saw was our second marriage. Your mother was too honest. We had thought each other dead—and—Newson became her husband."

This was the nearest approach Henchard could make to the full truth. As far as he personally was concerned he would have screened nothing; but he showed a respect for the young girl's sex and years worthy of a better man.

When he had gone on to give details which a whole series of slight and unregarded incidents in her past life strangely corroborated; when, in short, she believed his story to be true, she became greatly agitated, and turning round to the table flung her face upon it weeping.

"Don't cry—don't cry!" said Henchard, with vehement pathos, "I can't bear it, I won't bear it. I am your father; why should you cry? Am I so dreadful, so hateful to 'ee? Don't take against me, Elizabeth-Jane!" he cried, grasping her wet hand. "Don't take against me—though I was a drinking man once, and used your mother roughly—I'll be kinder to you than *he* was! I'll do anything, if you will only look upon me as your father!"

She tried to stand up and confront him trustfully; but she could not; she was troubled at his presence, like the brethren at the avowal of Joseph.[1]

"I don't want you to come to me all of a sudden," said Henchard in jerks, and moving like a great tree in a wind. "No, Elizabeth, I don't. I'll go away and not see you till tomorrow, or when you like; and then I'll show 'ee papers to prove my words. There, I am gone, and won't disturb you any more. . . . 'Twas I that chose your name, my daughter; your mother wanted it Susan. There, don't forget 'twas I gave you your name!" He went out at the door and shut her softly in, and she heard him go away into the garden. But he had not done. Before she had moved, or in any way recovered from the effect of his disclosure he reappeared.

"One word more, Elizabeth," he said. "You'll take my surname now—hey? Your mother was against it; but it will be much more pleasant to me. 'Tis legally yours, you know. But nobody need know that. You shall take it as if by choice. I'll talk to my lawyer—I don't know the law of it exactly; but will you do this—let me put a few lines into the newspaper that such is to be your name?"

"If it is my name I must have it, mustn't I?" she asked.

1. *Joseph:* reference to Bible, *Genesis* 30:22-24.

"Well, well; usage is everything in these matters."

"I wonder why mother didn't wish it?"

"Oh, some whim of the poor soul's. Now get a bit of paper and draw up a paragraph as I shall tell you. But let's have a light."

"I can see by the firelight," she answered. "Yes—I'd rather."

"Very well."

She got a piece of paper, and bending over the fender wrote at his dictation words which he had evidently got by heart from some advertisement or other—words to the effect that she, the writer, hitherto known as Elizabeth-Jane Newson, was going to call herself Elizabeth-Jane Henchard forthwith. It was done, and fastened up, and directed to the office of the *Casterbridge Chronicle*.

"Now," said Henchard, with the blaze of satisfaction that he always emitted when he had carried his point—though tenderness softened it this time—"I'll go upstairs and hunt for some documents that will prove it all to you. But I won't trouble you with them till tomorrow. Good night, my Elizabeth-Jane!"

He was gone before the bewildered girl could realize what it all meant, or adjust her filial sense to the new center of gravity. She was thankful that he had left her to herself for the evening, and sat down over the fire. Here she remained in silence, and wept—not for her mother now, but for the genial sailor Richard Newson, to whom she seemed doing a wrong.

Henchard in the meantime had gone upstairs. Papers of a domestic nature he kept in a drawer in his bedroom, and this he unlocked. Before turning them over he leaned back and indulged in reposeful thought. Elizabeth was his at last, and she was a girl of such good sense and kind heart that she would be sure to like him. He was the kind of man to whom some human object for pouring out his heat upon—were it emotive or were it choleric—was almost a necessity. The craving of his heart for the re-establishment of this tenderest human tie had been great during his wife's lifetime, and now he had submitted to its mastery without reluctance and without fear. He bent over the drawer again, and proceeded in his search.

Among the other papers had been placed the contents of his wife's little desk, the keys of which had been handed to him at her request. Here was the letter addressed to him with the restriction, *"Not to be opened till Elizabeth-Jane's wedding day."*

Mrs. Henchard, though more patient than her husband, had been no practical hand at anything. In sealing up the sheet, which was folded and tucked in without an envelope, in the old-fashioned way, she had overlaid the junction with a large mass of wax without the requisite under-touch of the same. The seal had cracked, and the letter was open. Henchard had no reason to suppose the restriction one of serious weight, and his feeling for his late wife had not been of the nature of deep respect. "Some trifling fancy or other of poor Susan's, I suppose," he said; and without curiosity he allowed his eyes to scan the letter:—

My dear Michael,—For the good of all three of us I have kept one thing a secret from you till now. I hope you will understand why; I think you will; though perhaps you may not forgive me. But, dear Michael, I have done it for the best. I shall be in my grave when you read this, and Elizabeth-Jane will have a home. Don't curse me, Mike—think of how I was situated. I can hardly write it, but here it is. Elizabeth-Jane is not your Elizabeth-Jane —the child who was in my arms when you sold me. No; she died three months after that, and this living one is my other husband's. I christened her by the same name we had given to the first, and she filled up the ache I felt at the other's loss. Michael, I am dying, and I might have held my tongue; but I could not. Tell her husband of this or not, as you may judge; and forgive, if you can, a woman you once deeply wronged, as she forgives you.

Susan Henchard.

Her husband regarded the paper as if it were a windowpane

through which he saw for miles. His lip twitched, and he seemed to compress his frame, as if to bear better. His usual habit was not to consider whether destiny were hard upon him or not—the shape of his ideas in cases of affliction being simply a moody "I am to suffer, I perceive." "This much scourging, then, is it for me." But now through his passionate head there stormed this thought—that the blasting disclosure was what he had deserved.

His wife's extreme reluctance to have the girl's name altered from Newson to Henchard was now accounted for fully. It furnished another illustration of that honesty in dishonesty which had characterized her in other things.

He remained unnerved and purposeless for near a couple of hours; till he suddenly said, "Ah—I wonder if it is true!"

He jumped up in an impulse, kicked off his slippers, and went with a candle to the door of Elizabeth-Jane's room, where he put his ear to the keyhole and listened. She was breathing profoundly. Henchard softly turned the handle, entered, and shading the light, approached the bedside. Gradually bringing the light from behind a screening curtain he held it in such a manner that it fell slantwise on her face without shining on her eyes. He steadfastly regarded her features.

They were fair: his were dark. But this was an unimportant preliminary. In sleep there come to the surface buried genealogical facts, ancestral curves, dead men's traits, which the mobility of daytime animation screens and overwhelms. In the present statuesque repose of the young girl's countenance Richard Newson's was unmistakably reflected. He could not endure the sight of her, and hastened away.

Misery taught him nothing more than defiant endurance of it. His wife was dead, and the first impulse for revenge died with the thought that she was beyond him. He looked out at the night as at a fiend. Henchard, like all his kind, was superstitious, and he could not help thinking that the concatenation of events this evening had produced was the scheme of some sinister intelligence bent on punishing him. Yet they had developed naturally. If he had not revealed his past history to Elizabeth he would not have searched the drawer for papers, and so on. The mockery was, that he should have no sooner taught a girl to claim the shelter of his paternity than he discovered her to have no kinship with him.

This ironical sequence of things angered him like an impish trick from a fellow creature. Like Prester John's,[2] his table had been spread, and infernal harpies had snatched up the food. He went out of the house, and moved sullenly onward down the pavement till he came to the bridge at the bottom of the High Street. Here he turned in upon a bypath on the river bank, skirting the northeastern limits of the town.

These precincts embodied the mournful phases of Casterbridge life, as the south avenues embodied its cheerful moods. The whole way along here was sunless, even in summer time; in spring, white frosts lingered here when other places were steaming with warmth; while in winter it was the seed field of all the aches, rheumatisms, and torturing cramps of the year. The Casterbridge doctors must have pined away for want of sufficient nourishment but for the configuration of the landscape on the northeastern side.

The river—slow, noiseless, and dark—the Schwarzwasser of Casterbridge—ran beneath a low cliff, the two together forming a defense which had rendered walls and artificial earthworks on this side unnecessary. Here were ruins of a Franciscan priory, and a mill attached to the same, the water of which roared down a back hatch like the voice of desolation. Above the cliff, and behind the river, rose a pile of buildings, and in the front of the pile a square mass cut into the sky. It was like a pedestal lacking its statue. This missing feature, without which the design remained incomplete, was, in truth, the corpse of a man; for the square mass formed the base of

2. *Prester John:* a legendary monk, subject of many fantastic stories.

the gallows, the extensive buildings at the back being the county jail. In the meadow where Henchard now walked the mob were wont to gather whenever an execution took place, and there to the tune of the roaring weir they stood and watched the spectacle.

The exaggeration which darkness imparted to the glooms of this region impressed Henchard more than he had expected. The lugubrious harmony of the spot with his domestic situation was too perfect for him, impatient of effects, scenes, and adumbrations. It reduced his heartburning to melancholy, and he exclaimed, "Why the deuce did I come here!" He went on past the cottage in which the old local hangman had lived and died, in times before that calling was monopolized over all England by a single gentleman; and climbed up by a steep back lane into the town.

For the sufferings of that night, engendered by his bitter disappointment, he might well have been pitied. He was like one who had half fainted, and could neither recover nor complete the swoon. In words he could blame his wife, but not in his heart; and had he obeyed the wise directions outside her letter this pain would have been spared him for long—possibly for ever, Elizabeth-Jane seeming to show no ambition to quit her safe and secluded maiden courses for the speculative path of matrimony.

The morning came after this night of unrest, and with it the necessity for a plan. He was far too self-willed to recede from a position, especially as it would involve humiliation. His daughter he had asserted her to be, and his daughter she should always think herself, no matter what hypocrisy it involved.

But he was ill-prepared for the first step in this new situation. The moment he came into the breakfast room Elizabeth advanced with open confidence to him and took him by the arm.

"I have thought and thought all night of it," she said frankly. "And I see that everything must be as you say. And

I am going to look upon you as the father that you are, and not to call you Mr. Henchard any more. It is so plain to me now. Indeed, Father, it is. For, of course, you would not have done half the things you have done for me, and let me have my own way so entirely, and bought me presents, if I had only been your stepdaughter! He—Mr. Newson—whom my poor mother married by such a strange mistake" (Henchard was glad that he had disguised matters here), "was very kind —O so kind!" (she spoke with tears in her eyes); "but that is not the same thing as being one's real father after all. Now, Father, breakfast is ready!" said she cheerfully.

Henchard bent and kissed her cheek. The moment and the act he had prefigured for weeks with a thrill of pleasure; yet it was no less than a miserable insipidity to him now that it had come. His reinstation of her mother had been chiefly for the girl's sake, and the fruition of the whole scheme was such dust and ashes as this.

. . . CHAPTER 20

OF ALL the enigmas which ever confronted a girl there can have been seldom one like that which followed Henchard's announcement of himself to Elizabeth as her father. He had done it in an ardor and an agitation which had half carried the point of affection with her; yet, behold, from the next morning onwards his manner was constrained as she had never seen it before.

The coldness soon broke out into open chiding. One grievous failing of Elizabeth's was her occasional pretty and picturesque use of dialect words—those terrible marks of the beast to the truly genteel.

It was dinner time—they never met except at meals—and she happened to say when he was rising from the table, wishing to show him something, "If you'll bide where you be a minute, Father, I'll get it."

" 'Bide where you be,' " he echoed sharply. "Good God,

are you only fit to carry wash to a pig trough, that ye use such words as those?"

She reddened with shame and sadness.

"I meant 'Stay where you are,' Father," she said, in a low, humble voice. "I ought to have been more careful."

He made no reply, and went out of the room.

The sharp reprimand was not lost upon her, and in time it came to pass that for "fay" she said "succeed"; that she no longer spoke of "dumbledores" but of "bumble bees"; no longer said of young men and women that they "walked together," but that they were "engaged"; that she grew to talk of "greggles" as "wild hyacinths"; that when she had not slept she did not quaintly tell the servants next morning that she had been "hag-rid," but that she had "suffered from indigestion."

These improvements, however, are somewhat in advance of the story. Henchard, being uncultivated himself, was the bitterest critic the fair girl could possibly have had of her own lapses—really slight now, for she read omnivorously. A gratuitous ordeal was in store for her in the matter of her handwriting. She was passing the dining-room door one evening, and had occasion to go in for something. It was not till she had opened the door that she knew the Mayor was there in the company of a man with whom he transacted business.

"Here, Elizabeth-Jane," he said, looking around at her, "just write down what I tell you—a few words of an agreement for me and this gentleman to sign. I am a poor tool with a pen."

"Be jowned, and so be I," said the gentleman.

She brought forward blotting book, paper, and ink, and sat down.

"Now then—'An agreement entered into this sixteenth day of October'—write that first."

She started the pen in an elephantine march across the sheet. It was a splendid round, bold hand of her own conception, a style that would have stamped a woman as Minerva's own[1] in more recent days. But other ideas reigned then: Henchard's creed was that proper young girls wrote ladies' hand—nay, he believed that bristling characters were as innate and inseparable a part of refined womanhood as sex itself. Hence when, instead of scribbling, like the Princess Ida,[2]—

> "In such a hand as when a field of corn
> Bows all its ears before the roaring East,"

Elizabeth-Jane produced a line of chain shot and sandbags, he reddened in angry shame for her, and peremptorily saying, "Never mind—I'll finish it," dismissed her there and then.

Her considerate disposition became a pitfall to her now. She was, it must be admitted, sometimes provokingly and unnecessarily willing to saddle herself with manual labors. She would go to the kitchen instead of ringing, "Not to make Phœbe come up twice." She went down on her knees, shovel in hand, when the cat overturned the coal scuttle; moreover, she would persistently thank the parlor maid for something, till one day, as soon as the girl was gone from the room, Henchard broke out with, "Good God, why dostn't leave off thanking that girl as if she were a goddess born! Don't I pay her a dozen pound a year to do things for 'ee?" Elizabeth shrank so visibly at the exclamation that he became sorry a few minutes after, and said that he did not mean to be rough.

These domestic exhibitions were the small protruding needle rocks which suggested rather than revealed what was underneath. But his passion had less terror for her than his coldness. The increasing frequency of the latter mood told her the sad news that he disliked her with a growing dislike. The more interesting that her appearance and manners became under the softening influences which she could now command, and in her wisdom did command, the more she seemed to estrange

1. *Minerva's* own: woman of wisdom.
2. *Princess Ida:* title character of Gilbert and Sullivan operetta (1884).

him. Sometimes she caught him looking at her with a louring invidiousness that she could hardly bear. Not knowing his secret it was a cruel mockery that she should for the first time excite his animosity when she had taken his surname.

But the most terrible ordeal was to come. Elizabeth had latterly been accustomed of an afternoon to present a cup of cider or ale and bread-and-cheese to Nance Mockridge, who worked in the yard wimbling hay bonds. Nance accepted this offering thankfully at first; afterwards as a matter of course. On a day when Henchard was on the premises he saw his stepdaughter enter the hay barn on this errand; and, as there was no clear spot on which to deposit the provisions, she at once set to work arranging two trusses of hay as a table, Mockridge meanwhile standing with her hands on her hips, easefully looking at the preparations on her behalf.

"Elizabeth, come here!" said Henchard; and she obeyed.

"Why do you lower yourself so confoundedly?" he said with suppressed passion. "Haven't I told you o't fifty times? Hey? Making yourself a drudge for a common workwoman of such a character as hers! Why, ye'll disgrace me to the dust!"

Now these words were uttered loud enough to reach Nance inside the barn door, who fired up immediately at the slur upon her personal character. Coming to the door she cried, regardless of consequences, "Come to that, Mr. Michael Henchard, I can let 'ee know she've waited on worse!"

"Then she must have had more charity than sense," said Henchard.

"Oh no, she hadn't. 'Twas not for charity but for hire; and at a public house in this town!"

"It is not true!" cried Henchard indignantly.

"Just ask her," said Nance, folding her naked arms in such a manner that she could comfortably scratch her elbows.

Henchard glanced at Elizabeth-Jane, whose complexion, now pink and white from confinement, lost nearly all of the former color. "What does this mean?" he said to her. "Anything or nothing?"

"It is true," said Elizabeth-Jane. "But it was only——"

"Did you do it, or didn't you? Where was it?"

"At the Three Mariners; one evening for a little while, when we were staying there."

Nance glanced triumphantly at Henchard, and sailed into the barn; for assuming that she was to be discharged on the instant she had resolved to make the most of her victory. Henchard, however, said nothing about discharging her. Unduly sensitive on such points by reason of his own past, he had the look of one completely ground down to the last indignity. Elizabeth followed him to the house like a culprit; but when she got inside she could not see him. Nor did she see him again that day.

Convinced of the scathing damage to his local repute and position that must have been caused by such a fact, though it had never before reached his own ears, Henchard showed a positive distaste for the presence of this girl, not his own, whenever he encountered her. He mostly dined with the farmers at the market room of one of the two chief hotels, leaving her in utter solitude. Could he have seen how she made use of those silent hours he might have found reason to reverse his judgment on her quality. She read and took notes incessantly, mastering facts with painful laboriousness, but never flinching from her self-imposed task. She began the study of Latin, incited by the Roman characteristics of the town she lived in. "If I am not well-informed it shall be by no fault of my own," she would say to herself through the tears that would occasionally glide down her peachy cheeks when she was fairly baffled by the portentous obscurity of many of these educational works.

Thus she lived on, a dumb, deep-feeling, great-eyed creature, construed by not a single contiguous being; quenching with patient fortitude her incipient interest in Farfrae, because it seemed to be one-sided, unmaidenly, and unwise. True, that for reasons best known to herself, she had, since Farfrae's dismissal, shifted her quarters from the back room affording a view of the yard (which she had occupied with such zest) to a front chamber overlooking the street; but as for the young man, whenever he passed the house he seldom or never turned his head.

Winter had almost come, and unsettled weather made her still more dependent upon indoor resources. But there were certain early winter days in Casterbridge—days of firmamental exhaustion which followed angry southwesterly tempests— when, if the sun shone, the air was like velvet. She seized on these days for her periodical visits to the spot where her mother lay buried—the still-used burial ground of the old Roman-British city, whose curious feature was this, its continuity as a place of sepulture. Mrs. Henchard's dust mingled with the dust of women who lay ornamented with glass hairpins and amber necklaces, and men who held in their mouths coins of Hadrian, Posthumus, and the Constantines.[3]

Half-past ten in the morning was about her hour for seeking this spot—a time when the town avenues were deserted as the avenues of Karnak.[4] Business had long since passed down them into its daily cells, and Leisure had not arrived there. So Elizabeth-Jane walked and read, or looked over the edge of the book to think, and thus reached the churchyard.

There, approaching her mother's grave, she saw a solitary dark figure in the middle of the gravel walk. This figure, too, was reading; but not from a book: the words which engrossed it being the inscription on Mrs. Henchard's tombstone. The personage was in mourning like herself, was about her age and size, and might have been her wraith or double, but for the fact that it was a lady much more beautifully dressed than she. Indeed, comparatively indifferent as Elizabeth-Jane was

3. *Hadrian . . . Constantines:* Roman emperors.
4. *Karnak:* ancient Egyptian city.

to dress, unless for some temporary whim or purpose, her eyes were arrested by the artistic perfection of the lady's appearance. Her gait, too, had a flexuousness about it, which seemed to avoid angularity of movement less from choice than from predisposition. It was a revelation to Elizabeth that human beings could reach this stage of external development —she had never suspected it. She felt all the freshness and grace to be stolen from herself on the instant by the neighborhood of such a stranger. And this was in face of the fact that Elizabeth could now have been writ handsome, while the young lady was simply pretty.

Had she been envious she might have hated the woman; but she did not do that—she allowed herself the pleasure of feeling fascinated. She wondered where the lady had come from. The stumpy and practical walk of honest homeliness which mostly prevailed there, the two styles of dress thereabout, the simple and the mistaken, equally avouched that this figure was no Casterbridge woman's, even if a book in her hand resembling a guidebook had not also suggested it.

The stranger presently moved from the tombstone of Mrs. Henchard, and vanished behind the corner of the wall. Elizabeth went to the tomb herself; beside it were two footprints distinct in the soil, signifying that the lady had stood there a long time. She returned homeward, musing on what she had seen, as she might have mused on a rainbow or the Northern Lights, a rare butterfly or a cameo.

Interesting as things had been out of doors, at home it turned out to be one of her bad days. Henchard, whose two years' mayoralty was ending, had been made aware that he was not to be chosen to fill a vacancy in the list of aldermen; and that Farfrae was likely to become one of the council. This caused the unfortunate discovery that she had played the waiting maid in the town of which he was Mayor to rankle in his mind yet more poisonously. He had learned by personal inquiry at the time that it was to Donald Farfrae—that treacherous upstart—that she had thus humiliated herself. And though Mrs. Stannidge seemed to attach no great importance to the incident—the cheerful souls at the Three Mariners having exhausted its aspects long ago—such was Henchard's haughty spirit that the simple thrifty deed was regarded as little less than a social catastrophe by him.

Ever since the evening of his wife's arrival with her daughter there had been something in the air which had changed his luck. That dinner at the King's Arms with his friends had been Henchard's Austerlitz: he had had his successes since, but his course had not been upward. He was not to be numbered among the aldermen—that peerage of burghers—as he had expected to be, and the consciousness of this soured him today.

"Well, where have you been?" he said to her with off-hand laconism.

"I've been strolling in the Walks and churchyard, father, till I feel quite leery." She clapped her hand to her mouth, but too late.

This was just enough to incense Henchard after the other crosses of the day. "I *won't* have you talk like that!" he thundered. " 'Leery,' indeed. One would think you worked upon a farm. One day I learn that you lend a hand in public houses. Then I hear you talk like a clodhopper. I'm burned, if it goes on, this house can't hold us two."

The only way of getting a single pleasant thought to go to sleep upon after this was by recalling the lady she had seen that day, and hoping she might see her again.

Meanwhile Henchard was sitting up, thinking over his jealous folly in forbidding Farfrae to pay his addresses to this girl who did not belong to him, when if he had allowed them to go on he might not have been encumbered with her. At last he said to himself with satisfaction as he jumped up and went to the writing table: "Ah! He'll think it means peace, and a marriage portion—not that I don't want my house to be troubled with her, and no portion at all!" He wrote as follows:—

Sir,—On consideration, I don't wish to interfere with your courtship of Elizabeth-Jane, if you care for her. I therefore withdraw my objection; excepting in this—that the business be not carried on in my house.—Yours,

M. Henchard.

Mr. Farfrae.

The morrow, being fairly fine, found Elizabeth-Jane again in the churchyard; but while looking for the lady she was startled by the apparition of Farfrae, who passed outside the gate. He glanced up for a moment from the pocketbook in which he appeared to be making figures as he went; whether or not he saw her he took no notice, and disappeared.

Unduly depressed by a sense of her own superfluity she thought he probably scorned her; and quite broken in spirit sat down on a bench. She fell into painful thoughts on her position, which ended with her saying quite loud, "O, I wish I was dead with dear Mother!"

Behind the bench was a little promenade where people sometimes walked instead of on the gravel. The bench seemed to be touched by something; she looked round, and a face was bending over her, veiled, but still distinct, the face of the young woman she had seen yesterday.

Elizabeth-Jane looked confounded for a moment, knowing she had been overheard, though there was pleasure in her confusion. "Yes, I heard you," said the lady, in a vivacious voice, answering her look. "What can have happened?"

"I don't—I can't tell you," said Elizabeth, putting her hand to her face to hide a quick flush that had come.

There was no movement or word for a few seconds; then the girl felt that the young lady was sitting down beside her.

"I guess how it is with you," said the latter. "That was your mother." She waved her hand toward the tombstone. Elizabeth looked up at her as if inquiring of herself whether there should be confidence. The lady's manner was so desirous, so anxious, that the girl decided there should be confidence. "It was my mother," she said, "my only friend."

"But your father, Mr. Henchard. He is living?"

"Yes, he is living," said Elizabeth-Jane.

"Is he not kind to you?"

"I've no wish to complain of him."

"There has been a disagreement?"

"A little."

"Perhaps you were to blame," suggested the stranger.

"I was—in many ways," sighed the meek Elizabeth. "I swept up the coals when the servant ought to have done it; and I said I was leery;—and he was angry with me."

The lady seemed to warm toward her for that reply. "Do you know the impression your words give me?" she said ingenuously. "That he is a hot-tempered man—a little proud—perhaps ambitious; but not a bad man." Her anxiety not to condemn Henchard while siding with Elizabeth was curious.

"O no; certainly not *bad*," agreed the honest girl. "And he has not ever been unkind to me till lately—since Mother died. But it has been very much to bear while it has lasted. All is owing to my defects, I dare-say; and my defects are owing to my history."

"What is your history?"

Elizabeth-Jane looked wistfully at her questioner. She found that her questioner was looking at her; turned her eyes down; and then seemed compelled to look back again. "My history is not gay or attractive," she said. "And yet I can tell it, if you really want to know."

The lady assured her that she did want to know; whereupon Elizabeth-Jane told the tale of her life as she understood it, which was in general the true one, except that the sale at the fair had no part therein.

Contrary to the girl's expectation her new friend was not shocked. This cheered her; and it was not till she thought of returning to that home in which she had been treated so roughly of late that her spirits fell.

"I don't know how to return," she murmured. "I think of going away. But what can I do? Where can I go?"

"Perhaps it will be better soon," said her friend gently. "So I would not go far. Now what do you think of this: I shall soon want somebody to live in my house, partly as house-keeper, partly as companion; would you mind coming to me? But perhaps——"

"O yes," cried Elizabeth, with tears in her eyes. "I would, indeed—I would do anything to be independent; for then perhaps my father might get to love me. But, ah!"

"What?"

"I am no accomplished person. And a companion to *you* must be that."

"O, not necessarily."

"Not? But I can't help using rural words sometimes, when I don't mean to."

"Never mind, I shall like to know them."

"And—O, I know I shan't do!"—she cried with a distressful laugh. "I accidentally learned to write round hand instead of ladies' hand. And, of course, you want some one who can write that?"

"Well, no."

"What, not necessary to write ladies' hand?" cried the joyous Elizabeth.

"Not at all."

"But where do you live?"

"In Casterbridge, or rather I shall be living here after twelve o'clock today."

Elizabeth expressed her astonishment.

"I have been staying at Budmouth for a few days while my house was getting ready. The house I am going into is that one they call High-Place Hall—the old stone one looking down the lane to the Market. Two or three rooms are fit for occupa-tion, though not all: I sleep there tonight for the first time. Now will you think over my proposal, and meet me here the first fine day next week, and say if you are still in the same mind?"

Elizabeth, her eyes shining at this prospect of a change

from an unbearable position, joyfully assented; and the two parted at the gate of the churchyard.

. . . CHAPTER 21

As a MAXIM glibly repeated from childhood remains practically unmarked till some mature experience enforces it, so did this High-Place Hall now for the first time really show itself to Elizabeth-Jane, though her ears had heard its name on a hundred occasions.

Her mind dwelt upon nothing else but the stranger, and the house, and her own chance of living there, all the rest of the day. In the afternoon she had occasion to pay a few bills in the town and do a little shopping, when she learned that what was a new discovery to herself had become a common topic about the streets. High-Place Hall was undergoing repair; a lady was coming there to live shortly; all the shop people knew it, and had already discounted the chance of her being a customer.

Elizabeth-Jane could, however, add a capping touch to information so new to her in the bulk. The lady, she said, had arrived that day.

When the lamps were lighted, and it was yet not so dark as to render chimneys, attics, and roofs invisible, Elizabeth, almost with a lover's feeling, thought she would like to look at the outside of High-Place Hall. She went up the street in that direction.

The Hall, with its gray *façade* and parapet, was the only residence of its sort so near the center of the town. It had, in the first place, the characteristics of a country mansion—birds' nests in its chimneys, damp nooks where fungi grew, and irregularities of surface direct from Nature's trowel. At night the forms of passengers were patterned by the lamps in black shadows upon the pale walls.

This evening motes of straw lay around, and other signs

of the premises having been in that lawless condition which accompanies the entry of a new tenant. The house was entirely of stone, and formed an example of dignity without great size. It was not altogether aristocratic, still less consequential, yet the old-fashioned stranger instinctively said "Blood built it, and Wealth enjoys it," however vague his opinions of those accessories might be.

Yet as regards the enjoying it the stranger would have been wrong, for until this very evening, when the new lady had arrived, the house had been empty for a year or two, while before that interval its occupancy had been irregular. The reason of its unpopularity was soon made manifest. Some of its rooms overlooked the marketplace; and such a prospect from such a house was not considered desirable or seemly by its would-be occupiers.

Elizabeth's eyes sought the upper rooms, and saw lights there. The lady had obviously arrived. The impression that this woman of comparatively practiced manner had made upon the studious girl's mind was so deep that she enjoyed standing under an opposite archway merely to think that the charming lady was inside the confronting walls, and to wonder what she was doing. Her admiration for the architecture of that front was entirely on account of the inmate it screened. Though for that matter the architecture deserved admiration, or at least study, on its own account. It was Palladian,[1] and like most architecture erected since the Gothic age was a compilation rather than a design. But its reasonableness made it impressive. It was not rich, but rich enough. A timely consciousness of the ultimate vanity of human architecture, no less than of other human things, had prevented artistic superfluity.

Men had till quite recently been going in and out with parcels and packing cases, rendering the door and hall within

1. *Palladian:* in the fashion of the Italian architect Andrea Palladio (1518-1580).

like a public thoroughfare. Elizabeth trotted through the open door in the dusk, but becoming alarmed at her own temerity she went quickly out again by another which stood open in the lofty wall of the back court. To her surprise she found herself in one of the little-used alleys of the town. Looking round at the door which had given her egress, by the light of the solitary lamp fixed in the alley, she saw that it was arched and old—older than the house itself. The door was studded, and the keystone of the arch was a mask. Originally the mask had exhibited a comic leer, as could still be discerned; but generations of Casterbridge boys had thrown stones at the mask, aiming at its open mouth; and the blows thereon had chipped off the lips and jaws as if they had been eaten away by disease. The appearance was so ghastly by the weakly lamp-glimmer that she could not bear to look at it—the first unpleasant feature of her visit.

The position of the queer old door and the odd presence of the leering mask suggested one thing above all others as appertaining to the mansion's past history—intrigue. By the alley it had been possible to come unseen from all sorts of quarters in the town—the old playhouse, the old bull stake, the old cockpit, the pool wherein nameless infants had been used to disappear. High-Place Hall could boast of its conveniences undoubtedly.

She turned to come away in the nearest direction homeward, which was down the alley, but hearing footsteps approaching in that quarter, and having no great wish to be found in such a place at such a time she quickly retreated. There being no other way out she stood behind a brick pier till the intruder should have gone his way.

Had she watched she would have been surprised. She would have seen that the pedestrian on coming up made straight for the arched doorway: that as he paused with his hand upon the latch the lamplight fell upon the face of Henchard.

But Elizabeth-Jane clung so closely to her nook that she

discerned nothing of this. Henchard passed in, as ignorant of her presence as she was ignorant of his identity, and disappeared in the darkness. Elizabeth came out a second time into the alley, and made the best of her way home.

Henchard's chiding, by begetting in her a nervous fear of doing anything definable as unladylike, had operated thus curiously in keeping them unknown to each other at a critical moment. Much might have resulted from recognition—at the least a query on either side in one and the selfsame form: What could he or she possibly be doing there?

Henchard, whatever his business at the lady's house, reached his own home only a few minutes later than Elizabeth-Jane. Her plan was to broach the question of leaving his roof this evening; the events of the day had urged her to the course. But its execution depended upon his mood, and she anxiously awaited his manner toward her. She found that it had changed. He showed no further tendency to be angry; he showed something worse. Absolute indifference had taken the place of irritability; and his coldness was such that it encouraged her to departure, even more than hot temper could have done.

"Father, have you any objection to my going away?" she asked.

"Going away! No—none whatever. Where are you going?"

She thought it undesirable and unnecessary to say anything at present about her destination to one who took so little interest in her. He would know that soon enough. "I have heard of an opportunity of getting more cultivated and finished, and being less idle," she answered, with hesitation. "A chance of a place in a household where I can have advantages of study, and seeing refined life."

"Then make the best of it, in Heaven's name—if you can't get cultivated where you are."

"You don't object?"

"Object—I? Ho—no! Not at all." After a pause he said, "But you won't have enough money for this lively scheme without help, you know? If you like I should be willing to make you an allowance, so that you be not bound to live upon the starvation wages refined folk are likely to pay 'ee."

She thanked him for this offer.

"It had better be done properly," he added after a pause. "A small annuity is what I should like you to have—so as to be independent of me—and so that I may be independent of you. Would that please ye?"

"Certainly."

"Then I'll see about it this very day." He seemed relieved to get her off his hands by this arrangement, and as far as they were concerned the matter was settled. She now simply waited to see the lady again.

The day and the hour came; but a drizzling rain fell. Elizabeth-Jane, having now changed her orbit from one of gay independence to laborious self-help, thought the weather good enough for such declined glory as hers, if her friend would only face it—a matter of doubt. She went to the boot room where her pattens had hung ever since her apotheosis; took them down, had their mildewed leathers blacked, and put them on as she had done in old times. Thus mounted, and with cloak and umbrella, she went off to the place of appointment—intending, if the lady were not there, to call at the house.

One side of the churchyard—the side toward the weather —was sheltered by an ancient thatched mud wall whose eaves overhung as much as one or two feet. At the back of the wall was a corn yard with its granary and barns—the place wherein she had met Farfrae many months earlier. Under the projection of the thatch she saw a figure. The young lady had come.

Her presence so exceptionally substantiated the girl's utmost hopes that she almost feared her good fortune. Fancies find room in the strongest minds. Here, in a churchyard old as civilization, in the worst of weathers, was a strange woman of curious fascinations never seen elsewhere: there might be some devilry about her presence. However, Elizabeth went on to the church tower, on whose summit the rope of a flag-staff rattled in the wind; and thus she came to the wall.

The lady had such a cheerful aspect in the drizzle that Elizabeth forgot her fancy. "Well," said the lady, a little of the whiteness of her teeth appearing with the word through the black fleece that protected her face, "have you decided?"

"Yes, quite," said the other eagerly.

"Your father is willing?"

"Yes."

"Then come along."

"When?"

"Now—as soon as you like. I had a good mind to send to you to come to my house, thinking you might not venture up here in the wind. But as I like getting out of doors, I thought I would come and see first."

"It was my own thought."

"That shows we shall agree. Then can you come today? My house is so hollow and dismal that I want some living thing there."

"I think I might be able to," said the girl, reflecting.

Voices were borne over to them at that instant on the wind and raindrops from the other side of the wall. There came such words as "sacks," "quarters," "threshing," "tailing," "next Saturday's market," each sentence being disorganized by the gusts like a face in a cracked mirror. Both the women listened.

"Who are those?" said the lady.

"One is my father. He rents that yard and barn."

The lady seemed to forget the immediate business in listening to the technicalities of the corn trade. At last she said suddenly, "Did you tell him where you were going to?"

"No."

"O—how was that?"

"I thought it safer to get away first—as he is so uncertain in his temper."

"Perhaps you are right. . . . Besides, I have never told you my name. It is Miss Templeman. . . . Are they gone—on the other side?"

"No. They have only gone up into the granary."

"Well, it is getting damp here. I shall expect you today—this evening, say, at six."

"Which way shall I come, ma'am?"

"The front way—round by the gate. There is no other that I have noticed."

Elizabeth-Jane had been thinking of the door in the alley.

"Perhaps, as you have not mentioned your destination, you may as well keep silent upon it till you are clear off. Who knows but that he may alter his mind?"

Elizabeth-Jane shook her head. "On consideration I don't fear it," she said sadly. "He has grown quite cold to me."

"Very well. Six o'clock then."

When they had emerged upon the open road and parted, they found enough to do in holding their bowed umbrellas to the wind. Nevertheless the lady looked in at the corn-yard gates as she passed them, and paused on one foot for a moment. But nothing was visible there save the ricks, and the hump-backed barn cushioned with moss, and the granary rising against the church tower behind, where the smacking of the rope against the flagstaff still went on.

Now Henchard had not the slightest suspicion that Eliza-beth-Jane's movement was to be so prompt. Hence when, just before six, he reached home and saw a fly[2] at the door from the King's Arms, and his stepdaughter, with all her little bags and boxes, getting into it, he was taken by surprise.

"But you said I might go, Father?" she explained through the carriage window.

"Said!—yes. But I thought you meant next month, or next year. 'Od seize it—you take time by the forelock! This, then,

2. *Fly:* carriage.

is how you be going to treat me for all my trouble about ye?"

"O Father! How can you speak like that? It is unjust of you!" she said with spirit.

"Well, well, have your own way," he replied. He entered the house, and, seeing that all her things had not yet been brought down, went up to her room to look on. He had never been there since she had occupied it. Evidences of her care, of her endeavors for improvement, were visible all around, in the form of books, sketches, maps, and little arrangements for tasteful effects. Henchard had known nothing of these efforts. He gazed at them, turned suddenly about, and came down to the door.

"Look here," he said, in an altered voice—he never called her by name now—"don't 'ee go away from me. It may be I've spoke roughly to you—but I've been grieved beyond everything by you—there's something that caused it."

"By me?" she said, with deep concern. "What have I done?"

"I can't tell you now. But if you'll stop, and go on living as my daughter, I'll tell you all in time."

But the proposal had come ten minutes too late. She was in the fly—was already, in imagination, at the house of the lady whose manner had such charms for her. "Father," she said, as considerately as she could, "I think it best for us that I go on now. I need not stay long; I shall not be far away; and if you want me badly I can soon come back again."

He nodded ever so slightly, as a receipt of her decision and no more. "You are not going far, you say. What will be your address, in case I wish to write to you? Or am I not to know?"

"Oh yes—certainly. It is only in the town—High-Place Hall."

"Where?" said Henchard, his face stilling.

She repeated the words. He neither moved nor spoke, and waving her hand to him in utmost friendliness she signified to the flyman to drive up the street.

... **CHAPTER 22**

We go back for a moment to the preceding night, to account for Henchard's attitude.

At the hour when Elizabeth-Jane was contemplating her stealthy reconnoitering excursion to the abode of the lady of her fancy, he had been not a little amazed at receiving a letter by hand in Lucetta's well-known characters. The self-repression, the resignation of her previous communication had vanished from her mood; she wrote with some of the natural lightness which had marked her in their early acquaintance.

High-Place Hall.

My dear Mr. Henchard,—Don't be surprised. It is for your good and mine, as I hope, that I have come to live at Casterbridge —for how long I cannot tell. That depends upon another; and he is a man, and a merchant, and a Mayor, and one who has the first right to my affections.

Seriously, *mon ami*,[1] I am not so light-hearted as I may seem to be from this. I have come here in consequence of hearing of the death of your wife—whom you used to think of as dead so many years before! Poor woman, she seems to have been a sufferer, though uncomplaining, and though weak in intellect not an imbecile. I am glad you acted fairly by her. As soon as I knew she was no more, it was brought home to me very forcibly by my conscience that I ought to endeavor to disperse the shade which my *étourderie*[2] flung over my name, by asking you to carry out your promise to me. I hope you are of the same mind, and that you will take steps to this end. As, however, I did not know how you were situated, or what had happened since our separation, I decided to come and establish myself here before communicating with you.

You probably feel as I do about this. I shall be able to see you in a day or two. Till then, farewell.—Yours,

Lucetta.

1. *Mon ami:* "my friend" (French).
2. *Étourderie:* "thoughtlessness" (French).

P.S.—I was unable to keep my appointment to meet you for a moment or two in passing through Casterbridge the other day. My plans were altered by a family event, which it will surprise you to hear of.

Henchard had already heard that High-Place Hall was being prepared for a tenant. He said with a puzzled air to the first person he encountered, "Who is coming to live at the Hall?"

"A lady of the name of Templeman, I believe, sir," said his informant.

Henchard thought it over. "Lucetta is related to her, I suppose," he said to himself. "Yes, I must put her in her proper position, undoubtedly."

It was by no means with the oppression that would once have accomplished the thought that he regarded the moral necessity now; it was, indeed, with interest, if not warmth. His bitter disappointment at finding Elizabeth-Jane to be none of his, and himself a childless man, had left an emotional void in Henchard that he unconsciously craved to fill. In this frame of mind, though without strong feeling, he had strolled up the alley and into High-Place Hall by the postern at which Elizabeth had so nearly encountered him. He had gone on thence into the court, and inquired of a man whom he saw unpacking china from a crate if Miss Le Sueur was living there. Miss Le Sueur had been the name under which he had known Lucetta—or "Lucette," as she had called herself at that time.

The man replied in the negative; that Miss Templeman only had come. Henchard went away, concluding that Lucetta had not as yet settled in.

He was in this interested stage of the inquiry when he witnessed Elizabeth-Jane's departure the next day. On hearing her announce the address there suddenly took possession of him the strange thought that Lucetta and Miss Templeman were one and the same person, for he could recall that in her season of intimacy with him the name of the rich relative whom he had deemed somewhat a mythical personage had been given as Templeman. Though he was not a fortune hunter, the possibility that Lucetta had been sublimed into a lady of means by some munificent testament on the part of this relative lent a charm to her image which it might not otherwise have acquired. He was getting on toward the dead level of middle age, when material things increasingly possess the mind.

But Henchard was not left long in suspense. Lucetta was rather addicted to scribbling, as had been shown by the torrent of letters after the *fiasco* in their marriage arrangements, and hardly had Elizabeth gone away when another note came to the Mayor's house from High-Place Hall.

"I am in residence," she said, "and comfortable, though getting here has been a wearisome undertaking. You probably know what I am going to tell you, or do you not? My good Aunt Templeman, the banker's widow, whose very existence you used to doubt, much more her affluence, has lately died, and bequeathed some of her property to me. I will not enter into details except to say that I have taken her name—as a means of escape from mine, and its wrongs.

"I am now my own mistress, and have chosen to reside in Casterbridge—to be tenant of High-Place Hall, that at least you may be put to no trouble if you wish to see me. My first intention was to keep you in ignorance of the changes in my life till you should meet me in the street; but I have thought better of this.

"You probably are aware of my arrangement with your daughter, and have doubtless laughed at the—what shall I call it?—practical joke (in all affection) of my getting her to live with me. But my first meeting with her was purely an accident. Do you see, Michael, partly why I have done it?—why, to give you an excuse for coming here as if to visit *her*, and thus to form my acquaintance naturally. She is a dear, good girl, and she thinks you have treated her with undue severity. You may have done so in your haste, but not deliberately, I am sure. As the result has

been to bring her to me I am not disposed to upbraid you.—In
haste, yours always,   LUCETTA."

The excitement which these announcements produced in
Henchard's gloomy soul was to him most pleasurable. He sat
over his dining table long and dreamily, and by an almost
mechanical transfer the sentiments which had run to waste
since his estrangement from Elizabeth-Jane and Donald Farfrae gathered around Lucetta before they had grown dry.
She was plainly in a very coming-on disposition for marriage.
But what else could a poor woman be who had given her
time and heart to him so thoughtlessly, at that former time, as
to lose her credit by it? Probably conscience no less than
affection had brought her here. On the whole he did not
blame her.

"The artful little woman!" he said, smiling (with reference
to Lucetta's adroit and pleasant maneuver with Elizabeth-
Jane).

To feel that he would like to see Lucetta was with Henchard to start for her house. He put on his hat and went. It
was between eight and nine o'clock when he reached her door.
The answer brought him was that Miss Templeman was engaged for that evening; but that she would be happy to see
him the next day.

"That's rather like giving herself airs!" he thought. "And
considering what we——" But after all, she plainly had not
expected him, and he took the refusal quietly. Nevertheless
he resolved not to go next day. "These cursed women—there's
not an inch of straight grain in 'em!" he said.

Let us follow the track of Mr. Henchard's thought as if
it were a clue line, and view the interior of High-Place Hall
on this particular evening.

On Elizabeth-Jane's arrival she had been phlegmatically
asked by an elderly woman to go upstairs and take off her
things. She had replied with great earnestness that she would
not think of giving that trouble, and on the instant divested

herself of her bonnet and cloak in the passage. She was then conducted to the first door on the landing, and left to find her way further alone.

The room disclosed was prettily furnished as a boudoir or small drawing room, and on a sofa with two cylindrical pillows reclined a dark-haired, large-eyed, pretty woman, of unmistakably French extraction on one side or the other. She was probably some years older than Elizabeth, and had a sparkling light in her eye. In front of the sofa was a small table, with a pack of cards scattered upon it faces upward.

The attitude had been so full of abandonment that she bounded up like a spring on hearing the door open.

Perceiving that it was Elizabeth she lapsed into ease, and came across to her with a reckless skip that innate grace only prevented from being boisterous.

"Why, you are late," she said, taking hold of Elizabeth-Jane's hands.

"There were so many little things to put up."

"And you seem dead-alive and tired. Let me try to enliven you by some wonderful tricks I have learned, to kill time. Sit there and don't move." She gathered up the pack of cards, pulled the table in front of her, and began to deal them rapidly, telling Elizabeth to choose some.

"Well, have you chosen?" she asked, flinging down the last card.

"No," stammered Elizabeth, arousing herself from a reverie. "I quite forgot, I was thinking of—you, and me—and how strange it is that I am here."

Miss Templeman looked at Elizabeth-Jane with interest, and laid down the cards. "Ah! Never mind," she said. "I'll lie here while you sit by me; and we'll talk."

Elizabeth drew up silently to the head of the sofa, but with obvious pleasure. It could be seen that though in years she was younger than her entertainer in manner and general vision she seemed more of the sage. Miss Templeman deposited herself on the sofa in her former flexuous position, and throwing her arm above her brow—somewhat in the pose of a well-known conception of Titian's[3]—talked up at Elizabeth-Jane invertedly across her forehead and arm.

"I must tell you something," she said. "I wonder if you have suspected it. I have only been mistress of a large house and fortune a little while."

"Oh—only a little while?" murmured Elizabeth-Jane, her countenance slightly falling.

"As a girl I lived about in garrison towns and elsewhere with my father, till I was quite flighty and unsettled. He was an officer in the army. I should not have mentioned this had I not thought it best you should know the truth."

"Yes, yes." She looked thoughtfully round the room—at the little square piano with brass inlayings, at the window curtains, at the lamp, at the fair and dark kings and queens on the card table, and finally at the inverted face of Lucetta Templeman, whose large lustrous eyes had such an odd effect upside down.

Elizabeth's mind ran on acquirements to an almost morbid degree. "You speak French and Italian fluently, no doubt," she said. "I have not been able to get beyond a wretched bit of Latin yet."

"Well, for that matter, in my native isle speaking French does not go for much. It is rather the other way."

"Where is your native isle?"

It was with rather more reluctance that Miss Templeman said, "Jersey. There they speak French on one side of the street and English on the other, and a mixed tongue in the middle of the road. But it is a long time since I was there. Bath is where my people really belong to, though my ancestors in Jersey were as good as anybody in England. They were the Le Sueurs, an old family who have done great things in their

3. *Titian:* Italian painter (1477-1576).

time. I went back and lived there after my father's death. But
I don't value such past matters, and am quite an English person in my feelings and tastes."

Lucetta's tongue had for a moment outrun her discretion.
She had arrived at Casterbridge as a Bath lady, and there were
obvious reasons why Jersey should drop out of her life. But
Elizabeth had tempted her to make free, and a deliberately
formed resolve had been broken.

It could not, however, have been broken in safer company.
Lucetta's words went no further, and after this day she was
so much upon her guard that there appeared no chance of her
identification with the young Jersey woman who had been
Henchard's dear comrade at a critical time. Not the least
amusing of her safeguards was her resolute avoidance of a
French word if one by accident came to her tongue more
readily than its English equivalent. She shirked it with the
suddenness of the weak Apostle at the accusation, "Thy
speech betrayeth thee!"

Expectancy sat visibly upon Lucetta the next morning. She
dressed herself for Mr. Henchard, and restlessly awaited his
call before midday; as he did not come she waited on through
the afternoon. But she did not tell Elizabeth that the person
expected was the girl's stepfather.

They sat in adjoining windows of the same room in Lucetta's great stone mansion, netting, and looking out upon
the market, which formed an animated scene. Elizabeth could
see the crown of her stepfather's hat among the rest beneath,
and was not aware that Lucetta watched the same object with
yet intenser interest. He moved about amid the throng, at this
point lively as an ant hill; elsewhere more reposeful, and
broken up by stalls of fruit and vegetables. The farmers as a
rule preferred the open *carrefour*[4] for their transactions, despite its inconvenient jostlings and the danger from crossing

4. *Carrefour:* crossway.

vehicles, to the gloomy sheltered market room provided for them. Here they surged on this one day of the week, forming a little world of leggings, switches, and sample bags; men of extensive stomachs, sloping like mountain sides; men whose heads in walking swayed as the trees in November gales; who in conversing varied their attitudes much, lowering themselves by spreading their knees, and thrusting their hands into the pockets of remote inner jackets. Their faces radiated tropical warmth; for though when at home their countenances varied with the seasons, their market faces all the year round were glowing little fires.

All overclothes here were worn as if they were an inconvenience, a hampering necessity. Some men were well-dressed; but the majority were careless in that respect, appearing in suits which were historical records of their wearer's deeds, sunscorchings, and daily struggles for many years past. Yet many carried ruffled checkbooks in their pockets which regulated at the bank hard by a balance of never less than four figures. In fact, what these gibbous human shapes specially represented was ready money—money insistently ready—not ready next year like a nobleman's—often not merely ready at the bank like a professional man's, but ready in their large plump hands.

It happened that today there rose in the midst of them all two or three tall apple trees standing as if they grew on the spot; till it was perceived that they were held by men from the cider districts who came here to sell them, bringing the clay of their country on their boots. Elizabeth-Jane, who had often observed them, said, "I wonder if the same trees come every week?"

"What trees?" said Lucetta, absorbed in watching for Henchard.

Elizabeth replied vaguely, for an incident checked her. Behind one of the trees stood Farfrae, briskly discussing a sample-bag with a farmer. Henchard had come up, accidentally encountering the younger man, whose face seemed to inquire, "Do we speak to each other?"

She saw her stepfather throw a shine into his eye which answered "No!" Elizabeth-Jane sighed.

"Are you particularly interested in anybody out there?" said Lucetta.

"O no," said her companion, a quick red shooting over her face.

Luckily Farfrae's figure was immediately covered by the apple tree.

Lucetta looked hard at her. "Quite sure?" she said.

"O yes," said Elizabeth-Jane.

Again Lucetta looked out. "They are all farmers, I suppose?" she said.

"No. There's Mr. Bulge—he's a wine merchant; there's Benjamin Brownlet—a horse dealer; and Kitson, the pig breeder; and Yopper, the auctioneer; besides maltsters, and millers—and so on." Farfrae stood out quite distinctly now; but she did not mention him.

The Saturday afternoon slipped on thus desultorily. The market changed from the sample-showing hour to the idle hour before starting homewards, when tales were told. Henchard had not called on Lucetta though he had stood so near. He must have been too busy, she thought. He would come on Sunday or Monday.

The days came but not the visitor, though Lucetta repeated her dressing with scrupulous care. She was disheartened. It may at once be declared that Lucetta no longer bore toward Henchard all that warm allegiance which had characterized her in their first acquaintance; the then unfortunate issue of things had chilled pure love considerably. But there remained a conscientious wish to bring about her union with him, now that there was nothing to hinder it—to right her position— which in itself was a happiness to sigh for. With strong social reasons on her side why their marriage should take place there had ceased to be any worldly reason on his why it should be postponed, since she had succeeded to fortune.

Tuesday was the great Candlemas fair. At breakfast she said to Elizabeth-Jane quite coolly: "I imagine your father may call to see you today. I suppose he stands close by in the marketplace with the rest of the corn dealers?"

She shook her head. "He won't come."

"Why?"

"He has taken against me," she said in a husky voice.

"You have quarreled more deeply than I know of."

Elizabeth, wishing to shield the man she believed to be her father from any charge of unnatural dislike, said "Yes."

"Then where you are is, of all places, the one he will avoid?"

Elizabeth nodded sadly.

Lucetta looked blank, twitched up her lovely eyebrows and lips, and burst into hysterical sobs. Here was a disaster—her ingenious scheme completely stultified.

"O, my dear Miss Templeman—what's the matter?" cried her companion.

"I like your company much!" said Lucetta, as soon as she could speak.

"Yes, yes—and so do I yours!" Elizabeth chimed in soothingly.

"But—but——" She could not finish the sentence, which was, naturally, that if Henchard had such a rooted dislike for the girl as now seemed to be the case, Elizabeth-Jane would have to be got rid of—a disagreeable necessity.

A provisional resource suggested itself. "Miss Henchard—will you go on an errand for me as soon as breakfast is over? —Ah, that's very good of you. Will you go and order——" Here she enumerated several commissions at sundry shops, which would occupy Elizabeth's time for the next hour or two, at least.

"And have you ever seen the museum?"

Elizabeth-Jane had not.

"Then you should do so at once. You can finish the morning by going there. It is an old house in a back street—I forget where—but you'll find out—and there are crowds of interesting things—skeletons, teeth, old pots and pans, ancient boots and shoes, birds' eggs—all charmingly instructive. You'll be sure to stay till you get quite hungry."

Elizabeth hastily put on her things and departed. "I wonder why she wants to get rid of me today!" she said sorrowfully as she went. That her absence, rather than her services or instruction, was in request, had been readily apparent to Elizabeth-Jane, simple as she seemed, and difficult as it was to attribute a motive for the desire.

She had not been gone ten minutes when one of Lucetta's servants was sent to Henchard's with a note. The contents were briefly:—

DEAR MICHAEL,—You will be standing in view of my house today for two or three hours in the course of your business, so please call and see me. I am sadly disappointed that you have not come before, for can I help anxiety about my own equivocal relation to you?—especially now my aunt's fortune has brought me more prominently before society? Your daughter's presence here may be the cause of your neglect; and I have therefore sent her away for the morning. Say you come on business—I shall be quite alone.   LUCETTA.

When the messenger returned her mistress gave directions that if a gentleman called he was to be admitted at once, and sat down to await results.

Sentimentally she did not much care to see him—his delays had wearied her; but it was necessary; and with a sigh she arranged herself picturesquely in the chair; first this way, then that; next so that the light fell over her head. Next she flung herself on the couch in the cyma-recta[5] curve which so became her, and with her arm over her brow looked towards the

5. *Cyma-recta:* hollow.

door. This, she decided, was the best position after all; and thus she remained till a man's step was heard on the stairs. Whereupon, Lucetta, forgetting her curve (for Nature was too strong for Art as yet), jumped up and ran and hid herself behind one of the window curtains in a freak of timidity. In spite of the waning of passion the situation was an agitating one—she had not seen Henchard since his (supposed) temporary parting from her in Jersey.

She could hear the servant showing the visitor into the room, shutting the door upon him, and leaving as if to go and look for her mistress. Lucetta flung back the curtain with a nervous greeting. The man before her was not Henchard.

. . . CHAPTER 23

A CONJECTURE that her visitor might be some other person had, indeed, flashed through Lucetta's mind when she was on the point of bursting out; but it was just too late to recede.

He was years younger than the Mayor of Casterbridge; fair, fresh, and slenderly handsome. He bore genteel cloth leggings with white buttons, polished boots with infinite lace holes, light cord breeches under a black velveteen coat and waistcoat; and he had a silver-topped switch in his hand. Lucetta blushed, and said with a curious mixture of pout and laugh on her face—"O, I've made a mistake!"

The visitor, on the contrary, did not laugh half a wrinkle.

"But I'm very sorry!" he said, in deprecating tones. "I came and I inquired for Miss Henchard, and they showed me up heere, and in no case would I have caught ye so unmannerly if I had known!"

"I was the unmannerly one," said she.

"But is it that I have come to the wrong house, madam?" said Mr. Farfrae, blinking a little in his bewilderment and nervously tapping his legging with his switch.

"O no, sir,—sit down. You must come and sit down now you are here," replied Lucetta kindly, to relieve his embarrassment. "Miss Henchard will be here directly."

Now this was not strictly true; but that something about the young man—that hyperborean crispness, stringency, and charm, as of a well-braced musical instrument, which had awakened the interest of Henchard, and of Elizabeth-Jane, and of the Three Mariners' jovial crew, at sight, made his unexpected presence here attractive to Lucetta. He hesitated, looked at the chair, thought there was no danger in it (though there was) and sat down.

Farfrae's sudden entry was simply the result of Henchard's permission to him to see Elizabeth if he were minded to woo her. At first he had taken no notice of Henchard's brusque letter; but an exceptionally fortunate business transaction put him on good terms with everybody, and revealed to him that he could undeniably marry if he chose. Then who so pleasing, thrifty, and satisfactory in every way as Elizabeth-Jane? Apart from her personal recommendations a reconciliation with his former friend Henchard would, in the natural course of things, flow from such a union. He therefore forgave the Mayor his curtness; and this morning on his way to the fair he had called at her house, where he learned that she was staying at Miss Templeman's. A little stimulated at not finding her ready and waiting—so fanciful are men!—he hastened on to High-Place Hall to encounter no Elizabeth but its mistress herself.

"The fair today seems a large one," she said when, by a natural deviation, their eyes sought the busy scene without. "Your numerous fairs and markets keep me interested. How many things I think of while I watch from here!"

He seemed in doubt how to answer, and the babble without reached them as they sat—voices as of wavelets on a lopping sea, one ever and anon rising above the rest. "Do you look out often?" he asked.

"Yes—very often."

"Do you look for anyone you know?"

Why should she have answered as she did?

"I look as at a picture merely. But," she went on, turning pleasantly to him, "I may do so now—I may look for you. You are always there, are you not? Ah—I don't mean it seriously! But it is amusing to look for somebody one knows in a crowd, even if one does not want him. It takes off the terrible oppressiveness of being surrounded by a throng, and having no point of junction with it through a single individual."

"Ay! Maybe you'll be very lonely, ma'am?"

"Nobody knows how lonely."

"But you are rich, they say?"

"If so, I don't know how to enjoy my riches. I came to Casterbridge thinking I should like to live here. But I wonder if I shall."

"Where did ye come from, ma'am?"

"The neighborhood of Bath."

"And I from near Edinboro," he murmured. "It's better to stay at home, and that's true; but a man must live where his money is made. It is a great pity, but it's always so! Yet I've done very well this year. O yes," he went on with ingenuous enthusiasm. "You see that man with the drab kerseymere coat? I bought largely of him in the autumn when wheat was down, and then afterwards when it rose a little I sold off all I had! It brought only a small profit to me; while the farmers kept theirs, expecting higher figures—yes, though the rats were gnawing the ricks hollow. Just when I sold the markets went lower, and I bought up the corn of those who had been holding back at less price than my first purchases. And then," cried Farfrae impetuously, his face alight, "I sold it a few weeks after, when it happened to go up again! And so, by contenting mysel' with small profits frequently repeated, I soon made five hundred pounds—yes!"—(bringing down his hand upon the table, and quite forgetting where he was)—"while others by keeping theirs in hand made nothing at all!"

Lucetta regarded him with a critical interest. He was quite

a new type of person to her. At last his eye fell upon the lady's
and their glances met.

"Ay, now, I'm wearying you!" he exclaimed.

She said, "No, indeed," coloring a shade.

"What then?"

"Quite otherwise. You are most interesting."

It was now Farfrae who showed the modest pink.

"I mean all you Scotchmen," she added in hasty correction.
"So free from Southern extremes. We common people are
all one way or the other—warm or cold, passionate or frigid.
You have both temperatures going on in you at the same time."

"But how do you mean that? Ye were best to explain clearly,
ma'am."

"You are animated—then you are thinking of getting on.
You are sad the next moment—then you are thinking of Scotland and friends."

"Yes. I think of home sometimes!" he said simply.

"So do I—as far as I can. But it was an old house where I
was born, and they pulled it down for improvements, so I
seem hardly to have any home to think of now."

Lucetta did not add, as she might have done, that the house
was in St. Helier, and not in Bath.

"But the mountains, and the mists and the rocks, they are
there! And don't they seem like home?"

She shook her head.

"They do to me—they do to me," he murmured. And his
mind could be seen flying away northwards. Whether its
origin were national or personal, it was quite true what Lucetta had said, that the curious double strands in Farfrae's
thread of life—the commercial and the romantic—were very
distinct at times. Like the colors in a variegated cord those con-
trasts could be seen intertwisted, yet not mingling.

"You are wishing you were back again," said she.

"Ah, no, ma'am," said Farfrae, suddenly recalling himself.

The fair without the windows was now raging thick and
loud. It was the chief hiring fair of the year, and differed quite

from the market of a few days earlier. In substance it was a whitey-brown crowd flecked with white—this being the body of laborers waiting for places. The long bonnets of the women, like wagon tilts, their cotton gowns and checked shawls, mixed with the carters' smockfrocks; for they, too, entered into the hiring. Among the rest, at the corner of the pavement, stood an old shepherd, who attracted the eyes of Lucetta and Farfrae by his stillness. He was evidently a chastened man. The battle of life had been a sharp one with him, for, to begin with, he was a man of small frame. He was now so bowed by hard work and years that, approaching from behind, a person could hardly see his head. He had planted the stem of his crook in the gutter and was resting upon the bow, which was polished to silver brightness by the long friction of his hands. He had quite forgotten where he was, and what he had come for, his eyes being bent on the ground. A little way off negotiations were proceeding which had reference to him; but he did not hear them, and there seemed to be passing through his mind pleasant visions of the hiring successes of his prime, when his skill laid open to him any farm for the asking.

The negotiations were between a farmer from a distant county and the old man's son. In these there was a difficulty. The farmer would not take the crust without the crumb of the bargain, in other words, the old man without the younger; and the son had a sweetheart on his present farm, who stood by, waiting the issue with pale lips.

"I'm sorry to leave ye, Nelly," said the young man with emotion. "But, you see, I can't starve Father, and he's out o' work at Lady-day. 'Tis only thirty-five mile."

The girl's lips quivered. "Thirty-five mile!" she murmured. "Ah! 'Tis enough! I shall never see 'ee again!" It was, indeed, a hopeless length of traction for Dan Cupid's magnet; for young men were young men at Casterbridge as elsewhere.

"O! no, no—I never shall," she insisted, when he pressed her hand; and she turned her face to Lucetta's wall to hide her weeping. The farmer said he would give the young man half an hour for his answer, and went away, leaving the group sorrowing.

Lucetta's eyes, full of tears, met Farfrae's. His, too, to her surprise, were moist at the scene.

"It is very hard," she said with strong feelings. "Lovers ought not to be parted like that! O, if I had my wish, I'd let people live and love at their pleasure!"

"Maybe I can manage that they'll not be parted," said Farfrae. "I want a young carter; and perhaps I'll take the old man too—yes; he'll not be very expensive, and doubtless he will answer my pairrpose somehow."

"O, you are so good!" she cried, delighted. "Go and tell them, and let me know if you have succeeded!"

Farfrae went out, and she saw him speak to the group. The eyes of all brightened; the bargain was soon struck. Farfrae returned to her immediately it was concluded.

"It is kindhearted of you, indeed," said Lucetta. "For my part, I have resolved that all my servants shall have lovers if they want them! Do make the same resolve!"

Farfrae looked more serious, waving his head a half turn. "I must be a little stricter than that," he said.

"Why?"

"You are a—a thriving woman; and I am a struggling hay-and-corn merchant."

"I am a very ambitious woman."

"Ah, well, I cannet explain. I don't know how to talk to ladies, ambitious or no; and that's true," said Donald with grave regret. "I try to be civil to a' folk—no more!"

"I see you are as you say," replied she, sensibly getting the upper hand in these exchanges of sentiment. Under this revelation of insight Farfrae again looked out of the window into the thick of the fair.

Two farmers met and shook hands, and being quite near the window their remarks could be heard as others' had been.

"Have you seen young Mr. Farfrae this morning?" asked

one. "He promised to meet me here at the stroke of twelve; but I've gone athwart and about the fair half a dozen times, and never a sign of him: though he's mostly a man to his word."

"I quite forgot the engagement," murmured Farfrae.

"Now you must go," said she; "must you not?"

"Yes," he replied. But he still remained.

"You had better go," she urged. "You will lose a customer."

"Now, Miss Templeman, you will make me angry," exclaimed Farfrae.

"Then suppose you don't go; but stay a little longer?"

He looked anxiously at the farmer who was seeking him, and just then ominously walked across to where Henchard was standing, and he looked into the room and at her. "I like staying; but I fear I must go!" he said. "Business ought not to be neglected, ought it?"

"Not for a single minute."

"It's true. I'll come another time—if I may, ma'am?"

"Certainly," she said. "What has happened to us today is very curious."

"Something to think over when we are alone, it's like to be?"

"Oh, I don't know that. It is commonplace after all."

"No, I'll not say that. O no!"

"Well, whatever it has been, it is now over; and the market calls you to be gone."

"Yes, yes. Market—business! I wish there were no business in the warrld."

Lucetta almost laughed—she would quite have laughed—but that there was a little emotion going in her at the time. "How you change!" she said. "You should not change like this."

"I have never wished such things before," said the Scotchman, with a simple, shamed, apologetic look for his weakness. "It is only since coming heere and seeing you!"

"If that's the case, you had better not look at me any longer. Dear me, I feel I have quite demoralized you!"

"But look or look not, I will see you in my thoughts. Well, I'll go—thank you for the pleasure of this visit."

"Thank you for staying."

"Maybe I'll get into my market mind when I've been out a few minutes," he murmured. "But I don't know—I don't know!"

As he went she said eagerly, "You may hear them speak of me in Casterbridge as time goes on. If they tell you I'm a coquette, which some may, because of the incidents of my life, don't believe it, for I am not."

"I swear I will not!" he said fervidly.

Thus the two. She had enkindled the young man's enthusiasm till he was quite brimming with sentiment; while he, from merely according her a new form of idleness had gone on to wake her serious solicitude. Why was this? They could not have told.

Lucetta as a young girl would hardly have looked at a tradesman. But her ups and downs, capped by her indiscretions with Henchard, had made her uncritical as to station. In her poverty she had met with repulse from the society to which she had belonged, and she had no great zest for renewing an attempt upon it now. Her heart longed for some ark into which it could fly and be at rest. Rough or smooth she did not care so long as it was warm.

Farfrae was shown out, it having entirely escaped him that he had called to see Elizabeth. Lucetta at the window watched him threading the maze of farmers and farmers' men. She could see by his gait that he was conscious of her eyes, and her heart went out to him for his modesty—pleaded with her sense of his unfitness that he might be allowed to come again. He entered the market house, and she could see him no more.

Three minutes later, when she had left the window, knocks, not of multitude but of strength, sounded through the house, and the waiting maid tripped up.

"The Mayor," she said.

Lucetta had reclined herself, and was looking dreamily through her fingers. She did not answer at once, and the maid repeated the information with the addition, "And he's afraid he hasn't much time to spare, he says."

"Oh! Then tell him that as I have a headache I won't detain him today."

The message was taken down, and she heard the door close.

Lucetta had come to Casterbridge to quicken Henchard's feelings with regard to her. She had quickened them, and now she was indifferent to the achievement.

Her morning view of Elizabeth-Jane as a disturbing element changed, and she no longer felt strongly the necessity of getting rid of the girl for her stepfather's sake. When the young woman came in, sweetly unconscious of the turn in the tide, Lucetta went up to her, and said quite sincerely—

"I'm so glad you've come. You'll live with me a long time, won't you?"

Elizabeth as a watchdog to keep her father off—what a new idea. Yet it was not unpleasing. Henchard had neglected her all these days, after compromising her indescribably in the past. The least he could have done when he found himself free and herself affluent, would have been to respond heartily and promptly to her invitation.

Her emotions rose, fell, undulated, filled her with wild surmise at their suddenness; and so passed Lucetta's experiences of that day.

. . . CHAPTER 24

Poor Elizabeth-Jane, little thinking what her malignant star had done to blast the budding attentions she had won from Donald Farfrae, was glad to hear Lucetta's words about remaining.

For in addition to Lucetta's house being a home, that raking view of the marketplace which it afforded had as much attraction for her as for Lucetta. The *carrefour* was like the regulation Open Place in spectacular dramas, where the incidents that occur always happen to bear on the lives of the adjoining residents. Farmers, merchants, dairymen, quacks, hawkers, appeared there from week to week, and disappeared as the afternoon wasted away. It was the node of all orbits.

From Saturday to Saturday was as from day to day with the two young women now. In an emotional sense they did not live at all during the intervals. Wherever they might go wandering on other days, on market day they were sure to be at home. Both stole sly glances out of the window at Farfrae's shoulders and poll. His face they seldom saw, for, either through shyness, or not to disturb his mercantile mood, he avoided looking toward their quarters.

Thus things went on, till a certain market morning brought a new sensation. Elizabeth and Lucetta were sitting at breakfast when a parcel containing two dresses arrived for the latter from London. She called Elizabeth from her breakfast, and entering her friend's bedroom Elizabeth saw the gowns spread out on the bed, one of a deep cherry color, the other lighter —a glove lying at the end of each sleeve, a bonnet at the top of each neck, and parasols across the gloves, Lucetta standing beside the suggested human figure in an attitude of contemplation.

"I wouldn't think so hard about it," said Elizabeth, marking the intensity with which Lucetta was alternating the question whether this or that would suit best.

"But settling upon new clothes is so trying," said Lucetta. "You are that person" (pointing to one of the arrangements), "for the whole of the coming spring: and one of the two, you don't know which, may turn out to be very objectionable."

It was finally decided by Miss Templeman that she would be the cherry-colored person at all hazards. The dress was pronounced to be a fit, and Lucetta walked with it into the front room, Elizabeth following her.

The morning was exceptionally bright for the time of the year. The sun fell so flat on the houses and pavement opposite Lucetta's residence that they poured their brightness into her rooms. Suddenly, after a rumbling of wheels, there were added to this steady light a fantastic series of circling irradiations upon the ceiling, and the companions turned to the window. Immediately opposite a vehicle of strange description had come to a standstill, as if it had been placed there for exhibition.

It was the new-fashioned agricultural implement called a horse drill, till then unknown, in its modern shape, in this part of the country, where the venerable seed lip was still used for sowing as in the days of the Heptarchy.[1] Its arrival created about as much sensation in the corn market as a flying machine would create at Charing Cross.[2] The farmers crowded round it, women drew near it, children crept under and into it. The machine was painted in bright hues of green, yellow, and red, and it resembled as a whole a compound of hornet, grasshopper, and shrimp, magnified enormously. Or it might have been likened to an upright musical instrument with the front gone. That was how it struck Lucetta. "Why, it is a sort of agricultural piano," she said.

"It has something to do with corn," said Elizabeth.

"I wonder who thought of introducing it here?"

Donald Farfrae was in the minds of both as the innovator, for though not a farmer he was closely leagued with farming operations. And as if in response to their thought he came up at that moment, looked at the machine, walked round it, and handled it as if he knew something about its make. The two watchers had inwardly started at his coming, and Elizabeth left the window, went to the back of the room, and stood as if absorbed in the paneling of the wall. She hardly knew that she had done this till Lucetta, animated by the conjunc-

1. *Heptarchy:* seven early English kingdoms.
2. *Charing Cross:* district in London.

tion of her new attire with the sight of Farfrae, spoke out:
"Let us go and look at the instrument, whatever it is."

Elizabeth-Jane's bonnet and shawl were pitchforked on in
a moment, and they went out. Among all the agriculturists
gathering round the only appropriate possessor of the new
machine seemed to be Lucetta, because she alone rivaled it
in color.

They examined it curiously; observed the rows of trumpet-
shaped tubes one within the other, the little scoops, like revolving salt spoons, which tossed the seed into the upper ends
of the tubes that conducted it to the ground; till somebody
said, "Good morning, Elizabeth-Jane." She looked up, and
there was her stepfather.

His greeting had been somewhat dry and thunderous, and
Elizabeth-Jane, embarrassed out of her equanimity, stam-
mered at random, "This is the lady I live with, Father—Miss
Templeman."

Henchard put his hand to his hat, which he brought down
with a great wave till it met his body at the knee. Miss Templeman bowed. "I am happy to become acquainted with you,
Mr. Henchard," she said. "This is a curious machine."

"Yes," Henchard replied; and he proceeded to explain it,
and still more forcibly to ridicule it.

"Who brought it here?" said Lucetta.

"Oh, don't ask me, ma'am!" said Henchard. "The thing—
why 'tis impossible it should act. 'Twas brought here by one
of our machinists on the recommendation of a jumped-up
jackanapes of a fellow who thinks——" His eye caught Elizabeth-Jane's imploring face, and he stopped, probably thinking
that the suit might be progressing.

He turned to go away. Then something seemed to occur
which his stepdaughter fancied must really be a hallucination
of hers. A murmur apparently came from Henchard's lips in
which she detected the words, "You refused to see me!" re-
proachfully addressed to Lucetta. She could not believe that

they had been uttered by her stepfather; unless, indeed, they might have been spoken to one of the yellow-gaitered farmers near them. Yet Lucetta seemed silent; and then all thought of the incident was dissipated by the humming of a song, which sounded as though from the interior of the machine. Henchard had by this time vanished into the market house, and both women glanced toward the corn drill. They could see behind it the bent back of a man who was pushing his head into the internal works to master their simple secrets. The hummed song went on—

> "Tw—s on a s—m—r aftern—n,
> A wee be—re the s—n w—nt d—n,
> When Kitty wi' a braw n—w g—wn
> C—me ow're the h—lls to Gowrie."

Elizabeth-Jane had apprehended the singer in a moment, and looked guilty of she did not know what. Lucetta next recognized him, and more mistress of herself said archly, "The 'Lass of Gowrie' from the inside of a seed drill—what a phenomenon!"

Satisfied at last with his investigation the young man stood upright, and met their eyes across the summit.

"We are looking at the wonderful new drill," Miss Templeman said. "But practically it is a stupid thing—is it not?" she added, on the strength of Henchard's information.

"Stupid? O no! " said Farfrae gravely. "It will revolutionize sowing heerabout! No more sowers flinging their seed about broadcast, so that some falls by the wayside and some among thorns, and all that. Each grain will go straight to its intended place, and nowhere else whatever!"

"Then the romance of the sower is gone for good," observed Elizabeth-Jane, who felt herself at one with Farfrae in Bible-reading at least. " 'He that observeth the wind shall not sow,' so the Preacher said; but his words will not be to the point any more. How things change!"

"Ay; ay. . . . It must be so!" Donald admitted, his gaze fixing itself on a blank point far away. "But the machines are already very common in the East and North of England," he added apologetically.

Lucetta seemed to be outside this train of sentiment, her acquaintance with the Scriptures being somewhat limited. "Is the machine yours?" she asked of Farfrae.

"Oh no, madam," said he, becoming embarrassed and deferential at the sound of her voice, though with Elizabeth-Jane he was quite at his ease. "No, no—I merely recommended that it should be got."

In the silence which followed Farfrae appeared only conscious of her; to have passed from perception of Elizabeth into a brighter sphere of existence than she appertained to. Lucetta, discerning that he was much mixed that day, partly in his mercantile mood and partly in his romantic one, said gaily to him—

"Well, don't forsake the machine for us," and went indoors with her companion.

The latter felt that she had been in the way, though why was unaccountable to her. Lucetta explained the matter somewhat by saying when they were again in the sitting room—

"I had occasion to speak to Mr. Farfrae the other day, and so I knew him this morning."

Lucetta was very kind toward Elizabeth that day. Together they saw the market thicken, and in course of time thin away with the slow decline of the sun towards the upper end of the town, its rays taking the street endways and enfilading the long thoroughfare from top to bottom. The gigs and vans disappeared one by one till there was not a vehicle in the street. The time of the riding world was over; the pedestrian world held sway. Field laborers and their wives and children trooped in from the villages for their weekly shopping, and instead of a rattle of wheels and a tramp of horses ruling the sound as earlier, there was nothing but the shuffle of many feet. All the implements were gone; all the farmers; all the moneyed class. The character of the town's trading had changed from bulk to multiplicity, and pence were handed now as pounds had been handled earlier in the day.

Lucetta and Elizabeth looked out upon this, for though it was night and the street lamps were lighted, they had kept their shutters unclosed. In the faint blink of the fire they spoke more freely.

"Your father was distant with you," said Lucetta.

"Yes." And having forgotten the momentary mystery of Henchard's seeming speech to Lucetta she continued, "It is because he does not think I am respectable. I have tried to be so more than you can imagine, but in vain! My mother's separation from my father was unfortunate for me. You don't know what it is to have shadows like that upon your life."

Lucetta seemed to wince. "I do not—of that kind precisely," she said, "but you may feel a—sense of disgrace—shame—in other ways."

"Have you ever had any such feeling?" said the younger innocently.

"O no," said Lucetta quickly. "I was thinking of—what happens sometimes when women get themselves in strange positions in the eyes of the world from no fault of their own."

"It must make them very unhappy afterwards."

"It makes them anxious; for might not other women despise them?"

"Not altogether despise them. Yet not quite like or respect them."

Lucetta winced again. Her past was by no means secure from investigation, even in Casterbridge. For one thing Henchard had never returned to her the cloud of letters she had written and sent him in her first excitement. Possibly they were destroyed; but she could have wished that they had never been written.

The rencounter with Farfrae and his bearing toward Lucetta made the reflective Elizabeth more observant of her brilliant and amiable companion. A few days afterwards, when her eyes met Lucetta's as the latter was going out, she somehow knew that Miss Templeman was nourishing a hope of seeing the attractive Scotchman. The fact was printed large all over Lucetta's cheeks and eyes to anyone who could read her as Elizabeth-Jane was beginning to do. Lucetta passed on and closed the street door.

A seer's spirit took possession of Elizabeth, impelling her to sit down by the fire and divine events so surely from data already her own that they could be held as witnessed. She followed Lucetta thus mentally—saw her encounter Donald somewhere as if by chance—saw him wear his special look when meeting women, with an added intensity because this one was Lucetta. She depicted his impassioned manner; beheld the indecision of both between their lothness to separate and their desire not to be observed; depicted their shaking of hands; how they probably parted with frigidity in their general contour and movements, only in the smaller features showing the spark of passion, thus invisible to all but themselves. This discerning silent witch had not done thinking of these things when Lucetta came noiselessly behind her and made her start.

It was all true as she had pictured—she could have sworn it. Lucetta had a heightened luminousness in her eye over and above the advanced color of her cheeks.

"You've seen Mr. Farfrae," said Elizabeth demurely.

"Yes," said Lucetta. "How did you know?"

She knelt down on the hearth and took her friend's hands excitedly in her own. But after all she did not say when or how she had seen him or what he had said.

That night she became restless; in the morning she was feverish; and at breakfast time she told her companion that she had something on her mind—something which concerned a person in whom she was interested much. Elizabeth was earnest to listen and sympathize.

"This person—a lady—once admired a man much—very much," she said tentatively.

"Ah," said Elizabeth-Jane.

"They were intimate—rather. He did not think so deeply of her as she did of him. But in an impulsive moment, purely out of reparation, he proposed to make her his wife. She agreed. But there was an unexpected hitch in the proceedings; though she had been so far compromised with him that she felt she could never belong to another man, as a pure matter of conscience, even if she should wish to. After that they were much apart, heard nothing of each other for a long time, and she felt her life quite closed up for her."

"Ah—poor girl!"

"She suffered much on account of him; though I should add that he could not altogether be blamed for what had happened. At last the obstacle which separated them was providentially removed; and he came to marry her."

"How delightful!"

"But in the interval she—my poor friend—had seen a man she liked better than him. Now comes the point: Could she in honor dismiss the first?"

"A new man she liked better—that's bad!"

"Yes," said Lucetta, looking pained at a boy who was swinging the town pump handle. "It is bad! Though you must remember that she was forced into an equivocal position with the first man by an accident—that he was not so well educated or refined as the second, and that she had discovered some qualities in the first that rendered him less desirable as a husband than she had at first thought him to be."

"I cannot answer," said Elizabeth-Jane thoughtfully. "It is so difficult. It wants a Pope to settle that!"

"You prefer not to, perhaps?" Lucetta showed in her appealing tone how much she leaned on Elizabeth's judgment.

"Yes, Miss Templeman," admitted Elizabeth. "I would rather not say."

Nevertheless, Lucetta seemed relieved by the simple fact of having opened out the situation a little, and was slowly convalescent of her headache. "Bring me a looking glass. How do I appear to people?" she said languidly.

"Well—a little worn," answered Elizabeth, eyeing her as a critic eyes a doubtful painting; fetching the glass she enabled Lucetta to survey herself in it, which Lucetta anxiously did.

"I wonder if I wear well, as times go!" she observed after a while.

"Yes—fairly."

"Where am I worst?"

"Under your eyes—I notice a little brownness there."

"Yes. That is my worst place, I know. How many years more do you think I shall last before I get hopelessly plain?"

There was something curious in the way in which Elizabeth, though the younger, had come to play the part of experienced sage in these discussions. "It may be five years," she said judicially. "Or, with a quiet life, as many as ten. With no love you might calculate on ten."

Lucetta seemed to reflect on this as on an unalterable, impartial verdict. She told Elizabeth-Jane no more of the past attachment she had roughly adumbrated as the experiences of a third person; and Elizabeth, who in spite of her philosophy was very tender-hearted, sighed that night in bed at the thought that her pretty, rich Lucetta did not treat her to the full confidence of names and dates in her confessions. For by the "she" of Lucetta's story Elizabeth had not been beguiled.

. . . **CHAPTER 25**

THE NEXT PHASE of the supersession of Henchard in Lucetta's heart was an experiment in calling on her performed by Farfrae with some apparent trepidation. Conventionally speaking he conversed with both Miss Templeman and her companion; but in fact it was rather that Elizabeth sat invisible in the room. Donald appeared not to see her at all, and answered her wise little remarks with curtly indifferent monosyllables, his looks and faculties hanging on the woman who could boast of a more Protean[1] variety in her phases, moods, opinions, and also principles, than could Elizabeth. Lucetta had persisted in dragging her into the circle; but she had remained like an awkward third point which that circle would not touch.

Susan Henchard's daughter bore up against the frosty ache of the treatment, as she had borne up under worse things, and contrived as soon as possible to get out of the inharmonious room without being missed. The Scotchman seemed hardly the same Farfrae who had danced with her and walked with her in a delicate poise between love and friendship—that period in the history of a love when alone it can be said to be unalloyed with pain.

She stoically looked from her bedroom window, and contemplated her fate as if it were written on the top of the church tower hard by. "Yes," she said at last, bringing down her palm upon the sill with a pat: "*He* is the second man of that story she told me!"

All this time Henchard's smoldering sentiments toward Lucetta had been fanned into higher and higher inflammation by the circumstances of the case. He was discovering that the young woman for whom he once felt a pitying warmth which had been almost chilled out of him by reflection, was, when now qualified with a slight inaccessibility and a more matured beauty, the very being to make him satisfied with life. Day after day proved to him, by her silence, that it was no use to think of bringing her round by holding aloof; so he gave in, and called upon her again, Elizabeth-Jane being absent.

1. *Protean:* Proteus, a sea god, could take many forms.

He crossed the room to her with a heavy tread of some awkwardness, his strong, warm gaze upon her—like the sun beside the moon in comparison with Farfrae's modest look— and with something of a hailfellow bearing, as, indeed, was not unnatural. But she seemed so transubstantiated by her change of position, and held out her hand to him in such cool friendship, that he became deferential, and sat down with a perceptible loss of power. He understood but little of fashion in dress, yet enough to feel himself inadequate in appearance beside her whom he had hitherto been dreaming of as almost his property. She said something very polite about his being good enough to call. This caused him to recover balance. He looked her oddly in the face, losing his awe.

"Why, of course I have called, Lucetta," he said. "What does that nonsense mean? You know I couldn't have helped myself if I had wished—that is, if I had any kindness at all. I've called to say that I am ready, as soon as custom will permit, to give you my name in return for your devotion, and what you lost by it in thinking too little of yourself and too much of me; to say that you can fix the day or month, with my full consent, whenever in your opinion it would be seemly: you know more of these things than I."

"It is full early yet," she said evasively.

"Yes, yes; I suppose it is. But you know, Lucetta, I felt directly my poor ill-used Susan died, and when I could not bear the idea of marrying again, that after what had happened between us it was my duty not to let any unnecessary delay occur before putting things to rights. Still, I wouldn't call in a hurry, because—well, you can guess how this money you've come into made me feel." His voice slowly fell; he was conscious that in this room his accents and manner wore a roughness not observable in the street. He looked about the room at the novel hangings and ingenious furniture with which she had surrounded herself.

"Upon my life I didn't know such furniture as this could be bought in Casterbridge," he said.

"Nor can it be," said she. "Nor will it till fifty years more of civilization have passed over the town. It took a wagon and four horses to get it here."

"H'm. It looks as if you were living on capital."

"O no, I am not."

"So much the better. But the fact is, your setting up like this makes my bearing toward you rather awkward."

"Why?"

An answer was not really needed, and he did not furnish one. "Well," he went on, "there's nobody in the world I would have wished to see enter into this wealth before you, Lucetta, and nobody, I am sure, who will become it more." He turned to her with congratulatory admiration so fervid that she shrank somewhat, notwithstanding that she knew him so well.

"I am greatly obliged to you for all that," said she, rather with an air of speaking ritual. The stint of reciprocal feeling was perceived, and Henchard showed chagrin at once—nobody was more quick to show that than he.

"You may be obliged or not for't. Though the things I say may not have the polish of what you've lately learned to expect for the first time in your life, they are real, my lady Lucetta."

"That's rather a rude way of speaking to me," pouted Lucetta, with stormy eyes.

"Not at all!" replied Henchard hotly. "But there, there, I don't wish to quarrel with 'ee. I come with an honest proposal for silencing your Jersey enemies, and you ought to be thankful."

"How can you speak so!" she answered, firing quickly. "Knowing that my only crime was the indulging in a foolish girl's passion for you with too little regard for correctness, and that I was what *I* call innocent all the time they called me guilty, you ought not to be so cutting! I suffered enough at that worrying time, when you wrote to tell me of your wife's return and my consequent dismissal, and if I am a little independent now, surely the privilege is due to me!"

"Yes, it is," he said. "But it is not by what is, in this life, but by what appears, that you are judged; and I therefore think you ought to accept me—for your own good name's sake. What is known in your native Jersey may get known here."

"How you keep on about Jersey! I am English!"

"Yes, yes. Well, what do you say to my proposal?"

For the first time in their acquaintance Lucetta had the move; and yet she was backward. "For the present let things be," she said with some embarrassment. "Treat me as an acquaintance; and I'll treat you as one. Time will——" she stopped; and he said nothing to fill the gap for awhile, there being no pressure of half acquaintance to drive them into speech if they were not minded for it.

"That's the way the wind blows, is it?" he said at last grimly, nodding an affirmative to his own thoughts.

A yellow flood of reflected sunlight filled the room for a few instants. It was produced by the passing of a load of newly trussed hay from the country, in a wagon marked with Farfrae's name. Beside it rode Farfrae himself on horseback. Lucetta's face became—as a woman's face becomes when the man she loves rises upon her gaze like an apparition.

A turn of the eye by Henchard, a glance from the window, and the secret of her inaccessibility would have been revealed. But Henchard in estimating her tone was looking down so plumb straight that he did not note the warm consciousness upon Lucetta's face.

"I shouldn't have thought it—I shouldn't have thought it of women!" he said emphatically by-and-by, rising and shaking himself into activity; while Lucetta was so anxious to divert him from any suspicion of the truth that she asked him to be in no hurry. Bringing him some apples she insisted upon paring one for him.

He would not take it. "No, no; such is not for me," he said drily, and moved to the door. At going out he turned his eye upon her.

"You came to live in Casterbridge entirely on my account," he said. "Yet now you are here you won't have anything to say to my offer!"

He had hardly gone down the staircase when she dropped upon the sofa and jumped up again in a fit of desperation. "I *will* love him!" she cried passionately; "as for *him*—he's hot-tempered and stern, and it would be madness to bind myself to him knowing that. I won't be a slave to the past—I'll love where I choose!"

Yet having decided to break away from Henchard one might have supposed her capable of aiming higher than Farfrae. But Lucetta reasoned nothing; she feared hard words from the people with whom she had been earlier associated; she had no relatives left; and with native lightness of heart took kindly to what fate offered.

Elizabeth-Jane, surveying the position of Lucetta between her two lovers from the crystalline sphere of a straightforward mind, did not fail to perceive that her father, as she called him, and Donald Farfrae became more desperately enamoured of her friend every day. On Farfrae's side it was the unforced passion of youth. On Henchard's the artificially stimulated coveting of a maturer age.

The pain she experienced from the almost absolute obliviousness to her existence that was shown by the pair of them became at times half dissipated by her sense of its humorousness. When Lucetta had pricked her finger they were as deeply concerned as if she were dying; when she herself had been seriously sick or in danger they uttered a conventional word of sympathy at the news, and forgot all about it immediately. But, as regarded Henchard, this perception of hers also caused her some filial grief; she could not help asking what she had done to be neglected so, after the professions of solicitude he had made. As regarded Farfrae, she thought, after honest reflection, that it was quite natural. What was she beside Lucetta?—as one of the "meaner beauties of the night," when the moon had risen in the skies.

She had learned the lesson of renunciation, and was as familiar with the wreck of each day's wishes as with the diurnal setting of the sun. If her earthly career had taught her few book philosophies it had at least well practiced her in this. Yet her experience had consisted less in a series of pure disappointments than in a series of substitutions. Continually it had happened that what she had desired had not been granted her, and that what had been granted her she had not desired. So she viewed with an approach to equanimity the now canceled days when Donald had been her undeclared lover, and wondered what unwished-for thing Heaven might send her in place of him.

. . . CHAPTER 26

It CHANCED that on a fine spring morning Henchard and Farfrae met in the chestnut walk which ran along the south wall of the town. Each had just come out from his early breakfast, and there was not another soul near. Henchard was reading a letter from Lucetta, sent in answer to a note from him, in which she made some excuse for not immediately granting him a second interview that he had desired.

Donald had no wish to enter into conversation with his former friend on their present constrained terms; neither would he pass him in scowling silence. He nodded, and Henchard did the same. They had receded from each other several paces when a voice cried "Farfrae!" It was Henchard's, who stood regarding him.

"Do you remember," said Henchard, as if it were presence of the thought and not of the man which made him speak, "do you remember my story of that second woman— who suffered for her thoughtless intimacy with me?"

"I do," said Farfrae.

"Do you remember my telling 'ee how it all began and how it ended?"

"Yes."

"Well, I have offered to marry her now that I can; but she won't marry me. Now what would you think of her—I put it to you?"

"Well, ye owe her nothing more now," said Farfrae heartily.

"It is true," said Henchard, and went on.

That he looked up from a letter to ask his questions completely shut out from Farfrae's mind all vision of Lucetta as the culprit. Indeed, her present position was so different from that of the young woman of Henchard's story as of itself to be sufficient to blind him absolutely to her identity. As for Henchard, he was reassured by Farfrae's words and manner against a suspicion which had crossed his mind. They were not those of a conscious rival.

Yet that there was rivalry by some one he was firmly persuaded. He could feel it in the air around Lucetta, see it in the turn of her pen. There was an antagonistic force in exercise, so that when he had tried to hang near her he seemed standing in a refluent current. That it was not innate caprice he was more and more certain. Her windows gleamed as if they did not want him; her curtains seemed to hang slyly, as if they screened an ousting presence. To discover whose presence that was—whether really Farfrae's after all, or another's—he exerted himself to the utmost to see her again; and at length succeeded.

At the interview, when she offered him tea, he made it a point to launch a cautious inquiry if she knew Mr. Farfrae.

O yes, she knew him, she declared; she could not help knowing almost everybody in Casterbridge, living in such a gazebo over the center and arena of the town.

"Pleasant young fellow," said Henchard.

"Yes," said Lucetta.

"We both know him," said kind Elizabeth-Jane, to relieve her companion's divined embarrassment.

There was a knock at the door; literally, three full knocks and a little one at the end.

"That kind of knock means half-and-half—somebody between gentle and simple," said the corn merchant to himself. "I shouldn't wonder therefore if it is he." In a few seconds surely enough Donald walked in.

Lucetta was full of little fidgets and flutters, which increased Henchard's suspicions without affording any special proof of their correctness. He was well-nigh ferocious at the sense of the queer situation in which he stood toward this woman. One who had reproached him for deserting her when calumniated, who had urged claims upon his consideration on that account, who had lived waiting for him, who at the first decent moment had come to ask him to rectify, by making her his, the false position into which she had placed herself for his sake; such she had been. And now he sat at her tea table eager to gain her attention, and in his amatory rage feeling the other man present to be a villain, just as any young fool of a lover might feel.

They sat stiffly side by side at the darkening table, like some Tuscan painting of the two disciples supping at Emmaus. Lucetta, forming the third and haloed figure, was opposite them; Elizabeth-Jane, being out of the game, and out of the group, could observe all from afar, like the evangelist who had to write it down: that there were long spaces of taciturnity, when all exterior circumstance was subdued to the touch of spoons and china, the click of a heel on the pavement under the window, the passing of a wheelbarrow or cart, the whistling of the carter, the gush of water into householders' buckets at the town pump opposite; the exchange of greetings among their neighbors, and the rattle of the yokes by which they carried off their evening supply.

"More bread and butter?" said Lucetta to Henchard and Farfrae equally, holding out between them a plateful of long slices. Henchard took a slice by one end and Donald by the other; each feeling certain he was the man meant; neither let go, and the slice came in two.

"Oh—I am sorry!" cried Lucetta, with a nervous titter. Farfrae tried to laugh; but he was too much in love to see the incident in any but a tragic light.

"How ridiculous of all three of them!" said Elizabeth to herself.

Henchard left the house with a ton of conjecture, though without a grain of proof, that the counter-attraction was Farfrae; and therefore he would not make up his mind. Yet to Elizabeth-Jane it was plain as the town pump that Donald and Lucetta were incipient lovers. More than once, in spite of her care, Lucetta had been unable to restrain her glance from flitting across into Farfrae's eyes like a bird to its nest. But Henchard was constructed upon too large a scale to discern such minutiæ as these by an evening light, which to him were as the notes of an insect that lie above the compass of the human ear.

But he was disturbed. And the sense of occult rivalry in suitorship was so much superadded to the palpable rivalry of their business lives. To the coarse materiality of that rivalry it added an inflaming soul.

The thus vitalized antagonism took the form of action by Henchard sending for Jopp, the manager originally displaced by Farfrae's arrival. Henchard had frequently met this man about the streets, observed that his clothing spoke of neediness, heard that he lived in Mixen Lane—a back slum of the town, the *pis aller*[1] of Casterbridge domiciliation—itself almost a proof that a man had reached a stage when he would not stick at trifles.

Jopp came after dark, by the gates of the storeyard, and

1. *Pis aller:* last resort.

felt his way through the hay and straw to the office where Henchard sat in solitude awaiting him.

"I am again out of a foreman," said the corn factor. "Are you in a place?"

"Not so much as a beggar's, sir."

"How much do you ask?"

Jopp named his price, which was very moderate.

"When can you come?"

"At this hour and moment, sir," said Jopp, who, standing hands-pocketed at the street corner till the sun had faded the shoulders of his coat to scarecrow green, had regularly watched Henchard in the marketplace, measured him, and learned him, by virtue of the power which the still man has in his stillness of knowing the busy one better than he knows himself. Jopp, too, had had a convenient experience; he was the only one in Casterbridge besides Henchard and the close-lipped Elizabeth who knew that Lucetta came truly from Jersey, and but proximately from Bath. "I know Jersey, too, sir," he said. "Was living there when you used to do business that way. O yes—have often seen ye there."

"Indeed! Very good. Then the thing is settled. The testimonials you showed me when you first tried for't are sufficient."

That characters deteriorate in time of need possibly did not occur to Henchard. Jopp said, "Thank you," and stood more firmly, in the consciousness that at last he officially belonged to that post.

"Now," said Henchard, digging his strong eyes into Jopp's face, "one thing is necessary to me, as the biggest corn-and-hay dealer in these parts. The Scotchman, who's taking the town trade so bold into his hands, must be cut out. D'ye hear? We two can't live side by side—that's clear and certain."

"I've seen it all," said Jopp.

"By fair competition I mean, of course," Henchard continued. "But as hard, keen, and unflinching as fair—rather more so. By such a desperate bid against him for the farmer's custom as will grind him into the ground—starve him out. I've capital, mind ye, and I can do it."

"I'm all that way of thinking," said the new foreman. Jopp's dislike of Farfrae as the man who had once usurped his place, while it made him a willing tool, made him, at the same time, commercially as unsafe a colleague as Henchard could have chosen.

"I sometimes think," he added, "that he must have some glass that he sees next year in. He has such a knack of making everything bring him fortune."

"He's deep beyond all honest men's discerning; but we must make him shallower. We'll undersell him, and over-buy him, and so snuff him out."

They then entered into specific details of the process by which this would be accomplished, and parted at a late hour.

Elizabeth-Jane heard by accident that Jopp had been engaged by her stepfather. She was so fully convinced that he was not the right man for the place that, at the risk of making Henchard angry, she expressed her apprehension to him when they met. But it was done to no purpose. Henchard shut up her argument with a sharp rebuff.

The season's weather seemed to favor their scheme. The time was in the years immediately before foreign competition had revolutionized the trade in grain; when still, as from the earliest ages, the wheat quotations from month to month depended entirely upon the home harvest. A bad harvest, or the prospect of one, would double the price of corn in a few weeks; and the promise of a good yield would lower it as rapidly. Prices were like the roads of the period, steep in gradient, reflecting in their phases the local conditions, without engineering, levelings, or averages.

The farmer's income was ruled by the wheat crop within his own horizon, and the wheat crop by the weather. Thus, in person, he became a sort of flesh-barometer, with feelers always directed to the sky and wind around him. The local atmosphere was everything to him; the atmospheres of other countries a matter of indifference. The people, too, who were not farmers, the rural multitude, saw in the god of the weather a more important personage than they do now. Indeed, the feeling of the peasantry in this matter was so intense as to be almost unrealizable in these equable days. Their impulse was well-nigh to prostrate themselves in lamentation before untimely rains and tempests, which came as the Alastor[2] of those households whose crime it was to be poor.

After midsummer they watched the weathercocks as men waiting in antechambers watch the lackey. Sun elated them;

2. *Alastor:* a nemesis.

English farmhouse interior in the 1800's.

quiet rain sobered them; weeks of watery tempest stupefied them. That aspect of the sky which they now regard as disagreeable they then beheld as maleficent.

It was June, and the weather was very unfavorable. Casterbridge, being as it were the bell board on which all the adjacent hamlets and villages sounded their notes, was decidedly dull. Instead of new articles in the shop windows those that had been rejected in the foregoing summer were brought out again; superseded reap hooks, badly shaped rakes, shopworn leggings, and time-stiffened watertights reappeared, furbished up as near to new as possible.

Henchard, backed by Jopp, read a disastrous garnering, and resolved to base his strategy against Farfrae upon that reading. But before acting he wished—what so many have wished—that he could know for certain what was at present only strong probability. He was superstitious—as such headstrong natures often are—and he nourished in his mind an idea bearing on the matter; an idea he shrank from disclosing even to Jopp.

In a lonely hamlet a few miles from the town—so lonely that what are called lonely villages were teeming by comparison—there lived a man of curious repute as a forecaster or weather prophet. The way to his house was crooked and miry—even difficult in the present unpropitious season. One evening when it was raining so heavily that ivy and laurel resounded like distant musketry, and an outdoor man could be excused for shrouding himself to his ears and eyes, such a shrouded figure on foot might have been perceived traveling in the direction of the hazel copse which dripped over the prophet's cot. The turnpike road became a lane, the lane a cart track, the cart track a bridle path, the bridle path a footway, the footway overgrown. The solitary walker slipped here and there, and stumbled over the natural springs formed by the brambles, till at length he reached the house, which, with its garden, was surrounded with a high, dense hedge. The cottage, comparatively a large one, had been built of mud by the occupier's own hands and thatched also by himself. Here he had always lived, and here it was assumed he would die.

He existed on unseen supplies; for it was an anomalous thing that while there was hardly a soul in the neighborhood but affected to laugh at this man's assertions, uttering the formula, "There's nothing in 'em," with full assurance on the surface of their faces, very few of them were unbelievers in their secret hearts. Whenever they consulted him they did it "for a fancy." When they paid him they said, "Just a trifle for Christmas," or "Candlemas,"[3] as the case might be.

He would have preferred more honesty in his clients, and less sham ridicule; but fundamental belief consoled him for superficial irony. As stated, he was enabled to live; people supported him with their backs turned. He was sometimes astonished that men could profess so little and believe so much at his house, when at church they professed so much and believed so little.

Behind his back he was called "Wide-oh," on account of his reputation; to his face "Mr." Fall.

The hedge of his garden formed an arch over the entrance, and a door was inserted as in a wall. Outside the door the tall traveler stopped, bandaged his face with a handkerchief as if he were suffering from toothache, and went up the path. The window shutters were not closed, and he could see the prophet within, preparing his supper.

In answer to the knock Fall came to the door, candle in hand. The visitor stepped back a little from the light, and said, "Can I speak to 'ee?" in significant tones. The other's invitation to come in was responded to by the country formula, "This will do, thank 'ee," after which the householder has no alternative but to come out. He placed the candle on the corner of the dresser, took his hat from a nail,

3. *Candlemas:* holiday occurring on February 2.

and joined the stranger in the porch, shutting the door behind him.

"I've long heard that you can—do things of a sort?" began the other, repressing his individuality as much as he could.

"Maybe so, Mr. Henchard," said the weathercaster.

"Ah—why do you call me that?" asked the visitor with a start.

"Because it's your name. Feeling you'd come I've waited for 'ee; and thinking you might be leery from your walk I laid two supper plates—look ye here." He threw open the door and disclosed the supper table, at which appeared a second chair, knife and fork, plate and mug, as he had declared.

Henchard felt like Saul at his reception by Samuel; he remained in silence for a few moments, then throwing off the disguise of frigidity which he had hitherto preserved he said, "Then I have not come in vain. . . . Now, for instance, can ye charm away warts?"

"Without trouble."

"Cure the evil?"

"That I've done—with consideration—if they will wear the toad bag by night as well as by day."

"Forecast the weather?"

"With labor and time."

"Then take this," said Henchard. "'Tis a crown piece. Now, what is the harvest fortnight to be? When can I know?"

"I've worked it out already, and you can know at once." (The fact was that five farmers had already been there on the same errand from different parts of the country.) "By the sun, moon, and stars, by the clouds, the winds, the trees, and grass, the candle flame and swallows, the smell of the herbs; likewise by the cats' eyes, the ravens, the leeches, the spiders, and the dungmixen, the last fortnight in August will be—rain and tempest."

"You are not certain, of course?"

"As one can be in a world where all's unsure. 'Twill be more like living in Revelations[4] this autumn than in England. Shall I sketch it out for 'ee in a scheme?"

"O no, no," said Henchard. "I don't altogether believe in forecasts, come to second thoughts on such. But I——"

"You don't—you don't—'tis quite understood," said Wide-oh, without a sound of scorn. "You have given me a crown because you've one too many. But won't you join me at supper, now 'tis waiting and all?"

Henchard would gladly have joined; for the savor of the stew had floated from the cottage into the porch with such appetizing distinctness that the meat, the onions, the pepper, and the herbs could be severally recognized by his nose. But as sitting down to hob-and-nob there would have seemed to mark him too implicitly as the weathercaster's apostle, he declined, and went his way.

The next Saturday Henchard bought grain to such an enormous extent that there was quite a talk about his purchases among his neighbors the lawyer, the wine merchant, and the doctor; also on the next, and on all available days. When his granaries were full to choking, all the weathercocks of Casterbridge creaked and set their faces in another direction, as if tired of the southwest. The weather changed; the sunlight, which had been like tin for weeks, assumed the hues of topaz. The temperament of the welkin passed from the phlegmatic to the sanguine; an excellent harvest was almost a certainty; and as a consequence prices rushed down.

All these transformations, lovely to the outsider, to the wrong-headed corn dealer were terrible. He was reminded of what he had well known before, that a man might gamble upon the square green areas of fields as readily as upon those of a card room.

Henchard had backed bad weather, and apparently lost. He

4. *Revelations:* last book of the New Testament.

had mistaken the turn of the flood for the turn of the ebb. His dealings had been so extensive that settlement could not long be postponed, and to settle he was obliged to sell off corn that he had bought only a few weeks before at figures higher by many shillings a quarter. Much of the corn he had never seen; it had not even been moved from the ricks in which it lay stacked miles away. Thus he lost heavily.

In the blaze of an early August day he met Farfrae in the marketplace. Farfrae knew of his dealings (though he did not guess their intended bearing on himself) and commiserated him; for since their exchange in words in the South Walk they had been on stiffly speaking terms. Henchard for the moment appeared to resent the sympathy; but he suddenly took a careless turn.

"Ho, no, no!—nothing serious, man!" he cried with fierce gaiety. "These things always happen, don't they? I know it has been said that figures have touched me right lately; but is that anything rare? The case is not so bad as folk make out perhaps. And dammy, a man must be a fool to mind the common hazards of trade!"

But he had to enter the Casterbridge Bank that day for reasons which had never before sent him there—and to sit a long time in the partners' room with a constrained bearing. It was rumored soon after that much real property as well as vast stores of produce, which had stood in Henchard's name in the town and neighborhood, was actually the possession of his bankers.

Coming down the steps of the bank he encountered Jopp. The gloomy transactions just completed within had added fever to the original sting of Farfrae's sympathy that morning, which Henchard fancied might be satire disguised, so that Jopp met with anything but a bland reception. The latter was in the act of taking off his hat to wipe his forehead, and saying, "A fine hot day," to an acquaintance.

"You can wipe and wipe, and say, 'A fine hot day,' can

ye!" cried Henchard in a savage undertone, imprisoning Jopp
between himself and the bank wall. "If it hadn't been for your
blasted advice it might have been a fine day enough! Why did
ye let me go on, hey?—when a word of doubt from you or
anybody would have made me think twice! For you can
never be sure of weather till 'tis past."

"My advice, sir, was to do what you thought best."

"A useful fellow! And the sooner you help somebody else
in that way the better!" Henchard continued his address to
Jopp in similar terms till it ended in Jopp's dismissal there and
then, Henchard turning upon his heel and leaving him.

"You shall be sorry for this, sir; sorry as a man can be!"
said Jopp, standing pale, and looking after the corn merchant
as he disappeared in the crowd of market men hard by.

. . . **CHAPTER 27**

IT WAS the eve of harvest. Prices being low Farfrae was buying. As was usual, after reckoning too surely on famine
weather the local farmers had flown to the other extreme, and
(in Farfrae's opinion) were selling off too recklessly—calculating with just a trifle too much certainty upon an abun-
dant yield. So he went on buying old corn at its comparatively
ridiculous price: for the produce of the previous year, though
not large, had been of excellent quality.

When Henchard had squared his affairs in a disastrous way,
and got rid of his burdensome purchases at a monstrous loss,
the harvest began. There were three days of excellent
weather, and then—"What if that curst conjuror should be
right after all!" said Henchard.

The fact was, that no sooner had the sickles begun to play
than the atmosphere suddenly felt as if cress would grow in it
without other nourishment. It rubbed people's cheeks like
damp flannel when they walked abroad. There was a gusty,

high, warm wind; isolated raindrops starred the window panes at remote distances: the sunlight would flap out like a quickly opened fan, throw the pattern of the window upon the floor of the room in a milky, colorless shine, and withdraw as suddenly as it had appeared.

From that day and hour it was clear that there was not to be so successful an ingathering after all. If Henchard had only waited long enough he might at least have avoided loss though he had not made a profit. But the momentum of his character knew no patience. At this turn of the scales he remained silent. The movements of his mind seemed to tend to the thought that some power was working against him.

"I wonder," he asked himself with eerie misgiving; "I wonder if it can be that somebody has been roasting a waxen image of me, or stirring an unholy brew to confound me! I don't believe in such power; and yet—what if they should ha' been doing it!" Even he could not admit that the perpetrator, if any, might be Farfrae. These isolated hours of superstition came to Henchard in time of moody depression, when all his practical largeness of view had oozed out of him.

Meanwhile Donald Farfrae prospered. He had purchased in so depressed a market that the present moderate stiffness of prices was sufficient to pile for him a large heap of gold where a little one had been.

"Why, he'll soon be Mayor!" said Henchard. It was indeed hard that the speaker should, of all others, have to follow the triumphal chariot of this man to the Capitol.

The rivalry of the masters was taken up by the men.

September-night shades had fallen upon Casterbridge; the clocks had struck half-past eight, and the moon had risen. The streets of the town were curiously silent for such a comparatively early hour. A sound of jangling horse bells and heavy wheels passed up the street. These were followed by angry voices outside Lucetta's house, which led her and Elizabeth-Jane to run to the windows, and pull up the blinds.

The neighboring Market House and Town Hall abutted against its next neighbor the church except in the lower story, where an arched thoroughfare gave admittance to a large square called Bull Stake. A stone post rose in the midst, to which the oxen had formally been tied for baiting with dogs to make them tender before they were killed in the adjoining shambles. In a corner stood the stocks.

The thoroughfare leading to this spot was now blocked by two four-horse wagons and horses, one laden with hay trusses, the leaders having already passed each other, and become entangled head to tail. The passage of the vehicles might have been practicable if empty; but built up with hay to the bedroom windows as one was, it was impossible.

"You must have done it a' purpose!" said Farfrae's wagoner. "You can hear my horses' bells half a mile such a night as this!"

"If ye'd been minding your business instead of zwailing along in such a gawk-hammer way, you would have zeed me!" retorted the wroth representative of Henchard.

However, according to the strict rule of the road it appeared that Henchard's man was most in the wrong; he therefore attempted to back into the High Street. In doing this the near hind wheel rose against the churchyard wall, and the whole mountainous load went over, two of the four wheels rising in the air, and the legs of the thill horse.

Instead of considering how to gather up the load the two men closed in a fight with their fists. Before the first round was quite over Henchard came upon the spot, somebody having run for him.

Henchard sent the two men staggering in contrary directions by collaring one with each hand, turned to the horse that was down, and extricated him after some trouble. He then inquired into the circumstances; and seeing the state of his wagon and its load began hotly rating Farfrae's man.

Lucetta and Elizabeth-Jane had by this time run down to

the street corner, whence they watched the bright heap of new hay lying in the moon's rays, and passed and re-passed by the forms of Henchard and the wagoners. The women had witnessed what nobody else had seen—the origin of the mishap; and Lucetta spoke.

"I saw it all, Mr. Henchard," she cried; "and your man was most in the wrong!"

Henchard paused in his harangue and turned. "Oh, I didn't notice you, Miss Templeman," said he. "My man in the wrong? Ah, to be sure; to be sure! But I beg your pardon notwithstanding. The other's is the empty wagon, and he must have been most to blame for coming on."

"No; I saw it, too," said Elizabeth-Jane. "And I can assure you he couldn't help it."

"You can't trust *their* senses!" murmured Henchard's man.

"Why not?" asked Henchard sharply.

"Why, you see, sir, all the women side with Farfrae—being a damn young dand—of the sort that he is—one that creeps into a maid's heart like the giddying worm into a sheep's brain— making crooked seem straight to their eyes!"

"But do you know who that lady is you talk about in such a fashion? Do you know that I pay my attentions to her, and have for some time? Just be careful!"

"Not I. I know nothing, sir, outside eight shillings a week."

"And that Mr. Farfrae is well aware of it? He's sharp in trade, but he wouldn't do anything so underhand as what you hint at."

Whether because Lucetta heard this low dialogue, or not, her white figure disappeared from her doorway inward, and the door was shut before Henchard could reach it to converse with her further. This disappointed him, for he had been sufficiently disturbed by what the man had said to wish to speak to her more closely. While pausing the old constable came up.

"Just see that nobody drives against that hay and wagon tonight, Stubberd," said the corn merchant. "It must bide till the morning, for all hands are in the fields still. And if any coach or road wagon wants to come along, tell 'em they must go around by the back street, and be hanged to 'em. . . . Any case tomorrow up in Hall?"

"Yes, sir. One in number, sir."

"Oh, what's that?"

"An old flagrant female, sir, swearing and committing a nuisance in a horrible profane manner against the church wall, sir, as if 'twere no more than a pothouse![1] That's all, sir."

"Oh. The Mayor's out o' town, isn't he?"

"He is, sir."

"Very well, then I'll be there. Don't forget to keep an eye on that hay. Good night t' 'ee."

During those moments Henchard had determined to follow up Lucetta notwithstanding her elusiveness, and he knocked for admission.

The answer he received was an expression of Miss Templeman's sorrow at being unable to see him again that evening because she had an engagement to go out.

Henchard walked away from the door to the opposite side of the street, and stood by his hay in a lonely reverie, the constable having strolled elsewhere, and the horses being removed. Though the moon was not bright as yet there were no lamps lighted, and he entered the shadow of one of the projecting jambs which formed the thoroughfare to Bull Stake; here he watched Lucetta's door.

Candlelights were flitting in and out of her bedroom, and it was obvious that she was dressing for the appointment, whatever the nature of that might be at such an hour. The lights disappeared, the clock struck nine, and almost at the moment Farfrae came around the opposite corner and knocked. That she had been waiting just inside for him was certain, for she instantly opened the door herself. They went together by

---

1. *Pothouse:* tavern.

the way of a back lane westward, avoiding the front street; guessing where they were going he determined to follow.

The harvest had been so delayed by the capricious weather that whenever a fine day occurred all sinews were strained to save what could be saved of the damaged crops. On account of the rapid shortening of the days the harvesters worked by moonlight. Hence tonight the wheat fields abutting on the two sides of the square formed by Casterbridge town were animated by the gathering hands. Their shouts and laughter had reached Henchard at the Market House while he stood there waiting, and he had little doubt from the turn which Farfrae and Lucetta had taken that they were bound for the spot.

Nearly the whole town had gone into the fields. The Casterbridge populace still retained the primitive habit of helping one another in time of need; and thus, though the corn belonged to the farming section of the little community—that inhabiting the Durnover quarter—the remainder was no less interested in the labor of getting it home.

Reaching the top of the lane Henchard crossed the shaded avenue on the walls, slid down the green rampart, and stood amongst the stubble. The "stitches" or shocks rose like tents about the yellow expanse, those in the distance becoming lost in the moonlit hazes.

He had entered at a point removed from the scene of immediate operations; but two others had entered at that place, and he could see them winding among the shocks. They were paying no regard to the direction of their walk, whose vague serpentining soon began to bear down toward Henchard. A meeting promised to be awkward, and he therefore stepped into the hollow of the nearest shock, and sat down.

"You have my leave," Lucetta was saying gaily. "Speak what you like."

"Well, then," replied Farfrae, with the unmistakable inflection of the lover pure, which Henchard had never heard in full resonance on his lips before, "you are sure to be much sought after for your position, wealth, talents, and beauty. But will ye resist the temptation to be one of those ladies with lots of admirers—ay—and be content to have only a homely one?"

"And he the speaker?" said she, laughing. "Very well, sir, what next?"

"Ah! I'm afraid that what I feel will make me forget my manners!"

"Then I hope you'll never have any, if you lack them only for that cause." After some broken words which Henchard lost she added, "Are you sure you won't be jealous?"

Farfrae seemed to assure her that he would not, by taking her hand.

"You are convinced, Donald, that I love nobody else," she presently said. "But I should wish to have my own way in some things."

"In everything! What special thing did you mean?"

"If I wished not to live always in Casterbridge, for instance, upon finding that I should not be happy here?"

Henchard did not hear the reply; he might have done so and much more, but he did not care to play the eavesdropper. They went on toward the scene of activity, where the sheaves were being handed, a dozen a minute, upon the carts and wagons which carried them away.

Lucetta insisted on parting from Farfrae when they drew near the work people. He had some business with them and, though he entreated her to wait a few minutes, she was inexorable, and tripped off homeward alone.

Henchard thereupon left the field and followed her. His state of mind was such on reaching Lucetta's door he did not knock but opened it, and walked straight up to her sitting room, expecting to find her there. But the room was empty, and he perceived that in his haste he had somehow passed her on the way hither. He had not to wait many minutes, however, for he soon heard her dress rustling in the hall, followed by a soft closing of the door. In a moment she appeared.

The light was so low that she did not notice Henchard at first. As soon as she saw him she uttered a little cry, almost of terror.

"How can you frighten me so?" she exclaimed, with a flushed face. "It is past ten o'clock, and you have no right to surprise me here at such a time."

"I don't know that I've not the right. At any rate I have the excuse. Is it so necessary that I should stop to think of manners and customs?"

"It is too late for propriety, and might injure me."

"I called an hour ago, and you would not see me, and I thought you were in when I called now. It is you, Lucetta, who are doing wrong. It is not proper in 'ee to throw me over like this. I have a little matter to remind you of, which you seem to forget."

She sank into a chair and turned pale.

"I don't want to hear it—I don't want to hear it!" she said through her hands, as he, standing close to the edge of her gown, began to allude to the Jersey days.

"But you ought to hear it," said he.

"It came to nothing; and through you. Then why not leave me the freedom I gained with such sorrow! Had I found that you proposed to marry me for pure love I might have felt bound now. But I soon learned that you had planned it out of mere charity—almost as an unpleasant duty—because I had nursed you, and compromised myself, and you thought you must repay me. After that I did not care for you so deeply as before."

"Why did you come here to find me, then?"

"I thought I ought to marry you for conscience' sake, since you were free, even though I—did not like you so well."

"And why then don't you think so now?"

She was silent. It was only too obvious that conscience had

ruled well enough till new love had intervened and usurped that rule. In feeling this she herself forgot for the moment her partially justifying argument—that having discovered Henchard's infirmities of temper, she had some excuse for not risking her happiness in his hands after once escaping them. The only thing she could say was, "I was a poor girl then; and now my circumstances have altered, so I am hardly the same person."

"That's true. And it makes the case awkward for me. But I don't want to touch your money. I am quite willing that every penny of your property shall remain to your personal use. Besides, that argument has nothing in it. The man you are thinking of is no better than I."

"If you were as good as he you would leave me!" she cried passionately.

This unluckily aroused Henchard. "You cannot in honor refuse me," he said. "And unless you give me your promise this very night to be my wife, before a witness, I'll reveal our intimacy—in common fairness to other men!"

A look of resignation settled upon her. Henchard saw its bitterness; and had Lucetta's heart been given to any other man in the world than Farfrae he would probably have had pity upon her at that moment. But the supplanter was the upstart (as Henchard called him) who had mounted into prominence upon his shoulders, and he could bring himself to show no mercy.

Without another word she rang the bell, and directed that Elizabeth-Jane should be fetched from her room. The latter appeared, surprised in the midst of her lucubrations. As soon as she saw Henchard she went across to him dutifully.

"Elizabeth-Jane," he said, taking her hand, "I want you to hear this." And turning to Lucetta: "Will you, or will you not, marry me?"

"If you—wish it, I must agree!"

"You say yes?"

"I do."

No sooner had she given the promise than she fell back in a fainting state.

"What dreadful thing drives her to say this, Father, when it is such a pain to her?" asked Elizabeth, kneeling down by Lucetta. "Don't compel her to do anything against her will! I have lived with her, and know that she cannot bear much."

"Don't be a no'thern simpleton!" said Henchard drily. "This promise will leave him free for you, if you want him, won't it?"

At this Lucetta seemed to wake from her swoon with a start.

"Him? Who are you talking about?" she said wildly.

"Nobody, as far as I am concerned," said Elizabeth firmly.

"Oh—well. Then it is my mistake," said Henchard. "But the business is between me and Miss Templeman. She agrees to be my wife."

"But don't dwell on it just now," entreated Elizabeth, holding Lucetta's hand.

"I don't wish to, if she promises," said Henchard.

"I have, I have," groaned Lucetta, her limbs hanging like flails, from very misery and faintness. "Michael, please don't argue it any more!"

"I will not," he said. And taking up his hat he went away.

Elizabeth-Jane continued to kneel by Lucetta. "What is this?" she said. "You called my father 'Michael' as if you knew him well? And how is it he has got his power over you, that you promise to marry him against your will? Ah—you have many secrets from me!"

"Perhaps you have some from me," Lucetta murmured with closed eyes, little thinking, however, so unsuspicious was she, that the secret of Elizabeth's heart concerned the young man who had caused this damage to her own.

"I would not—do anything against you at all!" stammered Elizabeth, keeping in all signs of emotion till she was ready to burst. "I cannot understand how my father can command you so; I don't sympathize with him in it at all. I'll go to him and ask him to release you."

"No, no," said Lucetta. "Let it all be."

. . . CHAPTER 28

THE NEXT MORNING Henchard went to the Town Hall below Lucetta's house, to attend petty sessions, being still a magistrate for the year by virtue of his late position as Mayor. In passing he looked up at her windows, but nothing of her was to be seen.

Henchard as a justice of the peace may at first seem to be an even greater incongruity than Shallow and Silence[1] themselves. But his rough and ready perceptions, his sledgehammer directness, had often served him better than nice legal knowledge in dispatching such simple business as fell to his hands in this court. Today Dr. Chalkfield, the Mayor for the year, being absent, the corn merchant took the big chair, his eyes still abstractedly stretching out of the window to the ashlar front of High-Place Hall.

There was one case only, and the offender stood before him. She was an old woman of mottled countenance, attired in a shawl of that nameless tertiary hue which comes, but cannot be made—a hue neither tawny, russet, hazel, nor ash; a sticky black bonnet that seemed to have been worn in the country of the Psalmist where the clouds drop fatness; and an apron that had been white in times so comparatively recent as still to contrast visibly with the rest of her clothes. The steeped aspect of the woman as a whole showed her to be no native of the countryside or even of a countrytown.

She looked cursorily at Henchard and the second magistrate, and Henchard looked at her, with a momentary pause, as if she had reminded him indistinctly of somebody or some-

1. *Shallow* . . . *Silence:* Shakespearean characters.

thing which passed from his mind as quickly as it had come. "Well, and what has she been doing?" he said, looking down at the charge sheet.

"She is charged, sir, with the offense of disorderly female and nuisance," whispered Stubberd.

"Where did she do that?" said the other magistrate.

"By the church, sir, of all the horrible places in the world! —I caught her in the act, your worship."

"Stand back then," said Henchard, "and let's hear what you've got to say."

Stubberd was sworn, the magistrate's clerk dipped his pen, Henchard being no note taker himself, and the constable began——

"Hearing a' illegal noise I went down the street at twenty-five minutes past eleven P.M. on the night of the fifth instinct, Hannah Dominy. When I had——"

"Don't go on so fast, Stubberd," said the clerk.

The constable waited, with his eyes on the clerk's pen, till the latter stopped scratching and said, "yes." Stubberd continued: "When I had proceeded to the spot I saw defendant at another spot, namely, the gutter." He paused, watching the point of the clerk's pen again.

"Gutter, yes, Stubberd."

"Spot measuring twelve feet nine inches or thereabouts, from where I——" Still careful not to outrun the clerk's penmanship Stubberd pulled up again; for having got his evidence by heart it was immaterial to him whereabouts he broke off.

"I object to that," spoke up the old woman, " 'spot measuring twelve feet nine or thereabouts from where I,' is not sound testimony!"

The magistrates consulted, and the second one said that the bench was of opinion that twelve feet nine inches from a man on his oath was admissible.

Stubberd, with a suppressed gaze of victorious rectitude at the old woman, continued: "Was standing myself. She was wambling about quite dangerous to the thoroughfare, and when I approached to draw near she committed the nuisance, and insulted me."

" 'Insulted me.' . . . Yes, what did she say?"

"She said, 'Put away that dee lantern,' she says."

"Yes."

"Says she, 'Dost hear, old turmit-head? Put away that dee lantern. I have floored fellows a dee sight finer-looking than a dee fool like thee, dee me if I haint,' she says."

"I object to that conversation!" interposed the old woman. "I was not capable enough to hear what I said, and what is said out of my hearing is not evidence."

There was another stoppage for consultation, a book was referred to, and finally Stubberd was allowed to go on again. The truth was that the old woman had appeared in court so many more times than the magistrates themselves, that they were obliged to keep a sharp lookout upon their procedure. However, when Stubberd had rambled on a little further Henchard broke in impatiently, "Come—we don't want to hear any more of them cust dees! Say the words out like a man, and don't be so modest, Stubberd; or else leave it alone!" Turning to the woman, "Now then, have you any questions to ask him, or anything to say?"

"Yes," she replied with a twinkle in her eye; and the clerk dipped his pen.

"Twenty years ago or thereabout I was selling furmity in a tent at Weydon Fair——"

" 'Twenty years ago'—well, that's beginning at the beginning; suppose you go back to the Creation!" said the clerk, not without satire.

But Henchard stared, and quite forgot what was evidence and what was not.

"A man and a woman with a little child came into my tent," the woman continued. "They sat down and has a basin apiece. Ah, Lord's my life! I was of a more respectable station in the world then than I am now, being a land smuggler in a large way of business; and I used to season my furmity with rum for them who asked for't. I did it for the man; and then he had more and more; till at last he quarreled with his wife, and offered to sell her to the highest bidder. A sailor came in and bid five guineas, and paid the money, and led her away. And the man who sold his wife in that fashion is the man sitting there in the great big chair." The speaker concluded by nodding her head at Henchard and folding her arms.

Everybody looked at Henchard. His face seemed strange, and in tint as if it had been powdered over with ashes. "We don't want to hear your life and adventures," said the second magistrate sharply, filling the pause which followed. "You've been asked if you've anything to say bearing on the case."

"That bears on the case. It proves that he's no better than I, and has no right to sit there in judgment upon me."

" 'Tis a concocted story," said the clerk. "So hold your tongue!"

"No—'tis true." The words came from Henchard. " 'Tis as true as the light," he said slowly. "And upon my soul it does prove that I'm no better than she! And to keep out of any temptation to treat her hard for her revenge, I'll leave her to you."

The sensation in the court was indescribably great. Henchard left the chair, and came out, passing through a group of people on the steps and outside that was much larger than usual; for it seemed that the old furmity dealer had mysteriously hinted to the denizens of the lane in which she had been lodging since her arrival, that she knew a queer thing or two about their great local man Mr. Henchard, if she chose to tell it. This had brought them hither.

"Why are there so many idlers round the Town Hall to-day?" said Lucetta to her servant when the case was over. She had risen late, and had just looked out of the window.

"Oh, please, ma'am, 'tis this larry about Mr. Henchard. A

woman has proved that before he became a gentleman he sold his wife for five guineas in a booth at a fair."

In all the accounts which Henchard had given her of the separation from his wife Susan for so many years, of his belief in her death, and so on, he had never clearly explained the actual and immediate cause of that separation. The story she now heard for the first time.

A gradual misery overspread Lucetta's face as she dwelt upon the promise wrung from her the night before. At bottom, then, Henchard was this. How terrible a contingency for a woman who should commit herself to his care.

During the day she went out to the Ring and to other places, not coming in till nearly dusk. As soon as she saw Elizabeth-Jane after her return indoors she told her that she had resolved to go away from home to the seaside for a few days—to Port-Bredy; Casterbridge was so gloomy.

Elizabeth seeing that she looked wan and disturbed, encouraged her in the idea, thinking a change would afford her relief. She could not help suspecting that the gloom which seemed to have come over Casterbridge in Lucetta's eyes might be partially owing to the fact that Farfrae was away from home.

Elizabeth saw her friend depart for Port-Bredy, and took charge of High-Place Hall till her return. After two or three days of solitude and incessant rain Henchard called at the house. He seemed disappointed to hear of Lucetta's absence, and though he nodded with outward indifference he went away handling his beard with a nettled mien.

The next day he called again. "Is she come now?" he asked.

"Yes. She returned this morning," replied his stepdaughter. "But she is not indoors. She has gone for a walk along the turnpike road to Port-Bredy. She will be home by dusk."

After a few words, which only served to reveal his restless impatience, he left the house again.

CHAPTER 29

AT THIS hour Lucetta was bounding along the road to Port-Bredy just as Elizabeth had announced. That she had chosen for her afternoon walk the road along which she had returned to Casterbridge three hours earlier in a carriage was curious —if anything should be called curious in concatenations of phenomena wherein each is known to have its accounting cause. It was the day of the chief market—Saturday—and Farfrae for once had been missed from his corn stand in the dealers' room. Nevertheless, it was known that he would be home that night—"for Sunday," as Casterbridge expressed it.

Lucetta, in continuing her walk, had at length reached the end of the ranked trees which bordered the highway in this and other directions out of the town. This end marked a mile; and here she stopped.

The spot was a vale between two gentle acclivities and the road, still adhering to its Roman foundation, stretched onward straight as a surveyor's line till lost to sight on the most distant ridge. There was neither hedge nor tree in the prospect now, the road clinging to the stubbly expanse of corn land like a stripe to an undulating garment. Near her was a barn—the single building of any kind within her horizon.

She strained her eyes up the lessening road, but nothing appeared thereon—not so much as a speck. She sighed one word—"Donald!" and turned her face to the town for retreat.

Here the case was different. A single figure was approaching her—Elizabeth-Jane's.

Lucetta, in spite of her loneliness, seemed a little vexed. Elizabeth's face, as soon as she recognized her friend, shaped itself into affectionate lines while yet beyond speaking distance. "I suddenly thought I would come and meet you," she said, smiling.

Lucetta's reply was taken from her lips by an unexpected

diversion. A by-road on her right hand descended from the fields into the highway at the point where she stood, and down the track a bull was rambling uncertainly toward her and Elizabeth, who, facing the other way, did not observe him.

In the latter quarter of each year cattle were at once the mainstay and the terror of families about Casterbridge and its neighborhood, where breeding was carried on with Abrahamic success.[1] The head of stock driven into and out of the town at this season to be sold by the local auctioneer was very large; and all these horned beasts, in traveling to and fro, sent women and children to shelter as nothing else could do. In the main the animals would have walked along quietly enough; but the Casterbridge tradition was that to drive stock it was indispensable that hideous cries, coupled with Yahoo[2] antics and gestures, should be used, large sticks flourished, stray dogs called in, and in general everything done that was likely to infuriate the viciously disposed and terrify the mild. Nothing was commoner than for a householder on going out of his parlor to find his hall or passage full of little children, nursemaids, aged women, or a ladies' school, who apologized for their presence by saying, "A bull passing down street from the sale."

Lucetta and Elizabeth regarded the animal in doubt, he meanwhile drawing vaguely toward them. It was a large specimen of the breed, in color rich dun, though disfigured at present by splotches of mud about his seamy sides. His horns were thick and tipped with brass; his two nostrils like the Thames Tunnel as seen in the perspective toys of yore. Between them, through the gristle of his nose, was a stout copper ring, welded on, and irremovable as Gurth's[3] collar of brass. To the ring was attached an ash staff about a yard long,

---

1. *Abrahamic success:* Abraham in the Bible was a successful cattle raiser.
2. *Yahoo:* subhuman characters in Swift's *Gulliver's Travels.*
3. *Gurth:* a serf in Sir Walter Scott's *Ivanhoe.*

which the bull with the motions of his head flung about like a flail.

It was not till they observed this dangling stick that the young women were really alarmed; for it revealed to them that the bull was an old one, too savage to be driven, which had in some way escaped, the staff being the means by which the drover controlled him and kept his horns at arm's length.

They looked round for some shelter or hiding place, and thought of the barn hard by. As long as they had kept their eyes on the bull he had shown some deference in his manner of approach; but no sooner did they turn their backs to seek the barn than he tossed his head and decided to thoroughly terrify them. This caused the two helpless girls to run wildly, whereupon the bull advanced in a deliberate charge.

The barn stood behind a green slimy pond, and it was closed save as to one of the usual pair of doors facing them, which had been propped open by a hurdle stake, and for this opening they made. The interior had been cleared by a recent bout of threshing except at one end, where there was a stack of dry clover. Elizabeth-Jane took in the situation. "We must climb up there," she said.

But before they had even approached it they heard the bull scampering through the pond without, and in a second he dashed into the barn, knocking down the hurdle stake in passing; the heavy door slammed behind him; and all three were imprisoned in the barn together. The mistaken creature saw them, and stalked toward the end of the barn into which they had fled. The girls doubled so adroitly that their pursuer was against the wall when the fugitives were already half way to the other end. By the time that his length would allow him to turn and follow them thither they had crossed over; thus the pursuit went on, the hot air from his nostrils blowing over them like a sirocco, and not a moment being attainable by Elizabeth or Lucetta in which to open the door. What might have happened had their situation continued cannot be said; but in a few moments a rattling of the door distracted their adversary's attention, and a man appeared. He ran forward toward the leading staff, seized it, and wrenched the animal's head as if he would snap it off. The wrench was in reality so violent that the thick neck seemed to have lost its stiffness and to become half-paralyzed, whilst the nose dropped blood. The premeditated human contrivance of the nose ring was too cunning for impulsive brute force, and the creature flinched.

The man was seen in the partial gloom to be large-framed and unhesitating. He led the bull to the door, and the light revealed Henchard. He made the bull fast without, and re-entered to the succor of Lucetta; for he had not perceived Elizabeth, who had climbed on to the clover heap. Lucetta was hysterical, and Henchard took her in his arms and carried her to the door.

"You—have saved me!" she cried, as soon as she could speak.

"I have returned you kindness," he responded tenderly. "You once saved me."

"How—comes it to be you—you?" she asked, not heeding his reply.

"I came out here to look for you. I have been wanting to tell you something these two or three days; but you have been away, and I could not. Perhaps you cannot talk now?"

"Oh—no! Where is Elizabeth?"

"Here am I!" cried the missing one cheerfully; and without waiting for the ladder to be placed she slid down the face of the clover stack to the floor.

Henchard supporting Lucetta on one side, and Elizabeth-Jane on the other, they went slowly along the rising road. They had reached the top and were descending again when Lucetta, now much recovered, recollected that she had dropped her muff in the barn.

"I'll run back," said Elizabeth-Jane. "I don't mind it at all, as I am not tired as you are." She thereupon hastened down again to the barn, the others pursuing their way.

Elizabeth soon found the muff, such an article being by no means small at that time. Coming out she paused to look for a moment at the bull, now rather to be pitied with his bleeding nose, having perhaps rather intended a practical joke than a murder. Henchard had secured him by jamming the staff into the hinge of the barn door, and wedging it there with a stake. At length she turned to hasten onward after her contemplation when she saw a green-and-black gig approaching from the contrary direction, the vehicle being driven by Farfrae.

His presence here seemed to explain Lucetta's walk that way. Donald saw her, drew up, and was hastily made acquainted with what had occurred. At Elizabeth-Jane mentioning how greatly Lucetta had been jeopardized, he exhibited an agitation different in kind no less than in intensity from any she had seen in him before. He became so absorbed in the circumstance that he scarcely had sufficient knowledge of what he was doing to think of helping her up beside him.

"She has gone on with Mr. Henchard, you say?" he inquired at last.

"Yes. He is taking her home. They are almost there by this time."

"And you are sure she can get home?"

Elizabeth-Jane was quite sure.

"Your stepfather saved her?"

"Entirely."

Farfrae checked his horse's pace; she guessed why. He was thinking that it would be best not to intrude on the other two just now. Henchard had saved Lucetta, and to provoke a possible exhibition of her deeper affection for himself was as ungenerous as it was unwise.

The immediate subject of their talk being exhausted she felt more embarrassed at sitting thus beside her past lover; but soon the two figures of the others were visible at the entrance to the town. The face of the woman was frequently turned back, but Farfrae did not whip on the horse. When these reached the town walls Henchard and his companion had disappeared down the street; Farfrae set down Elizabeth-Jane on her expressing a particular wish to alight there, and drove round to the stables at the back of his lodgings.

On this account he entered the house through his garden, and going up to his apartments found them in a particularly disturbed state, his boxes being hauled out upon the landing, and his bookcase standing in three pieces. These phenomena, however, seemed to cause him not the lease surprise. "When will everything be sent up?" he said to the mistress of the house, who was superintending.

"I am afraid not before eight, sir," said she. "You see we wasn't aware till this morning that you were going to move, or we could have been forwarder."

"A—well, never mind, never mind!" said Farfrae cheerily. "Eight o'clock will do well enough if it be not later. Now, don't ye be standing here talking, or it will be twelve, I doubt." Thus speaking he went out by the front door and up the street.

During this interval Henchard and Lucetta had had experiences of a different kind. After Elizabeth's departure for the muff the corn merchant opened himself frankly, holding her hand within his arm, though she would fain have withdrawn it. "Dear Lucetta, I have been very, very anxious to see you these two or three days," he said; "ever since I saw you last! I have thought over the way I got your promise that night. You said to me, 'If I were a man I should not insist.' That cut me deep. I felt that there was some truth in it. I don't want to make you wretched; and to marry me just now would do that as nothing else could—it is but too plain. Therefore I agree to an indefinite engagement—to put off all thought of marriage for a year or two."

"But—but—can I do nothing of a different kind?" said Lucetta. "I am full of gratitude to you—you have saved my life. And your care of me is like coals of fire on my head! I am a monied person now. Surely I can do something in return for your goodness—something practical?"

Henchard remained in thought. He had evidently not expected this. "There is one thing you might do, Lucetta," he said. "But not exactly of that kind."

"Then of what kind is it?" she asked with renewed misgiving.

"I must tell you a secret to ask it.—— You may have heard that I have been unlucky this year? I did what I have never done before—speculated rashly; and I lost. That's just put me in a strait."

"And you would wish me to advance some money?"

"No, no!" said Henchard, almost in anger. "I'm not the man to sponge on a woman, even though she may be so nearly my own as you. No, Lucetta; what you can do is this; and it would save me. My great creditor is Grower, and it is at his hands I shall suffer if at anybody's; while a fortnight's forbearance on his part would be enough to allow me to pull through. This may be got out of him in one way—that you would let it be known to him that you are my intended—that we are to be quietly married in the next fortnight.—— Now stop, you haven't heard all! Let him have this story, without, of course, any prejudice to the fact that the actual engagement between us is to be a long one. Nobody else need know: you could go with me to Mr. Grower and just let me speak to 'ee before him as if we were on such terms. We'll ask him to keep it secret. He will willingly wait then. At the fortnight's end I shall be able to face him; and I can coolly tell him all is postponed between us for a year or two. Not a soul in the town need know how you've helped me. Since you wish to be of use, there's your way."

It being now what the people called the "pinking in" of the day, that is, the quarter-hour just before dusk, he did not at first observe the result of his own words upon her.

"If it were anything else," she began, and the dryness of her lips was represented in her voice.

"But it is such a little thing!" he said, with a deep reproach.

"Less than you have offered—just the beginning of what you have so lately promised! I could have told him as much myself, but he would not have believed me."

"It is not because I won't—it is because I absolutely can't," she said, with rising distress.

"You are provoking!" he burst out. "It is enough to make me force you to carry out at once what you have promised."

"I cannot!" she insisted desperately.

"Why? When I have only within these few minutes released you from your promise to do the thing offhand."

"Because—he was a witness!"

"Witness? Of what?"

"If I must tell you——. Don't, don't upbraid me!"

"Well! Let's hear what you mean?"

"Witness of my marriage—Mr. Grower was!"

"Marriage?"

"Yes. With Mr. Farfrae. O Michael! I am already his wife. We were married this week at Port-Bredy. There were reasons against our doing it here. Mr. Grower was a witness because he happened to be at Port-Bredy at the time."

Henchard stood as if idiotized. She was so alarmed at his silence that she murmured something about lending him sufficient money to tide over the perilous fortnight.

"Married him?" said Henchard at length. "My good—what, married him whilst—bound to marry me?"

"It was like this," she explained, with tears in her eyes and quavers in her voice; "don't—don't be cruel! I loved him so much, and I thought you might tell him of the past—and that grieved me! And then, when I had promised you, I learned of the rumor that you had—sold your first wife at a fair like a horse or cow! How could I keep my promise after hearing that? I could not risk myself in your hands; it would have been letting myself down to take your name after such a scandal. But I knew I should lose Donald if I did not secure him at once—for you would carry out your threat of telling him of our former acquaintance, as long as there was a chance of keeping me for yourself by doing so. But you will not do so now, will you, Michael? For it is too late to separate us."

The notes of St. Peter's bells in full peal had been wafted to them while he spoke; and now the genial thumping of the town band, renowned for its unstinted use of the drumstick, throbbed down the street.

"Then this racket they are making is on account of it, I suppose?" said he.

"Yes—I think he has told them, or else Mr. Grower has. . . . May I leave you now? My—he was detained at Port-Bredy today, and sent me on a few hours before him."

"Then it is *his wife's* life I have saved this afternoon."

"Yes—and he will be forever grateful to you."

"I am much obliged to him. . . . O you false woman!" burst from Henchard. "You promised me!"

"Yes, yes! But it was under compulsion, and I did not know your past——"

"And now I've a mind to punish you as you deserve! One word to this brand-new husband of how you courted me, and your precious happiness is blown to atoms!"

"Michael—pity me, and be generous!"

"You don't deserve pity! You did; but you don't now."

"I'll help you to pay off your debt."

"A pensioner of Farfrae's wife—not I! Don't stay with me longer—I shall say something worse. Go home!"

She disappeared under the trees of the south walk as the band came round the corner, awaking the echoes of every stock and stone in celebration of her happiness. Lucetta took no heed, but ran up the back street and reached her own home unperceived.

. . . CHAPTER 30

FARFRAE'S words to his landlady had referred to the removal of his boxes and other effects from his late lodgings to Lucetta's house. The work was not heavy, but it had been much hindered on account of the frequent pauses necessitated by exclamations of surprise at the event, of which the good woman had been briefly informed by letter a few hours earlier.

At the last moment of leaving Port-Bredy, Farfrae, like John Gilpin,[1] had been detained by important customers, whom, even in the exceptional circumstances, he was not the man to neglect. Moreover, there was a convenience in Lucetta arriving first at her house. Nobody there as yet knew what had happened; and she was best in a position to break the news to the inmates, and give directions for her husband's accommodation. He had, therefore, sent on his two-days' bride in a hired brougham, whilst he went across the country to a certain group of wheat and barley ricks a few miles off, telling her the hour at which he might be expected the same evening. This accounted for her trotting out to meet him after their separation of four hours.

By a strenuous effort, after leaving Henchard she calmed herself in readiness to receive Donald at High-Place Hall when he came on from his lodgings. One supreme fact empowered her to this, the sense that come what would, she had secured him. Half an hour after her arrival he walked in, and she met him with a relieved gladness, which a month's perilous absence could not have intensified.

"There is one thing I have not done; and yet it is important," she said earnestly, when she had finished talking about the adventure with the bull. "That is, broken the news of our marriage to my dear Elizabeth-Jane."

"Ah, and you have not?" he said thoughtfully. "I gave her a lift from the barn homewards; but I did not tell her either; for I thought she might have heard of it in the town, and was keeping back her congratulations from shyness, and all that."

"She can hardly have heard of it. But I'll find out; I'll go

1. *John Gilpin:* character in a ballad by William Cowper (1782).

to her now. And, Donald, you don't mind her living on with me just the same as before? She is so quiet and unassuming."

"O no, indeed I don't," Farfrae answered with, perhaps, a faint awkwardness. "But I wonder if she would care to?"

"O yes!" said Lucetta eagerly. "I am sure she would like to. Besides, poor thing, she has no other home."

Farfrae looked at her and saw that she did not suspect the secret of her more reserved friend. He liked her all the better for the blindness. "Arrange as you like with her by all means," he said. "It is I who have come to your house, not you to mine."

"I'll run and speak to her," said Lucetta.

When she got upstairs to Elizabeth-Jane's room the latter had taken off her outdoor things, and was resting over a book. Lucetta found in a moment that she had not yet learned the news.

"I did not come down to you, Miss Templeman," she said simply. "I was coming to ask you if you had quite recovered from your fright, but I found you had a visitor. What are the bells ringing for, I wonder? And the band, too, is playing. Somebody must be married; or else they are practicing for Christmas."

Lucetta uttered a vague "Yes," and seating herself by the other woman looked musingly at her. "What a lonely creature you are," she presently said; "never knowing what's going on, or what people are talking about everywhere with keen interest. You should get out, and gossip about as other women do, and then you wouldn't be obliged to ask me a question of that kind. Well, now, I have something to tell you."

Elizabeth-Jane said she was so glad, and made herself receptive.

"I must go rather a long way back," said Lucetta, the difficulty of explaining herself satisfactorily to the pondering one beside her growing more apparent at each syllable. "You remember that trying case of conscience I told you of some time

ago—about the first lover and the second lover?" She let out
in jerky phrases a leading word or two of the story she had
told.

"O yes—I remember; the story of *your friend*," said Elizabeth drily, regarding the irises of Lucetta's eyes as though to
catch their exact shade. "The two lovers—the old and the new:
how she wanted to marry the second, but felt she ought to
marry the first; so that she neglected the better course to
follow the evil, like the poet Ovid[2] I've just been construing:
'Video meliora proboque, deteriora sequor.' "[3]

"O no; she didn't follow evil exactly!" said Lucetta hastily.

"But you said that she—or as I may say *you*"—answered
Elizabeth, dropping the mask, "were in honor and conscience
bound to marry the first?"

Lucetta's blush at being seen through came and went again
before she replied anxiously, "You will never breathe this,
will you, Elizabeth-Jane?"

"Certainly not, if you say not."

"Then I will tell you that the case is more complicated—
worse, in fact—than it seemed in my story. I and the first man
were thrown together in a strange way, and felt that we ought
to be united, as the world had talked of us. He was a widower,
as he supposed. He had not heard of his first wife for many
years. But the wife returned, and we parted. She is now dead;
and the husband comes paying me addresses again, saying,
'Now we'll complete our purpose.' But, Elizabeth-Jane, all
this amounts to a new courtship of me by him; I was absolved
from all vows by the return of the other woman."

"Have you not lately renewed your promise?" said the
younger with quiet surmise. She had divined Man Number
One.

"That was wrung from me by a threat."

2. *Ovid:* Roman poet (43 B.C.-17 A.D.).
3. "*Video . . . sequor:* I see the better and the right, [but] I follow the
worse."

"Yes, it was. But I think when anyone gets coupled up with a man in the past so unfortunately as you have done, she ought to become his wife if she can, even if she were not the sinning party."

Lucetta's countenance lost its sparkle. "He turned out to be a man I should be afraid to marry," she pleaded. "Really afraid! And it was not till after my renewed promise that I knew it."

"Then there is only one course left to honesty. You must remain a single woman."

"But think again! Do consider——"

"I am certain," interrupted her companion hardily. "I have guessed very well who the man is. My father; and I say it is him or nobody for you."

Any suspicion of impropriety was to Elizabeth-Jane like a red rag to a bull. Her craving for correctness of procedure was, indeed, almost vicious. Owing to her early troubles with regard to her mother a semblance of irregularity had terrors for her which those whose names are safeguarded from suspicion know nothing of. "You ought to marry Mr. Henchard or nobody—certainly not another man!" she went on with a quivering lip in whose movement two passions shared.

"I don't admit that!" said Lucetta passionately.

"Admit it or not, it is true!"

Lucetta covered her eyes with her right hand, as if she could plead no more, holding out her left to Elizabeth-Jane.

"Why, you *have* married him!" cried the latter, jumping up with pleasure after a glance at Lucetta's fingers. "When did you do it? Why did you not tell me, instead of teasing me like this? How very honorable of you! He did treat my mother badly once, it seems, in a moment of intoxication. And it is true that he is stern sometimes. But you will rule him entirely, I am sure, with your beauty and wealth and accomplishments. You are the woman he will adore, and we shall all three be happy together now."

"O, my Elizabeth-Jane!" cried Lucetta distressfully. 'Tis somebody else that I have married! I was so desperate—so afraid of being forced to anything else—so afraid of revelations that would quench his love for me, that I resolved to do it offhand, come what might, and purchase a week of happiness at any cost!"

"You—have—married Mr. Farfrae!" cried Elizabeth-Jane, in Nathan[4] tones.

Lucetta bowed. She had recovered herself.

"The bells are ringing on that account," she said. "My husband is downstairs. He will live here till a more suitable house is ready for us; and I have told him that I want you to stay with me just as before."

"Let me think of it alone," the girl quickly replied, corking up the turmoil of her feeling with grand control.

"You shall. I am sure we shall be happy together."

Lucetta departed to join Donald below, a vague uneasiness floating over her joy at seeing him quite at home there. Not on account of her friend Elizabeth did she feel it: for of the bearings of Elizabeth-Jane's emotions she had not the least suspicion; but on Henchard's alone.

Now the instant decision of Susan Henchard's daughter was to dwell in that house no more. Apart from her estimate of the propriety of Lucetta's conduct, Farfrae had been so nearly her avowed lover that she felt she could not abide there.

It was still early in the evening when she hastily put on her things and went out. In a few minutes, knowing the ground, she had found a suitable lodging, and arranged to enter it that night. Returning and entering noiselessly she took off her pretty dress and arrayed herself in a plain one, packing up the other to keep as her best; for she would have to be very economical now. She wrote a note to leave for Lucetta, who was closely shut up in the drawing room with Farfrae; and then

4. *Nathan:* Nahum, Old Testament prophet.

Elizabeth-Jane called a man with a wheelbarrow; and seeing her boxes put into it she trotted off down the street to her rooms. They were in the street in which Henchard lived, and almost opposite his door.

Here she sat down and considered the means of subsistence. The little annual sum settled on her by her stepfather would keep body and soul together. A wonderful skill in netting of all sorts—acquired in childhood by making seines in Newson's home—might serve her in good stead; and her studies, which were pursued unremittingly, might serve her in still better.

By this time the marriage that had taken place was known throughout Casterbridge; had been discussed noisily on curb-stones, confidentially behind counters, and jovially at the Three Mariners. Whether Farfrae would sell his business and set up for a gentleman on his wife's money, or whether he would show independence enough to stick to his trade in spite of his brilliant alliance, was a great point of interest.

. . . CHAPTER 31

THE RETORT of the furmity-woman before the magistrates had spread; and in four-and-twenty hours there was not a person in Casterbridge who remained unacquainted with the story of Henchard's mad freak at Weydon-Priors Fair, long years before. The amends he had made in after life were lost sight of in the dramatic glare of the original act. Had the incident been well known of old and always, it might by this time have grown to be lightly regarded as the rather tall wild oat, but well-nigh the single one, of a young man with whom the steady and mature (if somewhat headstrong) burgher of today had scarcely a point in common. But the act having lain as dead and buried ever since, the interspace of years was un-perceived; and the black spot of his youth wore the aspect of a recent crime.

Small as the police-court incident had been in itself, it formed the edge or turn in the incline of Henchard's fortunes. On that day—almost at that minute—he passed the ridge of prosperity and honor, and began to descend rapidly on the other side. It was strange how soon he sank in esteem. Socially he had received a startling fillip downwards; and, having already lost commercial buoyancy from rash transactions, the velocity of his descent in both aspects became accelerated every hour.

He now gazed more at the pavements and less at the house fronts when he walked about; more at the feet and leggings of men, and less into the pupils of their eyes with the blazing regard which formerly had made them blink.

New events combined to undo him. It had been a bad year for others besides himself, and the heavy failure of a debtor whom he had trusted generously completed the overthrow of his tottering credit. And now, in his desperation, he failed to preserve that strict correspondence between bulk and sample which is the soul of commerce in grain. For this, one of his men was mainly to blame; that worthy, in his great unwisdom, having picked over the sample of an enormous quantity of second-rate corn which Henchard had in hand, and removed the pinched, blasted, and smutted grains in great numbers. The produce if honestly offered would have created no scandal; but the blunder of misrepresentation, coming at such a moment, dragged Henchard's name into the ditch.

The details of his failure were of the ordinary kind. One day Elizabeth-Jane was passing the King's Arms, when she saw people bustling in and out more than usual when there was no market. A bystander informed her, with some surprise at her ignorance, that it was a meeting of commissioners under Mr. Henchard's bankruptcy. She felt quite tearful, and when she heard that he was present in the hotel she wished to go in and see him, but was advised not to intrude that day.

The room in which debtor and creditors had assembled

was a front one, and Henchard, looking out of the window, had caught sight of Elizabeth-Jane through the wire blind. His examination had closed, and the creditors were leaving. The appearance of Elizabeth threw him into a reverie; till, turning his face from the window, and towering above all the rest, he called their attention for a moment more. His countenance had somewhat changed from its flush of prosperity; the black hair and whiskers were the same as ever, but a film of ash was over the rest.

"Gentlemen," he said, "over and above the assets that we've been talking about, and that appear on the balance sheet, there be these. It all belongs to ye, as much as everything else I've got, and I don't wish to keep it from you, not I." Saying this, he took his gold watch from his pocket and laid it on the table; then his purse—the yellow canvas money bag, such as was carried by all farmers and dealers—untying it, and shaking the money out upon the table beside the watch. The latter he drew back quickly for an instant, to remove the hair guard made and given him by Lucetta. "There, now you have all I've got in the world," he said. "And I wish for your sakes 'twas more."

The creditors, farmers almost to a man, looked at the watch, and at the money, and into the street; when Farmer James Everdene of Weatherbury spoke.

"No, no, Henchard," he said warmly. "We don't want that. 'Tis honorable in ye; but keep it. What do you say, neighbors—do ye agree?"

"Ay, sure: we don't wish it at all," said Grower, another creditor.

"Let him keep it, of course," murmured another in the background—a silent, reserved young man named Boldwood; and the rest responded unanimously.

"Well," said the senior commissioner, addressing Henchard, "though the case is a desperate one, I am bound to admit that I have never met a debtor who behaved more fairly. I've proved the balance sheet to be as honestly made out as it could possibly be; we have had no trouble; there have been no evasions and no concealments. The rashness of dealing which led to this unhappy situation is obvious enough; but as far as I can see every attempt has been made to avoid wronging anybody."

Henchard was more affected by this than he cared to let them perceive, and he turned aside to the window again. A general murmur of agreement followed the commissioner's words; and the meeting dispersed. When they were gone Henchard regarded the watch they had returned to him. " 'Tisn't mine by rights," he said to himself. "Why the devil didn't they take it?—I don't want what don't belong to me!" Moved by a recollection he took the watch to the maker's just opposite, sold it there and then for what the tradesman offered, and went with the proceeds to one among the smaller of his creditors, a cottager of Durnover in straitened circumstances, to whom he handed the money.

When everything was ticketed that Henchard had owned, and the auctions were in progress, there was quite a sympathetic reaction in the town, which till then for some time past had done nothing but condemn him. Now that Henchard's whole career was pictured distinctly to his neighbors, and they could see how admirably he had used his one talent of energy to create a position of affluence out of absolutely nothing— which was really all he could show when he came to the town as a journeyman hay trusser, with his wimble and knife in his basket—they wondered and regretted his fall.

Try as she might, Elizabeth could never meet with him. She believed in him still, though nobody else did; and she wanted to be allowed to forgive him for his roughness to her, and to help him in his trouble.

She wrote to him; he did not reply. She then went to his house—the great house she had lived in so happily for a time —with its front of dun brick, vitrified here and there, and its heavy sash bars—but Henchard was to be found there no more. The ex-Mayor had left the home of his prosperity, and gone into Jopp's cottage by the Priory Mill—the sad purlieu to which he had wandered on the night of his discovery that she was not his daughter. Thither she went.

Elizabeth thought it odd that he had fixed on this spot to retire to, but assumed that necessity had no choice. Trees which seemed old enough to have been planted by the friars still stood around, and the back hatch of the original mill yet formed a cascade which had raised its terrific roar for centuries. The cottage itself was built of old stones from the long dismantled Priory, scraps of tracery, molded window jambs, and arch labels, being mixed in with the rubble of the walls.

In this cottage he occupied a couple of rooms, Jopp, whom Henchard had employed, abused, cajoled, and dismissed by turns, being the householder. But even here her stepfather could not be seen.

"Not by his daughter?" pleaded Elizabeth.

"By nobody—at present: that's his order," she was informed.

Afterwards she was passing by the corn stores and hay barns which had been the headquarters of his business. She knew that he ruled there no longer; but it was with amazement that she regarded the familiar gateway. A smear of decisive lead-colored paint had been laid on to obliterate Henchard's name, though its letters dimly loomed through like ships in a fog. Over these, in fresh white, spread the name of Farfrae.

Abel Whittle was edging his skeleton in at the wicket, and she said, "Mr. Farfrae is master here?"

"Yaas, Miss Henchet," he said, "Mr. Farfrae have bought the concern and all of we work folk with it; and 'tis better for us than 'twas—though I shouldn't say that to you as a daughter-law. We work harder, but we bain't made afeard now. It was fear made my few poor hairs so thin! No busting out, no slamming of doors, no meddling with yer eternal soul and all that; and though 'tis a shilling a week less I'm the richer man; for what's all the world if yer mind is always in a larry, Miss Henchet?"

The intelligence was in a general sense true; and Henchard's stores, which had remained in a paralyzed condition during the settlement of his bankruptcy, were stirred into activity again when the new tenant had possession. Thenceforward the full sacks, looped with the shining chain, went scurrying up and down under the cathead,[1] hairy arms were thrust out from the different doorways, and the grain was hauled in; trusses of hay were tossed anew in and out of the barns, and the wimbles creaked; while the scales and steelyards began to be busy where guesswork had formerly been the rule.

. . . CHAPTER 32

Two bridges stood near the lower part of Casterbridge town. The first, of weather-stained brick, was immediately at the end of High Street, where a diverging branch from that thoroughfare ran around to the low-lying Durnover lanes; so that the precincts of the bridge formed the merging point of respectability and indigence. The second bridge, of stone, was further out on the highway—in fact, fairly in the meadows, though still within the town boundary.

These bridges had speaking countenances. Every projection in each was worn down to obtuseness, partly by weather, more by friction from generations of loungers, whose toes and heels had from year to year made restless movements against these parapets, as they had stood there meditating on the aspect of affairs. In the case of the more friable bricks and stones even the flat faces were worn into hollows by the same mixed mechanism. The masonry of the top was clamped with

1. *Cathead:* beam.

iron at each point; since it had been no uncommon thing for desperate men to wrench the coping off and throw it down the river, in reckless defiance of the magistrates.

For to this pair of bridges gravitated all the failures of the town; those who had failed in business, in love, in sobriety, in crime. Why the unhappy hereabout usually chose the bridges for their meditations in preference to a railing, a gate, or a stile, was not so clear.

There was a marked difference of quality between the personages who haunted the near bridge of brick and the personages who haunted the far one of stone. Those of lowest character preferred the former, adjoining the town; they did not mind the glare of the public eye. They had been of comparatively no account during their successes; and, though they might feel dispirited, they had no particular sense of shame in their ruin. Their hands were mostly kept in their pockets; they wore a leather strap round their hips or knees, and boots that required a great deal of lacing, but seemed never to get any. Instead of sighing at their adversities they spat, and instead of saying the iron had entered into their souls they said they were down on their luck. Jopp in his times of distress had often stood here; so had Mother Cuxsom, Christopher Coney, and poor Abel Whittle.

The *misérables* who would pause on the remoter bridge were of a politer stamp. They included bankrupts, hypochondriacs, persons who were what is called "out of situation" from fault or lucklessness, the inefficient of the professional class—shabby-genteel men, who did not know how to get rid of the weary time between dinner and dark. The eyes of this species were mostly directed over the parapet upon the running water below. A man seen there looking thus fixedly into the river was pretty sure to be one whom the world did not treat kindly for some reason or other. While one in straits on the townward bridge did not mind who saw him so, and kept his back to the parapet to survey the passers-by, one in straits on this never faced the road, never turned his head at coming footsteps, but, sensitive to his own condition, watched the current whenever a stranger approached, as if some strange fish interested him, though every finned thing had been poached out of the river years before.

There and thus they would muse; if their grief were the grief of oppression they would wish themselves kings; if their grief were poverty, wish themselves millionaires; if sin, they would wish they were saints or angels; if despised love, that they were some much-courted Adonis[1] of county fame. Some had been known to stand and think so long with this fixed gaze downward that eventually they had allowed their poor carcasses to follow that gaze; and they were discovered the next morning out of reach of their troubles, either here or in the deep pool called Blackwater, a little higher up the river.

To this bridge came Henchard, as other unfortunates had come before him, his way thither being by the riverside path on the chilly edge of the town. Here he was standing one windy afternoon when Durnover church clock struck five. While the gusts were bringing the notes to his ears across the damp intervening flat a man passed behind him and greeted Henchard by name. Henchard turned slightly and saw that the comer was Jopp, his old foreman, now employed elsewhere, to whom, though he hated him, he had gone for lodgings because Jopp was the one man in Casterbridge whose observation and opinion the fallen corn merchant despised to the point of indifference.

Henchard returned him a scarcely perceptible nod and Jopp stopped.

"He and she are gone into their new house today," said Jopp.

"Oh," said Henchard absently. "Which house is that?"

"Your old one."

---

1. *Adonis:* handsome youth.

"Gone into my house?" And starting up Henchard added, "*My* house of all others in the town!"

"Well, as somebody was sure to live there, and you couldn't, it can do 'ee no harm that he's the man."

It was quite true: he felt that it was doing him no harm. Farfrae, who had already taken the yards and stores, had acquired possession of the house for the obvious convenience of its contiguity. And yet this act of his taking up residence within those roomy chambers while he, their former tenant, lived in a cottage, galled Henchard indescribably.

Jopp continued: "And you heard of that fellow who bought all the best furniture at your sale? He was bidding for no other than Farfrae all the while! It has never been moved out of the house, as he'd already got the lease."

"My furniture too! Surely he'll buy my body and soul likewise!"

"There's no saying he won't, if you be willing to sell." And having planted these wounds in the heart of his once imperious master Jopp went on his way; while Henchard stared and stared into the racing river till the bridge seemed moving backward with him.

The low land grew blacker, and the sky a deeper gray. When the landscape looked like a picture blotted in with ink, another traveler approached the great stone bridge. He was driving a gig, his direction being also townwards. On the round of the middle of the arch the gig stopped. "Mr. Henchard?" came from it in the voice of Farfrae. Henchard turned his face.

Finding that he had guessed rightly Farfrae told the man who accompanied him to drive home; while he alighted and went up to his former friend.

"I have heard that you think of emigrating, Mr. Henchard," he said. "Is it true? I have a real reason for asking."

Henchard withheld his answer for several instants, and then said, "Yes; it is true. I am going where you were going to a few years ago, when I prevented you and got you to bide here. 'Tis turn and turn about, isn't it! Do ye mind how we stood like this in the Chalk Walk when I persuaded 'ee to stay? You then stood without a chattel to your name, and I was the master of the house in Corn Street. But now I stand without a stick or a rag, and the master of that house is you."

"Yes, yes; that's so! It's the way o' the warrld," said Farfrae.

"Ha, ha, true!" cried Henchard, throwing himself into a mood of jocularity. "Up and down! I'm used to it. What's the odds after all!"

"Now listen to me, if it's no taking up your time," said Farfrae, "just as I listened to you. Don't go. Stay at home."

"But I can do nothing else, man!" said Henchard scornfully. "The little money I have will just keep body and soul together for a few weeks, and no more. I have not felt inclined to go back to journey work yet; but I can't stay doing nothing, and my best chance is elsewhere."

"No; but what I propose is this—if ye will listen. Come and live in your old house. We can spare some rooms very well—I am sure my wife would not mind it at all—until there's an opening for ye."

Henchard started. Probably the picture drawn by the unsuspecting Donald of himself under the same roof with Lucetta was too striking to be received with equanimity. "No, no," he said gruffly; "we should quarrel."

"You should hae a part to yourself," said Farfrae; "and nobody to interfere wi' you. It will be a deal healthier than down there by the river where you live now."

Still Henchard refused. "You don't know what you ask," he said. "However, I can do no less than thank 'ee."

They walked into the town together side by side, as they had done when Henchard persuaded the young Scotchman to remain. "Will you come in and have some supper?" said Farfrae when they reached the middle of the town, where their paths diverged right and left.

"No, no."

"By-the-bye, I had nearly forgot. I bought a good deal of your furniture."

"So I have heard."

"Well, it was no that I wanted it so very much for myself; but I wish ye to pick out all that you care to have—such things as may be endeared to ye by associations, or particularly suited to your use. And take them to your own house—it will not be depriving me; we can do with less very well, and I will have plenty of opportunities of getting more."

"What—give it to me for nothing?" said Henchard. "But you paid the creditors for it!"

"Ah, yes; but maybe it's worth more to you than it is to me."

Henchard was a little moved. "I—sometimes think I've wronged 'ee!" he said, in tones which showed the disquietude that the night shades hid in his face. He shook Farfrae abruptly by the hand, and hastened away as if unwilling to betray himself further. Farfrae saw him turn through the thoroughfare into Bull Stake and vanish down towards the Priory Mill.

Meanwhile Elizabeth-Jane, in an upper room no larger than the Prophet's[2] chamber, and with the silk attire of her palmy days packed away in a box, was netting with great industry between the hours which she devoted to studying such books as she could get hold of.

Her lodgings being nearly opposite her stepfather's former residence, now Farfrae's, she could see Donald and Lucetta speeding in and out of their door with all the abounding enthusiasm of their situation. She avoided looking that way as much as possible, but it was hardly in human nature to keep the eyes averted when the door slammed.

While living on thus quietly she heard the news that Henchard had caught cold and was confined to his room—possibly

2. *Prophet:* Mohammed, founder of Islam.

a result of standing about the meads in damp weather. She went off to his house at once. This time she was determined not to be denied admittance, and made her way upstairs. He was sitting up in the bed with a greatcoat round him, and at first resented her intrusion. "Go away—go away," he said. "I don't like to see 'ee!'"

"But, Father——"

"I don't like to see 'ee," he repeated.

However, the ice was broken, and she remained. She made the room more comfortable, gave directions to the people below, and by the time she went away had reconciled her stepfather to her visiting him.

The effect, either of her ministrations or of her mere presence, was a rapid recovery. He soon was well enough to go out; and now things seemed to wear a new color in his eyes. He no longer thought of emigration, and thought more of Elizabeth. The having nothing to do made him more dreary than any other circumstance; and one day, with better views of Farfrae than he had held for some time, and a sense that honest work was not a thing to be ashamed of, he stoically went down to Farfrae's yard and asked to be taken on as a journeyman hay-trusser. He was engaged at once. This hiring of Henchard was done through a foreman, Farfrae feeling that it was undesirable to come personally in contact with the ex-corn factor more than was absolutely necessary. While anxious to help him he was well aware by this time of his uncertain temper, and thought reserved relations best. For the same reason his orders to Henchard to proceed to this and that country farm trussing in the usual way were always given through a third person.

For a time these arrangements worked well, it being the custom to truss in the respective stack yards, before bringing it away, the hay bought at the different farms about the neighborhood; so that Henchard was often absent at such places the whole week long. When this was all done, and Henchard had become in a measure broken in, he came to work daily on the home premises like the rest. And thus the once flourishing merchant and Mayor and what not stood as a day laborer in the barns and granaries he formerly had owned.

"I have worked as a journeyman before now, ha'n't I?" he would say in his defiant way; "and why shouldn't I do it again?" But he looked a far different journeyman from the one he had been in his earlier days. Then he had worn clean, suitable clothes, light and cheerful in hue; leggings yellow as marigolds, corduroys immaculate as new flax, and a neckerchief like a flower garden. Now he wore the remains of an old blue cloth suit of his gentlemanly times, a rusty silk hat, and a once black satin smock, soiled and shabby. Clad thus he went to and fro still comparatively an active man—for he was not much over forty—and saw with the other men in the yard Donald Farfrae going in and out the green door that led to the garden, and the big house, and Lucetta.

At the beginning of the winter it was rumored about Casterbridge that Mr. Farfrae, already in the Town Council, was to be proposed for Mayor in a year or two.

"Yes; she was wise, she was wise in her generation!" said Henchard to himself when he heard of this one day on his way to Farfrae's hay barn. He thought it over as he wimbled his bonds, and the piece of news acted as a reviviscent breath to that old view of his—of Donald Farfrae as his triumphant rival who rode roughshod over him.

"A fellow of his age going to be Mayor, indeed!" he murmured with a corner-drawn smile on his mouth. "But 'tis her money that floats en upward. Ha-ha—how cust it is! Here be I, his former master, working for him as man, and he the man standing as master, with my house and my furniture and my what-you-may-call wife all his own."

He repeated these things a hundred times a day. During the whole period of his acquaintance with Lucetta he had never wished to claim her as his own so desperately as he now regretted her loss. It was no mercenary hankering after her fortune that moved him; though that fortune had been the means of making her so much the more desired by giving her the air of independence and sauciness which attracts men of his composition. It had given her servants, house, and fine clothing—a setting that invested Lucetta with a startling novelty in the eyes of him who had known her in her narrow days.

He accordingly lapsed into moodiness, and at every allusion to the possibility of Farfrae's near election to the municipal chair his former hatred of the Scotchman returned. Concurrently with this he underwent a moral change. It resulted in his significantly saying every now and then, in tones of recklessness, "Only a fortnight more!"—"Only a dozen days!" and so forth, lessening his figures day by day.

"Why d'ye say only a dozen days?" asked Solomon Longways as he worked beside Henchard in the granary weighing oats.

"Because in twelve days I shall be released from my oath."

"What oath?"

"The oath to drink no spirituous liquid. In twelve days it will be twenty-one years since I swore it, and then I mean to enjoy myself, please God!"

Elizabeth-Jane sat at her window one Sunday, and while there she heard in the street below a conversation which introduced Henchard's name. She was wondering what was the matter, when a third person who was passing by asked the question in her mind.

"Michael Henchard have busted out drinking after taking nothing for twenty-one years!"

Elizabeth-Jane jumped up, put on her things, and went out.

. . . **CHAPTER 33**

AT THIS DATE there prevailed in Casterbridge a convivial custom—scarcely recognized as such, yet none the less established.

On the afternoon of every Sunday a large contingent of the Casterbridge journeymen—steady churchgoers and sedate characters—having attended service, filed from the church doors across the way to the Three Mariners Inn. The rear was usually brought up by the choir, with their bass-viols, fiddles, and flutes under their arms.

The great point, the point of honor, on these sacred occasions was for each man to strictly limit himself to half-a-pint of liquor. This scrupulosity was so well understood by the landlord that the whole company was served in cups of that measure. They were all exactly alike—straight-sided, with two leafless lime trees done in eel-brown on the sides—one toward the drinker's lips, the other confronting his comrade. To wonder how many of these cups the landlord possessed altogether was a favorite exercise of children in the marvelous. Forty at least might have been seen at these times in the large room, forming a ring round the margin of the great sixteen-legged oak table, like the monolithic circle at Stonehenge[1] in its pristine days. Outside and above the forty cups came a circle of forty smoke jets from forty clay pipes; outside the pipes the countenances of the forty churchgoers, supported at the back by a circle of forty chairs.

The conversation was not the conversation of weekdays, but a thing altogether finer in point and higher in tone. They invariably discussed the sermon, dissecting it, weighing it, as above or below the average—the general tendency being to regard it as a scientific feat or performance which had no relation to their own lives, except as between critics and the thing criticized. The bass-viol player and the clerk usually spoke with more authority than the rest on account of their official connection with the preacher.

Now the Three Mariners was the inn chosen by Henchard as the place for closing his long term of dramless years. He had so timed his entry as to be well established in the large

---

1. *Stonehenge:* prehistoric monument site.

room by the time the forty churchgoers entered to their customary cups. The flush upon his face proclaimed at once that the vow of twenty-one years had lapsed, and the era of recklessness begun anew. He was seated on a small table, drawn up to the side of the massive oak board reserved for the churchmen, a few of whom nodded to him as they took their places and said, "How be ye, Mr. Henchard? Quite a stranger here."

Henchard did not take the trouble to reply for a few moments, and his eyes rested on his stretched-out legs and boots. "Yes," he said at length; "that's true. I've been down in spirit for weeks; some of ye know the cause. I am better now; but not quite serene. I want you fellows of the choir to strike up a tune; and what with that and this brew of Stannidge's, I am in hopes of getting altogether out of my minor key."

"With all my heart," said the first fiddle. "We've let back our strings, that's true; but we can soon pull 'em up again. Sound A, neighbors, and give the man a stave."

"I don't care a curse what the words be," said Henchard. "Hymns, ballets, or rantipole rubbish; the Rogue's March or the cherubim's warble—'tis all the same to me if 'tis good harmony, and well put out."

"Well—heh, heh—it may be we can do that, and not a man among us that have sat in the gallery less than twenty year," said the leader of the band. "As 'tis Sunday, neighbors, suppose we raise the Fourth Psa'am, to Samuel Wakely's tune, as improved by me?"

"Hang Samuel Wakely's tune, as improved by thee!" said Henchard. "Chuck across one of your psalters—old Wiltshire is the only tune worth singing—the psalm tune that would make my blood ebb and flow like the sea when I was a steady chap. I'll find some words to fit 'en." He took one of the psalters and began turning over the leaves.

Chancing to look out of the window at that moment he saw a flock of people passing by, and perceived them to be the congregation of the upper church, now just dismissed, their sermon having been a longer one than that the lower parish was favored with. Among the rest of the leading inhabitants walked Mr. Councillor Farfrae with Lucetta upon his arm, the observed and imitated of all the smaller tradesmen's womankind. Henchard's mouth changed a little, and he continued to turn over the leaves.

"Now then," he said, "Psalm the Hundred-and-Ninth, to the tune of Wiltshire: verses ten to fifteen. I gi'e ye the words:

> His seed shall orphans be, his wife
>   A widow plunged in grief;
> His vagrant children beg their bread
>   Where none can give relief.
>
> His ill-got riches shall be made
>   To usurers a prey;
> The fruit of all his toil shall be
>   By strangers borne away.
>
> None shall be found that to his wants
>   Their mercy will extend,
> Or to his helpless orphan seed
>   The least assistance lend.
>
> A swift destruction soon shall seize
>   On his unhappy race;
> And the next age his hated name
>   Shall utterly deface.

"I know the Psa'am—I know the Psa'am!" said the leader hastily; "but I would as lief not sing it. 'Twasn't made for singing. We chose it once when the gypsy stole the pa'son's mare, thinking to please him, but pa'son were quite upset. Whatever Servant David[2] were thinking about when he made a Psalm that nobody can sing without disgracing himself, I can't fathom! Now then, the Fourth Psalm, to Samuel Wakely's tune, as improved by me."

"'Od seize your sauce—I tell ye to sing the Hundred-and-

2. *David:* Biblical King David, known as the "Psalmist."

Ninth to Wiltshire, and sing it you shall!" roared Henchard. "Not a single one of all the droning crew of ye goes out of this room till that Psalm is sung!" He slipped off the table, seized the poker, and going to the door placed his back against it. "Now then, go ahead, if you don't wish to have your cust pates broke!"

"Don't 'ee, don't 'ee take on so!—As 'tis the Sabbath day, and 'tis Servant David's words and not ours, perhaps we don't mind for once, hey?" said one of the terrified choir, looking round upon the rest. So the instruments were turned and the comminatory verses sung.

"Thank ye, thank ye," said Henchard in a softened voice, his eyes growing downcast, and his manner that of a man much moved by the strains. "Don't you blame David," he went on in low tones, shaking his head without raising his eyes. "He knew what he was about when he wrote that! . . . If I could afford it, be hanged if I wouldn't keep a church choir at my own expense to play and sing to me at these low, dark times of my life. But the bitter thing is, that when I was rich I didn't need what I could have, and now I be poor I can't have what I need!"

While they paused, Lucetta and Farfrae passed again, this time homeward, it being their custom to take, like others, a short walk out on the highway and back, between church and tea time. "There's the man we've been singing about," said Henchard.

The players and singers turned their heads and saw his meaning. "Heaven forbid!" said the bass player.

"'Tis the man," repeated Henchard doggedly.

"Then if I'd known," said the performer on the clarinet solemnly, "that 'twas meant for a living man, nothing should have drawn out of my windpipe the breath for that Psalm, so help me!"

"Nor from mine," said the first singer. "But, thought I, as it was made so long ago perhaps there isn't much in it, so I'll oblige a neighbor; for there's nothing to be said against the tune."

"Ah, my boys, you've sung it," said Henchard triumphantly. "As for him, it was partly by his songs that he got over me, and heaved me out. . . . I could double him up like that—and yet I don't." He laid the poker across his knee, bent it as if it were a twig, flung it down, and came away from the door.

It was at this time that Elizabeth-Jane, having heard where her stepfather was, entered the room with a pale and agonized countenance. The choir and the rest of the company moved off, in accordance with their half-pint regulation. Elizabeth-Jane went up to Henchard, and entreated him to accompany her home.

By this hour the volcanic fires of his nature had burned down, and having drunk no great quantity as yet he was inclined to acquiesce. She took his arm, and together they went on. Henchard walked blankly, like a blind man, repeating to himself the last words of the singers—

> "And the next age his hated name
> Shall utterly deface."

At length he said to her, "I am a man to my word. I have kept my oath for twenty-one years; and now I can drink with a good conscience. . . . If I don't do for him—well, I am a fearful practical joker when I choose! He has taken away everything from me, and by heavens, if I meet him I won't answer for my deeds!"

These half-uttered words alarmed Elizabeth—all the more by reason of the still determination of Henchard's mien.

"What will you do?" she asked cautiously, while trembling with disquietude, and guessing Henchard's allusion only too well.

Henchard did not answer, and they went on till they had reached his cottage. "May I come in?" she said.

"No, no; not today," said Henchard; and she went away; feeling that to caution Farfrae was almost her duty, as it was certainly her strong desire.

As on the Sunday, so on the weekdays, Farfrae and Lucetta might have been seen flitting about the town like two butterflies—or rather like a bee and a butterfly in league for life. She seemed to take no pleasure in going anywhere except in her husband's company; and hence when business would not permit him to waste an afternoon she remained indoors waiting for the time to pass till his return, her face being visible to Elizabeth-Jane from her window aloft. The latter, however, did not say to herself that Farfrae should be thankful for such devotion, but, full of her reading, she cited Rosalind's[3] exclamation: "Mistress, know yourself; down on your knees and thank Heaven fasting for a good man's love."

She kept her eye upon Henchard also. One day he answered her inquiry for his health by saying that he could not endure Abel Whittle's pitying eyes upon him while they worked together in the yard. "He is such a fool," said Henchard, "that he can never get out of his mind the time when I was master there."

"I'll come and wimble for you instead of him, if you will allow me," said she. Her motive on going to the yard was to get an opportunity of observing the general position of affairs on Farfrae's premises now that her stepfather was a workman there. Henchard's threats had alarmed her so much that she wished to see his behavior when the two were face to face.

For two or three days after her arrival Donald did not make any appearance. Then one afternoon the green door opened, and through came, first Farfrae, and at his heels, Lucetta. Donald brought his wife forward without hesitation, it being obvious that he had no suspicion whatever of any antecedents in common between her and the now journeyman hay-trusser.

Henchard did not turn his eyes toward either of the pair,

----

3. *Rosalind:* character in Shakespeare's *As You Like It.*

keeping them fixed on the bond he twisted, as if that alone absorbed him. A feeling of delicacy, which ever prompted Farfrae to avoid anything that might seem like triumphing over a fallen rival, led him to keep away from the hay barn where Henchard and his daughter were working, and to go on to the corn department. Meanwhile Lucetta, never having been informed that Henchard had entered her husband's service, rambled straight on to the barn, where she came suddenly upon Henchard, and gave vent to a little "Oh!" which the happy and busy Donald was too far off to hear. Henchard, with withering humility of demeanor, touched the brim of his hat to her as Whittle and the rest had done, to which she breathed a dead-alive "Good afternoon."

"I beg your pardon, ma'am?" said Henchard, as if he had not heard.

"I said good afternoon," she faltered.

"O yes, good afternoon, ma'am," he replied, touching his hat again. "I am glad to see you, ma'am." Lucetta looked embarrassed, and Henchard continued: "For we humble workmen here feel it a great honor that a lady should look in and take an interest in us."

She glanced at him entreatingly; the sarcasm was too bitter, too unendurable.

"Can you tell me the time, ma'am?" he asked.

"Yes," she said hastily; "half-past four."

"Thank 'ee. An hour and a half longer before we are released from work. Ah, ma'am, we of the lower classes know nothing of the gay leisure that such as you enjoy!"

As soon as she could do so Lucetta left him, nodded and smiled to Elizabeth-Jane, and joined her husband at the other end of the enclosure, where she could be seen leading him away by the outer gates, so as to avoid passing Henchard again. That she had been taken by surprise was obvious. The result of this casual rencounter was that the next morning a note was put into Henchard's hand by the postman.

"Will you," said Lucetta, with as much bitterness as she

could put into a small communication, "will you kindly undertake not to speak to me in the biting undertones you used today, if I walk through the yard at any time? I bear you no ill will, and I am only too glad that you should have employment of my dear husband; but in common fairness treat me as his wife, and do not try to make me wretched by covert sneers. I have committed no crime, and done you no injury."

"Poor fool!" said Henchard with fond savagery, holding out the note. "To know no better than commit herself in writing like this! Why, if I were to show that to her dear husband —pooh!" He threw the letter into the fire.

Lucetta took care not to come again among the hay and corn. She would rather have died than run the risk of encountering Henchard at such close quarters a second time. The gulf between them was growing wider every day. Farfrae was always considerate to his fallen acquaintance; but it was impossible that he should not, by degrees, cease to regard the ex-corn merchant as more than one of his other workmen. Henchard saw this, and concealed his feelings under a cover of stolidity, fortifying his heart by drinking more freely at the Three Mariners every evening.

Often did Elizabeth-Jane, in her endeavors to prevent his taking other liquor, carry tea to him in a little basket at five o'clock. Arriving one day on this errand she found her stepfather was measuring up clover seed in the corn stores on the top floor, and she ascended to him. Each floor had a door opening into the air under a cat head, from which a chain dangled for hoisting the sacks.

When Elizabeth's head rose through the trap she perceived that the upper door was open, and that her stepfather and Farfrae stood just within it in conversation, Farfrae being nearest the dizzy edge, and Henchard a little way behind. Not to interrupt them she remained on the steps without raising her head any higher. While waiting thus she saw—or fancied she saw, for she had a terror of feeling certain—her stepfather slowly raise his hand to a level behind Farfrae's shoulders, a curious expression taking possession of his face. The young man was quite unconscious of the action, which was so indirect that, if Farfrae had observed it, he might almost have regarded it as an idle outstretching of the arm. But it would have been possible, by a comparatively light touch, to push Farfrae off his balance, and send him head over heels into the air.

Elizabeth felt quite sick at heart on thinking of what this *might* have meant. As soon as they turned she mechanically took the tea to Henchard, left it, and went away. Reflecting, she endeavored to assure herself that the movement was an idle eccentricity, and no more. Yet, on the other hand, his subordinate position in an establishment where he once had been master might be acting on him like an irritant poison; and she finally resolved to caution Donald.

. . . **CHAPTER 34**

NEXT MORNING, accordingly, she rose at five o'clock and went into the street. It was not yet light: a dense fog prevailed, and the town was as silent as it was dark, except that from the rectangular avenues which framed in the borough there came a chorus of tiny rappings, caused by the fall of water drops condensed on the boughs; now it was wafted from the West Walk, now from the South Walk; and then from both quarters simultaneously. She moved on to the bottom of Corn Street, and, knowing his time well, waited only a few minutes before she heard the familiar bang of his door, and then his quick walk toward her. She met him at the point where the last tree of the engirding avenue flanked the last house in the street.

He could hardly discern her till, glancing inquiringly, he said, "What—Miss Henchard—and are ye up so airly?"

She asked him to pardon her for waylaying him at such an unseemly time. "But I am anxious to mention something," she said. "And I wished not to alarm Mrs. Farfrae by calling."

"Yes?" said he, with the cheeriness of a superior. "And what may it be? It's very kind of ye, I'm sure."

She now felt the difficulty of conveying to his mind the exact aspect of possibilities in her own. But she somehow began, and introduced Henchard's name. "I sometimes fear," she said with an effort, "that he may be betrayed into some attempt to—insult you, sir."

"But we are the best of friends."

"Or to play some practical joke upon you, sir. Remember that he has been hardly used."

"But we are quite friendly."

"Or to do something—that would injure you—hurt you—wound you." Every word cost her twice its length of pain. And she could see that Farfrae was still incredulous. Henchard, a poor man in his employ, was not to Farfrae's view the Henchard who had ruled him. Yet he was not only the same man, but that man with his sinister qualities, formerly latent, quickened into life by his buffetings.

Farfrae, happy, and thinking no evil, persisted in making light of her fears. Thus they parted, and she went homeward, journeymen now being in the street, wagoners going to the harness makers for articles left to be repaired, farm horses going to the shoeing smiths, and the sons of labor showing themselves generally on the move. Elizabeth entered her lodging unhappily, thinking she had done no good, and only made herself appear foolish by her weak note of warning.

But Donald Farfrae was one of those men upon whom an incident is never absolutely lost. He revised impressions from a subsequent point of view, and the impulsive judgment of the moment was not always his permanent one. The vision of Elizabeth's earnest face in the rimy dawn came back to him several times during the day. Knowing the solidity of her character he did not treat her hints altogether as idle sounds.

But he did not desist from a kindly scheme on Henchard's account that engaged him just then; and when he met Lawyer Joyce, the town clerk, later in the day, he spoke of it as if nothing had occurred to damp it.

"About that little seedsman's shop," he said; "the shop overlooking the churchyard, which is to let. It is not for myself I want it, but for our unlucky fellow-townsman Henchard. It would be a new beginning for him, if a small one; and I have told the Council that I would head a private subscription among them to set him up in it—that I would be fifty pounds, if they would make up the other fifty among them."

"Yes, yes; so I've heard; and there's nothing to say against it for that matter," the town clerk replied, in his plain, frank way. "But, Farfrae, others see what you don't. Henchard hates 'ee—ay, hates 'ee; and 'tis right that you should know it. To my knowledge he was at the Three Mariners last night, saying in public that about you which a man ought not to say about another."

"Is that so—ah, is that so?" said Farfrae, looking down. "Why should he do it?" added the young man bitterly; "what harm have I done him that he should try to wrong me?"

"God only knows," said Joyce, lifting his eyebrows. "It shows much long-suffering in you to put up with him, and keep him in your employ."

"But I cannet discharge a man who was once a good friend to me? How can I forget that when I came here 'twas he enabled me to make a footing for mysel'? No, no. As long as I've a day's wark to offer he shall do it if he chooses. 'Tis not I who will deny him such a little as that. But I'll drop the idea of establishing him in a shop till I can think more about it."

It grieved Farfrae much to give up this scheme. But a damp having been thrown over it by these and other voices in the air, he went down and countermanded his orders. The then occupier of the shop was in it when Farfrae spoke to him, and feeling it necessary to give some explanation of his withdrawal from the negotiation Donald mentioned Henchard's name, and stated that the intentions of the Council had been changed.

The occupier was much disappointed, and straightway informed Henchard, as soon as he saw him, that a scheme of the Council for setting him up in a shop had been knocked on the head by Farfrae. And thus out of error enmity grew.

When Farfrae got indoors that evening the tea kettle was singing on the high hob of the semi-egg-shaped grate. Lucetta, light as a sylph, ran forward and seized his hands, whereupon Farfrae duly kissed her.

"Oh!" she cried playfully, turning to the window. "See—the blinds are not drawn down, and the people can look in—what a scandal!"

When the candles were lighted, the curtains drawn, and the twain sat at tea, she noticed that he looked serious. Without directly inquiring why she let her eyes linger solicitously on his face.

"Who has called?" he absently asked. "Any folk for me?"

"No," said Lucetta. "What's the matter, Donald?"

"Well—nothing worth talking of," he responded sadly.

"Then, never mind it. You will get through it. Scotchmen are always lucky."

"No—not always!" he said, shaking his head gloomily as he contemplated a crumb on the table. "I know many who have not been so! There was Sandy Macfarlane, who started to America to try his fortune, and he was drowned; and Archibald Leith, he was murdered! And poor Willie Dunbleeze and Maitland Macfreeze—they fell into bad courses, and went the way of all such!"

"Why—you old goosey—I was only speaking in a general sense; of course! You are always so literal. Now when we have finished tea, sing me that funny song about high-heeled shoon and siller tags, and the one-and-forty wooers."

"No, no. I couldna sing tonight! It's Henchard—he hates

me; so that I may not be his friend if I would. I would understand why there should be a wee bit envy; but I cannet see a reason for the whole intensity of what he feels. Now, can you, Lucetta? It is more like old-fashioned rivalry in love than just a bit of rivalry in trade."

Lucetta had grown somewhat wan. "No," she replied.

"I give him employment—I cannet refuse it. But neither can I blind myself to the fact that with a man of passions such as his, there is no safeguard for conduct!"

"What have you heard—O Donald, dearest?" said Lucetta in alarm. The words on her lips were "anything about me?"—but she did not utter them. She could not, however, suppress her agitation, and her eyes filled with tears.

"No, no—it is not so serious as ye fancy," declared Farfrae soothingly; though he did not know its seriousness so well as she.

"I wish you would do what we have talked of," mournfully remarked Lucetta. "Give up business, and go away from here. We have plenty of money, and why should we stay?"

Farfrae seemed seriously disposed to discuss this move, and they talked thereon till a visitor was announced. Their neighbor Alderman Vatt came in.

"You've heard, I suppose, of poor Doctor Chalkfield's death? Yes—died this afternoon at five," said Mr. Vatt. Chalkfield was the Councilman who had succeeded to the Mayoralty in the preceding November.

Farfrae was sorry at the intelligence, and Mr. Vatt continued: "Well, we know he's been going some days, and as his family is well provided for we must take it all as it is. Now I have called to ask 'ee this—quite privately. If I should nominate 'ee to succeed him, and there should be no particular opposition, will 'ee accept the chair?"

"But there are folk whose turn is before mine; and I'm over young, and may be thought pushing!" said Farfrae after a pause.

"Not at all. I don't speak for myself only, several have named it. You won't refuse?"

"We thought of going away," interposed Lucetta, looking at Farfrae anxiously.

"It was only a fancy," Farfrae murmured. "I wouldna refuse if it is the wish of a respectable majority in the Council."

"Very well, then, look upon yourself as elected. We have had older men long enough."

When he was gone Farfrae said musingly, "See now how it's ourselves that are ruled by the Powers above us! We plan this, but we do that. If they want to make me Mayor I will stay, and Henchard must rave as he will."

From this evening onward Lucetta was very uneasy. If she had not been imprudence incarnate she would not have acted as she did when she met Henchard by accident a day or two later. It was in the bustle of the market, when no one could readily notice their discourse.

"Michael," said she, "I must again ask you what I asked you months ago—to return me any letters or papers of mine that you may have—unless you have destroyed them? You must see how desirable it is that the time at Jersey should be blotted out, for the good of all parties."

"Why, bless the woman!—I packed up every scrap of your handwriting to give you in the coach—but you never appeared."

She explained how the death of her aunt had prevented her taking the journey on that day. "And what became of the parcel then?" she asked.

He could not say—he would consider. When she was gone he recollected that he had left a heap of useless papers in his former dining-room safe—built up in the wall of his old house —now occupied by Farfrae. The letters might have been amongst them.

A grotesque grin shaped itself on Henchard's face. Had that safe been opened?

On the very evening which followed this there was a great ringing of bells in Casterbridge, and the combined brass, wood, catgut, and leather bands played round the town with more prodigality of percussion notes than ever. Farfrae was Mayor—the two-hundredth odd of a series forming an elective dynasty dating back to the days of Charles I.—and the fair Lucetta was the courted of the town. . . . But, ah! that worm i' the bud—Henchard; what he could tell!

He, in the meantime, festering with indignation at some erroneous intelligence of Farfrae's opposition to the scheme for installing him in the little seed shop, was greeted with the news of the municipal election (which, by reason of Farfrae's comparative youth and his Scottish nativity—a thing unprecedented in the case—had an interest far beyond the ordinary). The bell-ringing and the band-playing, loud as Tamerlane's[1] trumpet, goaded the downfallen Henchard indescribably: the ousting now seemed to him to be complete.

The next morning he went to the corn yard as usual, and about eleven o'clock Donald entered through the green door, with no trace of the worshipful about him. The yet more emphatic change of places between him and Henchard which this election had established renewed a slight embarrassment in the manner of the modest younger man; but Henchard showed the front of one who had overlooked all this; and Farfrae met his amenities halfway at once.

"I was going to ask you," said Henchard, "about a packet that I may possibly have left in my old safe in the dining-room." He added particulars.

"If so, it is there now," said Farfrae. "I have never opened the safe at all as yet; for I keep ma papers at the bank, to sleep easy o' nights."

"It was not of much consequence—to me," said Henchard. "But I'll call for it this evening, if you don't mind?"

---

1. *Tamerlane:* Mongol conqueror (1336-1405).

It was quite late when he fulfilled his promise. He had primed himself with grog, as he did very frequently now, and a curl of sardonic humor hung on his lip as he approached the house, as though he were contemplating some terrible form of amusement. Whatever it was, the incident of his entry did not diminish its force, this being his first to the house since he had lived there as owner. The ring of the bell spoke to him like the voice of a familiar drudge who had been bribed to forsake him; the movements of the doors were revivals of dead days.

Farfrae invited him into the dining room, where he at once unlocked the iron safe built into the wall, *his*, Henchard's safe, made by an ingenious locksmith under his direction. Farfrae drew thence the parcel, and other papers, with apologies for not having returned them.

"Never mind," said Henchard drily. "The fact is they are letters mostly. . . . Yes," he went on, sitting down and unfolding Lucetta's passionate bundle, "here they be. That ever I should see 'em again! I hope Mrs. Farfrae is well after her exertions of yesterday?"

"She has felt a bit weary; and has gone to bed airly on that account."

Henchard returned to the letters, sorting them over with interest, Farfrae being seated at the other end of the dining table. "You don't forget, of course," he resumed, "that curious chapter in the history of my past which I told you of, and that you gave me some assistance in? These letters are, in fact, related to that unhappy business. Though, thank God, it is all over now."

"What became of the poor woman?" asked Farfrae.

"Luckily she married, and married well," said Henchard. "So that these reproaches she poured out on me do not now cause me any twinges, as they might otherwise have done. . . . Just listen to what an angry woman will say!"

Farfrae, willing to humor Henchard, though quite uninterested, and bursting with yawns, gave well-mannered attention.

" 'For me,' " Henchard read, " 'there is practically no future. A creature too unconventionally devoted to you—who feels it impossible that she can be wife of any other man; and who is yet no more to you than the first woman you meet in the street—such am I. I quite acquit you of any intention to wrong me, yet you are the door through which wrong has come to me. That in the event of your present wife's death you will place me in her position is a consolation so far as it goes—but how far does it go? Thus I sit here, forsaken by my few acqaintance, and forsaken by you!' "

"That's how she went on to me," said Henchard, "acres of words like that, when what had happened was what I could not cure."

"Yes," said Farfrae absently, "it is the way wi' women." But the fact was that he knew very little of the sex; yet detecting a sort of resemblance in style between the effusions of the woman he worshiped and those of the supposed stranger, he concluded that Aphrodite[2] ever spoke thus, whosesoever the personality she assumed.

Henchard unfolded another letter, and read it through likewise, stopping at the subscription as before. "Her name I don't give," he said blandly. "As I didn't marry her, and another man did, I can scarcely do that in fairness to her."

"Tr-rue, tr-rue," said Farfrae. "But why didn't you marry her when your wife Susan died?" Farfrae asked this and the other questions in the comfortably indifferent tone of one whom the matter very remotely concerned.

"Ah—well you may ask that!" said Henchard, the new-moon-shaped grin adumbrating itself again upon his mouth. "In spite of all her protestations, when I came forward to do so, as in generosity bound, she was not the woman for me."

2. *Aphrodite:* goddess of love.

"She had already married another—maybe?"

Henchard seemed to think it would be sailing too near the wind to descend further into particulars, and he answered "Yes."

"The young lady must have had a heart that bore transplanting very readily!"

"She had, she had," said Henchard emphatically.

He opened a third and fourth letter, and read. This time he approached the conclusion as if the signature were indeed coming with the rest. But again he stopped short. The truth was that, as may be divined, he had quite intended to effect a grand catastrophe at the end of this drama by reading out the name; he had come to the house with no other thought. But sitting here in cold blood he could not do it. Such a wrecking of hearts appalled even him. His quality was such that he could have annihilated them both in the heat of action; but to accomplish the deed by oral poison was beyond the nerve of his enmity.

. . . **CHAPTER 35**

As DONALD stated, Lucetta had retired early to her room because of fatigue. She had, however, not gone to rest, but sat in the bedside chair reading and thinking over the events of the day. At the ringing of the doorbell by Henchard she wondered who it should be that would call at that comparatively late hour. The dining room was almost under her bedroom; she could hear that somebody was admitted there, and presently the indistinct murmur of a person reading became audible.

The usual time for Donald's arrival upstairs came and passed, yet still the reading and conversation went on. This was very singular. She could think of nothing but that some extraordinary crime had been committed, and that the visitor, whoever he might be, was reading an account of it from a special edition of the *Casterbridge Chronicle*. At last she left the room, and descended the stairs. The dining-room door was ajar, and in the silence of the resting household the voice and the words were recognizable before she reached the lower flight. She stood transfixed. Her own words greeted her in Henchard's voice like spirits from the grave.

Lucetta leaned upon the banister with her cheek against the smooth handrail, as if she would make a friend of it in her misery. Rigid in this position, more and more words fell successively upon her ear. But what amazed her most was the tone of her husband. He spoke merely in the accents of a man who made a present of his time.

"One word," he was saying, as the crackling of paper denoted that Henchard was unfolding yet another sheet. "Is it quite fair to this young woman's memory to read at such length to a stranger what was intended for your eye alone?"

"Well, yes," said Henchard. "By not giving her name I make it an example of all womankind, and not a scandal to one."

"If I were you I would destroy them," said Farfrae, giving more thought to the letters than he had hitherto done. "As another man's wife it would injure the woman if it were known."

"No, I shall not destroy them," murmured Henchard, putting the letters away. Then he rose, and Lucetta heard no more.

She went back to her bedroom in a semi-paralyzed state. For very fear she could not undress, but sat on the edge of the bed, waiting. Would Henchard let out the secret in his parting words? Her suspense was terrible. Had she confessed all to Donald in their early acquaintance he might possibly have got over it, and married her just the same—unlikely as it had once seemed; but for her or any one else to tell him now would be fatal.

The door slammed; she could hear her husband bolting it.

After looking round in his customary way he came leisurely up the stairs. The spark in her eyes well nigh went out when he appeared round the bedroom door. Her gaze hung doubtful for a moment, then to her joyous amazement she saw that he looked at her with the rallying smile of one who had just been relieved of a scene that was irksome. She could hold out no longer, and sobbed hysterically.

When he had restored her Farfrae naturally enough spoke of Henchard. "Of all men he was the least desirable as a visitor," he said; "but it is my belief that he's just a bit crazed. He has been reading to me a long lot of letters relating to his past life; and I could do no less than indulge him by listening."

This was sufficient. Henchard, then, had not told. Henchard's last words to Farfrae, in short, as he stood on the doorstep, had been these: "Well—I'm much obliged to 'ee for listening. I may tell more about her some day."

Finding this, she was much perplexed as to Henchard's motives in opening the matter at all; for in such cases we attribute to an enemy a power of consistent action which we never find in ourselves or in our friends; and forget that abortive efforts from want of heart are as possible to revenge as to generosity.

Next morning Lucetta remained in bed, meditating how to parry this incipient attack. The bold stroke of telling Donald the truth, dimly conceived, was yet too bold; for she dreaded lest in doing so he, like the rest of the world, should believe that the episode was rather her fault than her misfortune. She decide to employ persuasion—not with Donald, but with the enemy himself. It seemed the only practicable weapon left her as a woman. Having laid her plan she rose, and wrote to him who kept her on these tenterhooks:—

"I overheard your interview with my husband last night, and saw the drift of your revenge. The very thought of it crushes me! Have pity on a distressed woman! If you could see me you would relent. You do not know how anxiety has told upon me lately. I will be at the Ring at the time you leave work—just before the sun goes down. Please come that way. I cannot rest till I have seen you face to face, and heard from your mouth that you will carry this horseplay no further."

To herself she said, on closing up this appeal: "If ever tears and pleadings have served the weak to fight the strong, let them do so now!"

With this view she made a toilette which differed from all she had ever attempted before. To heighten her natural attractions had hitherto been the unvarying endeavor of her adult life, and one in which she was no novice. But now she neglected this, and even proceeded to impair the natural presentation. Beyond a natural reason for her slightly drawn look, she had not slept all the previous night, and this had produced upon her pretty though slightly worn features the aspect of a countenance aging prematurely from extreme sorrow. She selected—as much from want of spirit as design—her poorest, plainest, and longest discarded attire.

To avoid the contingency of being recognized she veiled herself, and slipped out of the house quickly. The sun was resting on the hill like a drop of blood on an eyelid by the time she had got up the road opposite the amphitheater, which she speedily entered. The interior was shadowy, and emphatic of the absence of every living thing.

She was not disappointed in the fearful hope with which she awaited him. Henchard came over the top, descended, and Lucetta waited breathlessly. But having reached the arena she saw a change in his bearing: he stood still at a little distance from her; she could not think why.

Nor could anyone else have known. The truth was that in appointing this spot, and this hour, for the rendezvous, Lucetta had unwittingly backed up her entreaty by the strongest argument she could have used outside words, with this man of moods, glooms, and superstitions. Her figure in the midst of the huge enclosure, the unusual plainness of her dress, her attitude of hope and appeal, so strongly revived in his soul the memory of another ill-used woman who had stood there and thus in bygone days, and had now passed away into her rest, that he was unmanned, and his heart smote him for having attempting reprisals on one of a sex so weak. When he approached her, and before she had spoken a word, her point was half gained.

His manner as he had come down had been one of cynical carelessness; but he now put away his grim half-smile, and said in a kindly subdued tone, "Good night t'ye. Of course I'm glad to come if you want me."

"O, thank you," she said apprehensively.

"I am sorry to see 'ee looking so ill," he stammered with unconcealed compunction.

She shook her head. "How can you be sorry," she asked, "when you deliberately cause it?"

"What!" said Henchard uneasily. "Is it anything I have done that has pulled you down like that?"

"It is all your doing," said she. "I have no other grief. My happiness would be secure enough but for your threats. O Michael! Don't wreck me like this! You might think that you have done enough! When I came here I was a young woman; now I am rapidly becoming an old one. Neither my husband nor any other man will regard me with interest long."

Henchard was disarmed. His old feeling of supercilious pity for womankind in general was intensified by this suppliant appearing here as the double of the first. Moreover, that thoughtless want of foresight which had led to all her trouble remained with poor Lucetta still; she had come to meet him here in this compromising way without perceiving the risk. Such a woman was very small deer to hunt; he felt ashamed, lost all zest and desire to humiliate Lucetta there and then, and no longer envied Farfrae his bargain. He had married money, but nothing more. Henchard was anxious to wash his hands of the game.

"Well, what do you want me to do?" he said gently. I am

sure I shall be very willing. My reading of those letters was only a sort of practical joke, and I revealed nothing."

"To give me back the letters and any papers you may have that breathe of matrimony or worse."

"So be it. Every scrap shall be yours. . . . But, between you and me, Lucetta, he is sure to find out something of the matter, sooner or later."

"Ah!" she said with eager tremulousness; "but not till I have proved myself a faithful and deserving wife to him, and then he may forgive me everything!"

Henchard silently looked at her: he almost envied Farfrae such love as that, even now. "H'm—I hope so," he said. "But you shall have the letters without fail. And your secret shall be kept. I swear it."

"How good you are!—how shall I get them?"

He reflected, and said he would send them the next morning. "Now don't doubt me," he added. "I can keep my word."

. . . CHAPTER 36

RETURNING from her appointment Lucetta saw a man waiting by the lamp nearest to her own door. When she stopped to go in he came and spoke to her. It was Jopp.

He begged her pardon for addressing her. But he had heard that Mr. Farfrae had been applied to by a neighboring corn merchant to recommend a working partner; if so, he wished to offer himself. He could give good security, and had stated as much to Mr. Farfrae in a letter; but he would feel much obliged if Lucetta would say a word in his favor to her husband.

"It is a thing I know nothing about," said Lucetta coldly.

"But you can testify to my trustworthiness better than anybody, ma'am," said Jopp. "I was in Jersey several years, and knew you there by sight."

"Indeed," she replied. "But I knew nothing of you."

"I think, ma'am, that a word or two from you would secure for me what I covet very much," he persisted.

She steadily refused to have anything to do with the affair, and cutting him short, because of her anxiety to get indoors before her husband should miss her, left him on the pavement.

He watched her till she had vanished, and then went home. When he got there he sat down in the fireless chimney corner looking at the iron dogs, and the wood laid across them for heating the morning kettle. A movement upstairs disturbed him, and Henchard came down from his bedroom, where he seemed to have been rummaging boxes.

"I wish," said Henchard, "you would do me a service, Jopp, now—tonight, I mean, if you can. Leave this at Mrs. Farfrae's for her. I should take it myself, of course, but I don't wish to be seen there."

He handed a package in brown paper, sealed. Henchard had been as good as his word. Immediately on coming indoors he had searched over his few belongings; and every scrap of Lucetta's writing that he possessed was here. Jopp indifferently expressed his willingness.

"Well, how have ye got on today?" his lodger asked. "Any prospect of an opening?"

"I am afraid not," said Jopp, who had not told the other of his application to Farfrae.

"There never will be in Casterbridge," declared Henchard decisively. "You must roam further afield." He said good night to Jopp, and returned to his own part of the house.

Jopp sat on till his eyes were attracted by the shadow of the candle-snuff on the wall, and looking at the original he found that it had formed itself into a head like a red-hot cauliflower. Henchard's packet next met his gaze. He knew there had been something of the nature of wooing between Henchard and the now Mrs. Farfrae; and his vague ideas on the subject narrowed themselves down to these: Henchard had a parcel belonging to Mrs. Farfrae, and he had reasons for not returning that parcel to her in person. What could be inside it? So he went on and on till, animated by resentment at Lucetta's haughtiness, as he thought it, and curiosity to learn if there were any weak sides to this transaction with Henchard, he examined the package. The pen and all its relations being awkward tools in Henchard's hands he had affixed the seals without an impression, it never occurring to him that the efficacy of such a fastening depended on this. Jopp was far less of a tyro; he lifted one of the seals with his penknife, peeped in at the end thus opened, saw that the bundle consisted of letters; and, having satisfied himself thus far, sealed up the end again by simply softening the wax with the candle, and went off with the parcel as requested.

His path was by the river side at the foot of the town. Coming into the light at the bridge which stood at the end of High Street he beheld lounging thereon Mother Cuxsom and Nance Mockridge.

"We be just going down Mixen Lane way, to look into Peter's Finger afore creeping to bed," said Mrs. Cuxsom. "There's a fiddle and tambourine going on there. Lord, what's all the world—do ye come along too, Jopp—'twon't hinder ye five minutes."

Jopp had mostly kept himself out of this company, but present circumstances made him somewhat more reckless than usual, and without many words he decided to go to his destination that way.

Though the upper part of Durnover was mainly composed of a curious congeries of barns and farmsteads, there was a less picturesque side to the parish. This was Mixen Lane, now in great part pulled down.

Mixen Lane was the Adullam[1] of all the surrounding villages. It was the hiding place of those who were in distress, and in debt, and trouble of every kind. Farm laborers and other

1. *Adullam:* a biblical cave which was the hiding place of people in distress.

peasants, who combined a little poaching with their farming, and a little brawling and bibbing with their poaching, found themselves sooner or later in Mixen Lane. Rural mechanics too idle to mechanize, rural servants too rebellious to serve, drifted or were forced into Mixen Lane.

The lane and its surrounding thicket of thatched cottages stretched out like a spit into the moist and misty lowland. Much that was sad, much that was low, some things that were baneful, could be seen in Mixen Lane. Vice ran freely in and out certain of the doors of the neighborhood; recklessness dwelt under the roof with the crooked chimney; shame in some bow windows; theft (in times of privation) in the thatched and mud-walled houses by the sallows. Even slaughter had not been altogether unknown here. In a block of cottages up an alley there might have been erected an altar to disease in years gone by. Such was Mixen Lane in the times when Henchard and Farfrae were mayors.

Yet this mildewed leaf in the sturdy and flourishing Casterbridge plant lay close to the open country; not a hundred yards from a row of noble elms, and commanding a view across the moor of airy uplands and cornfields, and mansions of the great. A brook divided the moor from the tenements, and to outward view there was no way across it—no way to the houses but round about by the road. But under every householder's stairs there was kept a mysterious plank nine inches wide; which plank was a secret bridge.

If you, as one of those refugee householders, came in from business after dark—and this was the business time here—you stealthily crossed the moor, approached the border of the aforesaid brook, and whistled opposite the house to which you belonged. A shape thereupon made its appearance on the other side bearing the bridge on end against the sky; it was lowered; you crossed, and a hand helped you to land yourself, together with the pheasants and hares gathered from neighboring manors. You sold them slyly the next morning, and the

day after you stood before the magistrates with the eyes of all
your sympathizing neighbors concentrated on your back. You
disappeared for a time; then you were again found quietly
living in Mixen Lane.

Walking along the lane at dusk the stranger was struck by
two or three peculiar features therein. One was an intermittent rumbling from the back premises of the inn half way up;
this meant a skittle alley. Another was the extensive pre-
valence of whistling in the various domiciles—a piped note of
some kind coming from nearly every open door. Another
was the frequency of white aprons over dingy gowns among
the women around the doorways. A white apron is a suspicious vesture in situations where spotlessness is difficult; moreover, the industry and cleanliness which the white apron expressed were belied by the postures and gaits of the women
who wore it—their knuckles being mostly on their hips (an
attitude which lent them the aspect of two-handled mugs),
and their shoulders against doorposts; while there was a curious alacrity in the turn of each honest woman's head upon her
neck and in the twirl of her honest eyes, at any noise resembling a masculine footfall along the lane.

Yet amid so much that was bad needy respectability also
found a home. Under some of the roofs abode pure and virtuous souls whose presence there was due to the iron hand of
necessity, and to that alone. Families from decayed villages—
families of that once bulky, but now nearly extinct, section of
village society called "liviers," or lifeholders—copyholders and
others, whose roof trees had fallen for some reason or other,
compelling them to quit the rural spot that had been their
home for generations—came here, unless they chose to lie
under a hedge by the wayside.

The inn called Peter's Finger was the church of Mixen Lane.
It was centrally situate, as such places should be, and bore
about the same social relation to the Three Mariners as the
latter bore to the King's Arms. At first sight the inn was so

respectable as to be puzzling. The front door was kept shut, and the step was so clean that evidently but few persons entered over its sanded surface. But at the corner of the public house was an alley, a mere slit, dividing it from the next building. Halfway up the alley was a narrow door, shiny and paintless from the rub of infinite hands and shoulders. This was the actual entrance to the inn.

A pedestrian would be seen abstractedly passing along Mixen Lane; and then, in a moment, he would vanish, causing the gazer to blink like Ashton at the disappearance of Ravenswood. That abstracted pedestrian had edged into the slit by the adroit fillip of his person sideways; from the slit he edged into the tavern by a similar exercise of skill.

The company at the Three Mariners were persons of quality in comparison with the company which gathered here; though it must be admitted that the lowest fringe of the Mariners' party touched the crest of Peter's at points. Waifs and strays of all sorts loitered about here. The landlady was a virtuous woman who years ago had been unjustly sent to jail as an accessory to something or other after the fact. She underwent her twelvemonth, and had worn a martyr's countenance ever since, except at times of meeting the constable who apprehended her, when she winked her eye.

To this house Jopp and his acquaintances had arrived. The settles on which they sat down were thin and tall, their tops being guyed by pieces of twine to hooks in the ceiling; for when the guests grew boisterous the settles would rock and overturn without some such security. The thunder of bowls echoed from the backyard; swingels hung behind the blower of the chimney; and ex-poachers and ex-gamekeepers, whom squires had persecuted without cause, sat elbowing each other —men who in past times had met in fights under the moon, till lapse of sentences on the one part, and loss of favor and expulsion from service on the other, brought them here together to a common level, where they sat calmly discussing old times.

"Dos't mind how you could jerk a trout ashore with a bramble, and not ruffle the stream, Charl?" a deposed keeper was saying. " 'Twas at that I caught 'ee once, if you can mind?"

"That can I. But the worst larry for me was that pheasant business at Yalbury Wood. Your wife swore false that time, Joe—O, by Gad, she did—there's no denying it."

"How was that?" asked Jopp.

"Why—Joe closed wi' me, and we rolled down together, close to his garden hedge. Hearing the noise, out ran his wife with the oven pyle, and it being dark under the trees she couldn't see which was uppermost. 'Where beest thee, Joe, under or top?' she screeched. 'O—under, by Gad!' says he. She then began to rap down upon my skull, back, and ribs with the pyle till we'd roll over again. 'Where beest now, dear Joe, under or top?' she'd scream again. By George, 'twas through her I was took! And then when we got up in hall she swore that the cock pheasant was one of her rearing, when 'twas not your bird at all, Joe; 'twas Squire Brown's bird— that's whose 'twas—one that we'd picked off as we passed his wood, an hour afore. It did hurt my feelings to be so wronged! . . . . Ah well—'tis over now."

"I might have had 'ee days afore that," said the keeper. "I was within a few yards of 'ee dozens of times, with a sight more of birds than that poor one."

"Yes—'tis not our greatest doings that the world gets wind of," said the furmity woman, who, lately settled in this pur- lieu, sat among the rest. Having traveled a great deal in her time she spoke with cosmopolitan largeness of idea. It was she who presently asked Jopp what was the parcel he kept so snugly under his arm.

"Ah, therein lies a grand secret," said Jopp. "It is the passion of love. To think that a woman should love one man so well, and hate another so unmercifully."

"Who's the object of your meditation, sir?"

"One that stands high in this town. I'd like to shame her! Upon my life, 'twould be as good as a play to read her love letters, the proud piece of silk and waxwork! For 'tis her love letters that I've got here."

"Love letters? Then let's hear 'em, good soul," said Mother Cuxsom. "Lord, do ye mind, Richard, what fools we used to be when we were younger? Getting a schoolboy to write ours for us; and giving him a penny, do ye mind, not to tell other folks what he'd put inside, do ye mind?"

By this time Jopp had pushed his finger under the seals, and unfastened the letters, tumbling them over and picking up one here and there at random, which he read aloud. These passages soon began to uncover the secret which Lucetta had so earnestly hoped to keep buried, though the epistles, being allusive only, did not make it altogether plain.

"Mrs. Farfrae wrote that!" said Nance Mockridge. "'Tis a humbling thing for us, as respectable women, that one of the same sex could do it. And now she's vowed herself to another man!"

"So much the better for her," said the aged furmity woman. "Ah, I saved her from a real bad marriage, and she's never been the one to thank me."

"I say, what a good foundation for a skimmity ride," said Nance.

"True," said Mrs. Cuxsom, reflecting. "'Tis as good a ground for a skimmity ride as ever I knowed; and it ought not to be wasted. The last one seen in Casterbridge must have been ten years ago, if a day."

At this moment there was a shrill whistle, and the landlady said to the man who had been called Charl, "'Tis Jim coming in. Would ye go and let down the bridge for me?"

Without replying Charl and his comrade Joe rose, and receiving a lantern from her went out at the back door and down the garden path, which ended abruptly at the edge of the stream already mentioned. Beyond the stream was the open moor, from which a clammy breeze smote upon their faces as they advanced. Taking up the board that had lain in readiness one of them lowered it across the water, and the instant its further end touched the ground footsteps entered upon it, and there appeared from the shade a stalwart man with straps round his knees, a double-barreled gun under his arm and some birds slung up behind him. They asked him if he had had much luck.

"Not much," he said indifferently. "All safe inside?"

Receiving a reply in the affirmative he went on inwards, the others withdrawing the bridge and beginning to retreat in his rear. Before, however, they had entered the house a cry of "Ahoy" from the moor led them to pause.

The cry was repeated. They pushed the lantern into an outhouse, and went back to the brink of the stream.

"Ahoy—is this the way to Casterbridge?" said someone from the other side.

"Not in particular," said Charl. "There's a river afore 'ee."

"I don't care—here's for through it!" said the man in the moor. "I've had traveling enough for today."

"Stop a minute, then," said Charl, finding that the man was no enemy. "Joe, bring the plank and lantern; here's somebody that's lost his way. You should have kept along the turnpike road, friend, and not have strook across here."

"I should—as I see now. But I saw a light here, and says I to myself, that's an outlying house, depend on't."

The plank was now lowered; and the stranger's form shaped itself from the darkness. He was a middle-aged man, with hair and whiskers prematurely gray, and a broad and genial face. He had crossed on the plank without hesitation, and seemed to see nothing odd in the transit. He thanked them, and walked between them up the garden. "What place is this?" he asked, when they reached the door.

"A public house."

"Ah. Perhaps it will suit me to put up at. Now then, come

in and wet your whistle at my expense for the lift over you have given me."

They followed him into the inn, where the increased light exhibited him as one who would stand higher in an estimate by the eye than in one by the ear. He was dressed with a certain clumsy richness—his coat being furred, and his head covered by a cap of sealskin, which, though the nights were chilly, must have been warm for the daytime, spring being somewhat advanced. In his hand he carried a small mahogany case, strapped, and clamped with brass.

Apparently surprised at the kind of company which confronted him through the kitchen door, he at once abandoned his idea of putting up at the house; but taking the situation lightly, he called for glasses of the best, paid for them as he stood in the passage, and turned to proceed on his way by the front door. This was barred, and while the landlady was unfastening it the conversation about the skimmington was continued in the sitting room, and reached his ears.

"What do they mean by a 'skimmity-ride?' " he asked.

"O, sir!" said the landlady, swinging her long earrings with deprecating modesty; " 'tis a' old foolish thing they do in these parts when a man's wife is—well, not too particularly his own. But as a respectable householder I don't encourage it."

"Still, are they going to do it shortly? It is a good sight to see, I suppose?"

"Well, sir!" she simpered. And then, bursting into naturalness, and glancing from the corner of her eye, " 'Tis the funniest thing under the sun! And it costs money."

"Ah! I remember hearing of some such thing. Now I shall be in Casterbridge for two or three weeks to come, and should not mind seeing the performance. Wait a moment." He turned back, entered the sitting room, and said, "Here, good folks; I should like to see the old custom you are talking of, and I don't mind being something toward it—take that." He threw a sovereign on the table and returned to the landlady at the door, of whom, having inquired the way into the town, he took his leave.

"There were more where that one came from," said Charl, when the sovereign had been taken up and handed to the land- lady for safe keeping. "By George! We ought to have got a few more while we had him here."

"No, no," answered the landlady, "This is a respectable house, thank God! And I'll have nothing done but what's honorable!"

"Well," said Jopp; "now we'll consider the business begun, and will soon get it in train."

"We will!" said Nance. "A good laugh warms my heart more than a cordial, and that's the truth on't."

Jopp gathered up the letters, and it being now somewhat late he did not attempt to call at Farfrae's with them that night. He reached home, sealed them up as before, and delivered the parcel at its address next morning. Within an hour its con- tents were reduced to ashes by Lucetta, who, poor soul! was inclined to fall down on her knees in thankfulness that at last no evidence remained of the unlucky episode with Henchard in her past. For though hers had been rather the laxity of in- advertence than of intention, that episode, if known, was not the less likely to operate fatally between herself and her hus- band.

. . . CHAPTER 37

SUCH was the state of things when the current affairs of Casterbridge were interrupted by an event of such magnitude that its influence reached to the lowest social stratum there, stirring the depths of its society simultaneously with the prep- arations for the skimmington. It was one of those excitements which, when they move a country town, leave a permanent mark upon its chronicles, as a warm summer permanently marks the ring in the tree trunk corresponding to its date.

A Royal Personage was about to pass through the borough on his course further west, to inaugurate an immense engineering work out that way. He had consented to halt half an hour or so in the town, and to receive an address from the corporation of Casterbridge, which, as a representative center of husbandry, wished thus to express its sense of the great services he had rendered to agricultural science and economics, by his zealous promotion of designs for placing the art of farming on a more scientific footing.

Royalty had not been seen in Casterbridge since the days of the third King George, and then only by candlelight for a few minutes, when that monarch, on a night journey, had stopped to change horses at the King's Arms. The inhabitants therefore decided to make a thorough *fête carillonnée*[1] of the unwonted occasion. Half an hour's pause was not long, it is true; but much might be done in it by a judicious grouping of incidents, above all, if the weather were fine.

The address was prepared on parchment by an artist who was handy at ornamental lettering, and was laid on with the best gold leaf and colors that the sign painter had in his shop. The Council met on the Tuesday before the appointed day, to arrange the details of the procedure. While they were sitting, the door of the Council Chamber standing open, they heard a heavy footstep coming up the stairs. It advanced along the passage, and Henchard entered the room, in clothes of frayed and threadbare shabbiness, the very clothes which he had used to wear in the primal days when he had sat among them.

"I have a feeling," he said, advancing to the table and laying his hand upon the green cloth, "that I should like to join ye

---

1. *fête carillonnée:* holiday for bell-ringing.

in this reception of our illustrious visitor. I suppose I could walk with the rest?"

Embarrassed glances were exchanged by the Council, and Grower nearly ate the end of his quill pen off, so gnawed he it during the silence. Farfrae the young Mayor, who by virtue of his office sat in the large chair, intuitively caught the sense of the meeting, and as spokesman was obliged to utter it, glad as he would have been that the duty should have fallen to another tongue.

"I hardly see that it would be proper, Mr. Henchard," said he. "The Council are the Council, and as ye are no longer one of the body, there would be an irregularity in the proceeding. If ye were included, why not others?"

"I have a particular reason for wishing to assist at the ceremony."

Farfrae looked round. "I think I have expressed the feeling of the Council," he said.

"Yes, yes," from Dr. Bath, Lawyer Long, Alderman Tubber, and several more.

"Then I am not to be allowed to have anything to do with it officially?"

"I am afraid so; it is out of the question, indeed. But of course you can see the doings full well, such as they are to be, like the rest of the spectators."

Henchard did not reply to that very obvious suggestion, and, turning on his heel, went away.

It had been only a passing fancy of his, but opposition crystallized it into a determination. "I'll welcome his Royal Highness, or nobody shall!" he went about saying. "I am not going to be sat upon by Farfrae, or any of the rest of the paltry crew! You shall see."

The eventful morning was bright, a full-faced sun confronting early window gazers eastward, and all perceived (for they were practiced in weather lore) that there was permanence in the glow. Visitors soon began to flock in from county houses, villages, remote copses, and lonely uplands, the latter in oiled boots and tilt bonnets, to see the reception, or if not to see it, at any rate to be near it. There was hardly a workman in the town who did not put a clean shirt on. Solomon Longways, Christopher Coney, Buzzford, and the rest of that fraternity, showed their sense of the occasion by advancing their customary eleven o'clock pint to half-past ten; from which they found a difficulty in getting back to the proper hour for several days.

Henchard had determined to do no work that day. He primed himself in the morning with a glass of rum, and walking down the street met Elizabeth-Jane, whom he had not seen for a week. "It was lucky," he said to her, "my twenty-one years had expired before this came on, or I should never have had the nerve to carry it out."

"Carry out what?" said she, alarmed.

"This welcome I am going to give our royal visitor."

She was perplexed. "Shall we go and see it together?" she said.

"See it! I have other fish to fry. You see it. It will be worth seeing!"

She could do nothing to elucidate this, and decked herself out with a heavy heart. As the appointed time drew near she got sight again of her stepfather. She thought he was going to the Three Mariners; but no, he elbowed his way through the gay throng to the shop of Woolfrey, the draper. She waited in the crowd without.

In a few minutes he emerged, wearing, to her surprise, a brilliant rosette, while more surprising still, in his hand he carried a flag of somewhat homely construction, formed by tacking one of the small Union Jacks, which abounded in the town today, to the end of a deal wand—probably the roller from a piece of calico. Henchard rolled up his flag on the doorstep, put it under his arm, and went down the street.

Suddenly the taller members of the crowd turned their heads, and the shorter stood on tiptoe. It was said that the royal *cortège* approached. The railway had stretched out an arm towards Casterbridge at this time, but had not reached it by several miles as yet; so that the intervening distance, as well as the remainder of the journey, was to be traversed by road in the old fashion. People thus waited—the county families in their carriages, the masses on foot—and watched the far-stretching London highway to the ringing of bells and chatter of tongues.

From the background Elizabeth-Jane watched the scene. Some seats had been arranged from which ladies could witness the spectacle, and the front seat was occupied by Lucetta, the Mayor's wife, just at present. In the road under her eyes stood Henchard. She appeared so bright and pretty that, as it seemed, he was experiencing the momentary weakness of wishing for her notice. But he was far from attractive to a woman's eye, ruled as that is so largely by the superficies of things. He was not only a journeyman, unable to appear as he formerly had appeared, but he disdained to appear as well as he might. Everybody else, from the Mayor to the washerwoman, shone in new vesture according to means; but Henchard had doggedly retained the fretted and weather-beaten garments of bygone years.

Hence, alas, this occurred: Lucetta's eyes slid over him to this side and to that without anchoring on his features—as gaily dressed women's eyes will too often do on such occasions. Her manner signified quite plainly that she meant to know him in public no more.

But she was never tired of watching Donald, as he stood in animated converse with his friends a few yards off, wearing round his young neck the official gold chain with great square links, like that round the royal unicorn. Every trifling emotion that her husband showed as he talked had its reflex on her face and lips, which moved in little duplicates to his. She was living his part rather than her own, and cared for no one's situation but Farfrae's that day.

At length a man stationed at the furthest turn of the high

road, namely, on the second bridge of which mention has been made, gave a signal; and the Corporation in their robes proceeded from the front of the Town Hall to the archway erected at the entrance to the town. The carriages containing the royal visitor and his suite arrived at the spot in a cloud of dust, a procession was formed, and the whole came on to the Town Hall at a walking pace.

This spot was the center of interest. There were a few clear yards in front of the royal carriage, sanded; and into this space a man stepped before any one could prevent him. It was Henchard. He had unrolled his private flag, and removing his hat he staggered to the side of the slowing vehicle, waving the Union Jack to and fro with his left hand, while he blandly held out his right to the Illustrious Personage.

All the ladies said with bated breath, "O, look there!" and Lucetta was ready to faint. Elizabeth-Jane peeped through the shoulders of those in front, saw what it was, and was terrified; and then her interest in the spectacle as a strange phenomenon got the better of her fear.

Farfrae, with Mayoral authority, immediately rose to the occasion. He seized Henchard by the shoulder, dragged him back, and told him roughly to be off. Henchard's eyes met his, and Farfrae observed the fierce light in them despite his excitement and irritation. For a moment Henchard stood his ground rigidly; then by an unaccountable impulse gave way and retired. Farfrae glanced to the ladies' gallery, and saw that his Calpurnia's[2] cheek was pale.

"Why—it is your husband's old patron!" said Mrs. Blowbody, a lady of the neighborhood who sat beside Lucetta.

"Patron!" said Donald's wife with quick indignation.

"Do you say the man is an acquaintance of Mr. Farfrae's?" observed Mrs. Bath, the physician's wife, a newcomer to the town through her recent marriage with the doctor.

"He works for my husband," said Lucetta.

2. *Calpurnia:* Julius Caesar's wife.

"Oh—is that all? They have been saying to me that it was through him your husband first got a footing in Casterbridge. What stories people will tell!"

"They will indeed. It was not so at all. Donald's genius would have enabled him to get a footing anywhere, without anybody's help! He would have been just the same if there had been no Henchard in the world!"

It was partly Lucetta's ignorance of the circumstances of Donald's arrival which led her to speak thus; partly the sensation that everybody seemed bent on snubbing her at this triumphant time. The incident had occupied but a few moments, but it was necessarily witnessed by the Royal Personage, who, however, with practiced tact, affected not to have noticed anything unusual. He alighted, the Mayor advanced, the address was read; the Illustrious Personage replied, then said a few words to Farfrae, and shook hands with Lucetta as the Mayor's wife. The ceremony occupied but a few minutes, and the carriages rattled heavily as Pharaoh's chariots down Corn Street and out upon the Budmouth Road, in continuation of the journey coastward.

In the crowd stood Coney, Buzzford, and Longways. "Some difference between him now and when he zung at the Dree Mariners," said the first. " 'Tis wonderful how he could get a lady of her quality to go snacks wi' en in such quick time."

"True. Yet how folk do worship fine clothes! Now there's a better-looking woman than she that nobody notices at all, because she's akin to that hontish fellow Henchard."

"I could worship ye, Buzz, for saying that," remarked Nance Mockridge. "I do like to see the trimming pulled off such Christmas candles. I am quite unequal to the part of villain myself, or I'd gi'e all my small silver to see that lady toppered. . . . And perhaps I shall soon," she added significantly.

"That's not a noble passiont for a 'oman to keep up," said Longways.

Nance did not reply, but everyone knew what she meant.

The ideas diffused by the reading of Lucetta's letters at Peter's Finger had condensed into a scandal, which was spreading like a miasmatic fog through Mixen Lane, and thence up the back streets of Casterbridge.

This mixed assemblage of idlers known to each other presently fell apart into two bands by a process of natural selection, the frequenters of Peter's Finger going off Mixen Lane-wards, where most of them lived, while Coney, Buzzford, Longways, and that connection remained in the street.

"You know what's brewing down there, I suppose?" said Buzzford mysteriously to the others..

Coney looked at him. "Not the skimmity-ride?"

Buzzford nodded.

"I have my doubts if it will be carried out," said Longways. "If they are getting it up they are keeping it mighty close."

"I heard they were thinking of it a fortnight ago, at all events."

"If I were sure o't I'd lay information," said Longways emphatically. " 'Tis too rough a joke, and apt to wake riots in towns. We know that the Scotchman is a right enough man, and that his lady has been a right enough 'oman since she came here, and if there was anything wrong about her afore, that's their business, not ours."

Coney reflected. Farfrae was still liked in the community; but it must be owned that, as the Mayor and man of money, engrossed with affairs and ambitions, he had lost in the eyes of the poorer inhabitants something of that wondrous charm which he had had for them as a light-hearted penniless young man, who sang ditties as readily as the birds in the trees. Hence the anxiety to keep him from annoyance showed not quite the ardor that would have animated it in former days.

"Suppose we make inquiration into it, Christopher," continued Longways; "and if we find there's really anything in it, drop a letter to them most concerned, and advise 'em to keep out of the way?"

This course was decided on, and the group separated, Buzzford saying to Coney, "Come, my ancient friend; let's move on. There's nothing more to see here."

These well-intentioned ones would have been surprised had they known how ripe the great jocular plot really was. "Yes, tonight," Jopp had said to the Peter's party at the corner of Mixen Lane. "As a wind-up to the royal visit the hit will be all the more pat by reason of their great elevation today."

To him, at least, it was not a joke, but a retaliation.

. . . CHAPTER 38

THE PROCEEDINGS had been brief—too brief—to Lucetta, whom an intoxicating *Weltlust*[1] had fairly mastered; but they had brought her a great triumph nevertheless. The shake of the royal hand still lingered in her fingers; and the chit-chat she had overheard, that her husband might possibly receive the honor of knighthood, though idle to a degree, seemed not the wildest vision; stranger things had occurred to men so good and captivating as her Scotchman was.

After the collision with the Mayor, Henchard had withdrawn behind the ladies' stand; and there he stood, regarding with a stare of abstraction the spot on the lapel of his coat where Farfrae's hand had seized it. He put his own hand there, as if he could hardly realize such an outrage from one whom it had once been his wont to treat with ardent generosity. While pausing in this half-stupefied state the conversation of Lucetta with the other ladies reached his ears; and he distinctly heard her deny him—deny that he had assisted Donald, that he was anything more than a common journeyman.

He moved on homeward, and met Jopp in the archway to the Bull Stake. "So you've had a snub," said Jopp.

"And what if I have?" answered Henchard sternly.

"Why, I've had one too, so we are both under the same

1. *Weltlust:* desire for worldly experience.

cold shade." He briefly related his attempts to win Lucetta's intercession.

Henchard merely heard his story, without taking it deeply in. His own relation to Farfrae and Lucetta overshadowed all kindred ones. He went on saying brokenly to himself, "She has supplicated to me in her time; and now her tongue won't own me nor her eyes see me! . . . And he—how angry he looked. He drove me back as if I were a bull breaking fence. . . . I took it like a lamb, for I saw it could not be settled there. He can rub brine on a green wound! . . . But he shall pay for it, and she shall be sorry. It must come to a tussle—face to face; and then we'll see how a coxcomb can front a man!"

Without further reflection the fallen merchant, bent on some wild purpose, ate a hasty dinner and went forth to find Farfrae. After being injured by him as a rival, and snubbed by him as a journeyman, the crowning degradation had been reserved for this day—that he should be shaken at the collar by him as a vagabond in the face of the whole town.

The crowds had dispersed. But for the green arches which still stood as they were erected Casterbridge life had resumed its ordinary shape. Henchard went down Corn Street till he came to Farfrae's house, where he knocked, and left a message that he would be glad to see his employer at the granaries as soon as he conveniently could come there. Having done this he proceeded round to the back and entered the yard.

Nobody was present, for, as he had been aware, the laborers and carters were enjoying a half-holiday on account of the events of the morning—though the carters would have to return for a short time later on, to feed and litter down the horses. He had reached the granary steps and was about to ascend, when he said to himself aloud, "I'm stronger than he."

Henchard returned to a shed, where he selected a short piece of rope from several pieces that were lying about; hitching one end of this to a nail, he took the other in his right hand and turned himself bodily round, while keeping his arm against his side; by this contrivance he pinioned the arm effectively.

He now went up the ladders to the top floor of the corn stores.

It was empty except of a few sacks, and at the further end was the door often mentioned, opening under the cathead and chain that hoisted the sacks. He fixed the door open and looked over the sill. There was a depth of thirty or forty feet to the ground; here was the spot on which he had been standing with Farfrae when Elizabeth-Jane had seen him lift his arm, with many misgivings as to what the movement portended.

He retired a few steps into the loft and waited. From this elevated perch his eye could sweep the roofs round about, the upper parts of the luxurious chestnut trees, now delicate in leaves of a week's age, and the drooping boughs of the limes; Farfrae's garden and the green door leading therefrom. In course of time—he could not say how long—that green door opened and Farfrae came through. He was dressed as if for a journey. The low light of the nearing evening caught his head and face when he emerged from the shadow of the wall, warming them to a complexion of flame color. Henchard watched him with his mouth firmly set, the squareness of his jaw and the verticality of his profile being unduly marked.

Farfrae came on with one hand in his pocket, and humming a tune in a way which told that the words were most in his mind. They were those of the song he had sung when he arrived years before at the Three Mariners, a poor young man, adventuring for life and fortune, and scarcely knowing witherward:—

> "And here's a hand, my trusty fiere,
> And gie's a hand o' thine."

Nothing moved Henchard like an old melody. He sank back. "No; I can't do it!" he gasped. "Why does the infernal fool begin that now!"

At length Farfrae was silent, and Henchard looked out of the loft door. "Will ye come up here?" he said.

"Ay, man," said Farfrae. "I couldn't see ye. What's wrang?"

A minute later Henchard heard his feet on the lowest ladder. He heard him land on the first floor, ascend and land on the second, begin the ascent to the third. And then his head rose through the trap behind.

"What are you doing up here at this time?" he asked, coming forward. "Why didn't ye take your holiday like the rest of the men?" He spoke in a tone which had just severity enough in it to show that he remembered the untoward event of the forenoon, and his conviction that Henchard had been drinking.

Henchard said nothing; but going back he closed the stair hatchway, and stamped upon it so that it went tight into its frame; he next turned to the wondering young man, who by this time observed that one of Henchard's arms was bound to his side.

"Now," said Henchard quietly, "we stand face to face—man and man. Your money and your fine wife no longer lift 'ee above me as they did but now, and my poverty does not press me down."

"What does it all mean?" asked Farfrae simply.

"Wait a bit, my lad. You should ha' thought twice before you affronted to extremes a man who had nothing to lose. I've stood your rivalry, which ruined me, and your snubbing, which humbled me; but your hustling, that disgraced me, I won't stand!"

Farfrae warmed a little at this. "Ye'd no business there," he said.

"As much as anyone among ye! What, you forward stripling, tell a man of my age he'd no business there!" The anger vein swelled in his forehead as he spoke.

"You insulted royalty, Henchard; and 'twas my duty, as the chief magistrate, to stop you."

"Royalty be damned," said Henchard. "I am as loyal as you, come to that!"

"I am not here to argue. Wait till you cool doon, wait till you cool; and you will see things the same way as I do."

"You may be the one to cool first," said Henchard grimly. "Now this is the case. Here be we, in this four-square loft, to finish out that little wrestle you began this morning. There's the door, forty foot above ground. One of us two puts the other out by that door—the master stays inside. If he likes he may go down afterwards and give the alarm that the other has fallen out by accident—or he may tell the truth—that's his business. As the strongest man I've tied one arm to take no advantage of 'ee. D'ye understand? Then here's at 'ee!"

There was no time for Farfrae to do aught but one thing, to close with Henchard, for the latter had come on at once. It was a wrestling match, the object of each being to give his antagonist a back fall; and on Henchard's part, unquestionably, that it should be through the door.

At the outset Henchard's hold by his only free hand, the right, was on the left side of Farfrae's collar, which he firmly grappled, the latter holding Henchard by his collar with the contrary hand. With his right he endeavored to get hold of his antagonist's left arm, which, however, he could not do, so adroitly did Henchard keep it in the rear as he gazed upon the lowered eyes of his fair and slim antagonist.

Henchard planted the first toe forward, Farfrae crossing him with his; and thus far the struggle had very much the appearance of the ordinary wrestling of those parts. Several minutes were passed by them in this attitude, the pair rocking and writhing like trees in a gale, both preserving an absolute silence. By this time their breathing could be heard. Then Farfrae tried to get hold of the other side of Henchard's collar, which was resisted by the larger man exerting all his force in a wrenching movement, and this part of the struggle ended by his forcing Farfrae down on his knees by sheer pressure of one of his muscular arms. Hampered as he was, however, he could not keep him there, and Farfrae finding his feet again the struggle proceeded as before.

By a whirl Henchard brought Donald dangerously near

the precipice; seeing his position the Scotchman for the first time locked himself to his adversary, and all the efforts of that infuriated Prince of Darkness—as he might have been called from his appearance just now—were inadequate to lift or loosen Farfrae for a time. By an extraordinary effort he succeeded at last, though not until they had got far back again from the fatal door. In doing so Henchard contrived to turn Farfrae a complete somersault. Had Henchard's other arm been free it would have been all over with Farfrae then. But again he regained his feet, wrenching Henchard's arm considerably, and causing him sharp pain, as could be seen from the twitching of his face. He instantly delivered the younger man an annihilating turn by the left fore-hip, as it used to be expressed, and following up his advantage thrust him toward the door, never loosening his hold till Farfrae's fair head was hanging over the window sill, and his arm dangling down outside the wall.

"Now," said Henchard between his gasps, "this is the end of what you began this morning. Your life is in my hands."

"Then take it, take it!" said Farfrae. "Ye've wished to long enough!"

Henchard looked down upon him in silence, and their eyes met. "O Farfrae!—that's not true!" he said bitterly. "God is my witness that no man ever loved another as I did thee at one time. . . . And now—though I came here to kill 'ee, I cannot hurt thee! Go and give me in charge—do what you will—I care nothing for what comes of me!"

He withdrew to the back part of the loft, loosened his arm, and flung himself into a corner upon some sacks, in the abandonment of remorse. Farfrae regarded him in silence; then went to the hatch and descended through it. Henchard would fain have recalled him; but his tongue failed in its task, and the young man's steps died on his ear.

Henchard took his full measure of shame and self-reproach. The scenes of his first acquaintance with Farfrae rushed back upon him—that time when the curious mixture of romance and thrift in the young man's composition so commanded his heart that Farfrae could play upon him as on an instrument. So thoroughly subdued was he that he remained on the sacks in a crouching attitude, unusual for a man, and for such a man. Its womanliness sat tragically on the figure of so stern a piece of virility. He heard a conversation below, the opening of the coach-house door, and the putting in of a horse, but took no notice.

Here he stayed till the thin shades thickened to opaque obscurity, and the loft door became an oblong of gray light—the only visible shape around. At length he arose, shook the dust from his clothes wearily, felt his way to the hatch, and gropingly descended the steps till he stood in the yard.

"He thought highly of me once," he murmured. "Now he'll hate me and despise me forever!"

He became possessed by an overpowering wish to see Farfrae again that night, and by some desperate pleading to attempt the well-nigh impossible task of winning pardon for his late mad attack. But as he walked toward Farfrae's door he recalled the unheeded doings in the yard while he had lain above in a sort of stupor. Farfrae he remembered had gone to the stable and put the horse into the gig; while doing so Whittle had brought him a letter; Farfrae had then said that he would not go toward Budmouth as he had intended—that he was unexpectedly summoned to Weatherbury, and meant to call at Mellstock on his way thither, that place lying but one or two miles out of his course.

He must have come prepared for a journey when he first arrived in the yard, unsuspecting enmity; and he must have driven off (though in a changed direction) without saying a word to any one on what had occurred between themselves.

It would therefore be useless to call at Farfrae's house till very late.

There was no help for it but to wait till his return, though waiting was almost torture to his restless and self-accusing soul. He walked about the streets and outskirts of the town, lingering here and here till he reached the stone bridge of which mention has been made, an accustomed halting place with him now. Here he spent a long time, the purl of waters through the weirs meeting his ear, and the Casterbridge lights glimmering at no great distance off.

While leaning thus upon the parapet his listless attention was awakened by sounds of an unaccustomed kind from the town quarter. They were a confusion of rhythmical noises, to which the streets added yet more confusion by encumbering them with echoes. His first incurious thought that the clangor arose from the town band, engaged in an attempt to round off a memorable day by a burst of evening harmony, was contradicted by certain peculiarities of reverberation. But inexplicability did not rouse him to more than a cursory heed; his sense of degradation was too strong for the admission of foreign ideas; and he leaned against the parapet as before.

. . . **CHAPTER 39**

WHEN Farfrae descended out of the loft breathless from his encounter with Henchard, he paused at the bottom to recover himself. He arrived at the yard with the intention of putting the horse into the gig himself (all the men having a holiday), and driving to a village on the Budmouth Road. Despite the fearful struggle he decided still to persevere in his journey, so as to recover himself before going indoors and meeting the eyes of Lucetta. He wished to consider his course in a case so serious.

When he was just on the point of driving off Whittle arrived with a note badly addressed, and bearing the word "immediate" upon the outside. On opening it he was surprised to see that it was unsigned. It contained a brief request that

he would go to Weatherbury that evening about some business which he was conducting there. Farfrae knew nothing
that could make it pressing; but as he was bent upon going out
he yielded to the anonymous request, particularly as he had a
call to make at Mellstock which could be included in the
same tour. Thereupon he told Whittle of his change of direction, in words which Henchard had overheard; and set out
on his way. Farfrae had not directed his man to take the
message indoors, and Whittle had not been supposed to do
so on his own responsibility.

Now the anonymous letter was a well-intentioned but
clumsy contrivance of Longways and other of Farfrae's men
to get him out of the way for the evening, in order that the
satirical mummery should fall flat, if it were attempted. By
giving open information they would have brought down upon
their heads the vengeance of those among their comrades who
enjoyed these boisterous old games; and therefore the plan
of sending a letter recommended itself by its indirectness.

For poor Lucetta they took no protective measure, believing with the majority there was some truth in the scandal,
which she would have to bear as she best might.

It was about eight o'clock, and Lucetta was sitting in the
drawing room alone. Night had set in for more than half an
hour, but she had not had the candles lighted, for when Farfrae was away she preferred waiting for him by the firelight,
and, if it were not too cold, keeping one of the window sashes
a little way open that the sound of his wheels might reach her
ears early. She was leaning back in her chair, in a more hope-
ful mood than she had enjoyed since her marriage. The day
had been such a success; and the temporary uneasiness which
Henchard's show of effrontery had wrought in her disappeared with the quiet disappearance of Henchard himself
under her husband's reproof. The floating evidences of her
absurd passion for him, and its consequences, had been destroyed, and she really seemed to have no cause for fear.

The reverie in which these and other subjects mingled was disturbed by a hubbub in the distance, that increased moment by moment. It did not greatly surprise her, the afternoon having been given up to recreation by a majority of the populace since the passage of the royal equipages. But her attention was at once riveted to the matter by the voice of a maidservant next door, who spoke from an upper window across the street to some other maid even more elevated than she.

"Which way be they going now?" inquired the first with interest.

"I can't be sure for a moment," said the second, "because of the malter's chimbley. O yes—I can see 'em. Well, I declare, I declare!"

"What, what?" from the first, more enthusiastically.

"They are coming up Corn Street after all! They sit back to back!"

"What—two of 'em—are there two figures?"

"Yes. Two images on a donkey, back to back, their elbows tied to one another's! She's facing the head, and he's facing the tail."

"Is it meant for anybody particular?"

"Well—it mid be. The man has got on a blue coat and kerseymere leggings; he has black whiskers, and a reddish face. 'Tis a stuffed figure, with a false face."

The din was increasing now—then it lessened a little.

"There—I shan't see, after all!" cried the disappointed first maid.

"They have gone into a back street—that's all," said the one who occupied the enviable position in the attic. "There—now I have got 'em all endways nicely!"

"What's the woman like? Just say, and I can tell in a moment if 'tis meant for one I've in mind."

"My—why—'tis dressed just as *she* was dressed when she sat in the front seat at the time the playactors came to the Town Hall!"

Lucetta started to her feet; and almost at the instant the door of the room was quickly and softly opened. Elizabeth-Jane advanced into the firelight.

"I have come to see you," she said breathlessly. "I did not stop to knock—forgive me! I see you have not shut your shutters, and the window is open."

Without waiting for Lucetta's reply she crossed quickly to the window and pulled out one of the shutters. Lucetta glided to her side. "Let it be—hush!" she said peremptorily, in a dry voice, while she seized Elizabeth-Jane by the hand, and held up her finger. Their intercourse had been so low and hurried that not a word had been lost of the conversation without; which had thus proceeded:——

"Her neck is uncovered, and her hair in bands, and her back comb in place; she's got on a puce silk, and white stockings, and colored shoes."

Again Elizabeth-Jane attempted to close the window, but Lucetta held her by main force.

" 'Tis me!" she said, with a face pale as death. "A procession—a scandal—an effigy of me, and him!"

The look of Elizabeth betrayed that the latter knew it already.

"Let us shut it out," coaxed Elizabeth-Jane, noting that the rigid wildness of Lucetta's features were growing yet more rigid and wild with the nearing of the noise and laughter. "Let us shut it out!"

"It is of no use!" she shrieked out. "He will see it, won't he? Donald will see it! He is just coming home—and it will break his heart—he will never love me anymore—and O, it will kill me—kill me!"

Elizabeth-Jane was frantic now. "O, can't something be done to stop it?" she cried. "Is there nobody to do it—not one?"

She relinquished Lucetta's hands, and ran to the door. Lucetta herself, saying recklessly "I will see it!" turned to the window, threw up the sash, and went out upon the balcony. Elizabeth immediately followed her, and put her arm round her to pull her in. Lucetta's eyes were straight upon the spectacle of the uncanny revel, now advancing rapidly. The numerous lights around the two effigies threw them up into lurid distinctness; it was impossible to mistake the pair for other than the intended victims.

"Come in, come in," implored Elizabeth; "and let me shut the window!"

"She's me—she's me—even to the parasol—my green parasol!" cried Lucetta with a wild laugh as she stepped in. She stood motionless for one second—then fell heavily to the floor.

Almost at the instant of her fall the rude music of the skimmington ceased. The roars of sarcastic laughter went off in ripples, and the trampling died out like the rustle of a spent wind. Elizabeth was only indirectly conscious of this; she had rung the bell, and was bending over Lucetta, who remained convulsed on the carpet in the paroxysms of an epileptic seizure. She rang again and again, in vain; the probability being that the servants had all run out of the house to see more of the dæmonic Sabbath than they could see within.

At last Farfrae's man, who had been agape on the doorstep, came up; then the cook. The shutters, hastily pushed to by Elizabeth, were quite closed, a light was obtained, Lucetta carried to her room, and the man sent off for a doctor. While Elizabeth was undressing her she recovered consciousness; but as soon as she remembered what had passed the fit returned.

The doctor arrived with unhoped-for promptitude; he had been standing at his door, like others, wondering what the uproar meant. As soon as he saw the unhappy sufferer he said, in answer to Elizabeth's mute appeal, "This is serious."

"It is a fit," Elizabeth said.

"Yes. But a fit in the present state of her health means mischief. You must send at once for Mr. Farfrae. Where is he?"

"He has driven into the country, sir," said the parlor maid; "to some place on the Budmouth Road. He's likely to be back soon."

"Never mind; he must be sent for, in case he should not hurry." The doctor returned to the bedside again. The man was dispatched, and they soon heard him clattering out of the yard at the back.

Meanwhile Mr. Benjamin Grower, that prominent burgess of whom mention has been already made, hearing the din of cleavers, tongs, tambourines, kits, crouds, humstrums, serpents, rams' horns, and other historical kinds of music as he sat indoors in the High Street, had put on his hat and gone out to learn the cause. He came to the corner above Farfrae's, and soon guessed the nature of the proceedings; for being a native of the town he had witnessed such rough jests before. His first move was to search hither and thither for the constables; there were two in the town, shriveled men whom he ultimately found in hiding up an alley yet more shriveled than usual, having some not ungrounded fears that they might be roughly handled if seen.

"What can we two poor lammigers do against such a multitude!" expostulated Stubberd, in answer to Mr. Grower's chiding. " 'Tis tempting 'em to commit *felo-de-se*[1] upon us, and that would be the death of the perpetrator; and we wouldn't be the cause of a fellow creature's death on no account, not we!"

"Get some help, then! Here, I'll come with you. We'll see what a few words of authority can do. Quick now; have you got your staves?"

"We didn't want the folk to notice us as law officers, being so short-handed, sir; so we pushed our Gover'ment staves up this waterpipe."

"Out with 'em, and come along, for Heaven's sake! Ah, here's Mr. Blowbody; that's lucky." (Blowbody was the third of the three borough magistrates.)

---

1. *Felo de se:* Suicide (Latin).

"Well, what's the row?" said Blowbody. "Got their names —hey?"

"No. Now," said Grower to one of the constables, "you go with Mr. Blowbody round by the Old Walk and come up the street; and I'll go with Stubberd straight forward. By this plan we shall have 'em between us. Get their names only: no attack or interruption."

Thus they started. But as Stubberd with Mr. Grower advanced into Corn Street, whence the sounds had proceeded, they were surprised that no procession could be seen. They passed Farfrae's, and looked to the end of the street. The lamp flames waved, the Walk trees soughed, a few loungers stood about with their hands in their pockets. Everything was as usual.

"Have you seen a motley crowd making a disturbance?" Grower said magisterially to one of these in a fustian jacket, who smoked a short pipe and wore straps round his knees.

"Beg yer pardon, sir?" blandly said the person addressed, who was no other than Charl, of Peter's Finger. Mr. Grower repeated the words.

Charl shook his head to the zero of childlike ignorance. "No; we haven't seen anything; have we, Joe? And you was here afore I."

Joseph was quite as blank as the other in his reply.

"H'm—that's odd," said Mr. Grower. "Ah—here's a respectable man coming that I know by sight. Have you," he inquired, addressing the nearing shape of Jopp, "have you seen any gang of fellows making a devil of a noise—skimmington riding, or something of the sort?"

"O no—nothing, sir," Jopp replied, as if receiving the most singular news. "But I've not been far tonight, so perhaps——"

"Oh, 'twas here—just here," said the magistrate.

"Now I've noticed, come to think o't, that the wind in the Walk trees makes a peculiar poetical-like murmur tonight, sir; more than common; so perhaps 'twas that?" Jopp suggested, as he rearranged his hand in his greatcoat pocket (where it ingeniously supported a pair of kitchen tongs and a cow's horn, thrust up under his waistcoat).

"No, no, no—d'ye think I'm a fool? Constable, come this way. They must have gone into the back street."

Neither in back street nor in front street, however, could the disturbers be perceived; and Blowbody and the second constable, who came up at this time, brought similar intelligence. Effigies, donkeys, lanterns, band, all had disappeared like the crew of *Comus*.[2]

"Now," said Mr. Grower, "there's only one thing more we can do. Get ye half-a-dozen helpers, and go in a body to Mixen Lane, and into Peter's Finger. I'm much mistaken if you don't find a clue to the perpetrators there."

The rusty-jointed executors of the law mustered assistance as soon as they could, and the whole party marched off to the lane of notoriety. It was no rapid matter to get there at night, not a lamp or glimmer of any sort offering itself to light the way, except an occasional pale radiance through some window curtain, or through the chink of some door which could not be closed because of the smoky chimney within. At last they entered the inn boldly, by the till then bolted front door, after a prolonged knocking of loudness commensurate with the importance of their standing.

In the settles of the large room, guyed to the ceiling by cords as usual for stability, an ordinary group sat drinking and smoking with statuesque quiet of demeanor. The landlady looked mildly at the invaders, saying in honest accents, "Good evening, gentlemen; there's plenty of room. I hope there's nothing amiss?"

They looked round the room. "Surely," said Stubberd to one of the men, "I saw you by now in Corn Street—Mr. Grower spoke to 'ee?"

2. *Crew of Comus:* made to disappear by an enchantress. (See John Milton's *Comus*.)

The man, who was Charl, shook his head absently. "I've been here this last hour, hain't I, Nance?" he said to the woman who meditatively sipped her ale near him.

"Faith, that you have. I came in for my quiet supper-time half-pint, and you was here then, as was all the rest."

The other constable was facing the clock case, where he saw reflected in the glass a quick motion by the landlady. Turning sharply, he caught her closing the oven door.

"Something curious about that oven, ma'am!" he observed advancing, opening it, and drawing out a tambourine.

"Ah," she said apologetically, "that's what we keep here to use when there's a little quiet dancing. You see damp weather spoils it, so I put it there to keep it dry."

The constable nodded knowingly; but what he knew was nothing. Nohow could anything be elicited from this mute and inoffensive assembly. In a few minutes the investigators went out, and joining those of their auxiliaries who had been left at the door they pursued their way elsewhither.

. . . CHAPTER 40

Long before this time Henchard, weary of his ruminations on the bridge, had repaired toward the town. When he stood at the bottom of the street a procession burst upon his view, in the act of turning out of an alley just above him. The lanterns, horns, and multitude startled him; he saw the mounted images, and knew what it all meant.

They crossed the way, entered another street, and disappeared. He turned back a few steps and was lost in grave reflection, finally wending his way homeward by the obscure riverside path. Unable to rest there he went to his stepdaughter's lodging, and was told that Elizabeth-Jane had gone to Mrs. Farfrae's. Like one acting in obedience to a charm, and with a nameless apprehension, he followed in the same direc-

tion in the hope of meeting her, the roisterers having vanished.
Disappointed in this he gave the gentlest of pulls to the doorbell, and then learned particulars of what had occurred together with the doctor's imperative orders that Farfrae should
be brought home, and how they had set out to meet him on the
Budmouth Road.

"But he has gone to Mellstock and Weatherbury!" exclaimed Henchard, now unspeakably grieved. "Not Budmouth way at all."

But, alas! for Henchard; he had lost his good name. They
would not believe him, taking his words but as the frothy
utterances of recklessness. Though Lucetta's life seemed at
that moment to depend upon her husband's return (she being
in great mental agony lest he should never know the unexag-
gerated truth of her past relations with Henchard), no messenger was dispatched toward Weatherbury. Henchard, in a
state of bitter anxiety and contrition, determined to seek Farfrae himself.

To this end he hastened down the town, ran along the eastern road over Durnover Moor, up the hill beyond, and thus
onward in the moderate darkness of this spring night till he
reached a second and almost a third hill about three miles
distant. In Yalbury Bottom, or Plain, at the foot of the hill,
he listened. At first nothing, beyond his own heart-throbs, was
to be heard but the slow wind making its moan among the
masses of spruce and larch of Yalbury Wood which clothed
the heights on either hand; but presently there came the sound
of light wheels whetting their felloes against the newly stoned
patches of road, accompanied by the distant glimmer of lights.

He knew it was Farfrae's gig descending the hill from an
indescribable personality in its noise, the vehicle having been
his own till bought by the Scotchman at the sale of his effects.
Henchard thereupon retraced his steps along Yalbury Plain,
the gig coming up with him as its driver slackened speed
between two plantations.

It was a point in the highway near which the road to Mell-stock branched off from the homeward direction. By diverging to that village, as he had intended to do, Farfrae might probably delay his return by a couple of hours. It soon appeared that his intention was to do so still, the light swerving toward Cuckoo Lane, the by-road aforesaid. Farfrae's off gig-lamp flashed in Henchard's face. At the same time, Farfrae discerned his late antagonist.

"Farfrae—Mr. Farfrae!" cried the breathless Henchard, holding up his hand.

Farfrae allowed the horse to turn several steps into the branch lane before he pulled up. He then drew rein, and said "Yes?" over his shoulder, as one would toward a pronounced enemy.

"Come back to Casterbridge at once!" Henchard said. "There's something wrong at your house—requiring your return. I've run all the way here on purpose to tell ye."

Farfrae was silent, and at his silence Henchard's soul sank within him. Why had he not, before this, thought of what was only too obvious? He who, four hours earlier, had enticed Farfrae into a deadly wrestle stood now in the darkness of late nightime on a lonely road, inviting him to come a particular way, where an assailant might have confederates, instead of going his purposed way, where there might be a better opportunity of guarding himself from attack. Henchard could almost feel this view of things in course of passage through Farfrae's mind.

"I have to go to Mellstock," said Farfrae coldly, as he loosened his rein to move on.

"But," implored Henchard, "the matter is more serious than your business at Mellstock. It is—your wife! She is ill. I can tell you particulars as we go along."

The very agitation and abruptness of Henchard increased Farfrae's suspicion that this was a *ruse* to decoy him on to the next wood, where might be effectually compassed what, from policy or want of nerve, Henchard had failed to do earlier in the day. He started the horse.

"I know what you think," deprecated Henchard running after, almost bowed down with despair as he perceived the image of unscrupulous villainy that he assumed in his former friend's eyes. "But I am not what you think!" he cried hoarsely. "Believe me, Farfrae; I have come entirely on your own and your wife's account. She is in danger. I know no more; and they want you to come. Your man has gone the other way in a mistake. O Farfrae! Don't mistrust me—I am a wretched man; but my heart is true to you still!"

Farfrae, however, did distrust him utterly. He knew his wife was with child, but he had left her not long ago in perfect health; and Henchard's treachery was more credible than his story. He had in his time heard bitter ironies from Henchard's lips, and there might be ironies now. He quickened the horse's pace, and had soon risen into the high country lying between there and Mellstock, Henchard's spasmodic run after him lending yet more substance to his thought of evil purposes.

The gig and its driver lessened against the sky in Henchard's eyes; his exertions for Farfrae's good had been in vain. Over this repentent sinner, at least, there was to be no joy in heaven. He cursed himself like a less scrupulous Job,[1] as a vehement man will do when he loses self-respect, the last mental prop under poverty. To this he had come after a time of emotional darkness of which the adjoining woodland shade afforded inadequate illustration. Presently he began to walk back again along the way by which he had arrived. Farfrae should at all events have no reason for delay upon the road by seeing him there when he took his journey homeward later on.

Arriving at Casterbridge Henchard went again to Farfrae's

1. *Job:* Biblical figure who suffered much without complaint.

house to make inquiries. As soon as the door opened anxious faces confronted his from the staircase, hall, and landing; and they all said in grievous disappointment, "O—it is not he!" The manservant, finding his mistake, had long since returned, and all hopes had been centered upon Henchard.

"But haven't you found him?" said the doctor.

"Yes. . . . I cannot tell 'ee!" Henchard replied as he sank down on a chair within the entrance. "He can't be home for two hours."

"H'm," said the surgeon, returning upstairs.

"How is she?" asked Henchard of Elizabeth, who formed one of the group.

"In great danger, Father. Her anxiety to see her husband makes her fearfully restless. Poor woman—I fear they have killed her!"

Henchard regarded the sympathetic speaker for a few instants as if she struck him in a new light; then, without further remark, went out the door and onward to his lonely cottage. So much for man's rivalry, he thought. Death was to have the oyster, and Farfrae and himself the shells. But about Elizabeth-Jane; in the midst of his gloom she seemed to him as a pinpoint of light. He had liked the look of her face as she answered him from the stairs. There had been affection in it, and above all things what he desired now was affection from anything that was good and pure. She was not his own; yet, for the first time, he had a faint dream that he might get to like her as his own,—if she would only continue to love him.

Jopp was just going to bed when Henchard got home. As the latter entered the door Jopp said, "This is rather bad about Mrs. Farfrae's illness."

"Yes," said Henchard shortly, though little dreaming of Jopp's complicity in the night's harlequinade, and raising his eyes just sufficiently to observe that Jopp's face was lined with anxiety.

"Somebody has called for you," continued Jopp, when

Henchard was shutting himself into his own apartment. "A kind of traveler, or sea captain of some sort."

"Oh?—who could he be?"

"He seemed a well-be-doing man—had gray hair and a broadish face; but he gave no name, and no message."

"Nor do I gi'e him any attention." And, saying this, Henchard closed his door.

The divergence to Mellstock delayed Farfrae's return very nearly the two hours of Henchard's estimate. Among the other urgent reasons for his presence had been the need of his authority to send to Budmouth for a second physician; and when at length Farfrae did come back he was in a state bordering on distraction at his misconception of Henchard's motives.

A messenger was dispatched to Budmouth, late as it had grown; the night wore on, and the other doctor came in the small hours. Lucetta had been much soothed by Donald's arrival; he seldom or never left her side; and when, immediately after his entry, she had tried to lisp out to him the secret which so oppressed her, he checked her feeble words, lest talking should be dangerous, assuring her there was plenty of time to tell him everything.

Up to this time he knew nothing of the skimmington ride. The dangerous illness and miscarriage of Mrs. Farfrae was soon rumored through the town, and an apprehensive guess having been given as to its cause by the leaders in the exploit, compunction and fear threw a dead silence over all particulars of their orgy; while those immediately around Lucetta would not venture to add to her husband's distress by alluding to the subject.

What, and how much, Farfrae's wife ultimately explained to him of her past entanglement with Henchard, when they were alone in the solitude of that sad night, cannot be told. That she informed him of the bare facts of her peculiar intimacy with the corn merchant became plain from Farfrae's own statements. But in respect of her subsequent conduct— her motive in coming to Casterbridge to unite herself with Henchard—her assumed justification in abandoning him when she discovered reasons for fearing him (though in truth her inconsequent passion for another man at first sight had most to do with that abandonment)—her method of reconciling to her conscience a marriage with the second when she was in a measure committed to the first: to what extent she spoke of these things remained Farfrae's secret alone.

Besides the watchman who called the hours and weather in Casterbridge that night there walked a figure up and down Corn Street hardly less frequently. It was Henchard's, whose retiring to rest had proved itself a futility as soon as attempted; and he gave it up to go hither and thither, and make inquiries about the patient every now and then. He called as much on Farfrae's account as on Lucetta's, and on Elizabeth-Jane's even more than on either's. Shorn one by one of all other interests, his life seemed centering on the personality of the stepdaughter whose presence but recently he could not endure. To see her on each occasion of his inquiry at Lucetta's was a comfort to him.

The last of his calls was made about four o'clock in the morning, in the steely light of dawn. Lucifer[2] was fading into day across Durnover Moor, the sparrows were just alighting into the street, and the hens had begun to cackle from the outhouses. When within a few yards of Farfrae's he saw the door gently opened, and a servant raise her hand to the knocker, to untie the piece of cloth which had muffled it. He went across, the sparrows in his way scarcely flying up from the road litter, so little did they believe in human aggression at so early a time.

"Why do you take off that?" said Henchard.

2. *Lucifer:* the morning star.

She turned in some surprise at his presence, and did not answer for an instant or two. Recognizing him, she said, "Because they may knock as loud as they will; she will never hear it any more."

CHAPTER 41

HENCHARD went home. The morning having now fully broke he lit his fire, and sat abstractedly beside it. He had not sat there long when a gentle footstep approached the house and entered the passage, a finger tapping lightly at the door. Henchard's face brightened, for he knew the motions to be Elizabeth's. She came into his room, looking wan and sad.

"Have you heard?" she asked. "Mrs. Farfrae! She is—dead! Yes, indeed—about an hour ago!"

"I know it," said Henchard. "I have but lately come in from there. It is so very good of 'ee, Elizabeth, to come and tell me. You must be so tired out, too, with sitting up. Now do you bide here with me this morning. You can go and rest in the other room; and I will call 'ee when breakfast is ready."

To please him, and herself—for his recent kindliness was winning a surprised gratitude from the lonely girl—she did as he bade her, and lay down on a sort of couch which Henchard had rigged up out of a settle in the adjoining room. She could hear him moving about in his preparations; but her mind ran most strongly on Lucetta, whose death in such fullness of life and amid such cheerful hopes of maternity was appallingly unexpected. Presently she fell asleep.

Meanwhile her stepfather in the outer room had set the breakfast in readiness; but finding that she dozed he would not call her; he waited on, looking into the fire and keeping the kettle boiling with housewifely care, as if it were an honor to have her in his house. In truth, a great change had come over him with regard to her, and he was developing the dream

of a future lit by her filial presence, as though that way alone
could happiness lie.

He was disturbed by another knock at the door, and rose
to open it, rather deprecating a call from anybody just then.
A stoutly built man stood on the doorstep, with an alien, unfamiliar air about his figure and bearing—an air which might
have been called colonial by people of cosmopolitan experience. It was the man who had asked the way at Peter's Finger.
Henchard nodded, and looked inquiry.

"Good morning, good morning," said the stranger with
profuse heartiness. "Is it Mr. Henchard I am talking to?"

"My name is Henchard."

"Then I've caught 'ee at home—that's right. Morning's the
time for business, says I. Can I have a few words with you?"

"By all means," Henchard answered, showing the way in.

"You may remember me?" said his visitor, seating himself.

Henchard observed him indifferently, and shook his head.

"Well—perhaps you may not. My name is Newson."

Henchard's face and eyes seemed to die. The other did not
notice it. "I know the name well," Henchard said at last, looking on the floor.

"I make no doubt of that. Well, the fact is, I've been looking for 'ee this fortnight past. I landed at Havenpool and went
through Casterbridge on my way to Falmouth, and when I
got there, they told me you had some years before been living
at Casterbridge. Back came I again, and by long and by late
I got here by coach, ten minutes ago. 'He lives down by the
mill,' says they. So here I am. Now—that transaction between
us some twenty years agone—'tis that I've called about. 'Twas
a curious business. I was younger then than I am now, and
perhaps the less said about it, in one sense, the better."

"Curious business! 'Twas worse than curious. I cannot even
allow that I'm the man you met then. I was not in my senses,
and a man's senses are himself."

"We were young and thoughtless," said Newson. "How-

ever, I've come to mend matters rather than open arguments.
Poor Susan—hers was a strange experience."

"It was."

"She was a warm-hearted, homespun woman. She was not
what they call shrewd or sharp at all—better she had been."

"She was not."

"As you in all likelihood know, she was simpleminded
enough to think that the sale was in a way binding. She was as
guiltless o' wrongdoing in that particular as a saint in the
clouds."

"I know it, I know it. I found it out directly," said Henchard, still with averted eyes. "There lay the sting o't to me.
If she had seen it as what it was she would never have left me.
Never! But how should she be expected to know? What advantages had she? None. She could write her own name, and
no more."

"Well, it was not in my heart to undeceive her when the
deed was done," said the sailor of former days. "I thought, and
there was not much vanity in thinking it, that she would be
happier with me. She was fairly happy, and I never would
have undeceived her till the day of her death. Your child died;
she had another, and all went well. But a time came—mind me,
a time always does come. A time came—it was some after she
and I and the child returned from America—when somebody
she had confided her history to, told her my claim to her was a
mockery, and made a jest of her belief in my right. After that
she was never happy with me. She pined and pined, and
socked and sighed. She said she must leave me, and then came
the question of our child. Then a man advised me how to act,
and I did it, for I thought it was best. I left her at Falmouth,
and went off to sea. When I got to the other side of the
Atlantic there was a storm, and it was supposed that a lot of
us, including myself, had been washed overboard. I got ashore
at Newfoundland, and then I asked myself what I should do.
'Since I'm here, here I'll bide,' I thought to myself; ''twill be

most kindness to her, now she's taken against me, to let her believe me lost; for,' I thought, 'while she supposes us both alive she'll be miserable; but if she thinks me dead she'll go back to him, and the child will have a home.' I've never returned to this country till a month ago, and I found that, as I had supposed, she went to you, and my daughter with her. They told me in Falmouth that Susan was dead. But my Elizabeth-Jane—where is she?"

"Dead likewise," said Henchard doggedly. "Surely you learned that too?"

The sailor started up, and took an enervated pace or two down the room. "Dead!" he said, in a low voice. "Then what's the use of my money to me?"

Henchard, without answering, shook his head as if that were rather a question for Newson himself than for him.

"Where is she buried?" the traveler inquired.

"Beside her mother," said Henchard, in the same stolid tones.

"When did she die?"

"A year ago and more," replied the other without hesitation.

The sailor continued standing. Henchard never looked up from the floor. At last Newson said: "My journey hither has been for nothing! I may as well go as I came! It has served me right. I'll trouble you no longer."

Henchard heard the retreating footsteps of Newson upon the sanded floor, the mechanical lifting of the latch, the slow opening and closing of the door that was natural to a balked or dejected man; but he did not turn his head. Newson's shadow passed the window. He was gone.

Then Henchard, scarcely believing the evidence of his senses, rose from his seat amazed at what he had done. It had been the impulse of a moment. The regard he had lately acquired for Elizabeth, the new-sprung hope of his loneliness that she would be to him a daughter of whom he could feel as proud as of the actual daughter she still believed herself to be, had been stimulated by the unexpected coming of Newson to a greedy exclusiveness in relation to her; so that the sudden prospect of her loss had caused him to speak mad lies like a child, in pure mockery of consequences. He had expected questions to close in round him, and unmask his fabrication in five minutes; yet such questioning had not come. But surely they would come; Newson's departure could be but momentary; he would learn all by inquiries in the town; and return to curse him, and carry his last treasure away!

He hastily put on his hat, and went out in the direction that Newson had taken. Newson's back was soon visible up the road, crossing Bull-Stake. Henchard followed; and saw his visitor stop at the King's Arms, where the morning coach which had brought him waited half an hour for another coach which crossed there. The coach Newson had come by was now about to move again. Newson mounted; his luggage was put in, and in a few minutes the vehicle disappeared with him.

He had not so much as turned his head. It was an act of simple faith in Henchard's words—faith so simple as to be almost sublime. The young sailor who had taken Susan Henchard on the spur of the moment and on the faith of a glance at her face, more than twenty years before, was still living and acting under the form of the grizzled traveler who had taken Henchard's words on trust so absolute as to shame him as he stood.

Was Elizabeth-Jane to remain his by virtue of this hardy invention of a moment? "Perhaps not for long," said he. Newson might converse with his fellow travelers, some of whom might be Casterbridge people; and the trick would be discovered.

This probability threw Henchard into a defensive attitude, and instead of considering how best to right the wrong, and acquaint Elizabeth's father with the truth at once, he be-

thought himself of ways to keep the position he had accidentally won. Toward the young woman herself his affection
grew more jealously strong with each new hazard to which
his claim to her was exposed.

He watched the distant highway expecting to see Newson
return on foot, enlightened and indignant, to claim his child.
But no figure appeared. Possibly he had spoken to nobody on
the coach, but buried his grief in his own heart.

His grief!—what was it, after all, to that which he, Henchard, would feel at the loss of her? Newson's affection,
cooled by years, could not equal his who had been constantly
in her presence. And thus his jealous soul speciously argued
to excuse the separation of father and child.

He returned to the house half expecting that she would
have vanished. No; there she was—just coming out from the
inner room, the marks of sleep upon her eyelids, and exhibiting a generally refreshed air.

"O Father!" she said, smiling. "I had no sooner lain down
than I napped, though I did not mean to. I wonder I did not
dream about poor Mrs. Farfrae, after thinking of her so; but I
did not. How strange it is that we do not often dream of
latest events, absorbing as they may be."

"I am glad you have been able to sleep," he said, taking her
hand with anxious proprietorship—an act which gave her a
pleasant surprise.

They sat down to breakfast, and Elizabeth-Jane's thoughts
reverted to Lucetta. Their sadness added charm to a countenance whose beauty had ever lain in its meditative soberness.

"Father," she said, as soon as she recalled herself to the
outspread meal, "it is so kind of you to get this nice breakfast
with your own hands, and I idly asleep the while."

"I do it every day," he replied. "You have left me; everybody has left me; how should I live but by my own hands."

"You are very lonely, are you not?"

"Ay, child—to a degree that you know nothing of! It is my

own fault. You are the only one who has been near me for weeks. And you will come no more."

"Why do you say that? Indeed I will, if you would like to see me."

Henchard signified dubiousness. Though he had so lately hoped that Elizabeth-Jane might again live in his house as daughter, he would not ask her to do so now. Newson might return at any moment, and what Elizabeth would think of him for his deception it were best to bear apart from her.

When they had breakfasted his stepdaughter still lingered, till the moment arrived at which Henchard was accustomed to go to his daily work. Then she arose, and with assurances of coming again soon went up the hill in the morning sunlight.

"At this moment her heart is as warm toward me as mine is toward her; she would live with me here in this humble cottage for the asking! Yet before the evening probably he will have come; and then she will scorn me!"

This reflection, constantly repeated by Henchard to himself, accompanied him everywhere through the day. His mood was no longer that of the rebellious, ironical, reckless misadventurer; but the leaden gloom of one who has lost all that can make life interesting, or even tolerable. There would remain nobody for him to be proud of, nobody to fortify him; for Elizabeth-Jane would soon be but as a stranger, and worse. Susan, Farfrae, Lucetta, Elizabeth—all had gone from him, one after one, either by his fault or by his misfortune.

In place of them he had no interest, hobby, or desire. If he could have summoned music to his aid his existence might even now have been borne; for with Henchard music was of regal power. The merest trumpet or organ tone was enough to move him, and high harmonies transubstantiated him. But hard fate had ordained that he should be unable to call up this divine spirit in his need.

The whole land ahead of him was as darkness itself; there was nothing to come, nothing to wait for. Yet in the natural course of life he might possibly have to linger on earth another thirty or forty years—scoffed at; at best pitied.

The thought of it was unendurable.

To the east of Casterbridge lay moors and meadows through which much water flowed. The wanderer in this direction who should stand still for a few moments on a quiet night, might hear singular symphonies from these waters, as from a lampless orchestra, all playing in their sundry tones from near and far parts of the moor. At a hole in a rotten weir they executed a recitative; where a tributary brook fell over a stone breastwork they trilled cheerily; under an arch they performed a metallic cymbaling; and at Durnover Hole they hissed. The spot at which their instrumentation rose loudest was a place called Ten Hatches, whence during high springs there proceeded a very fugue of sounds.

The river here was deep and strong at all times, and the hatches on this account were raised and lowered by cogs and a winch. A path led from the second bridge over the highway (so often mentioned) to these Hatches, crossing the stream at their head by a narrow plank bridge. But after nightfall human beings were seldom found going that way, the path leading only to a deep reach of the stream called Blackwater, and the passage being dangerous.

Henchard, however, leaving the town by the east road, proceeded to the second, or stone bridge, and thence struck into this path of solitude, following its course beside the stream till the dark shapes of the Ten Hatches cut the sheen thrown upon the river by the weak luster that still lingered in the west. In a second or two he stood beside the weir hole where the water was at its deepest. He looked backwards and forwards, and no creature appeared in view. He then took off his coat and hat, and stood on the brink of the stream with his hands clasped in front of him.

While his eyes were bent on the water beneath there slowly became visible a something floating in the circular pool formed by the wash of centuries; the pool he was intending to make his deathbed. At first it was indistinct by reason of the shadow from the bank; but it emerged thence and took shape, which was that of a human body, lying stiff and stark upon the surface of the stream.

In the circular current imparted by the central flow the form was brought forward, till it passed under his eyes; and then he perceived with a sense of horror that it was *himself*. Not a man somewhat resembling him, but one in all respects his counterpart, his actual double, was floating as if dead in Ten Hatches Hole.

The sense of the supernatural was strong in this unhappy man, and he turned away as one might have done in the actual presence of an appalling miracle. He covered his eyes and bowed his head. Without looking again into the stream he took his coat and hat, and went slowly away.

Presently he found himself by the door of his own dwelling. To his surprise Elizabeth-Jane was standing there. She came forward, spoke, called him "Father" just as before. Newson, then, had not even yet returned.

"I thought you seemed very sad this morning," she said, "so I have come again to see you. Not that I am anything but sad myself. But everybody and everything seem against you so; and I know you must be suffering."

How this woman divined things! Yet she had not divined their whole extremity.

He said to her, "Are miracles still worked, do ye think, Elizabeth? I am not a read man. I don't know so much as I could wish. I have tried to peruse and learn all my life; but the more I try to know the more ignorant I seem."

"I don't quite think there are any miracles nowadays," she said.

"No interference in the case of desperate intentions, for instance? Well, perhaps not, in a direct way. Perhaps not. But will you come and walk with me, and I will show 'ee what I mean."

She agreed willingly, and he took her over the highway, and

by the lonely path to Ten Hatches. He walked restlessly, as if some haunting shade, unseen of her, hovered round him and troubled his glance. She would gladly have talked of Lucetta, but feared to disturb him. When they got near the weir he stood still, and asked her to go forward and look into the pool, and tell him what she saw.

She went, and soon returned to him. "Nothing," she said.

"Go again," said Henchard, "and look narrowly."

She proceeded to the river brink a second time. On her return, after some delay, she told him that she saw something floating round and round there; but what it was she could not discern. It seemed to be a bundle of old clothes.

"Are they like mine?" asked Henchard.

"Well—they are. Dear me—I wonder if—Father, let us go away!"

"Go and look once more; and then we will get home."

She went back, and he could see her stoop till her head was close to the margin of the pool. She started up, and hastened back to his side.

"Well," said Henchard; "what do you say now?"

"Let us go home."

"But tell me—do—what is it floating there?"

"The effigy," she answered hastily. "They must have thrown it into the river higher up amongst the willows at Blackwater, to get rid of it in their alarm at discovery by the magistrates; and it must have floated down here."

"Ah—to be sure—the image o' me! But where is the other? Why that one only? . . . That performance of theirs killed her, but kept me alive!"

Elizabeth-Jane thought and thought of these words "kept me alive," as they slowly retraced their way to the town, and at length guessed their meaning. "Father!—I will not leave you alone like this!" she cried. "May I live with you, and tend upon you as I used to do? I do not mind your being poor. I would have agreed to come this morning, but you did not ask me."

"May you come to me?" he cried bitterly. "Elizabeth, don't mock me! If you only would come!"

"I will," said she.

"How will you forgive all my roughness in former days? You cannot!"

"I have forgotten it. Talk of that no more."

Thus she assured him, and arranged their plans for reunion; and at length each went home. Then Henchard shaved for the first time during many days, and put on clean linen, and combed his hair; and was as a man resuscitated thenceforward.

The next morning the fact turned out to be as Elizabeth-Jane had stated; the effigy was discovered by a cowherd, and that of Lucetta a little higher up in the same stream. But as little as possible was said of the matter, and the figures were privately destroyed.

Despite this natural solution of the mystery Henchard no less regarded it as an intervention that the figure should have been floating there. Elizabeth-Jane heard him say, "Who is such a reprobate as I! And yet it seems that even I be in Somebody's hand!"

. . . CHAPTER 42

BUT THE EMOTIONAL conviction that he was in Somebody's hand began to die out of Henchard's breast as time slowly removed into distance the event which had given that feeling birth. The apparition of Newson haunted him. He would surely return.

Yet Newson did not arrive. Lucetta had been borne along the churchyard path; Casterbridge had for the last time turned its regard upon her, before proceeding to its work as if she had never lived. But Elizabeth remained undisturbed in the belief of her relationship to Henchard, and now shared his home. Perhaps, after all, Newson was gone for ever.

In due time the bereaved Farfrae had learned the, at least,

proximate cause of Lucetta's illness and death; and his first impulse was naturally enough to wreak vengeance in the name
of the law upon the perpetrators of the mischief. He resolved
to wait till the funeral was over ere he moved in the matter.
The time having come he reflected. Disastrous as the result
had been, it was obviously in no way foreseen or intended by
the thoughtless crew who arranged the motley procession.
The tempting prospect of putting to the blush people who
stand at the head of affairs—that supreme and piquant enjoyment of those who writhe under the heel of the same—had
alone animated them, so far as he could see; for he knew
nothing of Jopp's incitements. Other considerations were also
involved. Lucetta had confessed everything to him before her
death, and it was not altogether desirable to make much ado
about her history, alike for her sake, for Henchard's, and for
his own. To regard the event as an outward accident seemed,
to Farfrae, truest consideration for the dead one's memory, as
well as best philosophy.

Henchard and himself mutually forbore to meet. For Elizabeth's sake the former had fettered his pride sufficiently to
accept the small seed and root business which some of the
Town Council, headed by Farfrae, had purchased to afford
him a new opening. Had he been only personally concerned
Henchard, without doubt, would have declined assistance even
remotely brought about by the man whom he had so fiercely
assailed. But the sympathy of the girl seemed necessary to his
very existence; and on her account pride itself wore the garments of humility.

Here they settled themselves; and on each day of their
lives Henchard anticipated her every wish with a watchfulness in which paternal regard was heightened by a burning
jealous dread of rivalry. Yet that Newson would ever now
return to Casterbridge to claim her as a daughter there was
little reason to suppose. He was a wanderer and a stranger,
almost an alien; he had not seen his daughter for several years;

his affection for her could not in the nature of things be keen;
other interests would probably soon obscure his recollections
of her, and prevent any such renewal of inquiry into the past
as would lead to a discovery that she was still a creature of the
present. To satisfy his conscience somewhat Henchard repeated to himself that the lie which had retained for him the
coveted treasure had not been deliberately told to that end,
but had come from him as the last defiant word of a despair
which took no thought of consequences. Furthermore he
pleaded within himself that no Newson could love her as he
loved her, or would tend her to his life's extremity as he was
prepared to do cheerfully.

Thus they lived on in the shop overlooking the churchyard,
and nothing occurred to mark their days during the remainder
of the year. Going out but seldom, and never on a market day,
they saw Donald Farfrae only at rarest intervals, and then
mostly as a transitory object in the distance of the street. Yet
he was pursuing his ordinary avocations, smiling mechanically
to fellow tradesmen, and arguing with bargainers—as bereaved
men do after a while.

Time, "in his own gray style," taught Farfrae how to estimate his experience of Lucetta—all that it was, and all that it
was not. There are men whose hearts insist upon a dogged
fidelity to some image or cause thrown by chance into their
keeping, long after their judgment has pronounced it no
rarity—even the reverse, indeed; and without them the band
of the worthy is incomplete. But Farfrae was not of those. It
was inevitable that the insight, briskness, and rapidity of his
nature should take him out of the dead blank which his loss
threw about him. He could not but perceive that by the
death of Lucetta he had exchanged a looming misery for a
simple sorrow. After that revelation of her history, which
must have come sooner or later in any circumstances, it was
hard to believe that life with her would have been productive
of further happiness.

But as a memory, notwithstanding such conditions, Lucetta's image still lived on with him, her weaknesses provoking only the gentlest criticism, and her sufferings attenuating wrath at her concealments to a momentary spark now and then.

By the end of a year Henchard's little retail seed and grain shop, not much larger than a cupboard, had developed its trade considerably, and the stepfather and daughter enjoyed much serenity in the pleasant, sunny corner in which it stood. The quiet bearing of one who brimmed with an inner activity characterized Elizabeth-Jane at this period. She took long walks into the country two or three times a week, mostly in the direction of Budmouth. Sometimes it occurred to him that when she sat with him in the evening after these invigorating walks she was civil rather than affectionate; and he was troubled; one more bitter regret being added to those he had already experienced at having, by his severe censorship, frozen up her precious affection when originally offered.

She had her own way in everything now. In going and coming, in buying and selling, her word was law.

"You have got a new muff, Elizabeth," he said to her one day quite humbly.

"Yes; I bought it," she said.

He looked at it again as it lay on an adjoining table. The fur was of a glossy brown, and, though he was no judge of such articles, he thought it seemed an unusually good one for her to possess.

"Rather costly, I suppose, my dear, was it not?" he hazarded.

"It was rather above my figure," she said quietly. "But it is not showy."

"O no," said the netted lion, anxious not to pique her in the least.

Some little time after, when the year had advanced into another spring, he paused opposite her empty bedroom in passing it. He thought of the time when she had cleared out of his then large and handsome house in Corn Street, in consequence of his dislike and harshness, and he had looked into her chamber in just the same way. The present room was much humbler, but what struck him about it was the abundance of books lying everywhere. Their number and quality made the meager furniture that supported them seem absurdly disproportionate. Some, indeed many, must have been recently purchased; and though he encouraged her to buy in reason, he had no notion that she indulged her innate passion so extensively in proportion to the narrowness of their income. For the first time he felt a little hurt by what he thought her extravagance, and resolved to say a word to her about it. But, before he had found the courage to speak an event happened which set his thoughts flying in quite another direction.

The busy time of the seed trade was over; and the quiet weeks that preceded the hay season had come—setting their special stamp upon Casterbridge by thronging the market with wood rakes, new wagons in yellow, green, and red, formidable scythes, and pitchforks of prong sufficient to skewer up a small family. Henchard, contrary to his wont, went out one Saturday afternoon toward the market place, from a curious feeling that he would like to pass a few minutes on the spot of his former triumphs. Farfrae, to whom he was still a comparative stranger, stood a few steps below the Corn Exchange door—a usual position with him at this hour—and he appeared lost in thought about something he was looking at a little way off.

Henchard's eyes followed Farfrae's, and he saw that the object of his gaze was no sample-showing farmer, but his own stepdaughter, who had just come out of a shop over the way. She, on her part, was quite unconscious of his attention, and in this was less fortunate than those young women whose very plumes, like those of Juno's bird,[1] are set with Argus eyes whenever possible admirers are within ken.

1. *Juno's bird:* peacock. Argus had a hundred eyes, and was transformed to a peacock.

Henchard went away, thinking that perhaps there was nothing significant after all in Farfrae's look at Elizabeth-Jane at that juncture. Yet he could not forget that the Scotchman had once shown a tender interest in her, of a fleeting kind. Thereupon promptly came to the surface that idiosyncrasy of Henchard's which had ruled his courses from the beginning and had mainly made him what he was. Instead of thinking that a union between his cherished stepdaughter and the energetic thriving Donald was a thing to be desired for her good and his own, he hated the very possibility.

Time had been when such instinctive opposition would have taken shape in action. But he was not now the Henchard of former days. He schooled himself to accept her will, in this as in other matters, as absolute and unquestionable. He dreaded lest an antagonistic word should lose for him such regard as he had regained from her by his devotion, feeling that to retain this under separation was better than to incur her dislike by keeping her near.

But the mere thought of such separation fevered his spirit much, and in the evening he said, with the stillness of suspense: "Have you seen Mr. Farfrae today, Elizabeth?"

Elizabeth-Jane started at the question; and it was with some confusion that she replied "No."

"Oh—that's right—that's right. . . . It was only that I saw him in the street when we both were there." He was wondering if her embarrassment justified him in a new suspicion—that the long walks which she had latterly been taking, that the new books which had so surprised him, had anything to do with the young man. She did not enlighten him, and lest silence should allow her to shape thoughts unfavorable to their present friendly relations, he diverted the discourse into another channel.

Henchard was, by original make, the last man to act stealthily, for good or for evil. But the *solicitus timor*[2] of his love—

2. *Solicitus timor:* anxious fear.

the dependence upon Elizabeth's regard into which he had declined (or, in another sense, to which he had advanced)—denaturalized him. He would often weigh and consider for hours together the meaning of such and such a deed or phrase of hers, when a blunt settling question would formerly have been his first instinct. And now, uneasy at the thought of a passion for Farfrae which should entirely displace her mild sympathy with himself, he observed her going and coming more narrowly.

There was nothing secret in Elizabeth-Jane's movements beyond what habitual reserve induced; and it may at once be owned on her account that she was guilty of occasional conversations with Donald when they chanced to meet. Whatever the origin of her walks on the Budmouth Road, her return from those walks was often coincident with Farfrae's emergence from Corn Street for a twenty minutes' blow on that rather windy highway—just to winnow the seeds and chaff out of him before sitting down to tea, as he said. Henchard became aware of this by going to the Ring, and, screened by its enclosure, keeping his eye upon the road till he saw them meet. His face assumed an expression of extreme anguish.

"Of her, too, he means to rob me!" he whispered. "But he has the right. I do not wish to interfere."

The meeting, in truth, was of a very innocent kind, and matters were by no means so far advanced between the young people as Henchard's jealous grief inferred. Could he have heard such conversation as passed he would have been enlightened thus much:—

He.—"You like walking this way, Miss Henchard—and is it not so?" (uttered in his undulatory accents, and with an appraising, pondering gaze at her).

She.—"O yes. I have chosen this road latterly. I have no great reason for it."

He.—"But that may make a reason for others."

She (reddening).—"I don't know that. My reason, however, such as it is, is that I wish to get a glimpse of the sea every day."

He.—"Is it a secret why?"

She (reluctantly).—"Yes."

He (with the pathos of one of his native ballads).—"Ah, I doubt there will be any good in secrets! A secret cast a deep shadow over my life. And well you know what it was."

Elizabeth admitted that she did, but she refrained from confessing why the sea attracted her. She could not herself account for it fully, not knowing the secret possibly to be that, in addition to early marine associations, her blood was a sailor's.

"Thank you for those new books, Mr. Farfrae," she added shyly. "I wonder if I ought to accept so many!"

"Ay! Why not? It gives me more pleasure to get them for you, than you to have them!"

"It cannot!"

They proceeded along the road together till they reached the town, and their paths diverged.

Henchard vowed that he would leave them to their own devices, put nothing in the way of their courses, whatever they might mean. If he were doomed to be bereft of her, so it must be. In the situation which their marriage would create he could see no *locus standi*[3] for himself at all. Farfrae would never recognize him more than superciliously; his poverty ensured that, no less than his past conduct. And so Elizabeth would grow to be a stranger to him, and the end of his life would be friendless solitude.

With such a possibility impending he could not help watchfulness. Indeed, within certain lines, he had the right to keep an eye upon her as his charge. The meetings seemed to become matters of course with them on special days of the week.

---

3. *Locus standi:* standing place.

At last full proof was given him. He was standing behind a wall close to the place at which Farfrae encountered her. He heard the young man address her as "Dearest Elizabeth-Jane," and then kiss her, the girl looking quickly round to assure herself that nobody was near.

When they were gone their way Henchard came out from the wall, and mournfully followed them to Casterbridge. The chief looming trouble in this engagement had not decreased. Both Farfrae and Elizabeth-Jane, unlike the rest of the people, must suppose Elizabeth to be his actual daughter, from his own assertion while he himself had the same belief; and though Farfrae must have so far forgiven him as to have no objection to own him as a father-in-law, intimate they could never be. Thus would the girl, who was his only friend, be withdrawn from him by degrees through her husband's influence, and learn to despise him.

Had she lost her heart to any other man in the world than the one he had rivaled, cursed, wrestled with for life in days before his spirit was broken, Henchard would have said, "I am content." But content with the prospect as now depicted was hard to acquire.

There is an outer chamber of the brain in which thoughts unowned, unsolicited, and of noxious kind, are sometimes allowed to wander for a moment prior to being sent off whence they came. One of these thoughts sailed into Henchard's ken now.

Suppose he were to communicate to Farfrae the fact that his betrothed was not the child of Michael Henchard at all—legally, nobody's child; how would that correct and leading townsman receive the information? He might possibly forsake Elizabeth-Jane, and then she would be her stepsire's own again.

Henchard shuddered, and exclaimed, "God forbid such a thing! Why should I still be subject to these visitations of the devil, when I try so hard to keep him away?"

CHAPTER 43

WHAT HENCHARD saw thus early was, naturally enough, seen at a little later date by other people. That Mr. Farfrae "walked with that bankrupt Henchard's stepdaughter, of all women," became a common topic in the town, the simple perambulating term being used hereabout to signify a wooing; and the nineteen superior young ladies of Casterbridge, who had each looked upon herself as the only woman capable of making the merchant Councilman happy, indignantly left off going to the church Farfrae attended, left off conscious mannerisms, left off putting him in their prayers at night amongst their blood relations; in short, reverted to their natural courses.

Perhaps the only inhabitants of the town to whom this looming choice of the Scotchman's gave unmixed satisfaction were the members of the philosophic party, which included Longways, Christopher Coney, Billy Wills, Mr. Buzzford, and the like. The Three Mariners having been, years before, the house in which they had witnessed the young man and woman's first and humble appearance on the Casterbridge stage, they took a kindly interest in their career, not unconnected, perhaps, with visions of festive treatment at their hands hereafter. Mrs. Stannidge, having rolled into the large parlor one evening and said that it was a wonder such a man as Mr. Farfrae, "a pillow of the town," who might have chosen one of the daughters of the professional men or private residents, should stoop so low, Coney ventured to disagree with her.

"No, ma'am, no wonder at all. 'Tis she that's a stooping to he—that's my opinion. A widow man—whose first wife was no credit to him—what is it for a young perusing woman that's her own mistress and well liked? But as a neat patching up of things I see much good in it. When a man have put up a tomb of best marblestone to the other one, as he've done, and weeped his fill, and thought it all over, and said to hisself,

'T'other took me in; I knowed this one first; she's a sensible piece for a partner, and there's no faithful woman in high life now;'—well, he may do worse than not to take her, if she's tender-inclined."

Thus they talked at the Mariners. But we must guard against a too liberal use of the conventional declaration that a great sensation was caused by the prospective event, that all the gossips' tongues were set wagging thereby, and so on, even though such a declaration might lend some eclat to the career of our poor only heroine. When all has been said about busy rumorers, a superficial and temporary thing is the interest of anybody in affairs which do not directly touch them. It would be a truer representation to say that Casterbridge (ever excepting the nineteen young ladies) looked up for a moment at the news, and withdrawing its attention, went on laboring and victualing, bringing up its children, and burying its dead, without caring a tittle for Farfrae's domestic plans.

Not a hint of the matter was thrown out to her stepfather by Elizabeth herself or by Farfrae either. Reasoning on the cause of their reticence he concluded that, estimating him by his past, the throbbing pair were afraid to broach the subject, and looked upon him as an irksome obstacle whom they would be heartily glad to get out of the way. Embittered as he was against society, this moody view of himself took deeper and deeper hold of Henchard, till the daily necessity of facing mankind, and of them particularly Elizabeth-Jane, became well-nigh more than he could endure. His health declined; he became morbidly sensitive. He wished he could escape those who did not want him and hide his head for ever.

But what if he were mistaken in his views, and there were no necessity that his own absolute separation from her should be involved in the incident of her marriage?

He proceeded to draw a picture of the alternative—himself living like a fangless lion about the back rooms of a house in which his stepdaughter was mistress; an inoffensive old man, tenderly smiled on by Elizabeth, and good-naturedly tolerated by her husband. It was terrible to his pride to think of descending so low; and yet, for the girl's sake he might put up with anything; even from Farfrae; even snubbings and masterful tongue-scourgings. The privilege of being in the house she occupied would almost outweigh the personal humiliation.

Whether this were a dim possibility or the reverse, the courtship—which it evidently now was—had an absorbing interest for him.

Elizabeth, as has been said, often took her walks on the Budmouth Road, and Farfrae as often made it convenient to create an accidental meeting with her there. Two miles out, a quarter of a mile from the highway, was the prehistoric fort called Mai Dun, of huge dimensions and many ramparts, within or upon whose enclosures a human being, as seen from the road, was but an insignificant speck. Hitherward Henchard often resorted, glass in hand, and scanned the hedgeless *via*[1]—for it was the original track laid out by the legions of the Empire—to a distance of two or three miles, his object being to read the progress of affairs between Farfrae and his charmer.

One day Henchard was at this spot when a masculine figure came along the road from Budmouth, and lingered. Applying his telescope to his eye Henchard expected that Farfrae's features would be disclosed as usual. But the lenses revealed that today the man was not Elizabeth-Jane's lover.

It was one clothed as a merchant captain; and as he turned in his scrutiny of the road he revealed his face. Henchard lived a lifetime the moment he saw it. The face was Newson's.

Henchard dropped the glass, and for some seconds made no other movement. Newson waited, and Henchard waited—if that could be called a waiting which was a transfixture. But Elizabeth-Jane did not come. Something or other had caused

1. *Via:* Roman road.

her to neglect her customary walk that day. Perhaps Farfrae
and she had chosen another road for variety's sake. But what
did that amount to? She might be here tomorrow, and in any
case Newson, if bent on a private meeting and a revelation of
the truth to her, would soon make his opportunity.

Then he would tell her not only of his paternity, but of the
ruse by which he had been once sent away. Elizabeth's strict
nature would cause her for the first time to despise her stepfather, would root out his image as that of an arch-deceiver,
and Newson would reign in her heart in his stead.

But Newson did not see anything of her that morning. Having stood still awhile he at last retraced his steps, and Henchard felt like a condemned man who has a few hours' respite.
When he reached his own house he found her there.

"O Father!" she said innocently, "I have had a letter—a
strange one—not signed. Somebody has asked me to meet
him, either on the Budmouth Road at noon today, or in the
evening at Mr. Farfrae's. He says he came to see me some time
ago, but a trick was played him, so that he did not see me. I
don't understand it; but between you and me I think Donald
is at the bottom of the mystery, and that it is a relation of his
who wants to pass an opinion on his choice. But I did not like
to go till I had seen you. Shall I go?"

Henchard replied heavily, "Yes; go."

The question of his remaining in Casterbridge was forever
disposed of by this closing in of Newson on the scene. Henchard was not the man to stand the certainty of condemnation
on a matter so near his heart. And being an old hand at bearing
anguish in silence, and haughty withal, he resolved to make
as light as he could of his intention, while immediately taking
his measures.

He surprised the young woman whom he had looked upon
as his all in this world by saying to her, as if he did not care
about her more: "I am going to leave Casterbridge, Elizabeth-
Jane."

"Leave Casterbridge!" she cried, "and leave—me?"

"Yes, this little shop can be managed by you alone as well as by us both; I don't care about shops and streets and folk— I would rather get into the country by myself, out of sight, and follow my own ways, and leave you to yours."

She looked down and her tears fell silently. It seemed to her that this resolve of his had come on account of her attachment and its probable result. She showed her devotion to Farfrae, however, by mastering her emotion and speaking out.

"I am sorry you have decided on this," she said with difficult firmness. "For I thought it probable—possible—that I might marry Mr. Farfrae some little time hence, and I did not know that you disapproved of the step!"

"I approve of anything you desire to do, Izzy," said Henchard huskily. "If I did not approve it would be no matter! I wish to go away. My presence might make things awkward in the future; and, in short, it is best that I go."

Nothing that her affection could urge would induce him to reconsider his determination; for she could not urge what she did not know—that when she should learn he was not related to her other than as a stepparent she would refrain from despising him, and that when she knew what he had done to keep her in ignorance she would refrain from hating him. It was his conviction that she would not so refrain; and there existed as yet neither word nor event which could argue it away.

"Then," she said at last, "you will not be able to come to my wedding; and that is not as it ought to be."

"I don't want to see it—I don't want to see it!" he exclaimed; adding more softly, "but think of me sometimes in your future life—you'll do that, Izzy?—think of me when you are living as the wife of the richest, the foremost man in the town, and don't let my sins, *when you know them all*, cause 'ee to quite forget that though I loved 'ee late I loved 'ee well."

"It is because of Donald!" she sobbed.

"I don't forbid you to marry him," said Henchard. "Prom-

ise not to quite forget me when——" He meant when Newson should come.

She promised mechanically, in her agitation; and the same
evening at dusk Henchard left the town to whose development he had been one of the chief stimulants for many years.
During the day he had bought a new tool basket, cleaned
up his old hay knife and wimble, set himself up in fresh
leggings, knee-naps and corduroys, and in other ways gone
back to the working clothes of his young manhood, dis-
carding forever the shabby-genteel suit of cloth and rusty
silk hat that since his decline had characterized him in the
Casterbridge street as a man who had seen better days.

He went secretly and alone, not a soul of the many who
had known him being aware of his departure. Elizabeth-Jane
accompanied him as far as the second bridge on the highway
—for the hour of her appointment with the unguessed visitor
at Farfrae's had not yet arrived—and parted from him with
unfeigned wonder and sorrow, keeping him back a minute or
two before finally letting him go. She watched his form diminish across the moor, the yellow rush basket at his back
moving up and down with each tread, and the creases behind
his knees coming and going alternately till she could no longer
see them. Though she did not know it Henchard formed
at this moment much the same picture as he had presented
when entering Casterbridge for the first time nearly a quarter
of a century before; except, to be sure, that the serious
addition to his years had considerably lessened the spring of
his stride, that his state of hopelessness had weakened him,
and imparted to his shoulders, as weighted by the basket, a
perceptible bend.

He went on till he came to the first milestone, which stood
in the bank, half way up a steep hill. He rested his basket
on the top of the stone, placed his elbows on it, and gave
way to a convulsive twitch, which was worse than a sob,
because it was so hard and so dry.

"If I had only got her with me—if I only had!" he said.

"Hard work would be nothing to me then! But that was not to be. I—Cain—go alone as I deserve—an outcast and a vagabond. But my punishment is *not* greater than I can bear!"

He sternly subdued his anguish, shouldered his basket, and went on.

Elizabeth, in the meantime, had breathed him a sigh, recovered her equanimity, and turned her face to Casterbridge. Before she had reached the first house she was met in her walk by Donald Farfrae. This was evidently not their first meeting that day; they joined hands without ceremony, and Farfrae anxiously asked, "And is he gone—and did you tell him?—I mean of the other matter—not of ours."

"He is gone; and I told him all I knew of your friend. Donald, who is he?"

"Well, well, dearie; you will know soon about that. And Mr. Henchard will hear of it if he does not go far."

"He will go far—he's bent upon getting out of sight and sound!"

She walked beside her lover, and when they reached the Crossways, or Bow, turned with him into Corn Street instead of going straight on to her own door. At Farfrae's house they stopped and went in.

Farfrae flung open the door of the ground-floor sitting room, saying, "There he is waiting for you," and Elizabeth entered. In the armchair sat the broadfaced genial man who had called on Henchard on a memorable morning between one and two years before this time, and whom the latter had seen mount the coach and depart within half an hour of his arrival. It was Richard Newson. The meeting with the light-hearted father from whom she had been separated half-a-dozen years, as if by death, need hardly be detailed. It was an affecting one, apart from the question of paternity. Henchard's departure was in a moment explained. When the true facts came to be handled the difficulty of restoring her to her old belief in Newson was not so great as might have seemed likely, for Henchard's conduct itself was a proof that those

facts were true. Moreover, she had grown up under Newson's paternal care; and even had Henchard been her father
in nature, this father in early domiciliation might almost have
carried the point against him, when the incidents of her parting with Henchard had a little worn off.

Newson's pride in what she had grown up to be was more
than he could express. He kissed her again and again.

"I've saved you the trouble to come and meet me—ha-ha!"
said Newson. "The fact is that Mr. Farfrae here, he said,
'Come up and stop with me for a day or two, Captain Newson, and I'll bring her round.' 'Faith,' says I, 'so I will;' and
here I am."

"Well, Henchard is gone," said Farfrae, shutting the door.
"He has done it all voluntarily, and, as I gather from Elizabeth,
he has been very nice with her. I was got rather uneasy; but all
is as it should be, and we will have no more deefficulties at all."

"Now, that's very much as I thought," said Newson, looking into the face of each by turns. "I said to myself, ay, a
hundred times, when I tried to get a peep at her unknown
to herself—'Depend upon it, 'tis best that I should live on
quiet for a few days like this till something turns up for the
better.' I now know you are all right, and what can I wish
for more?"

"Well, Captain Newson, I will be glad to see ye here every
day now, since it can do no harm," said Farfrae. "And what
I've been thinking is that the wedding may as well be kept
under my own roof, the house being large, and you being in
lodgings by yourself—so that a great deal of trouble and
expense would be saved ye?—and 'tis a convenience when a
couple's married not to hae far to go to get home!"

"With all my heart," said Captain Newson; "since, as ye
say, it can do no harm, now poor Henchard's gone; though
I wouldn't have done it otherwise, or put myself in his way
at all; for I've already in my lifetime been an intruder into
his family quite as far as politeness can be expected to put up
with. But what do the young woman say herself about it?

Elizabeth, my child, come and hearken to what we be talking about, and not bide staring out o' the window as if ye didn't hear."

"Donald and you must settle it," murmured Elizabeth, still keeping up a scrutinizing gaze at some small object in the street.

"Well, then," continued Newson, turning anew to Farfrae with a face expressing thorough entry into the subject, "that's how we'll have it. And, Mr. Farfrae, as you provide so much, and house room, and all that, I'll do my part in the drinkables, and see to the rum and schiedam—maybe a dozen jars will be sufficient?—as many of the folk will be ladies, and perhaps they won't drink hard enough to make a high average in the reckoning? But you know best. I've provided for men and shipmates times enough, but I'm as ignorant as a child how many glasses of grog a woman, that's not a drinking woman, is expected to consume at these ceremonies?"

"Oh, none—we'll no want much of that—O no!" said Farfrae, shaking his head with appalled gravity. "Do you leave all to me."

When they had gone a little further in these particulars Newson, leaning back in his chair and smiling reflectively at the ceiling, said, "I've never told ye, or have I, Mr. Farfrae, how Henchard put me off the scent that time?"

He expressed ignorance of what the Captain alluded to.

"Ah, I thought I hadn't. I resolved that I would not, I remember, not to hurt the man's name. But now he's gone I can tell ye. Why, I came to Casterbridge nine or ten months before that day last week that I found ye out. I had been here twice before then. The first time I passed through the town on my way westward, not knowing Elizabeth lived here. Then hearing at some place—I forget where—that a man of the name of Henchard had been mayor here, I came back, and called at his house one morning. The old rascal!—he said Elizabeth-Jane had died years ago."

Elizabeth now gave earnest heed to his story.

"Now, it never crossed my mind that the man was selling me a packet," continued Newson. "And, if you'll believe me, I was that upset, that I went back to the coach that had brought me, and took passage onward without lying in the town half an hour. Ha-ha!—'twas a good joke, and well carried out, and I give the man credit for't!"

Elizabeth-Jane was amazed at the intelligence. "A joke?— O no!" she cried. "Then he kept you from me, Father, all those months, when you might have been here?"

The father admitted that such was the case.

"He ought not to have done it!" said Farfrae.

Elizabeth sighed. "I said I would never forget him. But O! I think I ought to forget him now!"

Newson, like a good many rovers and sojourners among strange men and strange moralities, failed to perceive the enormity of Henchard's crime, notwithstanding that he himself had been the chief sufferer therefrom. Indeed, the attack upon the absent culprit waxing serious, he began to take Henchard's part.

"Well, 'twas not ten words that he said, after all," Newson pleaded. "And how could he know that I should be such a simpleton as to believe him? 'Twas as much my fault as his, poor fellow!"

"No," said Elizabeth-Jane firmly, in her revulsion of feeling. "He knew your disposition—you always were so trusting, Father; I've heard my mother say so hundreds of times—and he did it to wrong you. After weaning me from you these five years by saying he was my father, he should not have done this."

Thus they conversed; and there was nobody to set before Elizabeth any extenuation of the absent one's deceit. Even had he been present Henchard might scarce have pleaded it, so little did he value himself or his good name.

"Well, well—never mind—it is all over and past," said Newson good-naturedly. "Now, about this wedding again."

... **CHAPTER 44**

MEANWHILE, the man of their talk had pursued his solitary way eastward till weariness overtook him, and he looked about for a place to rest. His heart was so exacerbated at parting from the girl that he could not face an inn, or even a household of the most humble kind; and entering a field he lay down under a wheat rick, feeling no want of food. The very heaviness of his soul caused him to sleep profoundly.

The bright autumn sun shining into his eyes across the stubble awoke him the next morning early. He opened his basket and ate for his breakfast what he had packed for his supper; and in doing so overhauled the remainder of his kit. Although everything he brought necessitated carriage at his own back, he had secreted among his tools a few of Elizabeth-Jane's cast-off belongings, in the shape of gloves, shoes, a scrap of her handwriting, and the like; and in his pocket he carried a curl of her hair. Having looked at these things he closed them up again, and went onward.

During five consecutive days Henchard's rush basket rode along upon his shoulder between the highway hedges, the new yellow of the rushes catching the eye of an occasional field laborer as he glanced through the quickset, together with the wayfarer's hat and head, and down-turned face, over which the twig shadows moved in endless procession. It now became apparent that the direction of his journey was Weydon Priors, which he reached on the afternoon of the sixth day.

The renowned hill whereon the annual fair had been held for so many generations was now bare of human beings, and almost of aught besides. A few sheep grazed thereabout, but these ran off when Henchard halted upon the summit. He deposited his basket upon the turf, and looked about with sad curiosity; till he discovered the road by which his wife and himself had entered on the upland so memorable to both, five-and-twenty years before.

"Yes, we came up that way," he said, after ascertaining his bearings. "She was carrying the baby, and I was reading a ballet sheet. Then we crossed about here—she so sad and weary, and I speaking to her hardly at all, because of my cursed pride and mortification at being poor. Then we saw the tent—that must have stood more this way." He walked to another spot; it was not really where the tent had stood but it seemed so to him. "Here we went in, and here we sat down. I faced this way. Then I drank, and committed my crime. It must have been just on that very pixy ring that she was standing when she said her last words to me before going off with him; I can hear their sound now, and the sound of her sobs: 'O Mike! I've lived with thee all this while, and had nothing but temper. Now I'm no more to 'ee—I'll try my luck else-where.' "

He experienced not only the bitterness of a man who finds, in looking back upon an ambitious course, that what he has sacrificed in sentiment was worth as much as what he has gained in substance; but the superadded bitterness of seeing his very recantation nullified. He had been sorry for all this long ago; but his attempts to replace ambition by love had been as fully foiled as his ambition itself. His wronged wife had foiled them by a fraud so grandly simple as to be almost a virtue. It was an odd sequence that out of all this tampering with social law came that flower of Nature, Elizabeth. Part of his wish to wash his hands of life arose from his perception of its contrarious inconsistencies—of Nature's jaunty readiness to support unorthodox social principles.

He intended to go on from this place—visited as an act of penance—into another part of the country altogether. But he could not help thinking of Elizabeth, and the quarter of the horizon in which she lived. Out of this it happened that the centrifugal tendency imparted by weariness of the world was counteracted by the centripetal influence of his love for his stepdaughter. As a consequence, instead of following a straight course yet further away from Casterbridge, Henchard gradually, almost unconsciously, deflected from that right line of his first intention; till, by degrees, his wandering, like that of the Canadian woodsman, became part of a circle of which Casterbridge formed the center. In ascending any particular hill he ascertained the bearings as nearly as he could by means of the sun, moon, or stars, and settled in his mind the exact direction in which Casterbridge and Elizabeth-Jane lay. Sneering at himself for his weakness he yet every hour— nay, every few minutes—conjectured her actions for the time being—her sitting down and rising up, her goings and comings, till thought of Newson's and Farfrae's counter-influence would pass like a cold blast over a pool, and efface her image. And then he would say of himself, "O you fool! All this about a daughter who is no daughter of thine!"

At length he obtained employment at his own occupation of hay trusser, work of that sort being in demand at this autumn time. The scene of his hiring was a pastoral farm near the old western highway, whose course was the channel of all such communications as passed between the busy centers of novelty and the remote Wessex boroughs. He had chosen the neighborhood of this artery from a sense that, situated here, though at a distance of fifty miles, he was virtually nearer to her whose welfare was so dear than he would be at a roadless spot only half as remote.

And thus Henchard found himself again on the precise standing which he had occupied a quarter of a century before. Externally there was nothing to hinder his making another start on the upward slope, and by his new lights achieving higher things than his soul in its half-formed state had been able to accomplish. But the ingenious machinery contrived by the gods for reducing human possibilities of amelioration to a minimum—which arranges that wisdom to do shall come *pari passu*[1] with the departure of zest for doing—stood in the way of all that. He had no wish to make an arena a second time of a world that had become a mere painted scene to him.

Very often, as his hay knife crunched down among the sweet-smelling grassy stems, he would survey mankind and say to himself: "Here and everywhere be folk dying before their time like frosted leaves, though wanted by their families, the country, and the world; while I, an outcast, an encumberer of the ground, wanted by nobody, and despised by all, live on against my will!"

He often kept an eager ear upon the conversation of those who passed along the road—not from a general curiosity by any means—but in the hope that among these travelers between Casterbridge and London some would, sooner or later, speak of the former place. The distance, however, was too great to lend much probability to his desire; and the highest result of his attention to wayside words was that he did indeed hear the name "Casterbridge" uttered one day by the driver of a road wagon. Henchard ran to the gate of the field he worked in, and hailed the speaker, who was a stranger.

"Yes—I've come from there, maister," he said, in answer to Henchard's inquiry. "I trade up and down, ye know; though, what with this traveling without horses that's getting so common, my work will soon be done."

"Anything moving in the old place, mid I ask?"

"All the same as usual."

"I've heard that Mr. Farfrae, the late mayor, is thinking of getting married. Now is that true or not?"

"I couldn't say for the life o' me. O no, I should think not."

"But yes, John—you forget," said a woman inside the wagon tilt. "What were them packages we carr'd there at the beginning o' the week? Surely they said a wedding was coming off soon—on Martin's Day[2]?"

---

1. *Pari passu:* in the same step (Latin).
2. *Martin's Day:* November 11.

The man declared he remembered nothing about it; and the wagon went on jangling over the hill.

Henchard was convinced that the woman's memory served her well. The date was an extremely probable one, there being no reason for delay on either side. He might, for that matter, write and inquire of Elizabeth; but his instinct for sequestration had made the course difficult. Yet before he left her she had said that for him to be absent from her wedding was not as she wished it to be.

The remembrance would continually revive in him now that it was not Elizabeth and Farfrae who had driven him away from them, but his own haughty sense that his presence was no longer desired. He had assumed the return of Newson without absolute proof that the Captain meant to return; still less that Elizabeth-Jane would welcome him; and with no proof whatever that if he did return he would stay. What if he had been mistaken in his views; if there had been no necessity that his own absolute separation from her he loved should be involved in these untoward incidents? To make one more attempt to be near her: to go back; to see her, to plead his cause before her, to ask forgiveness for his fraud, to endeavor strenuously to hold his own right in her love; it was worth the risk of repulse, ay, of life itself.

But how to initiate this reversal of all his former resolves without causing husband and wife to despise him for his inconsistency was a question which made him tremble and brood.

He cut and cut his trusses two days more, and then he concluded his hesitancies by a sudden reckless determination to go to the wedding festivity. Neither writing nor message would be expected of him. She had regretted his decision to be absent—his unanticipated presence would fill the little unsatisfied corner that would probably have place in her just heart without him.

To intrude as little of his personality as possible upon a gay event with which that personality could show nothing in keeping, he decided not to make his appearance till evening —when stiffness would have worn off, and a gentle wish to let bygones be bygones would exercise its sway in all hearts.

He started on foot, two mornings before St. Martin-tide, allowing himself about sixteen miles to perform for each of the three days' journey, reckoning the wedding day as one. There were only two towns, Melchester and Shottsford, of any importance along his course, and at the latter he stopped on the second night, not only to rest, but to prepare himself for the next evening.

Possessing no clothes but the working suit he stood in—now stained and distorted by their two months of hard usage, he entered a shop to make some purchases which should put him, externally at any rate, a little in harmony with the prevailing tone of the morrow. A rough yet respectable coat and hat, a new shirt and neckcloth, were the chief of these; and having satisfied himself that in appearance at least he would not now offend her, he proceeded to the more interesting particular of buying her some present.

What should that present be? He walked up and down the street, regarding dubiously the display in the shop windows, from a gloomy sense that what he might most like to give her would be beyond his miserable pocket. At length a caged goldfinch met his eye. The cage was a plain and small one, the shop humble, and on inquiry he concluded he could afford the modest sum asked. A sheet of newspaper was tied round the little creature's wire prison, and with the wrapped-up cage in his hand Henchard sought a lodging for the night.

Next day he set out upon the last stage, and was soon within the district which had been his dealing ground in by-gone years. Part of the distance he traveled by carrier, seating himself in the darkest corner at the back of that trader's van; and as the other passengers, mainly women going short journeys, mounted and alighted in front of Henchard, they talked over much local news, not the least portion of this being the wedding then in course of celebration at the town they were nearing. It appeared from their accounts that the town band had been hired for the evening party, and, lest the convivial instincts of that body should get the better of their skill, the further step had been taken of engaging the string band from Budmouth, so that there would be a reserve of harmony to fall back upon in case of need.

He heard, however, but few particulars beyond those known to him already, the incident of the deepest interest on the journey being the soft pealing of the Casterbridge bells, which reached the travelers' ears while the van paused on the top of Yalbury Hill to have the drag lowered. The time was just after twelve o'clock.

Those notes were a signal that all had gone well; that there had been no slip 'twixt cup and lip in this case; that Elizabeth-Jane and Donald Farfrae were man and wife.

Henchard did not care to ride any further with his chattering companions after hearing this sound. Indeed, it quite unmanned him; and in pursuance of his plan of not showing himself in Casterbridge street till evening, lest he should mortify Farfrae and his bride, he alighted here, with his bundle and bird cage, and was soon left as a lonely figure on the broad white highway.

It was the hill near which he had waited to meet Farfrae, almost two years earlier, to tell him of the serious illness of his wife Lucetta. The place was unchanged; the same larches sighed the same notes; but Farfrae had another wife—and, as Henchard knew, a better one. He only hoped that Elizabeth-Jane had obtained a better home than had been hers at the former time.

He passed the remainder of the afternoon in a curious high-strung condition, unable to do much but think of the approaching meeting with her, and sadly satirize himself for his

emotions thereon, as a Samson[3] shorn. Such an innovation on
Casterbridge customs as a flitting of bridegroom and bride
from the town immediately after the ceremony was not
likely, but if it should have taken place he would wait till their
return. To assure himself on this point he asked a market man
when near the borough if the newly-married couple had gone
away, and was promptly informed that they had not; they
were at that hour, according to all accounts, entertaining a
houseful of guests at their home in Corn Street.

Henchard dusted his boots, washed his hands at the river
side, and proceeded up the town under the feeble lamps. He
need have made no inquiries beforehand, for on drawing near
Farfrae's residence it was plain to the least observant that
festivity prevailed within, and that Donald himself shared it,
his voice being distinctly audible in the street, giving strong
expression to a song of his dear native country that he loved so
well as never to have revisited it. Idlers were standing on the
pavement in front; and wishing to escape the notice of these
Henchard passed quickly on to the door.

It was wide open; the hall was lighted extravagantly, and
people were going up and down the stairs. His courage failed
him; to enter footsore, laden, and poorly dressed into the
midst of such resplendency was to bring needless humiliation
upon her he loved, if not to court repulse from her husband.
Accordingly he went round into the street at the back that he
knew so well, entered the garden, and came quietly into the
house through the kitchen, temporarily depositing the bird
and cage under a bush outside, to lessen the awkwardness of
his arrival.

Solitude and sadness had so emolliated Henchard that he
now feared circumstances he would formerly have scorned,
and he began to wish that he had not taken upon himself to

3. *Samson:* Biblical hero who was weakened when his hair was cut.

arrive at such a juncture. However, his progress was made unexpectedly easy by his discovering alone in the kitchen an elderly woman who seemed to be acting as provisional house-keeper during the convulsions from which Farfrae's establishment was just then suffering. She was one of those people whom nothing surprises, and though to her, a total stranger, his request must have seemed odd, she willingly volunteered to go up and inform the master and mistress of the house that "a humble old friend" had come.

On second thoughts she said he had better not wait in the kitchen, but come up into the little back parlor, which was empty. He thereupon followed her thither, and she left him. Just as she had got across the landing to the door of the best parlor a dance was struck up, and she returned to say that she would wait till that was over before announcing him—Mr. and Mrs. Farfrae having both joined in the figure.

The door of the front room had been taken off its hinges to give more space, and that of the room Henchard sat in being ajar, he could see fractional parts of the dancers whenever the gyrations brought them near the doorway, chiefly in the shape of the skirts of dresses and streaming curls of hair; together with about three-fifths of the band in profile, including the restless shadow of a fiddler's elbow, and the tip of the bass-viol bow.

The gaiety jarred upon Henchard's spirits; and he could not quite understand why Farfrae, a much-sobered man, and a widower, who had had his trials, should have cared for it all, notwithstanding the fact that he was quite a young man still, and quickly kindled to enthusiasm by dance and song. That the quiet Elizabeth, who had long ago appraised life at a moderate value, and who knew in spite of her maidenhood that marriage was as a rule no dancing matter, should have had zest for this revelry surprised him still more. However, young people could not be quite old people, he concluded, and custom was omnipotent.

With the progress of the dance the performers spread out somewhat, and then for the first time he caught a glimpse of the once despised daughter who had mastered him, and made his heart ache. She was in a dress of white silk or satin, he was not near enough to say which—snowy white, without a tinge of milk or cream; and the expression of her face was one of nervous pleasure rather than of gaiety. Presently Farfrae came round, his exuberant Scotch movement making him conspicuous in a moment. The pair were not dancing together, but Henchard could discern that whenever the changes of the figure made them the partners of a moment their emotions breathed a much subtler essence than at other times.

By degrees Henchard became aware that the measure was trod by someone who out-Farfraed Farfrae in saltatory intenseness. This was strange, and it was stranger to find that the eclipsing personage was Elizabeth-Jane's partner. The first time that Henchard saw him he was sweeping grandly round, his head quivering and low down, his legs in the form of an X and his back toward the door. The next time he came round in the other direction, his white waistcoat preceding his face, and his toes preceding his white waistcoat. That happy face—Henchard's complete discomfiture lay in it. It was Newson's, who had indeed come and supplanted him.

Henchard pushed to the door, and for some seconds made no other movement. He rose to his feet, and stood like a dark ruin, obscured by "the shade from his own soul upthrown."

But he was no longer the man to stand these reverses unmoved. His agitation was great, and he would fain have been gone, but before he could leave the dance had ended, the housekeeper had informed Elizabeth-Jane of the stranger who awaited her, and she entered the room immediately.

"Oh—it is—Mr. Henchard!" she said, starting back.

"What; Elizabeth?" he cried, as he seized her hand. "What do you say?—*Mr.* Henchard? Don't, don't scourge me like that! Call me worthless old Henchard—anything—but don't

'ee be so cold as this! O my maid—I see you have another—
a real father in my place. Then you know all; but don't give
all your thought to him! Do ye save a little room for me!"

She flushed up, and gently drew her hand away. "I could
have loved you always—I would have, gladly," said she. "But
how can I when I know you have deceived me so—so bitterly
deceived me! You persuaded me that my father was not my
father—allowed me to live on in ignorance of the truth for
years; and then when he, my warm-hearted real father, came
to find me, cruelly sent him away with a wicked invention
of my death, which nearly broke his heart. O how can I love
as I once did a man who has served us like this!"

Henchard's lips half parted to begin an explanation. But
he shut them up like a vise, and uttered not a sound. How
should he, there and then, set before her with any effect the
palliatives of his great faults—that he had himself been deceived in her identity at first, till informed by her mother's
letter that his own child had died; that, in the second accusation, his lie had been the last desperate throw of a gamester
who loved her affection better than his own honor? Among
the many hindrances to such a pleading not the least was this,
that he did not sufficiently value himself to lessen his sufferings by strenuous appeal or elaborate argument.

Waiving, therefore, his privilege of self-defense, he regarded only her discomposure. "Don't ye distress yourself on
my account," he said, with proud superiority. "I would not
wish it—at such a time, too, as this. I have done wrong in
coming to 'ee—I see my error. But it is only for once, so forgive it. I'll never trouble 'ee again, Elizabeth-Jane—no, not
to my dying day! Good night. Good-bye!"

Then, before she could collect her thoughts, Henchard
went out from her rooms, and departed from the house by the
back way as he had come; and she saw him no more.

CHAPTER 45

IT WAS about a month after the day which closed as in the
last chapter. Elizabeth-Jane had grown accustomed to the
novelty of her situation, and the only difference between
Donald's movements now and formerly was that he hastened
indoors rather more quickly after business hours than he had
been in the habit of doing for some time.

Newson had stayed in Casterbridge three days after the
wedding party (whose gaiety, as might have been surmised,
was of his making rather than of the married couple's), and
was stared at and honored as became the returned Crusoe of
the hour. But whether or not because Casterbridge was difficult to excite by dramatic returns and disappearances, through
having been for centuries an assize town, in which sensational
exits from the world, antipodean absences, and such like, were
half-yearly occurrences, the inhabitants did not altogether lose
their equanimity on his account. On the fourth morning he
was discovered disconsolately climbing a hill, in his craving
to get a glimpse of the sea from somewhere or other. The
contiguity of salt water proved to be such a necessity of his
existence that he preferred Budmouth as a place of residence,
notwithstanding the society of his daughter in the other town.
Thither he went, and settled in lodgings in a green-shuttered
cottage which had a bow window, jutting out sufficiently to
afford glimpses of a vertical strip of blue sea to anyone opening the sash, and leaning forward far enough to look through
a narrow lane of tall intervening houses.

Elizabeth-Jane was standing in the middle of her upstairs
parlor, critically surveying some re-arrangement of articles
with her head to one side, when the housemaid came in with
the announcement, "Oh, please ma'am, we know now how
that bird cage came there."

In exploring her new domain during the first week of residence, gazing with critical satisfaction on this cheerful room and that, penetrating cautiously into dark cellars, sallying forth with gingerly tread to the garden, now leaf-strewn by autumn winds, and thus, like a wise field marshal, estimating the capabilities of the site whereon she was about to open her housekeeping campaign—Mrs. Donald Farfrae had discovered in a screened corner a new bird cage, shrouded in newspaper, and at the bottom of the cage a little ball of feathers—the dead body of a goldfinch. Nobody could tell her how the bird and cage had come there; though that the poor little songster had been starved to death was evident. The sadness of the incident had made an impression on her. She had not been able to forget it for days, despite Farfrae's tender banter; and now when the matter had been nearly forgotten it was again revived.

"Oh, please ma'm, we know how that bird cage came there. That farmer's man who called on the evening of the wedding —he was seen wi' it in his hand as he came up the street; and 'tis thoughted that he put it down while he came in with his message, and then went away forgetting where he had left it."

This was enough to set Elizabeth thinking, and in thinking she seized hold of the idea, at one feminine bound, that the caged bird had been brought by Henchard for her as a wedding gift and token of repentance. He had not expressed to her any regrets or excuses for what he had done in the past; but it was a part of his nature to extenuate nothing, and live on as one of his own worst accusers. She went out, looked at the cage, buried the starved little singer, and from that hour her heart softened toward the self-alienated man.

When her husband came in she told him her solution of the bird-cage mystery; and begged Donald to help her in finding out, as soon as possible, whither Henchard had banished himself, that she might make her peace with him; try to do something to render his life less that of an outcast, and more tolerable to him. Although Farfrae had never so passionately liked Henchard as Henchard had liked him, he had, on the other hand, never so passionately hated in the same direction as his former friend had done; and he was therefore not the least indisposed to assist Elizabeth-Jane in her laudable plan.

But it was by no means easy to set about discovering Henchard. He had apparently sunk into the earth on leaving Mr. and Mrs. Farfrae's door. Elizabeth-Jane remembered what he had once attempted; and trembled.

But though she did not know it Henchard had become a changed man since then—as far, that is, as change of emotional basis can justify such a radical phrase; and she needed not to fear. In a few days Farfrae's inquiries elicited that Henchard had been seen by one who knew him walking steadily along the Melchester highway eastward, at twelve o'clock at night —in other words, retracing his steps on the road by which he had come.

This was enough; and the next morning Farfrae might have been discovered driving his gig out of Casterbridge in that direction, Elizabeth-Jane sitting beside him, wrapped in a thick flat fur—the victorine of the period—her complexion somewhat richer than formerly, and an incipient matronly dignity, which the serene Minerva-eyes[1] of one "whose gestures beamed with mind" made becoming, settling on her face. Having herself arrived at a promising haven from at least the grosser troubles of her life, her object was to place Henchard in some similar quietude before he should sink into that lower stage of existence which was only too possible to him now.

After driving along the highway for a few miles they made further inquiries, and learned of a road mender, who had been working thereabouts for weeks, that he had observed such a man at the time mentioned; he had left the Melchester coach road at Weatherbury by a forking highway which skirted the north of Egdon Heath. Into this road they directed the horse's head, and soon were bowling across

1. *Minerva-eyes:* eyes of wisdom.

that ancient country whose surface never had been stirred
to a finger's depth, save by the scratchings of rabbits, since
brushed by the feet of the earliest tribes. The tumuli these
had left behind, dun and shagged with heather, jutted roundly
into the sky from the uplands, as though they were the full
breasts of Diana[2] Multimammia supinely extended there.

They searched Egdon, but found no Henchard. Farfrae
drove onward, and by the afternoon reached the neighborhood of some extension of the heath to the north of Angle-
bury, a prominent feature of which, in the form of a blasted
clump of firs on the summit of a hill, they soon passed under.
That the road they were following had, up to this point,
been Henchard's track on foot they were pretty certain;
but the ramifications which now began to reveal themselves in
the route made further progress in the right direction a matter
of pure guesswork, and Donald strongly advised his wife to
give up the search in person, and trust to other means for obtaining news of her stepfather. They were now a score of
miles at least from home, but, by resting the horse for a couple
of hours at a village they had just traversed, it would be possible to get back to Casterbridge that same day; while to go
much further afield would reduce them to the necessity of
camping out for the night; "and that will make a hole in a
sovereign," said Farfrae. She pondered the position, and
agreed with him.

He accordingly drew rein, but before reversing their direction paused a moment and looked vaguely round upon the
wide country which the elevated position disclosed. While
they looked a solitary human form came from under the
clump of trees, and crossed ahead of them. The person was
some laborer; his gait was shambling, his regard fixed in front
of him as absolutely as if he wore blinkers; and in his hand
he carried a few sticks. Having crossed the road he descended

2. *Diana:* Roman goddess.

into a ravine, where a cottage revealed itself, which he entered.

"If it were not so far away from Casterbridge I should say that must be poor Whittle. 'Tis just like him," observed Elizabeth-Jane.

"And it may be Whittle, for he's never been to the yard these three weeks, going away without saying any word at all; and I owing him for two days' work, without knowing who to pay it to."

The possibility led them to alight, and at least make an inquiry at the cottage. Farfrae hitched the reins to the gate post, and they approached what was of humble dwellings surely the humblest. The walls, built of kneaded clay originally faced with a trowel, had been worn by years of rain-washings to a lumpy crumbling surface, channeled and sunken from its plane, its gray rents held together here and there by a leafy strap of ivy which could scarcely find substance enough for the purpose. The rafters were sunken, and the thatch of the roof in ragged holes. Leaves from the fence had been blown into the corners of the doorway, and lay there undisturbed. The door was ajar; Farfrae knocked; and he who stood before them was Whittle, as they had conjectured.

His face showed marks of deep sadness, his eyes lighting on them with an unfocused gaze; and he still held in his hand the few sticks he had been out to gather. As soon as he recognized them he started.

"What; Abel Whittle; is it that ye are heere?" said Farfrae.

"Ay, yes, sir! You see he was kind-like to Mother when she wer here below, though 'a was rough to me."

"Who are you talking of?"

"O sir—Mr. Henchet! Didn't ye know it? He's just gone—about half an hour ago, by the sun; for I've got no watch to my name."

"Not—dead?" faltered Elizabeth-Jane.

"Yes, ma'am, he's gone! He was kind-like to Mother when

she wer here below, sending her the best ship coal, and hardly
any ashes from it at all; and taties, and such-like that were
very needful to her. I seed en go down street on the night of
your worshipful's wedding to the lady at yer side, and I
thought he looked low and faltering. And I followed en over
Grey's Bridge, and he turned an zeed me, and said, 'You go
back!' But I followed, and he turned again, and said, 'Do you
hear, sir? Go back!' But I zeed that he was low, and I followed
on still. Then 'a said, 'Whittle, what do ye follow me for when
I've told ye to go back all these times?' And I said, 'Because,
sir, I see things be bad with 'ee, and ye wer kind-like to
Mother if ye were rough to me, and I would fain be kind-like
to you.' Then he walked on, and I followed; and he never
complained at me no more. We walked on like that all night;
and in the blue o' the morning, when 'twas hardly day, I
looked ahead o' me, and I zeed that he wambled, and could
hardly drag along. By that time we had got past here, but I
had seen that this house was empty as I went by, and I got him
to come back; and I took down the boards from the windows,
and helped him inside. 'What, Whittle,' he said, 'and can ye
really be such a poor fond fool as to care for such a wretch as
I!' Then I went on further, and some neighborly woodmen
lent me a bed, and a chair, and a few other traps, and we
brought 'em here, and made him as comfortable as we could.
But he didn't gain strength, for you see, ma'am, he couldn't
eat—no, no appetite at all—and he got weaker; and today he
died. One of the neighbors have gone to get a man to measure
him."

"Dear me—is that so!" said Farfrae.

As for Elizabeth, she said nothing.

"Upon the head of his bed he pinned a piece of paper, with
some writing upon it," continued Abel Whittle. "But not
being a man o' letters, I can't read writing; so I don't know
what it is. I can get it and show ye."

They stood in silence while he ran into the cottage; returning in a moment with a crumpled scrap of paper. On it there was penciled as follows:—

MICHAEL HENCHARD'S WILL

That Elizabeth-Jane Farfrae be not told of my death, or made to grieve on account of me.

& that I be not bury'd in consecrated ground.
& that no sexton be asked to toll the bell.
& that nobody is wished to see my dead body.
& that no murners walk behind me at my funeral.
& that no flours be planted on my grave.
& that no man remember me.
To this I put my name.

MICHAEL HENCHARD.

"What are we to do?" said Donald, when he had handed the paper to her.

She could not answer distinctly. "O Donald!" she said at last through her tears, "what bitterness lies there! O I would not have minded so much if it had not been for my unkindness at that last parting! . . . But there's no altering—so it must be."

What Henchard had written in the anguish of his dying was respected as far as practicable by Elizabeth-Jane, though less from a sense of the sacredness of last words, as such, than from her independent knowledge that the man who wrote them meant what he said. She knew the directions to be a piece of the same stuff that his whole life was made of, and hence were not to be tampered with to give herself a mournful pleasure, or her husband credit for large-heartedness.

All was over at last, even her regrets for having misunderstood him on his last visit, for not having searched him out sooner, though these were deep and sharp for a good while. From this time forward Elizabeth-Jane found herself in a latitude of calm weather, kindly and grateful in itself, and doubly so after the Capharnaum[3] in which some of her preceding years had been spent. As the lively and sparkling emotions of her early married life cohered into an equable serenity, the finer movements of her nature found scope in discovering to the narrow-lived ones around her the secret (as she had once learned it) of making limited opportunities endurable; which she deemed to consist in the cunning enlargement, by a species of microscopic treatment, of those minute forms of satisfaction that offer themselves to everybody not in positive pain; which, thus handled, have much of the same inspiriting effect upon life as wider interests cursorily embraced.

Her teaching had a reflex action upon herself, insomuch that she thought she could perceive no great personal difference between being respected in the nether parts of Casterbridge and glorified at the uppermost end of the social world. Her position was, indeed, to a marked degree one that, in the common phrase, afforded much to be thankful for. That she was not demonstratively thankful was no fault of hers. Her experience had been of a kind to teach her, rightly or wrongly, that the doubtful honor of a brief transit through a sorry world hardly called for effusiveness, even when the path was suddenly irradiated at some halfway point by day beams rich as hers. But her strong sense that neither she nor any human being deserved less than was given, did not blind her to the fact that there were others receiving less who had deserved much more. And in being forced to class herself among the fortunate she did not cease to wonder at the persistence of the unforeseen, when the one to whom such unbroken tranquillity had been accorded in the adult stage was she whose youth had seemed to teach that happiness was but the occasional episode in a general drama of pain.

3. *Capharnaum:* a ruined city in Palestine, hence a ruin.

To Enrich Your Reading

Reading a novel can be a richer experience if we ask ourselves questions as we go along. The running dialogue about what is going on—why the characters act the way they do, what connections are there between this event and that, what do we think of this person's behavior, etc.—provides much of our pleasure. The following questions are intended to stimulate this dialogue:

CHAPTERS 1 TO 6

1. What in Henchard's situation makes his strange bargain of the opening chapter believable?
2. When the words *temperament* and *character* are applied to an individual, *temperament* usually refers to his emotional tendencies, *character* to his deepest beliefs and strength of will. What qualities of temperament and character are displayed by Henchard in the bargain incident and in his reaction the following day?
3. What additional traits (of character? temperament? something else, perhaps?) would you think Henchard had to have in order to achieve his rise in Casterbridge?
4. Why does Susan pursue her search for Henchard despite her earlier acceptance of the bargain? What does this show about her?

CHAPTERS 7 TO 15

5. What qualities in Farfrae win Henchard's friendship?

6. While it lasts, how would you describe Henchard's friendship for Farfrae? To what extent is it based on business expediency? Give evidence for your opinion.

7. What is the cause of their first quarrel? What underlying situation makes the effects of the quarrel on Henchard more bitter?

8. *Ambivalence* means having two opposite (ambi) tendencies at the same time. What ambivalence do you find in a) Henchard's treatment of Abel, b) his feeling for Farfrae during the quarrel, and c) his treatment of Susan?

CHAPTERS 16 TO 23

9. Comment on Farfrae's reaction to the note from Henchard requesting that he discontinue attentions to Elizabeth-Jane.

10. Explain Mother Cuxsom's remarks after Susan's death: ". . . why should death rob life of fourpence? . . . her wishes and ways will all be as nothing." What do these remarks contribute to the scene and to the novel as a whole?

11. What effect does Henchard's premature reading of Susan's letter have on his relationship with Elizabeth-Jane? What might have developed had he not read the letter? In your opinion, does the author let too much of his story flow from this chance action? Explain your opinion. (Be on the lookout for later situations in which chance plays an important part.)

12. Why is Henchard finally reluctant to let Elizabeth-Jane leave his house?

13. To what extent is Lucetta frank in her dealings with Elizabeth-Jane? Explain your view.

14. What feelings lead Lucetta to prefer Farfrae over Henchard?

CHAPTERS 24 TO 28

15. What circumstances lead to Henchard's speculation that a "power" outside himself has caused his financial loss?
16. What other evidence is there of a superstitious streak in Henchard?
17. What connection is there between his readiness to surrender to superstition and the manner of his hiring and firing Jopp?
18. Henchard's action in admitting to the truth of the furmity woman's accusation and then withdrawing as her judge appears very honorable. How consistent do you find this behavior with his actions in the preceding scene?

CHAPTERS 29 TO 37

19. "You ought to marry Mr. Henchard or nobody—certainly not another man!" is Elizabeth-Jane's advice to Lucetta. Explain the reasoning behind this view. Might Elizabeth-Jane have any deeper motives she herself is not aware of?
20. How is Henchard's ruin accepted by his creditors? His former workmen, now employed by Farfrae? How do these reactions each illuminate the kind of man Henchard is?
21. What is Henchard's intention in picking up the letters from Farfrae's house? Why does he stop short of carrying it out? ·
22. What are the motives of those who plan the skimmity ride? Do you think they represent the forces of virtue and justice? Explain your opinion.
23. "He drove me back as if I were a bull breaking fence," is Henchard's reflection on Farfrae's treatment of him during the royal visit. In what ways is *bull* an apt image for Henchard? Recall another occasion in which a bull and Henchard are associated.

CHAPTERS 38 TO 45

24. What makes Henchard stop short of taking Farfrae's life in the granary? What previous incident does this call to mind? In what sense does Henchard seem to have conquered a "bull" a second time?

25. Tell why you think Henchard was right or wrong in lying to Newson.

26. As Henchard leaves Casterbridge, he says, "I—Cain—go alone as I deserve—an outcast and a vagabond. But my punishment is not greater than I can bear!" What does this show about the effects of Henchard's experience? Explain the reference to Cain.

27. Describe Elizabeth-Jane's treatment of Henchard immediately after the disclosure of his lie and later at the wedding party. What similarity is there to her earlier judgment of Lucetta?

28. How does the solution of the "bird-cage mystery" affect the views of Elizabeth-Jane? Describe her philosophy of life as she grows older. Is it an acceptable philosophy for you?

SETTING

Setting is usually defined as the place and time of a story—in a word, where and when it is "set." In the hands of a skillful writer it is also something more. It is an atmosphere—a feeling about the place and time that adds meaning to the action.

In all the novels of Thomas Hardy the setting is roughly the same, a rural section of southern England in the nineteenth century. Hardy gives this area a name, Wessex, and establishes an entire geography for it, including waterways, towns, and roads. Although fictitious, Wessex corresponds to a real place that Hardy knew well. The town of Casterbridge, for example, is Dorchester, where the author had a home during a large part of his adult life. Yet the actuality of Wessex is less important than its particular atmospheric uses in the novels. The following questions will help you to recognize some of these uses in *The Mayor of Casterbridge:*

1. How does the atmosphere of the fair at Weydon-Priors help you to accept the strange opening action?
2. Describe Casterbridge in terms of its size and its connection to the countryside. What makes this place more suitable than a large metropolitan city for a tale of the rise and fall of a man like Henchard?
3. The Ring (the Roman amphitheater) and the execution gibbet are remnants of other eras. In which incidents in the story do these places figure? What point is made by bringing up reminders of the past in the narration of current incidents?
4. In what ways do the two inns, The Three Mariners and Peter's Finger, contribute to the story? How are they different from one another? How do they add to our understanding of Casterbridge? In what ways do the comments of their patrons contribute to the novel? (If you have read any ancient Greek plays, what feature of these plays do the patrons remind you of?)
5. What atmosphere is evoked by the two bridges outside of town? How are the bridges different from one another? How do they figure in the story?

Style and Vocabulary

Hardy's words in *The Mayor of Casterbridge* are generally expressive and exact. They reveal both the actual appearances of things and their moods. In depicting the ruins of the Roman amphitheater, he writes, ". . . the whole was grown over with grass, which now, at the end of summer, was bearded with withered bends that formed waves under the brush of the wind. . . ." Why is *bearded* a well-chosen word? Find other passages that use words with similar skill.

In presenting the conversations of his characters, Hardy demonstrates a sensitivity to their peculiarities of speech and dialect. Henchard speaks in country idiom like the other Wessex natives. ("I did for myself that way thoroughly. I married at eighteen, like the fool that I was; and this is the consequence o't.") Yet the bitter force of the individual man comes out.

See if you can identify the speaker of the following quotations. Be guided not only by *what* is said but by *how* it is said.

1. "I'll no' press ye, sir—I'll no' press ye. I respect your vow."
2. ". . . Come indoors with me and have some supper. Now you shall! I am determined on't."
3. "Yes, yes, . . . I have seen him, and it is enough for me! Now I only want to go—pass away—die."
4. "Ah—I don't mean it seriously! But it is amusing looking for somebody one knows in a crowd, even if one does not want him."
5. ". . . it is so kind of you to get this nice breakfast with your own hands, and I idly asleep the while."

When describing the scene settings, Hardy uses longer words, as well as sentences, than he does elsewhere. This slowing down permits us to savor the atmosphere. It also provides a pleasing contrast with the styles expressing the speech and action of the characters. Occasionally, a less familiar, abstract word (e.g., *aperture*) is used instead of the concrete term (e.g., *opening*). While this is not always an advantage, an alert reader need not be thrown off. By seeing the troublesome word as part of its phrase, sentence, or paragraph, he can usually grasp its meaning without breaking the spell to look it up in a dictionary. (e.g., " . . . a wimble for hay-bonds being also visible in the *aperture*." The clue here is *visible*.)

Below in column 1 are ten of the more difficult words in Chapter One. Exercise your skill in skimming by finding these words in the text, then choose from the twenty possible meanings in column 2 the meaning that applies to each. Write the original word and your choice of its meaning in your notebook. Check the accuracy of your choices with a dictionary. This exercise should prove to you how efficient you can be in comprehending words from their uses in context.

Column 1	*Column 2*
1. desultory	give-and-take
2. reciprocity	introduction
3. taciturnity	conveyance
4. nimbus	meagerness
5. sundry	earthly
6. ochreous	theoretical
7. penuriousness	two-faced
8. hypothetical	derogatory
9. abjure	richness
10. terrestrial	renounce
	common
	dried-up
	various
	cloud
	careless
	green
	silence
	hurtful
	yellowish
	diplomacy

To enlarge your vocabulary, make a list of unfamiliar words after you finish each chapter. Skimming back will help you find them. Guess each meaning from the word's context, and check your guesses by consulting a dictionary. Try using the words in conversation or writing some time during the day. This will help make them a part of your permanent vocabulary.

Related Activities

1. Many important episodes in the life of a character are *not* specifically shown in a novel. They may be summarized in a sentence or hinted at, but they are not presented in full.
   a. State at least one such episode in the lives of: Henchard, Susan, Farfrae, Elizabeth-Jane. Why do you think these episodes are treated so scantily?
   b. Select one such episode and, applying your imagination to whatever you know of the character and situation, write a "chapter" depicting it.
2. Casterbridge is an imaginary place, although it is made to seem very real. From the particulars given in the story, draw a map of the town's layout and main features. Include important buildings and aspects of the surrounding countryside.
3. For outside reading choose another novel set in an imaginary, realistically created place. The following titles, with the fictional location indicated in parentheses, are some from which you might choose. Perhaps your librarian will help you to find others.
   Babbitt by Sinclair Lewis (Zenith)
   Look Homeward, Angel by Thomas Wolfe (Catawba)
   Intruder in the Dust by William Faulkner (Yoknapatawpha County)
   Hard Times by Charles Dickens (Coketown)
   Report on the book to the class, describing the kind of place created, the extent to which, in your opinion, it is

like a real place, and the influence it has on the main characters. Tell how you think Henchard might have fared, had he been placed there. How important is the environment? How important is the man?

4. Look up in a good encyclopedia or other resource book (e.g., *Seeing Roman Britain* by Leonard Cottrell) information on Roman ruins in England. Present your findings to the class, using appropriate illustrations.

5. Write a description of two people entering a place you know well. You may fictionalize, but make the people and place seem real by highlighting the most significant and vivid details. Try to create a dominant feeling about the scene that grows out of the way the people fit in with and react to their surroundings. Study Hardy's technique in the opening chapter of *The Mayor of Casterbridge* for hints.

PYGMALION
A Romance in Five Acts

George Bernard Shaw

A PLAY

GEORGE BERNARD SHAW

The Author and the Play

It is a happy coincidence that the names of Shakespeare and Shaw share the same first three letters. On library shelves their works stand close to one another, which is where they belong. For if Shakespeare is the greatest playwright in the history of the English theater, George Bernard Shaw is the greatest of the twentieth century. By another coincidence, Shaw claims descent from the historical subject of Shakespeare's great play *Macbeth*.

George Bernard Shaw was born of English and—if we go back far enough—Scottish ancestry in Dublin, Ireland, on July 26, 1856. His parents were unhappily married, and early in Shaw's life they separated, his mother moving with her children to London, where she set up as a music teacher. A strong personality, Mrs. Shaw had a profound influence on her son, giving him a background in music and otherwise encouraging his artistic bents. At the age of fifteen, young Shaw held a clerical job in a real-estate office. Restive in these prosaic surroundings, he left after four years, and for about a decade following he permitted himself to be supported by his mother while he worked on five unsuccessful novels and poorly paid literary hack work. It was during this period that he developed an interest in radical social ideas and was active in behalf of reform movements.

Shaw's first regular literary employment was writing music criticism for a newspaper, by which he attracted attention for his understanding and wit. Abandoning the novel at this time, he turned to the writing of dramatic criticism, political tracts, and, finally, plays. Although the unpleasant social themes of his early dramatic efforts brought trouble from the censors, they attracted considerable critical notice, and Shaw began to write almost exclusively for the theater. His first "success" was a satire on war, *Arms and the Man*, presented in 1894. Other popular plays soon followed, including *The Devil's Disciple, Candida*, and *Man and Superman*. The third ranks with Shaw's best works of subsequent years, among which is the selection in this volume, *Pygmalion*, as well as *Heartbreak House, Androcles and the Lion, Caesar and Cleopatra, Major Barbara, Back to Methuselah*, and *Saint Joan*.

Shaw's career as a playwright began in his middle thirties, but his extraordinarily long life permitted him to more than make up for his late start. He was reportedly still at work on a play when on November 2, 1950, at the age of 94, he died following an injury suffered while gardening. He also married late, at the age of 42, and outlived his wife by seven years.

Important as he was as a playwright, Shaw also enjoyed world-wide fame as a "personality." He was a man of cantankerous opinions and great outspokenness, and he had an instinctive gift, once he had an audience, for commanding attention. His views in favor of vegetarianism and a more phonetic alphabet, and in opposition to vaccination and animal vivisection, became as well known as his important social ideas on the use of state controls to promote man's evolution. His almost mystical, optimistic belief in the Life Force, by which man can make his own evolution, received international attention, as much through his vigorous lecturing and pamphleteering as through his plays. Shaw found that he had so much to say on issues raised in his plays that he wrote prefaces, epilogues, and appendices that frequently took up more space in the published volumes than the plays themselves.

A unique quality in all of Shaw's writings is their gaiety. Somber as the theme may be, and however outraged the author at a social wrong, Shaw employs wit, paradox, and humor in his presentation. There is no repressing the man's high spirits which, though they soften anger—or perhaps because they do—nevertheless get the message across.

Pygmalion is one of Shaw's gayest, most charming comedies. It is also, like all of his plays, partly social satire. The amiable inventiveness of plot and the colorful, humorous characterizations are a disguised lecture platform for Shaw's criticisms of society. At no time do the criticisms get in the way, however; in fact, they are vital outgrowths of both situation and character.

The title derives from the old Greek myth of the sculptor Pygmalion, who created a statue that was so life-like an expression of his ideal that he fell in love with it. Out of sympathy for his plight, the gods allowed the statue to come alive as a beautiful woman, Galatea. It is a very real question whether the Pygmalion of the play, the speech teacher Henry Higgins, falls in love with his Galatea, Eliza Doolittle, but in attempting to shape the clay of a lowly personality through his art he simulates the artist of mythology.

Henry Higgins is an artist of phonetics—the sounds of speech. He is capable of pinpointing a person's origin by listening to a few fragments of his conversation. More important, he can, through his teaching, radically alter a person's speech patterns so that the person may be thought to have come from another region, and, with additional training in manners, a different social class. On a bet, he undertakes to transform a London slum girl with appalling speech and gauche manners into a cultured lady accepted in the highest ranks of British society. Eliza Doolittle, Higgins' pupil, is no passive instrument, however. Beneath her acquired social veneer is the spunky, independent creature of the slum alleys.

The clash of personalities between the hard-driving, single-minded artist-teacher, Higgins, and his very apt but not always tractable pupil, Eliza, is one of the great comic man-woman battles in all literature. As a team, the two must be ranked with Kate and Petruchio and Beatrice and Benedick of Shakespeare's *The Taming of the Shrew* and *Much Ado About Nothing*. And, like Shakespeare, with whom Shaw was not too modest to compare himself, Shaw provided his hero and heroine with minor character foils of great richness and charm. Eliza's father, Alfred Doolittle, is a shrewd, witty cockney of awesome loquaciousness and originality of mind. When on the scene, he is always in danger of running away with the play. Higgins' formidable mother, his colleague Pickering, and the various other persons of the drama are in their own rights amusing caricatures.

It has been said that one of Shaw's great dramatic gifts was his ability to bring out "the idea in the man." Each person possesses as part of his humanity a set of ideas that he uses to justify himself. Shaw brings out these ideas, and their inevitable clash with the ideas of others, with unique lucidity. Higgins thus is a spokesman for cool intellect, bachelorhood, and the social transformations to be accomplished by good speech. Eliza speaks for the primacy of personality and womanly feelings over the scientist's callous manipulations. Her gifted father expresses a variety of paradoxical social views, upholding the "undeserving poor," attacking "middle-class morality," and suggesting the uses and abuses of money.

Through these characters and their ideas, as well as through the basic situation in which social barriers are breached through an artifice, Shaw presents a penetrating though good-natured satire of society. If a "crash course" in speech and manners can change the class status of an Eliza Doolittle, how foolish are the ways and pretensions of the socially favored! More hopefully, how much education and money can do to improve the lot of us all! Lest we get too optimistic, however, there are the admonitions of Alfred Doolittle against being "intimidated." There is such a thing as too much improvement, which saps the fun from life.

All of this is presented with such liveliness, wit, and joy that it is not surprising *Pygmalion* has been often revived on the stage with great success. Moreover, in 1938 the play was made into an Academy Award-winning motion picture and in 1956 transformed into the brilliant Broadway musical *My Fair Lady*. In 1964 *My Fair Lady* appeared on film, and a mammoth audience is now acquainted with Shaw's own *Pygmalion*. For this audience, as well as for those who are still unfamiliar with the Higgins-Eliza tale, a reading of *Pygmalion* as originally written by Shaw will be a special delight.

A Note on Shaw's Language

Certain deviations from accepted American punctuation and spelling practices appear in the text of this play. They are Shaw's own innovations, left unchanged out of deference to one of the playwright's favorite causes, language reform. Shaw considered himself a language simplifier and consequently dropped the apostrophe in most contractions and the unsounded vowels in certain words. Curiously, one of his "changes" has been accepted practice in this country for a long time, the omission of the letter *u* in the British -*our* ending (*colour, color*).

Since the play is, in part, about speech, Shaw appended to it a note on his use of the upside down *e* (ə) to represent the indefinite vowel sounds, for which, according to the author, "our wretched alphabet has no letter." He was sufficiently considerate of our present habits, however, to use this symbol sparingly.

There are two versions of the play, one as originally written in 1912 and another as revised by Shaw for the 1938 movie and "for stages furnished with exceptionally elaborate machinery." Since the latter version is fuller, and represents Shaw's most recent text, that is the one used here.[1]

1. The scenes set off by asterisks are those added later.

L*ondon at* 11:15 P.M. *Torrents of heavy summer rain. Cab whistles blowing frantically in all directions. Pedestrians running for shelter into the portico of St Paul's church (not Wren's cathedral but Inigo Jones's[1] church in Covent Garden vegetable market), among them a lady and her daughter in evening dress. All are peering out gloomily at the rain, except one man with his back turned to the rest, wholly preoccupied with a notebook in which he is writing.*

The church clock strikes the first quarter.

THE DAUGHTER. (*In the space between the central pillars, close to the one on her left.*)   I'm getting chilled to the bone. What can Freddy be doing all this time? He's been gone twenty minutes.

THE MOTHER. (*On her daughter's right.*)   Not so long. But he ought to have got us a cab by this.

A BYSTANDER. (*On the lady's right.*)   He wont get no cab not until half-past eleven, missus, when they come back after dropping their theater fares.

THE MOTHER.   But we must have a cab. We cant stand here until half-past eleven. Its too bad.

THE BYSTANDER.   Well, it aint my fault, missus.

THE DAUGHTER.   If Freddy had a bit of gumption, he would have got one at the theater door.

THE MOTHER.   What could he have done, poor boy?

1. *Wren . . . Jones:* Christopher Wren (1632-1723), Inigo Jones (1573-1652), architects.

THE DAUGHTER. Other people got cabs. Why couldnt he? (*Freddy rushes in out of the rain from the Southampton Street side, and comes between them closing a dripping umbrella. He is a young man of twenty, in evening dress, very wet round the ankles.*)

THE DAUGHTER. Well, havnt you got a cab?

FREDDY. Theres not one to be had for love or money.

THE MOTHER. Oh, Freddy, there must be one. You cant have tried.

THE DAUGHTER. It's too tiresome. Do you expect us to go and get one ourselves?

FREDDY. I tell you theyre all engaged. The rain was so sudden: nobody was prepared; and everybody had to take a cab. Ive been to Charing Cross one way and nearly to Ludgate Circus the other; and they were all engaged.

THE MOTHER. Did you try Trafalgar Square?

FREDDY. There wasnt one at Trafalgar Square.

THE DAUGHTER. Did you try?

FREDDY. I tried as far as Charing Cross Station. Did you expect me to walk to Hammersmith?

THE DAUGHTER. You havnt tried at all.

THE MOTHER. You really are very helpless, Freddy. Go again; and dont come back until you have found a cab.

FREDDY. I shall simply get soaked for nothing.

THE DAUGHTER. And what about us? Are we to stay here all night in this draught, with next to nothing on? You selfish pig—

FREDDY. Oh, very well: I'll go, I'll go. (*He opens his umbrella and dashes off Strandwards, but comes into collision with a flower girl who is hurrying in for shelter, knocking her basket out of her hands. A blinding flash of lightning, followed instantly by a rattling peal of thunder, orchestrates the incident.*)

THE FLOWER GIRL. Nah then, Freddy: look wh' y' gowin, deah.

FREDDY. Sorry. (*He rushes off.*).

THE FLOWER GIRL. (*Picking up her scattered flowers and replacing them in the basket.*) Theres menners f' yer! Tɔ-oo banches o voylets trod into the mad. (*She sits down on the plinth of the column, sorting her flowers, on the lady's right. She is not at all a romantic figure. She is perhaps eighteen, perhaps twenty, hardly older. She wears a little sailor hat of black straw that has long been exposed to the dust and soot of London and has seldom if ever been brushed. Her hair needs washing rather badly: its mousy color can hardly be natural. She wears a shoddy black coat that reaches nearly to her knees and is shaped to her waist. She has a brown skirt with a coarse apron. Her boots are much the worse for wear. She is no doubt as clean as she can afford to be; but compared to the ladies she is very dirty. Her features are no worse than theirs; but their condition leaves something to be desired; and she needs the services of a dentist.*)

THE MOTHER. How do you know my son's name is Freddy, pray?

THE FLOWER GIRL. Ow, eez yɔ-ooa san, is e? Wal, fewd dan y' dɔ-ooty bawmz a mather should, eed now bettern to spawl a pore gel's flahrzn than ran awy athaht pyin. Will ye-oo py me f'them?[2] (*Here, with apologies, this desperate attempt to represent her dialect without a phonetic alphabet must be abandoned as unintelligible outside London.*).

THE DAUGHTER. Do nothing of the sort, mother. The idea!

THE MOTHER. Please allow me, Clara. Have you any pennies?

THE DAUGHTER. No. Ive nothing smaller than sixpence.

THE FLOWER GIRL. (*Hopefully.*) I can give you change for a tanner, kind lady.

---

2. Oh, he's your son, is he? Well, if you'd done your duty by him as a mother should, he'd know better than to spoil a poor girl's flowers, then run away without paying. Will you pay me for them?

THE MOTHER. (*To Clara.*)　Give it to me. (*Clara parts reluctantly.*) Now. (*To the girl.*) This is for your flowers.

THE FLOWER GIRL.　Thank you kindly, lady.

THE DAUGHTER.　Make her give you the change. These things are only a penny a bunch.

THE MOTHER.　Do hold your tongue, Clara. (*To the girl.*) You can keep the change.

THE FLOWER GIRL.　Oh, thank you, lady.

THE MOTHER.　Now tell me how you know that young gentleman's name.

THE FLOWER GIRL.　I didn't.

THE MOTHER.　I heard you call him by it. Dont try to deceive me.

THE FLOWER GIRL. (*Protesting.*)　Who's trying to deceive you? I called him Freddy or Charlie same as you might yourself if you was talking to a stranger and wished to be pleasant.

THE DAUGHTER.　Sixpence thrown away! Really, mamma, you might have spared Freddy that. (*She retreats in disgust behind the pillar.*)

　　(*An elderly gentleman of the amiable military type rushes into the shelter and closes a dripping umbrella. He is in the same plight as Freddy, very wet about the ankles. He is in evening dress, with a light overcoat. He takes the place left vacant by the daughter.*)

THE GENTLEMAN.　Phew!

THE MOTHER. (*To the gentleman.*)　Oh, sir, is there any sign of its stopping?

THE GENTLEMAN.　I'm afraid not. It started worse than ever about two minutes ago. (*He goes to the plinth beside the flower girl, puts up his foot on it, and stoops to turn down his trouser ends.*)

THE MOTHER.　Oh dear! (*She retires sadly and joins her daughter.*)

THE FLOWER GIRL. (*Taking advantage of the military gentle-*

man's proximity to establish friendly relations with him.)
If it's worse, it's a sign it's nearly over. So cheer up, Captain,
and buy a flower off a poor girl.

THE GENTLEMAN.   I'm sorry. I havnt any change.

THE FLOWER GIRL.   I can give you change, Captain.

THE GENTLEMAN.   For a sovereign? Ive nothing less.

THE FLOWER GIRL.   Garn! Oh do buy a flower off me, Captain. I can change half-a-crown. Take this for tuppence.

THE GENTLEMAN.   Now dont be troublesome: theres a good
girl. (*Trying his pockets.*) I really havnt any change—Stop:
heres three hapence, if thats any use to you. (*He retreats to
the other pillar.*)

THE FLOWER GIRL. (*Disappointed, but thinking three half-
pence better than nothing.*)   Thank you, sir.

THE BYSTANDER. (*To the girl.*)   You be careful: give him a
flower for it. Theres a bloke here behind taking down every
blessed word youre saying. (*All turn to the man who is taking notes.*)

THE FLOWER GIRL. (*Springing up terrified.*)   I aint done nothing wrong by speaking to the gentleman. Ive a right to sell
flowers if I keep off the curb. (*Hysterically.*) I'm a respectable girl: so help me, I never spoke to him except to ask him
to buy a flower off me.

(*General hubbub, mostly sympathetic to the flower girl,
but deprecating her excessive sensibility. Cries of* Dont
start hollerin. Who's hurting you? Nobody's going to
touch you. Whats the good of fussing? Steady on. Easy
easy, etc., *come from the elderly staid spectators, who pat
her comfortingly. Less patient ones bid her shut her head,
or ask her roughly what is wrong with her. A remoter
group, not knowing what the matter is, crowd in and increase the noise with question and answer:* Whats the
row? What she do? Where is he? A tec[3] taking her down.

3. *Tec:* detective.

W'nat! him? Yes: him over there. Took money off the
gentleman, etc.)

THE FLOWER GIRL. (*Breaking through them to the gentleman,
crying wildly.*) Oh, sir, dont let him charge me. You
dunno what it means to me. Theyll take away my character
and drive me on the streets for speaking to gentlemen.
They—

THE NOTE TAKER. (*Coming forward on her right, the rest
crowding after him.*) There! there! there! there! who's
hurting you, you silly girl? What do you take me for?

THE BYSTANDER. It's aw rawt: e's a gentleman: Look at his
bɔ-oots. (*Explaining to the note taker.*) She thought you
was a copper's nark, sir.

THE NOTE TAKER. (*With quick interest.*) Whats a copper's
nark?

THE BYSTANDER. (*Inept at definition.*) It's a—well, it's a copper's nark, as you might say. What else would you call it?
A sort of informer.

THE FLOWER GIRL. (*Still hysterical.*) I take my Bible oath I
never said a word—

THE NOTE TAKER. (*Overbearing but good-humored.*) Oh,
shut up, shut up. Do I look like a policeman?

THE FLOWER GIRL. (*Far from reassured.*) Then what did you
take down my words for? How do I know whether you
took me down right? You just show me what youve wrote
about me. (*The note taker opens his book and holds it
steadily under her nose, though the pressure of the mob trying to read it over his shoulders would upset a weaker man.*)
What's that? That aint proper writing. I cant read that.

THE NOTE TAKER. I can. (*Reads, reproducing her pronunciation exactly.*) "Cheer ap, Keptin; 'n' baw ya flahr orf a pore
gel."

THE FLOWER GIRL. (*Much distressed.*) It's because I called
him Captain. I meant no harm. (*To the gentleman.*) Oh, sir,

dont let him lay a charge agen me for a word like that. You—

THE GENTLEMAN. Charge! I make no charge. (*To the note taker.*) Really, sir, if you are a detective, you need not begin protecting me against molestation by young women until I ask you. Anybody could see that the girl meant no harm.

THE BYSTANDERS GENERALLY. (*Demonstrating against police espionage.*) Course they could. What business is it of yours? You mind your own affairs. He wants promotion, he does. Taking down people's words! Girl never said a word to him. What harm if she did? Nice thing a girl cant shelter from the rain without being insulted, etc., etc., etc., (*She is conducted by the more sympathetic demonstrators back to her plinth, where she resumes her seat and struggles with her emotion.*)

THE BYSTANDER. He aint a tec. He's a blooming busybody: thats what he is. I tell you, look at his bɔ-oots.

THE NOTE TAKER. (*Turning on him genially.*) And how are all your people down at Selsey?

THE BYSTANDER. (*Suspiciously.*) Who told you my people come from Selsey?

THE NOTE TAKER. Never you mind. They did. (*To the girl.*) How do you come to be up so far east? You were born in Lisson Grove.

THE FLOWER GIRL. (*Appalled.*) Oh, what harm is there in my leaving Lisson Grove? It wasnt fit for a pig to live in; and I had to pay four-and-six a week. (*In tears.*) Oh, boo—hoo—oo—

THE NOTE TAKER. Live where you like; but stop that noise.

THE GENTLEMAN. (*To the girl.*) Come, come! he cant touch you: you have a right to live where you please.

A SARCASTIC BYSTANDER. (*Thrusting himself between the note taker and the gentleman.*) Park Lane, for instance. I'd like to go into the housing question with you, I would.

THE FLOWER GIRL. (*Subsiding into a brooding melancholy over her basket, and talking very low-spiritedly to herself.*) I'm a good girl, I am.

THE SARCASTIC BYSTANDER. (*Not attending to her.*)   Do you know where *I* come from?

THE NOTE TAKER. (*Promptly.*)   Hoxton.
(*Titterings. Popular interest in the note taker's perform-ance increases.*)

THE SARCASTIC ONE. (*Amazed.*)   Well, who said I didnt? Bly me! you know everything, you do.

THE FLOWER GIRL. (*Still nursing her sense of injury.*)   Aint no call to meddle with me, he aint.

THE BYSTANDER. (*To her.*)   Of course he aint. Dont you stand it from him. (*To the note taker.*) See here: what call have you to know about people what never offered to meddle with you?

THE FLOWER GIRL.   Let him say what he likes. I dont want to have no truck with him.

THE BYSTANDER.   You take us for dirt under your feet, dont you? Catch you taking liberties with a gentleman!

THE SARCASTIC BYSTANDER.   Yes: tell him where he come from if you want to go fortune-telling.

THE NOTE TAKER.   Cheltenham, Harrow, Cambridge,[4] and India.

THE GENTLEMAN.   Quite right.
(*Great laughter. Reaction in the note taker's favor. Ex-clamations of* He knows all about it. Told him proper. Hear him tell the toff where he come from? *etc.*)

THE GENTLEMAN.   May I ask, sir, do you do this for your living at a music hall?

THE NOTE TAKER.   I've thought of that. Perhaps I shall some day.

---

4. *Harrow, Cambridge:* Harrow is a famed boys' preparatory school and Cambridge one of the great English universities.

(*The rain has stopped, and the persons on the outside of the crowd begin to drop off.*)

THE FLOWER GIRL. (*Resenting the reaction.*) He's no gentleman, he aint, to interfere with a poor girl.

THE DAUGHTER. (*Out of patience, pushing her way rudely to the front and displacing the gentleman, who politely retires to the other side of the pillar.*) What on earth is Freddy doing? I shall get pneumownia if I stay in this draught any longer.

THE NOTE TAKER. (*To himself, hastily making a note of her pronunciation of "monia."*) Earlscourt.

THE DAUGHTER. (*Violently.*) Will you please keep your impertinent remarks to yourself.

THE NOTE TAKER. Did I say that out loud? I didn't mean to. I beg your pardon. Your mother's Epsom, unmistakably.

THE MOTHER. (*Advancing between the daughter and the note taker.*) How very curious! I was brought up in Largelady Park, near Epsom.

THE NOTE TAKER. (*Uproariously amused.*) Ha! ha! What a devil of a name! Excuse me. (*To the daughter.*) You want a cab, do you?

THE DAUGHTER. Dont dare speak to me.

THE MOTHER. Oh please, please, Clara. (*Her daughter repudiates her with an angry shrug and retires haughtily.*) We should be so grateful to you, sir, if you found us a cab. (*The note taker produces a whistle.*) Oh, thank you. (*She joins her daughter.*)

(*The note taker blows a piercing blast.*)

THE SARCASTIC BYSTANDER. There! I knowed he was a plainclothes copper.

THE BYSTANDER. That aint a police whistle: thats a sporting whistle.

THE FLOWER GIRL. (*Still preoccupied with her wounded feelings.*) He's no right to take away my character. My character is the same to me as any lady's.

THE NOTE TAKER.   I dont know whether youve noticed it;
but the rain stopped about two minutes ago.

THE BYSTANDER.   So it has. Why didn't you say so before?
And us losing our time listening to your silliness! (*He walks
off toward the Strand.*)

THE SARCASTIC BYSTANDER.   I can tell where you come from.
You come from 'Anwell. Go back there.

THE NOTE TAKER. (*Helpfully.*)   Hanwell.

THE SARCASTIC BYSTANDER. (*Affecting great distinction of
speech.*)   Thenk you, teacher. Haw haw! So long. (*He
touches his hat with mock respect and strolls off.*)

THE FLOWER GIRL.   Frightening people like that! How would
he like it himself?

THE MOTHER.   It's quite fine now, Clara. We can walk to a
motor bus. Come. (*She gathers her skirts above her ankles
and hurries off toward the Strand.*)

THE DAUGHTER.   But the cab—(*Her mother is out of hearing.*)
Oh, how tiresome! (*She follows angrily.*)

   (*All the rest have gone except the note taker, the gentleman, and the flower girl, who sits arranging her basket,
   and still pitying herself in murmurs.*)

THE FLOWER GIRL.   Poor girl! Hard enough for her to live
without being worrited and chivied.[5]

THE GENTLEMAN. (*Returning to his former place on the note
taker's left.*)   How do you do it, may I ask?

THE NOTE TAKER.   Simply phonetics. The science of speech.
Thats my profession: also my hobby. Happy is the man who
can make a living by his hobby! You can spot an Irishman
or a Yorkshireman by his brogue. *I* can place any man
within six miles. I can place him within two miles in London. Sometimes within two streets.

THE FLOWER GIRL.   Ought to be ashamed of himself, unmanly
coward!

---

5. *Worrited and chivied:* bothered and annoyed.

THE GENTLEMAN.   But is there a living in that?

THE NOTE TAKER.   Oh yes. Quite a fat one. This is an age of upstarts. Men begin in Kentish Town with £80 a year, and end in Park Lane with a hundred thousand. They want to drop Kentish Town; but they give themselves away every time they open their mouths. Now I can teach them—

THE FLOWER GIRL.   Let him mind his own business and leave a poor girl—

THE NOTE TAKER. (*Explosively*.)   Woman: cease this detestable boohooing instantly; or else seek the shelter of some other place of worship.

THE FLOWER GIRL. (*With feeble defiance*.)   Ive a right to be here if I like, same as you.

THE NOTE TAKER.   A woman who utters such depressing and disgusting sounds has no right to be anywhere——no right to live. Remember that you are a human being with a soul and the divine gift of articulate speech; that your native language is the language of Shakespear and Milton[6] and the Bible; and dont sit there crooning like a bilious pigeon.

THE FLOWER GIRL. (*Quite overwhelmed, looking up at him in mingled wonder and deprecation without daring to raise her head*.)   Ah-ah-ah-ow-ow-ow-oo!

THE NOTE TAKER. (*Whipping out his book*.)   Heavens! What a sound! (*He writes; then holds out the book and reads, reproducing her vowels exactly*.) Ah-ah-ah-ow-ow-ow-oo!

THE FLOWER GIRL. (*Tickled by the performance, and laughing in spite of herself*.)   Garn!

THE NOTE TAKER.   You see this creature with her curbstone English: the English that will keep her in the gutter to the end of her days. Well, sir, in three months I could pass that girl off as a duchess at an ambassador's garden party. I could even get her a place as lady's maid or shop assistant, which requires better English.

---

6. *Shakespear . . . Milton:* William Shakespeare (1564-1616) and John Milton (1608-1674), English poets.

"Ah-ah-ah-ow-ow-ow-oo!"

THE FLOWER GIRL. What's that you say?

THE NOTE TAKER. Yes, you squashed cabbage leaf, you disgrace to the noble architecture of these columns, you incarnate insult to the English language: I could pass you off as the Queen of Sheba. (*To the gentleman.*) Can you believe that?

THE GENTLEMAN. Of course I can. I am myself a student of Indian dialects; and—

THE NOTE TAKER. (*Eagerly.*) Are you? Do you know Colonel Pickering, the author of Spoken Sanscrit?

THE GENTLEMAN. I am Colonel Pickering. Who are you?

THE NOTE TAKER. Henry Higgins, author of Higgins's Universal Alphabet.

PICKERING. (*With enthusiasm.*) I came from India to meet you.

HIGGINS. I was going to India to meet you.

PICKERING. Where do you live?

HIGGINS. 27A Wimpole Street. Come and see me tomorrow.

PICKERING. I'm at the Carlton. Come with me now and lets have a jaw over some supper.

HIGGINS. Right you are.

THE FLOWER GIRL. (*To Pickering, as he passes her.*) Buy a flower, kind gentleman. I'm short for my lodging.

PICKERING. I really havnt any change. I'm sorry. (*He goes away.*)

HIGGINS. (*Shocked at the girl's mendacity.*) Liar. You said you could change half a crown.

THE FLOWER GIRL. (*Rising in desperation.*) You ought to be stuffed with nails, you ought. (*Flinging the basket at his feet.*) Take the whole blooming basket for sixpence.

(*The church clock strikes the second quarter.*)

HIGGINS. (*Hearing in it the voice of God, rebuking him for his Pharisaic[7] want of charity to the poor girl.*) A re-

---

7. *Pharisaic:* like the Pharisees, hypocritical practitioners of religion.

minder. (*He raises his hat solemnly, then throws a handful of money into the basket and follows Pickering.*)

THE FLOWER GIRL. (*Picking up a half-crown.*) Ah-ow-ooh! (*Picking up a couple of florins.*) Aaah-ow-ooh! (*Picking up several coins.*) Aaaaah-ow-ooh! (*Picking up a half-sovereign.*) Aaaaaaaaaaah-ow-ooh!!!

FREDDY. (*Springing out of a taxicab.*) Got one at last. Hallo! (*To the girl.*) Where are the two ladies that were here?

THE FLOWER GIRL. They walked to the bus when the rain stopped.

FREDDY. And left me with a cab on my hands! Damnation!

THE FLOWER GIRL. (*With grandeur.*) Never mind, young man. I'm going home in a taxi. (*She sails off to the cab. The driver puts his hand behind him and holds the door firmly shut against her. Quite understanding his mistrust, she shows him her handful of money.*) A taxi fare aint no object to me, Charlie. (*He grins and opens the door.*) Here. What about the basket?

THE TAXIMAN. Give it here. Tuppence extra.

ELIZA. No. I dont want nobody to see it. (*She crushes it into the cab and gets in, continuing the conversation through the window.*) Good-by, Freddy.

FREDDY. (*Dazedly raising his hat.*) Good-by.

TAXIMAN. Where to?

ELIZA. Bucknam Pellis (Buckingham Palace.)

TAXIMAN. What d'ye mean—Bucknam Pellis?

ELIZA. Dont you know where it is? In the Green Park, where the King lives. Good-by, Freddy. Dont let me keep you standing there. Good-by.

FREDDY. Good-by. (*He goes.*)

TAXIMAN. Here? Whats this about Bucknam Pellis? What business have you at Bucknam Pellis?

ELIZA. Of course I havnt none. But I wasn't going to let him know that. You drive me home.

TAXIMAN.   And wheres home?

ELIZA.   Angel Court, Drury Lane, next Meiklejohn's oil shop.

TAXIMAN.   That sounds more like it, Judy. (*He drives off*).

*   *   *   *   *   *

Let us follow the taxi to the entrance to Angel Court, a narrow little archway between two shops, one of them Meiklejohn's oil shop. When it stops there, Eliza gets out, dragging her basket with her.

ELIZA.   How much?

TAXIMAN.   (*Indicating the taximeter.*)   Cant you read? A shilling.

ELIZA.   A shilling for two minutes!!

TAXIMAN.   Two minutes or ten: it's all the same.

ELIZA.   Well, I dont call it right.

TAXIMAN.   Ever been in a taxi before?

ELIZA. (*With dignity.*)   Hundreds and thousands of times, young man.

TAXIMAN. (*Laughing at her.*)   Good for you, Judy. Keep the shilling, darling, with best love from all at home. Good luck! (*He drives off.*)

ELIZA. (*Humiliated.*)   Impidence!

(*She picks up the basket and trudges up the alley with it to her lodging: a small room with very old wallpaper hanging loose in the damp places. A broken pane in the window is mended with paper. A portrait of a popular actor and a fashion plate of ladies' dresses, all wildly beyond poor Eliza's means, both torn from newspapers, are pinned up on the wall. A birdcage hangs in the window, but its tenant died long ago: it remains as a memorial only. These are the only visible luxuries; the rest is the irreducible minimum of poverty's needs: a wretched bed heaped with all sorts of coverings that have any warmth in them, a draped packing case with a basin and jug on it and a*

*little looking glass over it, a chair and table, the refuse of
some suburban kitchen, and an American alarm clock on
the shelf above the unused fireplace: the whole lighted
with a gas lamp with a penny in the slot meter. Rent: four
shillings a week.*

*Here Eliza, chronically weary, but too excited to go to
bed, sits, counting her new riches and dreaming and planning what to do with them, until the gas goes out, when
she enjoys for the first time the sensation of being able to
put in another penny without grudging it. This prodigal
mood does not extinguish her gnawing sense of need for
economy sufficiently to prevent her from calculating that
she can dream and plan in bed more cheaply and warmly
than sitting up without a fire. So she takes off her shawl
and skirt and adds them to the miscellaneous bedclothes.
Then she kicks off her shoes and gets into bed without
any further change.)*

Next day at 11 A.M. Higgins' laboratory in Wimpole Street. It is a room on the first floor, looking on the street, and was meant for the drawing room. The double doors are in the middle of the back wall, and persons entering find in the corner to their right two tall file cabinets at right angles to one another against the walls. In this corner stands a flat writing table, on which are a phonograph, a laryngoscope,[1] a row of tiny organ pipes with a bellows, a set of lamp chimneys for singing flames with burners attached to a gas plug in the wall by an India rubber tube, several tuning forks of different sizes, a life-size image of half a human head, showing in section the vocal organs, and a box containing a supply of wax cylinders for the phonograph.

Further down the room, on the same side, is a fireplace, with a comfortable leather-covered easy chair at the side of the hearth nearest the door, and a coal scuttle. There is a clock on the mantlepiece. Between the fireplace and the phonograph table is a stand for newspapers.

On the other side of the central door, to the left of the visitor, is a cabinet of shallow drawers. On it is a telephone and the telephone directory. The corner beyond, and most of the side wall, is occupied by a grand piano, with the keyboard at the end furthest from the door, and a bench for the players extending the full length of the keyboard. On the piano is a dessert dish heaped with fruit and sweets, mostly chocolates.

The middle of the room is clear. Besides the easy chair, the

---

1. *Laryngoscope:* medical instrument for examining the larynx.

piano bench, and two chairs at the phonograph table, there is one stray chair. It stands near the fireplace. On the walls, engravings: mostly Piranesis[2] and mezzotint portraits. No paintings.

Pickering is seated at the table, putting down some cards and a tuning fork which he has been using. Higgins is standing up near him, closing two or three file drawers which are hanging out. He appears in the morning light as a robust, vital, appetizing sort of man of forty or thereabouts, dressed in a professional-looking black frock coat with a white linen collar and black silk tie. He is of energetic, scientific type, heartily, even violently interested in everything that can be studied as a scientific subject, and careless about himself and other people, including their feelings. He is, in fact, but for his years and size, rather like a very impetuous baby "taking notice" eagerly and loudly, and requiring almost as much watching to keep him out of unintended mischief. His manner varies from genial bullying when he is in a good humor to stormy petulance when anything goes wrong; but he is so entirely frank and void of malice that he remains likable even in his least reasonable moments.

HIGGINS. (*As he shuts the last drawer.*)   Well, I think thats the whole show.

PICKERING.   It's really amazing. I havnt taken half of it in, you know.

HIGGINS.   Would you like to go over any of it again?

PICKERING. (*Rising and coming to the fireplace, where he plants himself with his back to the fire.*)   No, thank you: not now. I'm quite done up for this morning.

HIGGINS. (*Following him, and standing beside him on his left.*) Tired of listening to sounds?

PICKERING.   Yes. It's a fearful strain. I rather fancied myself

2. *Piranesis:* works of Giovanni Piranesi, Italian painter (1720-1778).

because I can pronounce twenty-four distinct vowel sounds; but your hundred and thirty beat me. I cant hear a bit of difference between most of them.

HIGGINS. (*Chuckling, and going over to the piano to eat sweets.*) Oh, that comes with practice. You hear no difference at first; but you keep on listening, and presently you find theyre all as different as A from B. (*Mrs. Pearce looks in: she is Higgins's housekeeper.*) Whats the matter?

MRS. PEARCE. (*Hesitating, evidently perplexed.*) A young woman asks to see you, sir.

HIGGINS. A young woman! What does she want?

MRS. PEARCE. Well, sir, she says youll be glad to see her when you know what she's come about. She's quite a common girl, sir. Very common indeed. I should have sent her away, only I thought perhaps you wanted her to talk into your machines. I hope Ive not done wrong; but really you see such queer people sometimes—youll excuse me, I'm sure, sir—

HIGGINS. Oh, thats all right, Mrs. Pearce. Has she an interesting accent?

MRS. PEARCE. Oh, something dreadful, sir, really. I dont know how you can take an interest in it.

HIGGINS. (*To Pickering.*) Lets have her up. Show her up, Mrs. Pearce. (*He rushes across to his working table and picks out a cylinder to use on the phonograph.*)

MRS. PEARCE. (*Only half resigned to it.*) Very well, sir. It's for you to say. (*She goes downstairs.*)

HIGGINS. This is rather a bit of luck. I'll show you how I make records. We'll set her talking, and I'll take it down first in Bell's Visible Speech, then in broad Romic, and then we'll get her on the phonograph so that you can turn her on as often as you like with the written transcript before you.

MRS. PEARCE. (*Returning.*) This is the young woman, sir.

(*The flower girl enters in state. She has a hat with three ostrich feathers, orange, sky-blue, and red. She has a*

*nearly clean apron, and the shoddy coat has been tidied a
little. The pathos of this deplorable figure, with its innocent vanity and consequential air, touches Pickering,
who has already straightened himself in the presence of
Mrs. Pearce. But as to Higgins, the only distinction he
makes between men and women is that when he is neither
bullying nor exclaiming to the heavens against some
feather-weight cross, he coaxes women as a child coaxes
its nurse when it wants to get anything out of her.*)

HIGGINS. (*Brusquely, recognizing her with unconcealed disappointment, and at once, babylike, making an intolerable
grievance of it.*)   Why, this is the girl I jotted down last
night. She's no use: I've got all the records I want of the
Lisson Grove lingo, and I'm not going to waste another
cylinder on it. (*To the girl.*) Be off with you: I dont want
you.

THE FLOWER GIRL.   Dont you be so saucy. You aint heard
what I come for yet. (*To Mrs. Pearce, who is waiting at the
door for further instructions.*) Did you tell him I come in a
taxi?

MRS. PEARCE.   Nonsense, girl! What do you think a gentleman like Mr. Higgins cares what you came in?

THE FLOWER GIRL.   Oh, we are proud! He aint above giving
lessons, not him: I heard him say so. Well, I aint come here
to ask for any compliment; and if my money's not good
enough I can go elsewhere.

HIGGINS.   Good enough for what?

THE FLOWER GIRL.   Good enough for yə-oo. Now you know,
dont you? I've come to have lessons, I am. And to pay for
em tə-oo: make no mistake.

HIGGINS. (*Stupent.*)   Well!!! (*Recovering his breath with a
gasp.*) What do you expect me to say to you?

THE FLOWER GIRL.   Well, if you was a gentleman, you might
ask me to sit down, I think. Dont I tell you I'm bringing you
business?

HIGGINS.   Pickering: shall we ask this baggage to sit down, or shall we throw her out of the window?

THE FLOWER GIRL.   (*Running away in terror to the piano, where she turns at bay.*) Ah-ah-oh-ow-ow-ow-oo! (*Wounded and whimpering.*) I wont be called a baggage when Ive offered to pay like any lady.

   (*Motionless, the two men stare at her from the other side of the room, amazed.*)

PICKERING. (*Gently.*)   But what is it you want?

THE FLOWER GIRL.   I want to be a lady in a flower shop stead of sellin at the corner of Tottenham Court Road. But they wont take me unless I can talk more genteel. He said he could teach me. Well, here I am ready to pay him—not asking any favor—and he treats me zif I was dirt.

MRS. PEARCE.   How can you be such a foolish ignorant girl as to think you could afford to pay Mr. Higgins?

THE FLOWER GIRL.   Why shouldnt I? I know what lessons cost as well as you do; and I'm ready to pay.

HIGGINS.   How much?

THE FLOWER GIRL. (*Coming back to him, triumphant.*)   Now youre talking! I thought youd come off it when you saw a chance of getting back a bit of what you chucked at me last night. (*Confidentially.*) Youd had a drop in, hadnt you?

HIGGINS. (*Peremptorily.*)   Sit down.

THE FLOWER GIRL.   Oh, if youre going to make a compliment of it—

HIGGINS. (*Thundering at her.*)   Sit down.

MRS. PEARCE. (*Severely.*)   Sit down, girl. Do as youre told.

THE FLOWER GIRL.   Ah-ah-ah-ow-od-oo! (*She stands, half rebellious, half bewildered.*)

PICKERING. (*Very courteous.*)   Wont you sit down? (*He places the stray chair near the hearthrug between himself and Higgins.*)

ELIZA. (*Coyly.*)   Dont mind if I do. (*She sits down. Pickering returns to the hearthrug.*)

HIGGINS.   Whats your name?

THE FLOWER GIRL.   Liza Doolittle.

HIGGINS. (*Declaiming gravely.*)

    Eliza, Elizabeth, Betsy and Bess,

    They went to the woods to get a bird's nes':

PICKERING.   They found a nest with four eggs in it:

HIGGINS.   They took one apiece, and left three in it.

    (*They laugh at their own fun.*)

ELIZA.   Oh, dont be silly.

MRS. PEARCE. (*Placing herself behind Eliza's chair.*) You mustnt speak to the gentleman like that.

ELIZA.   Well, why wont he speak sensible to me?

HIGGINS.   Come back to business. How much do you propose to pay me for the lessons?

ELIZA.   Oh, I know whats right. A lady friend of mine gets French lessons for eighteenpence an hour from a real French gentleman. Well, you wouldnt have the face to ask me the same for teaching me my own language as you would for French; so I wont give you more than a shilling. Take it or leave it.

HIGGINS. (*Walking up and down the room, rattling his keys and his cash in his pockets.*) You know, Pickering, if you consider a shilling, not as a simple shilling, but as a percentage of this girl's income, it works out as fully equivalent to sixty or seventy guineas from a millionaire.

PICKERING.   How so?

HIGGINS.   Figure it out. A millionaire has about £150 a day. She earns about half-a-crown.

ELIZA. (*Haughtily.*)   Who told you I only—

HIGGINS. (*Continuing.*)   She offers me two-fifths of her day's income for a lesson. Two-fifths of a millionaire's income for a day would be somewhere about £60. It's handsome. By George, it's enormous! It's the biggest offer I ever had.

ELIZA. (*Rising, terrified.*)   Sixty pounds! What are you talking about? I never offered you sixty pounds. Where would I get—

HIGGINS.   Hold your tongue.

ELIZA. (*Weeping.*)   But I aint got sixty pounds. Oh—

MRS. PEARCE.   Don't cry, you silly girl. Sit down. Nobody is going to touch your money.

HIGGINS.   Somebody is going to touch you, with a broomstick, if you dont stop snivelling. Sit down.

ELIZA. (*Obeying slowly.*)   Ah-ah-ah-ow-oo-o! One would think you was my father.

HIGGINS.   If I decide to teach you, I'll be worse than two fathers to you. Here! (*He offers her his silk handkerchief.*)

ELIZA.   Whats this for?

HIGGINS.   To wipe your eyes. To wipe any part of your face that feels moist. Remember: thats your handkerchief, and thats your sleeve. Dont mistake the one for the other if you wish to become a lady in a shop.

(*Eliza, utterly bewildered, stares helplessly at him.*)

MRS. PEARCE.   It's no use talking to her like that, Mr. Higgins: she doesnt understand you. Besides, youre quite wrong: she doesnt do it that way at all. (*She takes the handkerchief.*).

ELIZA. (*Snatching it.*)   Here! You give me that handkerchief. He gev it to me, not to you.

PICKERING. (*Laughing.*)   He did. I think it must be regarded as her property, Mrs. Pearce.

MRS. PEARCE. (*Resigning herself.*)   Serve you right, Mr. Higgins.

PICKERING.   Higgins: I'm interested. What about the ambassador's garden party? I'll say youre the greatest teacher alive if you make that good. I'll bet you all the expenses of the experiment you cant do it. And I'll pay for the lessons.

ELIZA.   Oh, you are real good. Thank you, Captain.

HIGGINS. (*Tempted, looking at her.*)   It's almost irresistible. She's so deliciously low—so horribly dirty—

ELIZA. (*Protesting extremely*.)   Ah-ah-ah-ah-ow-ow-oo-oo!!!
I aint dirty: I washed my face and hands afore I come, I did.

PICKERING.   Youre certainly not going to turn her head with
flattery, Higgins.

MRS. PEARCE. (*Uneasy*.)   Oh, dont say that, sir: theres more
ways than one of turning a girl's head; and nobody can do
it better than Mr. Higgins, though he may not always mean
it. I do hope, sir, you wont encourage him to do anything
foolish.

HIGGINS. (*Becoming excited as the idea grows on him*.)
What is life but a series of inspired follies? The difficulty is
to find them to do. Never lose a chance: it doesnt come
every day. I shall make a duchess of this draggletailed guttersnipe.

ELIZA. (*Strongly deprecating this view of her*.)   Ah-ah-ah-
ow-ow-oo!

HIGGINS. (*Carried away*.)   Yes: in six months—in three if she
has a good ear and a quick tongue—I'll take her anywhere
and pass her off as anything. We'll start today: now! this
moment! Take her away and clean her, Mrs. Pearce. Monkey Brand, if it wont come off any other way. Is there a
good fire in the kitchen?

MRS. PEARCE. (*Protesting*.)   Yes; but—

HIGGINS. (*Storming on*.)   Take all her clothes off and burn
them. Ring up Whitely or somebody for new ones. Wrap
her up in brown paper till they come.

ELIZA.   Youre no gentleman, youre not, to talk of such
things. I'm a good girl, I am; and I know what the like of
you are, I do.

HIGGINS.   We want none of your Lisson Grove prudery here,
young woman. Youve got to learn to behave like a duchess.
Take her away, Mrs. Pearce. If she gives you any trouble,
wallop her.

ELIZA. (*Springing up and running between Pickering and
Mrs. Pearce for protection*.)   No! I'll call the police, I will.

MRS. PEARCE.   But Ive no place to put her.

HIGGINS.   Put her in the dustbin.

ELIZA.   Ah-ah-ah-ow-ow-oo!

PICKERING.   Oh come, Higgins! Be reasonable.

MRS. PEARCE. (*Resolutely.*)   You must be reasonable, Mr. Higgins: really you must. You cant walk over everybody like this.

(*Higgins, thus scolded, subsides. The hurricane is succeeded by a zephyr of amiable surprise.*)

HIGGINS. (*With professional exquisiteness of modulation.*)   I walk over everybody! My dear Mrs. Pearce, my dear Pickering, I never had the slightest intention of walking over anyone. All I propose is that we should be kind to this poor girl. We must help her to prepare and fit herself for her new station in life. If I did not express myself clearly it was because I did not wish to hurt her delicacy, or yours.

(*Eliza, reassured, steals back to her chair.*)

MRS. PEARCE. (*To Pickering.*)   Well, did you ever hear anything like that, sir?

PICKERING. (*Laughing heartily.*)   Never, Mrs. Pearce: never.

HIGGINS. (*Patiently.*)   Whats the matter?

MRS. PEARCE.   Well, the matter is, sir, that you cant take a girl up like that as if you were picking up a pebble on the beach.

HIGGINS.   Why not?

MRS. PEARCE.   Why not! But you dont know anything about her. What about her parents? She may be married.

ELIZA.   Garn!

HIGGINS.   There! As the girl very properly says, Garn! Married indeed! Dont you know that a woman of that class looks a worn out drudge of fifty a year after she's married?

ELIZA.   Whood marry me?

HIGGINS. (*Suddenly resorting to the most thrillingly beautiful low tones in his best elocutionary style.*)   By George, Eliza, the streets will be strewn with the bodies of men shooting themselves for your sake before Ive done with you.

MRS. PEARCE.   Nonsense, sir. You mustnt talk like that to her.

ELIZA. (*Rising and squaring herself determinedly.*)   I'm going away. He's off his chump, he is. I dont want no balmies teaching me.

HIGGINS. (*Wounded in his tenderest point by her insensibility to his elocution.*)   Oh, indeed! I'm mad, am I? Very well, Mrs. Pearce: you neednt order the new clothes for her. Throw her out.

ELIZA. (*Whimpering.*)   Nah-ow. You got no right to touch me.

MRS. PEARCE.   You see now what comes of being saucy. (*Indicating the door.*) This way, please.

ELIZA. (*Almost in tears.*)   I didnt want no clothes. I wouldnt have taken them. (*She throws away the handkerchief.*) I can buy my own clothes.

HIGGINS. (*Deftly retrieving the handkerchief and intercepting her on her reluctant way to the door.*)   Youre an ungrateful wicked girl. This is my return for offering to take you out of the gutter and dress you beautifully and make a lady of you.

MRS. PEARCE.   Stop, Mr. Higgins. I wont allow it. It's you that are wicked. Go home to your parents, girl: and tell them to take better care of you.

ELIZA.   I aint got no parents. They told me I was big enough to earn my own living and turned me out.

MRS. PEARCE.   Wheres your mother?

ELIZA.   I aint got no mother. Her that turned me out was my sixth stepmother. But I done without them. And I'm a good girl, I am.

HIGGINS.   Very well, then, what on earth is all this fuss about? The girl doesnt belong to anybody—is no use to anybody but me. (*He goes to Mrs. Pearce and begins coaxing.*) You can adopt her, Mrs. Pearce: I'm sure a daughter would be a great amusement to you. Now dont make any more fuss. Take her downstairs; and—

MRS. PEARCE. But whats to become of her? Is she to be paid anything? Do be sensible, sir.

HIGGINS. Oh, pay her whatever is necessary: put it down in the housekeeping book. (*Impatiently.*) What on earth will she want with money? She'll have her food and her clothes. She'll only drink if you give her money.

ELIZA. (*Turning on him.*) Oh you are a brute. It's a lie: nobody ever saw the sign of liquor on me. (*To Pickering.*) Oh, sir: youre a gentleman: dont let him speak to me like that.

PICKERING. (*In good-humored remonstrance.*) Does it occur to you, Higgins, that the girl has some feelings?

HIGGINS. (*Looking critically at her.*) Oh no, I dont think so. Not any feelings that we need bother about. (*Cheerily.*) Have you, Eliza?

ELIZA. I got my feelings same as anyone else.

HIGGINS. (*To Pickering, reflectively.*) You see the difficulty?

PICKERING. Eh? What difficulty?

HIGGINS. To get her to talk grammar. The mere pronunciation is easy enough.

ELIZA. I dont want to talk grammar. I want to talk like a lady in a flower shop.

MRS. PEARCE. Will you please keep to the point, Mr. Higgins. I want to know on what terms the girl is to be here. Is she to have any wages? And what is to become of her when youve finished your teaching? You must look ahead a little.

HIGGINS. (*Impatiently.*) Whats to become of her if I leave her in the gutter? Tell me that, Mrs. Pearce.

MRS. PEARCE. Thats her own business, not yours, Mr. Higgins.

HIGGINS.   Well, when Ive done with her, we can throw her
back into the gutter; and then it will be her own business
again; so thats all right.

ELIZA.   Oh, youve no feeling heart in you: you dont care for
nothing but yourself. (*She rises and takes the floor resolutely.*) Here! Ive had enough of this. I'm going. (*Making
for the door.*) You ought to be ashamed of yourself, you
ought.

HIGGINS.   (*Snatching a chocolate cream from the piano, his
eyes suddenly beginning to twinkle with mischief.*)   Have
some chocolates, Eliza.

ELIZA.   (*Halting, tempted.*)   How do I know what might be
in them? Ive heard of girls being drugged by the like of you.
(*Higgins whips out his penknife; cuts a chocolate in two;
puts one half into his mouth and bolts it; and offers her
the other half.*)

HIGGINS.   Pledge of good faith, Eliza. I eat one half: you eat
the other. (*Eliza opens her mouth to retort: he pops the half
chocolate into it.*) You shall have boxes of them, barrels of
them, every day. You shall live on them. Eh?

ELIZA.   (*Who has disposed of the chocolate after being nearly
choked by it.*)   I wouldnt have ate it, only I'm too ladylike
to take it out of my mouth.

HIGGINS.   Listen, Eliza. I think you said you came in a taxi.

ELIZA.   Well, what if I did? Ive as good a right to take a taxi
as anyone else.

HIGGINS.   You have, Eliza; and in future you shall have as
many taxis as you want. You shall go up and down and
round the town in a taxi every day. Think of that, Eliza.

MRS. PEARCE.   Mr. Higgins: youre tempting the girl. It's not
right. She should think of the future.

HIGGINS.   At her age! Nonsense! Time enough to think of the
future when you havnt any future to think of. No, Eliza: do
as this lady does: think of other people's futures; but never

think of your own. Think of chocolates, and taxis, and gold, and diamonds.

ELIZA. No: I dont want no gold and no diamonds. I'm a good girl, I am. (*She sits down again, with an attempt at dignity.*)

HIGGINS. You shall remain so, Eliza, under the care of Mrs. Pearce. And you shall marry an officer in the Guards, with a beautiful moustache: the son of a marquis, who will disinherit him for marrying you, but will relent when he sees your beauty and goodness—

PICKERING. Excuse me, Higgins; but I really must interfere. Mrs. Pearce is quite right. If this girl is to put herself in your hands for six months for an experiment in teaching, she must understand thoroughly what she's doing.

HIGGINS. How can she? She's incapable of understanding anything. Besides, do any of us understand what we are doing? If we did, would we ever do it?

PICKERING. Very clever, Higgins; but not to the present point. (*To Eliza.*) Miss Doolittle—

ELIZA. (*Overwhelmed.*) Ah-ah-ow-oo!

HIGGINS. There! Thats all youll get out of Eliza. Ah-ah-ow-oo! No use explaining. As a military man you ought to know that. Give her orders: thats enough for her. Eliza: you are to live here for the next six months, learning how to speak beautifully, like a lady in a florist's shop. If youre good and do whatever youre told, you shall sleep in a proper bedroom, and have lots to eat, and money to buy chocolates and take rides in taxis. If youre naughty and idle you will sleep in the back kitchen among the black beetles, and be walloped by Mrs. Pearce with a broomstick. At the end of six months you shall go to Buckingham Palace in a carriage, beautifully dressed. If the King finds out youre not a lady, you will be taken by the police to the Tower of London, where your head will be cut off as a warning to other presumptuous flower girls. If you are not found out, you shall have a present of seven-and-sixpence to start life with as a lady in a shop. If you refuse this offer you will be a most ungrateful wicked girl; and the angels will weep for you. (*To Pickering.*) Now are you satisfied, Pickering? (*To Mrs. Pearce.*) Can I put it more plainly and fairly, Mrs. Pearce?

MRS. PEARCE. (*Patiently.*)   I think youd better let me speak to the girl properly in private. I dont know that I can take charge of her or consent to the arrangement at all. Of course I know you dont mean her any harm; but when you get what you call interested in people's accents, you never think or care what may happen to them or you. Come with me, Eliza.

HIGGINS.   Thats all right. Thank you, Mrs. Pearce. Bundle her off to the bathroom.

ELIZA. (*Rising reluctantly and suspiciously.*)   Youre a great bully, you are. I wont stay here if I dont like. I wont let nobody wallop me. I never asked to go to Bucknam Palace, I didn't. I was never in trouble with the police, not me. I'm a good girl—

MRS. PEARCE.   Dont answer back, girl. You dont understand the gentleman. Come with me. (*She leads the way to the door, and holds it open for Eliza.*).

ELIZA. (*As she goes out.*)   Well, what I say is right. I wont go near the King, not if I'm going to have my head cut off. If I'd known what I was letting myself in for, I wouldnt have come here. I always been a good girl; and I never offered to say a word to him; and I don't owe him nothing; and I dont care; and I wont be put upon; and I have my feelings the same as anyone else—

(*Mrs. Pearce shuts the door; and Eliza's plaints are no longer audible.*)

*   *   *   *   *   *

Eliza is taken upstairs to the third floor, greatly to her surprise; for she expected to be taken down to the scullery. There Mrs. Pearce opens a door and takes her into a spare bedroom.

MRS. PEARCE.   I will have to put you here. This will be your bedroom.

ELIZA.   O-h, I couldnt sleep here, missus. It's too good for the likes of me. I should be afraid to touch anything. I aint a duchess yet, you know.

MRS. PEARCE.   You have got to make yourself as clean as the room: then you wont be afraid of it. And you must call me Mrs. Pearce, not missus. (*She throws open the door of the dressing room, now modernized as a bathroom.*).

ELIZA.   Gawd! whats this? Is this where you wash clothes? Funny sort of copper I call it.

MRS. PEARCE.   It is not a copper. This is where we wash ourselves, Eliza, and where I am going to wash you.

ELIZA.   You expect me to get into that and wet myself all over! Not me. I should catch my death. I knew a woman did it every Saturday night; and she died of it.

MRS. PEARCE.   Mr. Higgins has the gentlemen's bathroom downstairs; and he has a bath every morning, in cold water.

ELIZA.   Ugh! He's made of iron, that man.

MRS. PEARCE.   If you are to sit with him and the Colonel and be taught you will have to do the same. They wont like the smell of you if you dont. But you can have the water as hot as you like. There are two taps: hot and cold.

ELIZA.   (*Weeping.*)   I couldnt. I dursnt. It's not natural: it would kill me. Ive never had a bath in my life: not what youd call a proper one.

MRS. PEARCE.   Well, dont you want to be clean and sweet and decent, like a lady? You know you cant be a nice girl inside if youre a dirty slut outside.

ELIZA.   Boohoo!!!!

MRS. PEARCE.   Now stop crying and go back into your room and take off all your clothes. Then wrap yourself in this

(*Taking down a gown from its peg and handing it to her.*) and come back to me. I will get the bath ready.

ELIZA. (*All tears.*)   I cant. I wont. I'm not used to it. Ive never took off all my clothes before. It's not right: it's not decent.

MRS. PEARCE.   Nonsense, child. Dont you take off all your clothes every night when you go to bed?

ELIZA. (*Amazed.*)   No. Why should I? I should catch my death. Of course I take off my skirt.

MRS. PEARCE.   Do you mean that you sleep in the under-clothes you wear in the daytime?

ELIZA.   What else have I to sleep in?

MRS. PEARCE.   You will never do that again as long as you live here. I will get you a proper nightdress.

ELIZA.   Do you mean change into cold things and lie awake shivering all night? You want to kill me, you do.

MRS. PEARCE.   I want to change you from a frowzy slut to a clean respectable girl fit to sit with the gentlemen in the study. Are you going to trust me and do what I tell you or be thrown out and sent back to your flower basket?

ELIZA.   But you dont know what the cold is to me. You dont know how I dread it.

MRS. PEARCE.   Your bed wont be cold here: I will put a hot water bottle in it. (*Pushing her into the bedroom.*) Off with you and undress.

ELIZA.   Oh, if only I'd known what a dreadful thing it is to be clean I'd never have come. I didnt know when I was well off. I– (*Mrs. Pearce pushes her through the door, but leaves it partly open lest her prisoner should take to flight.*).

(*Mrs. Pearce puts on a pair of white rubber sleeves and fills the bath, mixing hot and cold and testing the result with the bath thermometer. She perfumes it with a hand-ful of bath salts and adds a palmful of mustard. She then takes a formidable looking long-handled scrubbing brush and soaps it profusely with a ball of scented soap.*)

Eliza comes back with nothing on but the bath gown huddled tightly round her, a piteous spectacle of abject terror.)

MRS. PEARCE. Now come along. Take that thing off.

ELIZA. Oh I couldnt, Mrs. Pearce: I reely couldnt. I never done such a thing.

MRS. PEARCE. Nonsense. Here: step in and tell me whether its hot enough for you.

ELIZA. Ah-oo! Ah-oo! It's too hot.

MRS. PEARCE. *(Deftly snatching the gown away and throwing Eliza down on her back.)* It wont hurt you. *(She sets to work with the scrubbing brush.)*

(Eliza's screams are heartrending.)

* * * * * *

Meanwhile the Colonel has been having it out with Higgins about Eliza. Pickering has come from the hearth to the chair and seated himself astride of it with his arms on the back to cross-examine him.

PICKERING. Excuse the straight question, Higgins. Are you a man of good character where women are concerned?

HIGGINS. *(Moodily.)* Have you ever met a man of good character where women are concerned?

PICKERING. Yes: very frequently.

HIGGINS. *(Dogmatically, lifting himself on his hands to the level of the piano, and sitting on it with a bounce.)* Well, I havnt. I find that the moment I let a woman make friends with me, she becomes jealous, exacting, suspicious, and a damned nuisance. I find that the moment I let myself make friends with a woman, I become selfish and tyrannical. Women upset everything. When you let them into your life, you find that the woman is driving at one thing and youre driving at another.

PICKERING. At what, for example?

HIGGINS. *(Coming off the piano restlessly.)* Oh, Lord knows!

I suppose the woman wants to live her own life; and the man wants to live his; and each tries to drag the other on to the wrong track. One wants to go north and the other south; and the result is that both have to go east, though they both hate the east wind. (*He sits down on the bench at the keyboard.*) So here I am, a confirmed old bachelor, and likely to remain so.

PICKERING. (*Rising and standing over him gravely.*) Come, Higgins! You know what I mean. If I'm to be in this business I shall feel responsible for that girl. I hope it's understood that no advantage is to be taken of her position.

HIGGINS. What! That thing! Sacred, I assure you. (*Rising to explain.*) You see, she'll be a pupil; and teaching would be impossible unless pupils were sacred. Ive taught scores of American millionairesses how to speak English: the best looking women in the world. I'm seasoned. They might as well be blocks of wood. *I* might as well be a block of wood. It's—

(*Mrs. Pearce opens the door. She has Eliza's hat in her hand. Pickering retires to the easy chair at the hearth and sits down.*)

HIGGINS. (*Eagerly.*) Well, Mrs. Pearce: Is it all right?

MRS. PEARCE. (*At the door.*) I just wish to trouble you with a word, if I may, Mr. Higgins.

HIGGINS. Yes, certainly. Come in. (*She comes forward.*) Dont burn that, Mrs. Pearce. I'll keep it as a curiosity. (*He takes the hat.*)

MRS. PEARCE. Handle it carefully, sir, please. I had to promise her not to burn it; but I had better put it in the oven for a while.

HIGGINS. (*Putting it down hastily on the piano.*) Oh! thank you. Well, what have you to say to me?

PICKERING. Am I in the way?

MRS. PEARCE. Not in the least, sir. Mr. Higgins: will you please be very particular what you say before the girl?

HIGGINS. (*Sternly.*) Of course. I'm always particular about what I say. Why do you say this to me?

MRS. PEARCE. (*Unmoved.*) No, sir: youre not at all particular when youve mislaid anything or when you get a little impatient. Now it doesnt matter before me: I'm used to it. But you really must not swear before the girl.

HIGGINS. (*Indignantly.*) *I* swear! (*Most emphatically.*) I never swear. I detest the habit. What the devil do you mean?

MRS. PEARCE. (*Stolidly.*) Thats what I mean, sir. You swear a great deal too much. I dont mind your damning and blasting, and what the devil and where the devil and who the devil—

HIGGINS. Mrs. Pearce: this language from your lips! Really!

MRS. PEARCE. (*Not to be put off.*)—but there is a certain word I must ask you not to use. The girl used it herself when she began to enjoy the bath. It begins with the same letter as bath. She knows no better: she learnt it at her mother's knee. But she must not hear it from your lips.

HIGGINS. (*Loftily.*) I cannot charge myself with having ever uttered it, Mrs. Pearce. (*She looks at him steadfastly. He adds, hiding an uneasy conscience with a judicial air.*) Except perhaps in a moment of extreme and justifiable excitement.

MRS. PEARCE. Only this morning, sir, you applied it to your boots, to the butter, and to the brown bread.

HIGGINS. Oh, that! Mere alliteration, Mrs. Pearce, natural to a poet.

MRS. PEARCE. Well, sir, whatever you choose to call it, I beg you not to let the girl hear you repeat it.

HIGGINS. Oh, very well, very well. Is that all?

MRS. PEARCE. No, sir. We shall have to be very particular with this girl as to personal cleanliness.

HIGGINS. Certainly. Quite right. Most important.

MRS. PEARCE. I mean not to be slovenly about her dress or untidy in leaving things about.

HIGGINS. (*Going to her solemnly*.)　　Just so. I intended to call your attention to that. (*He passes on to Pickering, who is enjoying the conversation immensely*.) It is these little things that matter, Pickering. Take care of the pence and the pounds will take care of themselves is as true of personal habits as of money. (*He comes to anchor on the hearthrug, with the air of a man in an unassailable position*.)

MRS. PEARCE.　　Yes, sir. Then might I ask you not to come down to breakfast in your dressing-gown, or at any rate not use it as a napkin to the extent you do, sir. And if you would be so good as not to eat everything off the same plate, and to remember not to put the porridge saucepan out of your hand on the clean tablecloth, it would be a better example to the girl. You know you nearly choked yourself with a fishbone in a jam only last week.

HIGGINS. (*Routed from the hearthrug and drifting back to the piano*.)　　I may do these things sometimes in absence of mind; but surely I dont do them habitually. (*Angrily*.) By the way: my dressing-gown smells most damnably of benzine.

MRS. PEARCE.　　No doubt it does, Mr. Higgins. But if you will wipe your fingers—

HIGGINS. (*Yelling*.)　　Oh very well, very well: I'll wipe them in my hair in future.

MRS. PEARCE.　　I hope youre not offended, Mr. Higgins.

HIGGINS. (*Shocked at finding himself thought capable of an unamiable sentiment.*)　　Not at all, not at all. Youre quite right, Mrs. Pearce: I shall be particularly careful before the girl. Is that all?

MRS. PEARCE.　　No, sir. Might she use some of those Japanese dresses you brought from abroad? I really cant put her back into her old things.

HIGGINS.　　Certainly. Anything you like. Is that all?

MRS. PEARCE.　　Thank you, sir. Thats all. (*She goes out.*)

HIGGINS.　　You know, Pickering, that woman has the most extraordinary ideas about me. Here I am, a shy, diffident sort of man. Ive never been able to feel really grown-up and tremendous, like other chaps. And yet she's firmly persuaded that I'm an arbitrary overbearing bossing kind of person. I cant account for it.

(*Mrs. Pearce returns.*)

MRS. PEARCE. If you please, sir, the trouble's beginning already. Theres a dustman[3] downstairs, Alfred Doolittle, wants to see you. He says you have his daughter here.

PICKERING. (*Rising.*) Phew! I say!

HIGGINS. (*Promptly.*) Send the blackguard up.

MRS. PEARCE. Oh, very well, sir. (*She goes out.*)

PICKERING. He may not be a blackguard, Higgins.

HIGGINS. Nonsense. Of course he's a blackguard.

PICKERING. Whether he is or not, I'm afraid we shall have some trouble with him.

HIGGINS. (*Confidently.*) Oh no: I think not. If theres any trouble he shall have it with me, not I with him. And we are sure to get something interesting out of him.

PICKERING. About the girl?

HIGGINS. No. I mean his dialect.

PICKERING. Oh!

MRS. PEARCE. (*At the door.*) Doolittle, sir. (*She admits Doolittle and retires.*)

(*Alfred is an elderly but vigorous dustman, clad in the costume of his profession, including a hat with a back brim covering his neck and shoulders. He has well marked and rather interesting features, and seems equally free from fear and conscience. He has a remarkably expressive voice, the result of a habit of giving vent to his feelings without reserve. His present pose is that of wounded honor and stern resolution.*)

DOOLITTLE. (*At the door, uncertain which of the two gentlemen is his man.*) Professor Iggins?

HIGGINS. Here. Good morning. Sit down.

3. *Dustman:* trash collector.

DOOLITTLE. Morning, Governor. (*He sits down magisterially*.) I come about a very serious matter, Governor.

HIGGINS. (*To Pickering*.) Brought up in Hounslow. Mother Welsh, I should think. (*Doolittle opens his mouth, amazed. Higgins continues*.) What do you want, Doolittle?

DOOLITTLE. (*Menacingly*.) I want my daughter, that's what I want. See?

HIGGINS. Of course you do. Youre her father, arnt you? You dont suppose anyone else wants her, do you? I'm glad to see you have some spark of family feeling left. She's upstairs. Take her away at once.

DOOLITTLE. (*Rising, fearfully taken aback*.) What!

HIGGINS. Take her away. Do you suppose I'm going to keep your daughter for you?

DOOLITTLE. (*Remonstrating*.) Now, now, look here, Governor. Is this reasonable? Is it fairity to take advantage of a man like this? The girl belongs to me. You got her. Where do I come in? (*He sits down again*.)

HIGGINS. Your daughter had the audacity to come to my house and ask me to teach her how to speak properly so that she could get a place in a flower shop. This gentleman and my housekeeper have been here all the time. (*Bullying him*.) How dare you come here and attempt to blackmail me? You sent her here on purpose.

DOOLITTLE. (*Protesting*.) No, Governor.

HIGGINS. You must have. How else could you possibly know that she is here?

DOOLITTLE. Don't take a man up like that, Governor.

HIGGINS. The police shall take you up. This is a plant—a plot to extort money by threats. I shall telephone for the police. (*He goes resolutely to the telephone and opens the directory*.)

DOOLITTLE. Have I asked you for a brass farthing? I leave it to the gentleman here: have I said a word about money?

HIGGINS. (*Throwing the book aside and marching down on Doolittle with a poser*.) What else did you come for?

DOOLITTLE. (*Sweetly.*)   Well, what would a man come for? Be human, Governor.

HIGGINS. (*Disarmed.*)   Alfred: did you put her up to it?

DOOLITTLE.   So help me, Governor, I never did. I take my Bible oath I aint seen the girl these two months past.

HIGGINS.   Then how did you know she was here?

DOOLITTLE. (*"Most musical, most melancholy."*)   I'll tell you, Governor, if youll only let me get a word in. I'm willing to tell you. I'm wanting to tell you. I'm waiting to tell you.

HIGGINS.   Pickering: this chap has a certain natural gift of rhetoric. Observe the rhythm of his native woodnotes wild. "I'm willing to tell you: I'm wanting to tell you: I'm waiting to tell you." Sentimental rhetoric! thats the Welsh strain in him. It also accounts for his mendacity and dishonesty.

PICKERING.   Oh, please, Higgins: I'm west country myself. (*To Doolittle.*) How did you know the girl was here if you didnt send her?

DOOLITTLE.   It was like this, Governor. The girl took a boy in the taxi to give him a jaunt. Son of her landlady, he is. He hung about on the chance of her giving him another ride home. Well, she sent him back for her luggage when she heard you was willing for her to stop here. I met the boy at the corner of Long Acre and Endell Street.

HIGGINS.   Public house. Yes?

DOOLITTLE.   The poor man's club, Governor: why shouldnt I?

PICKERING.   Do let him tell his story, Higgins.

DOOLITTLE.   He told me what was up. And I ask you, what was my feelings and my duty as a father? I says to the boy, "You bring me the luggage," I says—

PICKERING.   Why didnt you go for it yourself?

DOOLITTLE.   Landlady wouldnt have trusted me with it, Governor. She's that kind of woman: you know. I had to give the boy a penny afore he trusted me with it, the little swine.

I brought it to her just to oblige you like, and make myself agreeable. Thats all.

HIGGINS.   How much luggage?

DOOLITTLE.   Musical instrument, Governor. A few pictures, a trifle of jewelry, and a bird-cage. She said she didnt want no clothes. What was I to think from that, Governor? I ask you as a parent what was I to think?

HIGGINS.   So you came to rescue her from worse than death, eh?

DOOLITTLE.   (*Appreciatively: relieved at being so well understood.*)   Just so, Governor. Thats right.

PICKERING.   But why did you bring her luggage if you intended to take her away?

DOOLITTLE.   Have I said a word about taking her away? Have I now?

HIGGINS. (*Determinedly.*)   Youre going to take her away, double quick. (*He crosses to the hearth and rings the bell.*)

DOOLITTLE. (*Rising.*)   No, Governor. Dont say that. I'm not the man to stand in my girl's light. Heres a career opening for her, as you might say; and—

(*Mrs. Pearce opens the door and awaits orders.*)

HIGGINS.   Mrs. Pearce: this is Eliza's father. He has come to take her away. Give her to him. (*He goes back to the piano, with an air of washing his hands of the whole affair.*)

DOOLITTLE.   No. This is a misunderstanding. Listen here—

MRS. PEARCE.   He cant take her away, Mr. Higgins: how can he? You told me to burn her clothes.

DOOLITTLE.   Thats right. I cant carry the girl through the streets like a blooming monkey, can I? I put it to you.

HIGGINS.   You have put it to me that you want your daughter. Take your daughter. If she has no clothes go out and buy her some.

DOOLITTLE. (*Desperate.*)   Wheres the clothes she come in? Did I burn them or did your missus here?

MRS. PEARCE.   I am the housekeeper, if you please. I have

sent for some clothes for your girl. When they come you can take her away. You can wait in the kitchen. This way, please.

(*Doolittle, much troubled, accompanies her to the door; then hesitates; finally turns confidentially to Higgins.*)

DOOLITTLE. Listen here, Governor. You and me is men of the world, aint we?

HIGGINS. Oh! Men of the world, are we? Youd better go, Mrs. Pearce.

MRS. PEARCE. I think so, indeed, sir. (*She goes, with dignity.*)

PICKERING. The floor is yours, Mr. Doolittle.

DOOLITTLE. (*To Pickering.*) I thank you, Governor. (*To Higgins, who takes refuge on the piano bench, a little overwhelmed by the proximity of his visitor; for Doolittle has a professional flavor of dust about him.*). Well, the truth is, Ive taken a sort of fancy to you, Governor; and if you want the girl, I'm not so set on having her back home again but what I might be open to an arrangement. Regarded in the light of a young woman, she's a fine handsome girl. As a daughter she's not worth her keep; and so I tell you straight. All I ask is my rights as a father; and youre the last man alive to expect me to let her go for nothing; for I can see youre one of the straight sort, Governor. Well, whats a five-pound note to you? And whats Eliza to me? (*He turns to his chair and sits down judicially.*)

PICKERING. I think you ought to know, Doolittle, that Mr. Higgins's intentions are entirely honorable.

DOOLITTLE. Course they are, Governor. If I thought they wasnt, I'd ask fifty.

HIGGINS. (*Revolted.*) Do you mean to say that you would sell your daughter for £50?

DOOLITTLE. Not in a general way I would; but to oblige a gentleman like you I'd do a good deal, I do assure you.

PICKERING. Have you no morals, man?

DOOLITTLE. (*Unabashed.*)   Cant afford them, Governor. Neither could you if you was as poor as me. Not that I mean any harm, you know. But if Liza is going to have a bit out of this, why not me too?

HIGGINS. (*Troubled.*)   I dont know what to do, Pickering. There can be no question that as a matter of morals it's a positive crime to give this chap a farthing. And yet I feel a sort of rough justice in his claim.

DOOLITTLE.   Thats it, Governor. Thats all I say. A father's heart, as it were.

PICKERING.   Well, I know the feeling; but really it seems hardly right—

DOOLITTLE.   Dont say that, Governor. Dont look at it that way. What am I, Governors both? I ask you, what am I? I'm one of the undeserving poor: thats what I am. Think of what that means to a man. It means that he's up agen middle class morality all the time. If theres anything going, and I put in for a bit of it, it's always the same story: "Youre undeserving; so you cant have it." But my needs is as great as the most deserving widow's that ever got money out of six different charities in one week for the death of the same husband. I dont need less than a deserving man: I need more. I dont eat less hearty than him; and I drink a lot more. I want a bit of amusement, cause I'm a thinking man. I want cheerfulness and a song and a band when I feel low. Well, they charge me just the same for everything as they charge the deserving. What is middle class morality? Just an excuse for never giving me anything. Therefore, I ask you, as two gentlemen, not to play that game on me. I'm playing straight with you. I aint pretending to be deserving. I'm undeserving; and I mean to go on being undeserving. I like it, and thats the truth. Will you take advantage of a man's nature to do him out of the price of his own daughter what he's brought up and fed and clothed by the sweat of his brow until she's growed big enough to be interesting to

"He could choose between a seat in the Cabinet and a popular pulpit in Wales."

you two gentlemen? Is five pounds unreasonable? I put it to you; and I leave it to you.

HIGGINS. (*Rising, and going over to Pickering.*) Pickering: if we were to take this man in hand for three months, he could choose between a seat in the Cabinet and a popular pulpit in Wales.

PICKERING. What do you say to that, Doolittle?

DOOLITTLE. Not me, Governor, thank you kindly. Ive heard all the preachers and all the prime ministers—for I'm a thinking man and game for politics or religion or social reform same as all the other amusements—and I tell you it's a dog's life any way you look at it. Undeserving poverty is my line. Taking one station in society with another, it's—it's—well, it's the only one that has any ginger in it, to my taste.

HIGGINS. I suppose we must give him a fiver.

PICKERING. He'll make a bad use of it, I'm afraid.

DOOLITTLE. Not me, Governor, so help me I wont. Dont you be afraid that I'll save it and spare it and live idle on it. There wont be a penny of it left by Monday: I'll have to go to work same as if I'd never had it. It wont pauperize me, you bet. Just one good spree for myself and the missus, giving pleasure to ourselves and employment to others, and satisfaction to you to think it's not been throwed away. You couldnt spend it better.

HIGGINS. (*Taking out his pocket book and coming between Doolittle and the piano.*) This is irresistible. Lets give him ten. (*He offers two notes to the dustman.*)

DOOLITTLE. No, Governor. She wouldnt have the heart to spend ten; and perhaps I shouldnt neither. Ten pounds is a lot of money: it makes a man feel prudent like; and then good-by to happiness. You give me what I ask you, Governor: not a penny more, and not a penny less.

PICKERING. Why dont you marry that missus of yours? I rather draw the line at encouraging that sort of immorality.

DOOLITTLE. Tell her so, Governor: tell her so. *I'm* willing. It's me that suffers by it. Ive no hold on her. I got to be agreeable to her. I got to give her presents. I got to buy her clothes something sinful. I'm a slave to that woman, Governor, just because I'm not her lawful husband. And she knows it too. Catch her marrying me! Take my advice, Governor: marry Eliza while she's young and dont know no better. If you dont you'll be sorry for it after. If you do, she'll be sorry for it after; but better her than you, because youre a man, and she's only a woman and dont know how to be happy anyhow.

HIGGINS. Pickering: if we listen to this man another minute, we shall have no convictions left. (*To Doolittle.*) Five pounds I think you said.

DOOLITTLE. Thank you kindly, Governor.

HIGGINS. Youre sure you wont take ten?

DOOLITTLE. Not now. Another time, Governor.

HIGGINS. (*Handing him a five-pound note.*) Here you are.

DOOLITTLE. Thank you, Governor. Good morning. (*He hurries to the door, anxious to get away with his booty. When he opens it he is confronted with a dainty and exquisitely clean young Japanese lady in a simple blue cotton kimono printed cunningly with small white jasmine blossoms. Mrs. Pearce is with her. He gets out of her way deferentially and apologizes.*) Beg pardon, miss.

THE JAPANESE LADY. Garn! Dont you know your own daughter?

DOOLITTLE.	⎧ *Exclaiming* ⎫	Bly me! It's Eliza!
HIGGINS.	⎨ *simul-* ⎬	Whats that? This!
PICKERING.	⎩ *taneously.* ⎭	By Jove!

ELIZA. Dont I look silly?

HIGGINS. Silly?

MRS. PEARCE. (*At the door.*) Now, Mr. Higgins, please dont say anything to make the girl conceited about herself.

HIGGINS. (*Conscientiously.*) Oh! Quite right, Mrs. Pearce. (*To Eliza.*) Yes: damned silly.

MRS. PEARCE. Please, sir.

HIGGINS. (*Correcting himself.*) I mean extremely silly.

ELIZA.   I should look all right with my hat on. (*She takes up her hat; puts it on; and walks across the room to the fireplace with a fashionable air.*)

HIGGINS.   A new fashion, by George! And it ought to look horrible!

DOOLITTLE. (*With fatherly pride.*)   Well, I never thought she'd clean up as good looking as that, Governor. She's a credit to me, aint she?

ELIZA.   I tell you, it's easy to clean up here. Hot and cold water on tap, just as much as you like, there is. Woolly towels, there is; and a towel horse so hot, it burns your fingers. Soft brushes to scrub yourself, and a wooden bowl of soap smelling like primroses. Now I know why ladies is so clean. Washing's a treat for them. Wish they could see what it is for the like of me!

HIGGINS.   I'm glad the bathroom met with your approval.

ELIZA.   It didnt: not all of it; and I dont care who hears me say it. Mrs. Pearce knows.

HIGGINS.   What was wrong, Mrs. Pearce?

MRS. PEARCE. (*Blandly.*)   Oh, nothing, sir. It doesnt matter.

ELIZA.   I had a good mind to break it. I didn't know which way to look. But I hung a towel over it, I did.

HIGGINS.   Over what?

MRS. PEARCE.   Over the looking-glass, sir.

HIGGINS.   Doolittle: you have brought your daughter up too strictly.

DOOLITTLE.   Me! I never brought her up at all, except to give her a lick of a strap now and again. Dont put it on me, Governor. She aint accustomed to it, you see: thats all. But shell soon pick up your free-and-easy ways.

ELIZA.   I'm a good girl, I am; and I wont pick up no free-and-easy ways.

HIGGINS.   Eliza: if you say again that youre a good girl, your father shall take you home.

ELIZA.   Not him. You dont know my father. All he come here for was to touch you for some money to get drunk on.

DOOLITTLE. Well, what else would I want money for? To put into the plate in church, I suppose. (*She puts out her tongue at him. He is so incensed by this that Pickering presently finds it necessary to step between them.*) Dont you give me none of your lip; and dont let me hear you giving this gentleman any of it neither, or youll hear from me about it. See?

HIGGINS. Have you any further advice to give her before you go, Doolittle? Your blessing, for instance.

DOOLITTLE. No, Governor: I aint such a mug as to put up my children to all I know myself. Hard enough to hold them in without that. If you want Eliza's mind improved, Governor, you do it yourself with a strap. So long, gentlemen. (*He turns to go.*)

HIGGINS. (*Impressively.*) Stop. Youll come regularly to see your daughter. It's your duty, you know. My brother is a clergyman; and he could help you in your talks with her.

DOOLITTLE. (*Evasively.*) Certainly, I'll come, Governor. Not just this week, because I have a job at a distance. But later on you may depend on me. Afternoon, gentlemen. Afternoon, maam. (*He touches his hat to Mrs. Pearce, who disdains the salutation and goes out. He winks at Higgins, thinking him probably a fellow-sufferer from Mrs. Pearce's difficult disposition, and follows her.*).

ELIZA. Dont you believe the old liar. He'd as soon you set a bulldog on him as a clergyman. You wont see him again in a hurry.

HIGGINS. I don't want to, Eliza. Do you?

ELIZA. Not me. I dont want never to see him again, I dont. He's a disgrace to me, he is, collecting dust, instead of working at his trade.

PICKERING. What is his trade, Eliza?

ELIZA. Talking money out of other people's pockets into his own. His proper trade's a navvy[4]; and he works at it some-

4. *Navvy:* unskilled laborer.

times too—for exercise—and earns good money at it. Aint you going to call me Miss Doolittle any more?

PICKERING. I beg your pardon, Miss Doolittle. It was a slip of the tongue.

ELIZA. Oh, I dont mind; only it sounded so genteel. I should just like to take a taxi to the corner of Tottenham Court Road and get out there and tell it to wait for me, just to put the girls in their place a bit. I wouldn't speak to them, you know.

PICKERING. Better wait till we get you something really fashionable.

HIGGINS. Besides, you shouldnt cut your old friends now that you have risen in the world. Thats what we call snobbery.

ELIZA. You dont call the like of them my friends now, I should hope. Theyve took it out of me often enough with their ridicule when they had the chance; and now I mean to get a bit of my own back. But if I'm to have fashionable clothes, I'll wait. I should like to have some. Mrs. Pearce says youre going to give me some to wear in bed at night different to what I wear in the daytime; but it do seem a waste of money when you could get something to show. Besides, I never could fancy changing into cold things on a winter night.

MRS. PEARCE. (*Coming back.*) Now, Eliza. The new things have come for you to try on.

ELIZA. Ah-ow-oo-ooh! (*She rushes out.*)

MRS. PEARCE. (*Following her.*) Oh, dont rush about like that, girl. (*She shuts the door behind her.*)

HIGGINS. Pickering: we have taken on a stiff job.

PICKERING. (*With conviction.*) Higgins: we have.

* * * * * *

There seems to be some curiosity as to what Higgins' lessons to Eliza were like. Well, here is a sample: the first one.

Picture Eliza, in her new clothes, and feeling her inside put out of step by a lunch, dinner, and breakfast of a kind to which it is unaccustomed, seated with Higgins and the Colonel in the study, feeling like a hospital out-patient at a first encounter with the doctors.

Higgins, constitutionally unable to sit still, discomposes her still more by striding restlessly about. But for the reassuring presence and quietude of her friend the Colonel she would run for her life, even back to Drury Lane.

HIGGINS. Say your alphabet.

ELIZA. I know my alphabet. Do you think I know nothing? I dont need to be taught like a child.

HIGGINS. (*Thundering.*) Say your alphabet.

PICKERING. Say it, Miss Doolittle. You will understand presently. Do what he tells you; and let him teach you in his own way.

ELIZA. Oh well, if you put it like that—Ahyee, bəyee, cəyee, dəyee—

HIGGINS. (*With the roar of a wounded lion.*) Stop. Listen to this, Pickering. This is what we pay for as elementary education. This unfortunate animal has been locked up for nine years in school at our expense to teach her to speak and read the language of Shakespear and Milton. And the result is Ahyee, Bə-yee, Cə-yee, Dəyee. (*To Eliza.*) Say A, B, C, D.

ELIZA. (*Almost in tears.*) But I'm sayin it. Ahyee, Bəyee, Cə-yee—

HIGGINS. Stop. Say a cup of tea.

ELIZA. A cappətə-ee.

HIGGINS. Put your tongue forward until it squeezes against the top of your lower teeth. Now say cup.

ELIZA. C-c-c—I cant. C-Cup.

PICKERING. Good. Splendid, Miss Doolittle.

HIGGINS. By Jupiter, she's done it the first shot. Pickering: we shall make a duchess of her. (*To Eliza.*) Now do you think you could possibly say tea? Not tə-yee, mind: if you ever say bə-yee cə-yee də-yee again you shall be dragged round the room three times by the hair of your head. (*Fortissimo.*) T, T, T, T.

ELIZA. (*Weeping.*)   I cant hear no difference cep that it sounds more genteel-like when you say it.

HIGGINS.   Well, if you can hear that difference, what the devil are you crying for? Pickering: give her a chocolate.

PICKERING.   No, no. Never mind crying a little, Miss Doolittle: you are doing very well; and the lessons wont hurt. I promise you I wont let him drag you round the room by your hair.

HIGGINS.   Be off with you to Mrs. Pearce and tell her about it. Think about it. Try to do it by yourself: and keep your tongue well forward in your mouth instead of trying to roll it up and swallow it. Another lesson at half-past four this afternoon. Away with you.

(*Eliza, still sobbing, rushes from the room.*)

And that is the sort of ordeal poor Eliza has to go through for months before we meet her again on her first appearance in London society of the professional class.

And that is the sort of ordeal poor Eliza has to go through for months. . . .

It is Mrs. Higgins' at-home day. Nobody has yet arrived. Her drawing room, in a flat on Chelsea Embankment, has three windows looking on the river; and the ceiling is not so lofty as it would be in an older house of the same pretension. The windows are open, giving access to a balcony with flowers in pots. If you stand with your face to the windows, you have the fireplace on your left and the door in the right-hand wall close to the corner nearest the windows.

Mrs. Higgins was brought up on Morris and Burne Jones;[1] and her room, which is very unlike her son's room in Wimpole Street, is not crowded with furniture and little tables and knickknacks. In the middle of the room there is a big ottoman; and this, with the carpet, the Morris wallpapers, and the Morris chintz window curtains and brocade covers of the ottoman and its cushions, supply all the ornament, and are much too handsome to be hidden by odds and ends of useless things. A few good oil paintings from the exhibitions in the Grosvenor Gallery thirty years ago (the Burne Jones, not the Whistler[2] side of them) are on the walls. The only landscape is a Cecil Lawson on the scale of a Rubens. There is a portrait of Mrs. Higgins as she was when she defied the fashion in her youth in one of the beautiful Rossettian costumes which, when caricatured by people who did not understand, led to the absurdities of popular estheticism in the eighteen-seventies.

1. *Morris . . . Burne Jones:* William Morris (1834-1896), Edward Burne-Jones (1833-1898), designed furniture.
2. *Whistler:* James Abbott McNeill Whistler (1834-1903), painter. Other references are to artists and poets.

In the corner diagonally opposite the door Mrs. Higgins, now over sixty and long past taking the trouble to dress out of the fashion, sits writing at an elegantly simple writing table with a bell button within reach of her hand. There is a Chippendale chair further back in the room between her and the window nearest her side. At the other side of the room, further forward, is an Elizabethan chair roughly carved in the taste of Inigo Jones. On the same side a piano in a decorated case. The corner between the fireplace and the window is occupied by a divan cushioned in Morris chintz.

It is between four and five in the afternoon.

The door is opened violently, and Higgins enters with his hat on.

MRS. HIGGINS. (*Dismayed.*) Henry! (*Scolding him.*) What are you doing here today? It is my at-home day: you promised not to come. (*As he bends to kiss her, she takes his hat off, and presents it to him.*)

HIGGINS. Oh bother! (*He throws the hat down on the table.*)

MRS. HIGGINS. Go home at once.

HIGGINS. (*Kissing her.*) I know, mother. I came on purpose.

MRS. HIGGINS. But you mustnt. I'm serious, Henry. You offend all my friends: they stop coming whenever they meet you.

HIGGINS. Nonsense! I know I have no small talk; but people dont mind. (*He sits on the settee.*)

MRS. HIGGINS. Oh! dont they? Small talk indeed! what about your large talk? Really, dear, you mustnt stay.

HIGGINS. I must. Ive a job for you. A phonetic job.

MRS. HIGGINS. No use, dear. I'm sorry; but I cant get around your vowels; and though I like to get pretty postcards in your patent shorthand, I always have to read the copies in ordinary writing you so thoughtfully send me.

HIGGINS. Well, this isnt a phonetic job.

MRS. HIGGINS. You said it was.

HIGGINS. Not your part of it. Ive picked up a girl.

MRS. HIGGINS.   Does that mean that some girl has picked you up?

HIGGINS.   Not at all. I dont mean a love affair.

MRS. HIGGINS.   What a pity!

HIGGINS.   Why?

MRS. HIGGINS.   Well, you never fall in love with anyone under forty-five. When will you discover that there are some rather nice-looking young women about?

HIGGINS.   Oh, I cant be bothered with young women. My idea of a lovable woman is somebody as like you as possible. I shall never get into the way of seriously liking young women: some habits lie too deep to be changed. (*Rising abruptly and walking about, jingling his money and his keys in his trouser pockets.*) Besides, theyre all idiots.

MRS. HIGGINS.   Do you know what you would do if you really loved me, Henry?

HIGGINS.   Oh bother! What? Marry, I suppose.

MRS. HIGGINS.   No. Stop fidgeting and take your hands out of your pockets. (*With a gesture of despair, he obeys and sits down again.*) Thats a good boy. Now tell me about the girl.

HIGGINS.   Shes coming to see you.

MRS. HIGGINS.   I dont remember asking her.

HIGGINS.   You didnt. *I* asked her. If youd known her you wouldnt have asked her.

MRS. HIGGINS.   Indeed! Why?

HIGGINS.   Well, it's like this. She's a common flower girl. I picked her off the curbstone.

MRS. HIGGINS.   And invited her to my at-home!

HIGGINS. (*Rising and coming to her to coax her.*)   Oh, thatll be all right. Ive taught her to speak properly; and she has strict orders as to her behavior. She's to keep to two subjects: the weather and everybody's health—Fine day and How do you do, you know—and not to let herself go on things in general. That will be safe.

MRS. HIGGINS. Safe! To talk about our health! About our insides! Perhaps about our outsides! How could you be so silly, Henry?

HIGGINS. (*Impatiently.*) Well, she must talk about something. (*He controls himself and sits down again.*) Oh, she'll be all right, dont you fuss. Pickering is in it with me. Ive a sort of bet on that I'll pass her off as a duchess in six months. I started on her some months ago; and she's getting on like a house on fire. I shall win my bet. She has a quick ear; and she's easier to teach than my middle-class pupils because she's had to learn a complete new language. She talks English almost as you talk French.

MRS. HIGGINS. Thats satisfactory, at all events.

HIGGINS. Well, it is and it isnt.

MRS. HIGGINS. What does that mean?

HIGGINS. You see, Ive got her pronunciation all right: but you have to consider not only how a girl pronounces, but what she pronounces; and that's where—

(*They are interrupted by the parlormaid, announcing guests.*)

THE PARLORMAID. Mrs. and Miss Eynsford Hill. (*She withdraws.*)

HIGGINS. Oh Lord! (*He rises; snatches his hat from the table; and makes for the door; but before he reaches it his mother introduces him.*)

(*Mrs. and Miss Eynsford Hill are the mother and daughter who sheltered from the rain in Covent Garden. The mother is well bred, quiet, and has the habitual anxiety of straitened means. The daughter has acquired a gay air of being very much at home in society: the bravado of genteel poverty.*)

MRS. EYNSFORD HILL. (*To Mrs. Higgins.*) How do you do? (*They shake hands.*)

MISS EYNSFORD HILL. How do you do? (*She shakes.*)

MRS. HIGGINS. (*Introducing.*) My son Henry.

MRS. EYNSFORD HILL.   Your celebrated son! I have so longed to meet you, Professor Higgins.

HIGGINS.   (*Glumly, making no movement in her direction.*) Delighted. (*He backs against the piano and bows brusquely.*)

MISS EYNSFORD HILL. (*Going to him with confident familiarity.*)   How do you do?

HIGGINS. (*Staring at her.*)   Ive seen you before somewhere. I havnt the ghost of a notion where; but Ive heard your voice. (*Drearily.*) It doesnt matter. Youd better sit down.

MRS. HIGGINS.   I'm sorry to say that my celebrated son has no manners. You mustnt mind him.

MISS EYNSFORD HILL. (*Gaily.*)   I dont. (*She sits in the Elizabethan chair.*)

MRS. EYNSFORD HILL. (*A little bewildered.*)   Not at all. (*She sits on the ottoman between her daughter and Mrs. Higgins, who has turned her chair away from the writing-table.*)

HIGGINS.   Oh, have I been rude? I didnt mean to be.

(*He goes to the central window, through which, with his back to the company, he contemplates the river and the flowers in Battersea Park on the opposite bank as if they were a frozen desert.*

The parlormaid returns, ushering in Pickering.)

THE PARLORMAID.   Colonel Pickering. (*She withdraws.*)

PICKERING.   How do you, Mrs. Higgins?

MRS. HIGGINS.   So glad youve come. Do you know Mrs. Eynsford Hill—Miss Eynsford Hill? (*Exchange of bows. The Colonel brings the Chippendale chair a little forward between Mrs. Hill and Mrs. Higgins, and sits down.*)

PICKERING.   Has Henry told you what weve come for?

HIGGINS. (*Over his shoulder.*)   We were interrupted: damn it!

MRS. HIGGINS.   Oh Henry, Henry, really!

MRS. EYNSFORD HILL. (*Half rising.*)   Are we in the way?

MRS. HIGGINS. (*Rising and making her sit down again.*)No, no. You couldnt have come more fortunately: we want you to meet a friend of ours.

HIGGINS. (*Turning hopefully.*) Yes, by George! We want two or three people. You'll do as well as anybody else.
    (*The parlormaid returns, ushering Freddy.*)

THE PARLORMAID. Mr. Eynsford Hill.

HIGGINS. (*Almost audibly, past endurance.*) God of Heaven! another of them.

FREDDY. (*Shaking hands with Mrs. Higgins.*) Ahdedo?

MRS. HIGGINS. Very good of you to come. (*Introducing.*) Colonel Pickering.

FREDDY. (*bowing.*) Ahdedo?

MRS. HIGGINS. I dont think you know my son, Professor Higgins.

FREDDY. (*Going to Higgins.*) Ahdedo?

HIGGINS. (*Looking at him much as if he were a pickpocket.*) I'll take my oath Ive met you before somewhere. Where was it?

FREDDY. I dont think so.

HIGGINS. (*Resignedly.*) It dont matter, anyhow. Sit down.
    (*He shakes Freddy's hand, and almost slings him on to the ottoman with his face to the window; then comes round to the other side of it.*)

HIGGINS. Well, here we are, anyhow! (*He sits down on the ottoman next Mrs. Eynsford Hill, on her left.*) And now, what the devil are we going to talk about until Eliza comes?

MRS. HIGGINS. Henry, you are the life and soul of the Royal Society's[3] soirées; but really youre rather trying on more commonplace occasions.

HIGGINS. Am I? Very sorry. (*Beaming suddenly.*)I suppose I am, you know. (*Uproariously.*) Ha, ha!

3. *Royal Society:* group of learned men.

MISS EYNSFORD HILL. (*Who considers Higgins quite eligible matrimonially.*) I sympathize. *I* havnt any small talk. If people would only be frank and say what they really think!

HIGGINS. (*Relapsing into gloom.*) Lord forbid!

MRS. EYNSFORD HILL. (*Taking up her daughter's cue.*) But why?

HIGGINS. What they think they ought to think is bad enough, Lord knows; but what they really think would break up the whole show. Do you suppose it would be really agreeable if I were to come out now with what *I* really think?

MISS EYNSFORD HILL. (*Gaily.*) Is it so very cynical?

HIGGINS. Cynical! Who the dickens said it was cynical! I mean it wouldnt be decent.

MRS. EYNSFORD HILL. (*Seriously.*) Oh! I'm sure you dont mean that, Mr. Higgins.

HIGGINS. You see, we're all savages, more or less. We're supposed to be civilized and cultured—to know all about poetry and philosophy and art and science, and so on; but how many of us know even the meanings of these names? (*To Miss Hill.*) What do you know of poetry? (*To Mrs. Hill.*) What do you know of science? (*Indicating Freddy.*) What does he know of art or science or anything else? What the devil do you imagine I know of philosophy?

MRS. HIGGINS. (*Warningly.*) Or of manners, Henry?

THE PARLORMAID. (*Opening the door.*) Miss Doolittle. (*She withdraws.*)

HIGGINS. (*Rising hastily and running to Mrs. Higgins.*) Here she is, mother. (*He stands on tiptoe and makes signs over his mother's head to Eliza to indicate to her which lady is her hostess.*)

(*Eliza, who is exquisitely dressed, produces an impression of such remarkable distinction and beauty as she enters that they all rise, quite fluttered. Guided by Hig-*

gins' *signals, she comes to Mrs. Higgins with studied grace.*)

ELIZA. (*Speaking with pedantic correctness of pronunciation and great beauty of tone.*) How do you do, Mrs. Higgins? (*She gasps slightly in making sure of the H in Higgins, but is quite successful.*) Mr. Higgins told me I might come.

MRS. HIGGINS. (*Cordially.*) Quite right: I'm very glad indeed to see you.

PICKERING. How do you do, Miss Doolittle?

ELIZA. (*Shaking hands with him.*) Colonel Pickering, is it not?

MRS. EYNSFORD HILL. I feel sure we have met before, Miss Doolittle. I remember your eyes.

ELIZA. How do you do? (*She sits down on the ottoman gracefully in the place just left vacant by Higgins.*)

MRS. EYNSFORD HILL. (*Introducing.*) My daughter Clara.

ELIZA. How do you do?

CLARA. (*Impulsively.*) How do you do? (*She sits down on the ottoman beside Eliza, devouring her with her eyes.*)

FREDDY. (*Coming to their side of the ottoman.*) Ive certainly had the pleasure.

MRS. EYNSFORD HILL. (*Introducing.*) My son Freddy.

ELIZA. How do you do?

(*Freddy bows and sits down in the Elizabethan chair, infatuated.*)

HIGGINS. (*Suddenly.*) By George, yes: it all comes back to me! (*They stare at him.*) Covent Garden! (*Lamentably.*) What a damned thing!

MRS. HIGGINS. Henry, please! (*He is about to sit on the edge of the table.*) Don't sit on my writing-table: you'll break it.

HIGGINS. (*Sulkily.*) Sorry.

(*He goes to the divan, stumbling into the fender and over the fire-irons on his way; extricating himself with*

muttered imprecations; and finishing his disastrous jour-
ney by throwing himself so impatiently on the divan that
he almost breaks it. Mrs. Higgins looks at him, but con-
trols herself and says nothing.
    A long and painful pause ensues.)

MRS. HIGGINS. (*At last, conversationally.*) Will it rain, do
you think?

ELIZA. The shallow depression in the west of these islands
is likely to move in an easterly direction. There are no indications of any great change in the barometrical situation.

FREDDY. Ha! ha! how awfully funny!

ELIZA. What is wrong with that, young man? I bet I got it
right.

FREDDY. Killing!

MRS. EYNSFORD HILL. I'm sure I hope it wont turn cold.
Theres so much influenza about. It runs right through our
whole family regularly every spring.

ELIZA. (*Darkly.*) My aunt died of influenza: so they said.

MRS. EYNSFORD HILL. (*Clicks her tongue sympathetically.*)!!!

ELIZA. (*In the same tragic tone.*) But it's my belief they done
the woman in.

MRS. HIGGINS. (*Puzzled.*) Done her in?

ELIZA. Y-e-e-e-es, Lord love you! Why should she die of influenza? She come through diphtheria right enough the year
before. I saw her with my own eyes. Fairly blue with it, she
was. They all thought she was dead; but my father he kept
ladling gin down her throat til she came to so sudden that
she bit the bowl off the spoon.

MRS. EYNSFORD HILL. (*Startled.*) Dear me!

ELIZA. (*Piling up the indictment.*) What call would a woman with such strength in her have to die of influenza?
What become of her new straw hat that should have come
to me? Somebody pinched it; and what I say is, them as
pinched it done her in.

MRS. EYNSFORD HILL. What does doing her in mean?

HIGGINS. (*Hastily.*) Ah, thats the new small talk. To do a person in means to kill them.

MRS. EYNSFORD HILL. (*To Eliza, horrified.*) You surely dont believe that your aunt was killed?

ELIZA. Do I not! Them she lived with would have killed her for a hat-pin, let alone a hat.

MRS. EYNSFORD HILL. But it cant have been right for your father to pour spirits down her throat like that. It might have killed her.

ELIZA. Not her. Gin was mother's milk to her. Besides, he'd poured so much down his own throat that he knew the good of it.

MRS. EYNSFORD HILL. Do you mean that he drank?

ELIZA. Drank! My word! Something chronic.

MRS. EYNSFORD HILL. How dreadful for you!

ELIZA. Not a bit. It never did no harm what I could see. But then he did not keep it up regular. (*Cheerfully.*) On the burst, as you might say, from time to time. And always more agreeable when he had a drop in. When he was out of work, my mother used to give him fourpence and tell him to go out and not come back until he'd drunk himself cheerful and loving-like. Theres lots of women has to make their husbands drunk to make them fit to live with. (*Now quite at her ease.*) You see, it's like this. If a man has a bit of conscience, it always takes him when he's sober; and then it makes him low-spirited. A drop of booze just takes that off and makes him happy. (*To Freddy, who is in convulsions of suppressed laughter.*)Here! what are you sniggering at?

FREDDY. The new small talk. You do it so awfully well.

ELIZA. If I was doing it proper, what was you laughing at? (*To Higgins.*) Have I said anything I oughtnt?

MRS. HIGGINS. (*Interposing.*) Not at all, Miss Doolittle.

ELIZA. Well, thats a mercy, anyhow. (*Expansively.*) What I always say is—

HIGGINS. (*Rising and looking at his watch.*)   Ahem!

ELIZA. (*Looking round at him; taking the hint, and rising.*) Well: I must go. (*They all rise. Freddy goes to the door.*) So pleased to have met you. Good-by. (*She shakes hands with Mrs. Higgins.*)

MRS. HIGGINS.   Good-by.

ELIZA.   Good-by, Colonel Pickering.

PICKERING.   Good-by, Miss Doolittle. (*They shake hands.*)

ELIZA. (*Nodding to the others.*) Good-by, all.

FREDDY. (*Opening the door for her.*)   Are you walking across the park, Miss Doolittle? If so—

ELIZA. (*With perfectly elegant diction.*)   Walk! Not bloody likely. (*Sensation.*) I am going in a taxi. (*She goes out.*)
   (*Pickering gasps and sits down. Freddy goes out on the balcony to catch another glimpse of Eliza.*)

MRS. EYNSFORD HILL. (*Suffering from shock.*)   Well, I really cant get used to the new ways.

CLARA. (*Throwing herself discontentedly into the Elizabethan chair.*)   Oh, it's all right, mamma, quite right. People will think we never go anywhere or see anybody if you are so old-fashioned.

MRS. EYNSFORD HILL.   I daresay I am very old-fashioned; but I do hope you wont begin using that expression, Clara. I have got accustomed to hear you talking about men as rotters, and calling everything filthy and beastly; though I do think it horrible and unladylike. But this last is really too much. Dont you think so, Colonel Pickering?

PICKERING.   Dont ask me. Ive been away in India for several years; and manners have changed so much that I sometimes dont know whether I'm at a respectable dinnertable or in a ship's forecastle.

CLARA.   It's all a matter of habit. Theres no right or wrong in it. Nobody means anything by it. And it's so quaint, and gives such a smart emphasis to things that are not in themselves very witty. I find the new small talk delightful and quite innocent.

MRS. EYNSFORD HILL. (*Rising.*)   Well, after that, I think it's time for us to go.

   (*Pickering and Higgins rise.*)

CLARA. (*Rising.*)   Oh yes: we have three at-homes to go to still. Good-by, Mrs. Higgins. Good-by, Colonel Pickering. Good-by, Professor Higgins.

HIGGINS. (*Coming grimly at her from the divan, and accompanying her to the door.*)   Good-by. Be sure you try on that small talk at the three at-homes. Dont be nervous about it. Pitch it in strong.

CLARA. (*All smiles.*)   I will. Good-by. Such nonsense, all this early Victorian prudery!

HIGGINS. (*Tempting her.*)   Such damned nonsense!

CLARA.   Such bloody nonsense!

MRS. EYNSFORD HILL. (*Convulsively.*)   Clara!

CLARA.   Ha! ha! (*She goes out radiant, conscious of being thoroughly up-to-date, and is heard descending the stairs in a stream of silvery laughter.*)

FREDDY. (*To the heavens at large.*)   Well, I ask you—(*He gives it up, and comes to Mrs. Higgins.*) Good-by.

MRS. HIGGINS. (*Shaking hands.*)   Good-by. Would you like to meet Miss Doolittle again?

FREDDY. (*Eagerly.*)   Yes, I should, most awfully.

MRS. HIGGINS.   Well, you know my days.

FREDDY.   Yes, Thanks awfully. Good-by. (*He goes out.*)

MRS. EYNSFORD HILL.   Good-by, Mr. Higgins.

HIGGINS.   Good-by. Good-by.

MRS. EYNSFORD HILL. (*To Pickering.*)   It's no use. I shall never be able to bring myself to use that word.

PICKERING.   Dont. It's not compulsory, you know. Youll get on quite well without it.

MRS. EYNSFORD HILL.   Only, Clara is so down on me if I am not positively reeking with the latest slang. Good-by.

PICKERING.   Good-by. (*They shake hands.*)

MRS. EYNSFORD HILL. (*To Mrs. Higgins.*)   You mustnt mind Clara. (*Pickering, catching from her lowered tone that this is not meant for him to hear, discreetly joins Higgins at the window.*) We're so poor! and she gets so few parties, poor child! She doesnt quite know. (*Mrs. Higgins, seeing that her eyes are moist, takes her hand sympathetically and goes with her to the door.*) But the boy is nice. Dont you think so?

MRS. HIGGINS. Oh, quite nice. I shall always be delighted to see him.

MRS. EYNSFORD HILL. Thank you, dear. Good-by. (*She goes out.*)

HIGGINS. (*Eagerly.*) Well? Is Eliza presentable? (*He swoops on his mother and drags her to the ottoman, where she sits down in Eliza's place with her son on her left.*)
    (*Pickering returns to his chair on her right.*)

MRS. HIGGINS. You silly boy, of course she's not presentable. She's a triumph of your art and of her dressmaker's; but if you suppose for a moment that she doesn't give herself away in every sentence she utters, you must be perfectly cracked about her.

PICKERING. But dont you think something might be done? I mean something to eliminate the sanguinary element from her conversation.

MRS. HIGGINS. Not as long as she is in Henry's hands.

HIGGINS. (*Aggrieved.*) Do you mean that my language is improper?

MRS. HIGGINS. No, dearest: it would be quite proper—say on a canal barge; but it would not be proper for her at a garden party.

HIGGINS. (*Deeply injured.*) Well I must say—

PICKERING. (*Interrupting him.*) Come, Higgins: you must learn to know yourself. I havent heard such language as yours since we used to review the volunteers in Hyde Park twenty years ago.

HIGGINS. (*Sulkily.*) Oh, well, if you say so, I suppose I dont always talk like a bishop.

MRS. HIGGINS. (*Quieting Henry with a touch.*) Colonel Pickering: will you tell me what is the exact state of things in Wimpole Street?

PICKERING. (*Cheerfully, as if this completely changed the subject.*) Well, I have come to live there with Henry. We work together at my Indian Dialects; and we think it more convenient—

MRS. HIGGINS. Quite so. I know all about that: it's an excellent arrangement. But where does this girl live?

HIGGINS. With us, of course. Where should she live?

MRS. HIGGINS. But on what terms? Is she a servant? If not, what is she?

PICKERING. (*Slowly.*) I think I know what you mean, Mrs. Higgins.

HIGGINS. Well, dash me if *I* do! Ive had to work at the girl every day for months to get her to her present pitch. Besides, she's useful. She knows where my things are, and remembers my appointments and so forth.

MRS. HIGGINS. How does your housekeeper get on with her?

HIGGINS. Mrs. Pearce? Oh, she's jolly glad to get so much taken off her hands; for before Eliza came, she used to have to find things and remind me of my appointments. But she's got some silly bee in her bonnet about Eliza. She keeps saying "You dont think, sir": doesnt she, Pick?

PICKERING. Yes: thats the formula. "You dont think, sir." Thats the end of every conversation about Eliza.

HIGGINS. As if I ever stop thinking about the girl and her confounded vowels and consonants. I'm worn out, thinking about her, and watching her lips and her teeth and her tongue, not to mention her soul, which is the quaintest of the lot.

MRS. HIGGINS. You certainly are a pretty pair of babies, playing with your live doll.

HIGGINS. Playing! The hardest job I ever tackled: make no mistake about that, mother. But you have no idea how frightfully interesting it is to take a human being and change her into a quite different human being by creating a new speech for her. It's filling up the deepest gulf that separates class from class and soul from soul.

PICKERING. (*Drawing his chair closer to Mrs. Higgins and bending over to her eagerly.*) Yes: it's enormously interesting. I assure you, Mrs. Higgins, we take Eliza very seriously. Every week—every day almost—there is some new change. (*Closer again.*) We keep records of every stage—dozens of gramophone disks and photographs—

HIGGINS. (*Assailing her at the other ear.*) Yes, by George: it's the most absorbing experiment I ever tackled. She regularly fills our lives up: doesn't she, Pick?

PICKERING.   We're always talking Eliza.

HIGGINS.   Teaching Eliza.

PICKERING.   Dressing Eliza.

MRS. HIGGINS.   What!

HIGGINS.   Inventing new Elizas.

HIGGINS.   (*Speaking together.*)   You know, she has the most extraordinary quickness of ear:

PICKERING.   I assure you, my dear Mrs. Higgins, that girl

HIGGINS.   just like a parrot. Ive tried her with every

PICKERING.   is a genius. She can play the piano quite beautifully.

HIGGINS.   possible sort of sound that a human being can make—

PICKERING.   We have taken her to classical concerts and to music

HIGGINS.   Continental dialects, African dialects, Hottentot

PICKERING.   halls; and it's all the same to her: she plays everything

HIGGINS. ⟩ (*Speaking* ⟨clicks, things it took me years to get
                together.) ⟩ hold of; and

PICKERING. ⟩   ⟨she hears right off when she comes
                         ⟨ home, whether it's

HIGGINS. ⟩   ⟨she picks them up like a shot, right
                       ⟨ away, as if she had

PICKERING. ⟩   ⟩Beethoven and Brahms or Lehar and
                        ⟨ Lionel Monckton;[4]

HIGGINS. ⟩   ⟨been at it all her life.
PICKERING. ⟩   ⟩though six months ago, she'd never
                        ⟨ as much as touched a piano—

MRS. HIGGINS. (*Putting her fingers in her ears, as they are by
this time shouting one another down with an intolerable
noise.*)   Sh-sh-sh—sh! (*They stop.*)

PICKERING.   I beg your pardon. (*He draws his chair back
apologetically.*)

HIGGINS.   Sorry. When Pickering starts shouting nobody
can get a word in edgeways.

MRS. HIGGINS.   Be quiet, Henry. Colonel Pickering, dont you
realize that when Eliza walked in Wimpole Street, something walked in with her?

PICKERING.   Her father did. But Henry soon got rid of him.

MRS. HIGGINS.   It would have been more to the point if her
mother had. But as her mother didnt something else did.

PICKERING.   But what?

MRS. HIGGINS. (*Unconsciously dating herself by the word.*)
A problem.

PICKERING.   Oh, I see. The problem of how to pass her off as
a lady.

HIGGINS.   I'll solve that problem. Ive half solved it already.

MRS. HIGGINS.   No, you two infinitely stupid male creatures:
the problem of what is to be done with her afterwards.

4. *Beethoven . . . Monckton:* music composers.

HIGGINS. I dont see anything in that. She can go her own way, with all the advantages I have given her.

MRS. HIGGINS. The advantages of that poor woman who was here just now! The manners and habits that disqualify a fine lady from earning her own living without giving her a fine lady's income! Is that what you mean?

PICKERING. (*Indulgently, being rather bored.*) Oh, that will be all right, Mrs. Higgins. (*He rises to go.*)

HIGGINS. (*Rising also.*) We'll find her some light employment.

PICKERING. She's happy enough. Dont you worry about her. Good-by. (*He shakes hands as if he were consoling a frightened child, and makes for the door.*)

HIGGINS. Anyhow, theres no good bothering now. The thing's done. Good-by, mother. (*He kisses her, and follows Pickering.*)

PICKERING. (*Turning for a final consolation.*) There are plenty of openings. We'll do whats right. Good-by.

HIGGINS. (*To Pickering as they go out together.*) Lets take her to the Shakespear exhibition at Earls Court.

PICKERING. Yes, lets. Her remarks will be delicious.

HIGGINS. She'll mimic all the people for us when we get home.

PICKERING. Ripping. (*Both are heard laughing as they go downstairs.*)

MRS. HIGGINS. (*Rises with an impatient bounce, and returns to her work at the writing-table. She sweeps a litter of disarranged papers out of the way; snatches a sheet of paper from her stationery case; and tries resolutely to write. At the third time she gives it up; flings down her pen; grips the table angrily and exclaims.*) Oh, men! men!! men!!!

*   *   *   *   *   *

Clearly Eliza will not pass as a duchess yet; and Higgins' bet remains unwon. But the six months are not yet *exhausted and just in time Eliza does actually pass as a princess. For a glimpse of how she did it imagine an Embassy in London one summer evening after dark. The hall door has an awning and a carpet across to the curb, because a grand reception is in progress. A small crowd is lined up to see the guests arrive.*

A Rolls-Royce car drives up. Pickering in evening dress, with medals and orders, alights, and hands out Eliza, in opera cloak, evening dress, diamonds, fan, flowers and all accessories. Higgins follows. The car drives off; and the three go up the steps and into the house, the door opening for them as they approach.

Inside the house they find themselves in a spacious hall from which the grand staircase rises. On the left are the arrangements for the gentlemen's cloaks. The male guests are depositing their hats and wraps there.

On the right is a door leading to the ladies's cloakroom. Ladies are going in cloaked and coming out in splendor. Pickering whispers to Eliza and points out the ladies' room. She goes into it. Higgins and Pickering take off their overcoats and take tickets for them from the attendant.

One of the guests, occupied in the same way, has his back turned. Having taken his ticket, he turns round and reveals himself as an important looking young man with an astonishingly hairy face. He has an enormous moustache, flowing out into luxuriant whiskers. Waves of hair cluster on his brow. His hair is cropped closely at the back, and glows with oil. Otherwise he is very smart. He wears several worthless orders. He is evidently a foreigner, guessable as a whiskered Pandour[5] from Hungary; but in spite of the ferocity of his moustache he is amiable and genially voluble.

5. *Pandour:* member of a middle-European mounted military police.

Recognizing Higgins, he flings his arms wide apart and approaches him enthusiastically.

WHISKERS.   Maestro, maestro! (*He embraces Higgins and kisses him on both cheeks.*) You remember me?

HIGGINS.   No I don't. Who the devil are you?

WHISKERS.   I am your pupil: your first pupil, your best and greatest pupil. I am little Nepommuck, the marvelous boy. I have made your name famous throughout Europe. You teach me phonetic. You cannot forget ME.

HIGGINS.   Why don't you shave?

NEPOMMUCK.   I have not your imposing appearance, your chin, your brow. Nobody notice me when I shave. Now I am famous: they call me Hairy Face Dick.

HIGGINS.   And what are you doing here among all these swells?

NEPOMMUCK.   I am interpreter. I speak 32 languages. I am indispensable at these international parties. You are great cockney specialist: you place a man anywhere in London the moment he open his mouth. I place any man in Europe.

(*A footman hurries down the grand staircase and comes to Nepommuck.*)

FOOTMAN.   You are wanted upstairs. Her excellency cannot understand the Greek gentleman.

NEPOMMUCK.   Thank you, yes, immediately.

(*The footman goes and is lost in the crowd.*)

NEPOMMUCK. (*To Higgins.*)   This Greek diplomatist pretends he cannot speak nor understand English. He cannot deceive me. He is the son of a Clerkenwell watchmaker. He speaks English so villainously that he dare not utter a word of it without betraying his origin. I help him to pretend; but I make him pay through the nose. I make them all pay. Ha ha! (*He hurries upstairs.*)

PICKERING.   Is this fellow really an expert? Can he find out Eliza and blackmail her?

HIGGINS.   We shall see. If he finds her out I lose my bet.

(*Eliza comes from the cloakroom and joins them.*)

PICKERING.   Well, Eliza, now for it. Are you ready?

ELIZA.   Are you nervous, Colonel?

PICKERING.   Frightfully. I feel exactly as I felt before my first battle. It's the first time that frightens.

ELIZA.   It is not the first time for me, Colonel. I have done this fifty times—hundreds of times—in my little piggery in Angel Court in my day-dreams. I am in a dream now. Promise me not to let Professor Higgins wake me; for if he does I shall forget everything and talk as I used to in Drury Lane.

PICKERING.   Not a word, Higgins. (*To Eliza.*) Now, ready?

ELIZA.   Ready.

PICKERING.   Go.

(*They mount the stairs, Higgins last. Pickering whispers to the footman on the first landing.*)

FIRST LANDING FOOTMAN.   Miss Doolittle, Colonel Pickering, Professor Higgins.

SECOND LANDING FOOTMAN.   Miss Doolittle, Colonel Pickering, Professor Higgins.

(*At the top of the staircase the Ambassador and his wife, with Nepommuck at her elbow, are receiving.*)

HOSTESS. (*Taking Eliza's hand.*)   How d'ye do?

HOST. (*Same play.*)   How d'ye do? How d'ye do, Pickering?

ELIZA. (*With a beautiful gravity that awes her hostess.*) How do you do? (*She passes on to the drawingroom.*)

HOSTESS.   Is that your adopted daughter, Colonel Pickering? She will make a sensation.

PICKERING.   Most kind of you to invite her for me. (*He passes on.*)

HOSTESS. (*To Nepommuck.*)   Find out all about her.

NEPOMMUCK. (*Bowing.*)   Excellency—(*He goes into the crowd.*)

HOST.   How d'ye do, Higgins? You have a rival here to-night. He introduced himself as your pupil. Is he any good?

"Is that your adopted daughter, Colonel Pickering?"

HIGGINS. He can learn a language in a fortnight—knows dozens of them. A sure mark of a fool. As a phonetician, no good whatever.

HOSTESS. How d'ye do, Professor?

HIGGINS. How do you do? Fearful bore for you, this sort of thing. Forgive my part in it. (*He passes on.*)

(*In the drawingroom and its suite of salons the reception is in full swing. Eliza passes through. She is so intent on her ordeal that she walks like a somnambulist in a desert instead of a débutante in a fashionable crowd. They stop talking to look at her, admiring her dress, her jewels, and her strangely attractive self. Some of the younger ones at the back stand on their chairs to see.*

The Host and Hostess come in from the staircase and mingle with their guests. Higgins, gloomy and contemptuous of the whole business, comes into the group where they are chatting.)

HOSTESS. Ah, here is Professor Higgins: he will tell us. Tell us all about the wonderful young lady, Professor.

HIGGINS. (*Almost morosely.*) What wonderful young lady?

HOSTESS. You know very well. They tell me there has been nothing like her in London since people stood on their chairs to look at Mrs. Langtry.[6]

(*Nepommuck joins the group, full of news.*)

HOSTESS. Ah, here you are at last, Nepommuck. Have you found out all about the Doolittle lady?

NEPOMMUCK. I have found out all about her. She is a fraud.

HOSTESS. A fraud! Oh no.

NEPOMMUCK. YES, yes. She cannot deceive me. Her name cannot be Doolittle.

HIGGINS. Why?

NEPOMMUCK. Because Doolittle is an English name. And she is not English.

---

6. *Mrs. Langtry:* Lily Langtry, a famous actress.

HOSTESS.   Oh, nonsense! she speaks English perfectly.

NEPOMMUCK.   Too perfectly. Can you show me any English woman who speaks English as it should be spoken? Only foreigners who have been taught to speak it speak it well.

HOSTESS.   Certainly she terrified me by the way she said How d'ye do. I had a schoolmistress who talked like that; and I was mortally afraid of her. But if she is not English what is she?

NEPOMMUCK.   Hungarian.

ALL THE REST.   Hungarian!

NEPOMMUCK.   Hungarian. And of royal blood. I am Hungarian. My blood is royal.

HIGGINS.   Did you speak to her in Hungarian?

NEPOMMUCK.   I did. She was very clever. She said "Please speak to me in English: I do not understand French." French! She pretend not to know the difference between Hungarian and French. Impossible: she knows both.

HIGGINS.   And the blood royal? How did you find that out?

NEPOMMUCK.   Instinct, maestro, instinct. Only the Magyar races can produce that air of the divine right, those resolute eyes. She is a princess.

HOST.   What do you say, Professor?

HIGGINS.   I say an ordinary London girl out of the gutter and taught to speak by an expert. I place her in Drury Lane.

NEPOMMUCK.   Ha ha ha! Oh, maestro, maestro, you are mad on the subject of cockney dialects. The London gutter is the whole world for you.

HIGGINS. (*To the Hostess.*)   What does your Excellency say?

HOSTESS.   Oh, of course I agree with Nepommuck. She must be a princess at least.

HOST.   Not necessarily legitimate, of course. Morganatic[7] perhaps. But that is undoubtedly her class.

HIGGINS.   I stick to my opinion.

---

7. *Morganatic:* of mixed royal and commoner origin.

HOSTESS.   Oh, you are incorrigible.

(*The group breaks up, leaving Higgins isolated. Picker-ing joins him.*)

PICKERING.   Where is Eliza? We must keep an eye on her.

(*Eliza joins them.*)

ELIZA.   I dont think I can bear much more. The people all stare so at me. An old lady has just told me that I speak exactly like Queen Victoria. I am sorry if I have lost your bet. I have done my best; but nothing can make me the same as these people.

PICKERING.   You have not lost it, my dear. You have won it ten times over.

HIGGINS.   Let us get out of this. I have had enough of chattering to these fools.

PICKERING.   Eliza is tired; and I am hungry. Let us clear out and have supper somewhere.

The Wimpole Street laboratory. Midnight. Nobody in the room. The clock on the mantelpiece strikes twelve. The fire is not alight: it is a summer night.

Presently Higgins and Pickering are heard on the stairs.

HIGGINS. (*Calling down to Pickering.*) I say, Pick: lock up, will you? I shant be going out again.

PICKERING. Right. Can Mrs. Pearce go to bed? We dont want anything more, do we?

HIGGINS. Lord, no!

> (*Eliza opens the door and is seen on the lighted landing in all the finery in which she has just won Higgins's bet for him. She comes to the hearth, and switches on the electric lights there. She is tired; her pallor contrasts strongly with her dark eyes and hair, and her expression is almost tragic. She takes off her cloak, puts her fan and gloves on the piano, and sits down on the bench, brooding and silent. Higgins, in evening dress, with overcoat and hat, comes in, carrying a smoking jacket which he has picked up downstairs. He takes off the hat and overcoat; throws them carelessly on the newspaper stand; disposes of his coat in the same way; puts on the smoking jacket; and throws himself wearily into the easychair at the hearth. Pickering, similarly attired, comes in. He also takes off his hat and overcoat, and is about to throw them on Higgins's when he hesitates.*)

PICKERING. I say: Mrs. Pearce will row if we leave these things lying about in the drawing room.

HIGGINS. Oh, chuck them over the bannisters into the hall. She'll find them there in the morning and put them away all right. She'll think we were drunk.

PICKERING. We are, slightly. Are there any letters?

HIGGINS. I didnt look. (*Pickering takes the overcoats and hats and goes downstairs. Higgins begins half singing, half yawning an air from* La Fanciulla del Golden West.[1] *Suddenly he stops and exclaims.*) I wonder where the devil my slippers are!

(*Eliza looks at him darkly; then rises suddenly and leaves the room.*

Higgins yawns again, and resumes his song.

Pickering returns, with the contents of the letter-box in his hand.)

PICKERING. Only circulars, and this coroneted billet-doux for you. (*He throws the circulars into the fender, and posts himself on the hearth-rug, with his back to the grate.*)

HIGGINS. (*Glancing at the billet-doux.*) Money-lender. (*He throws the letter after the circulars.*)

(*Eliza returns with a pair of large down-at-heel slippers. She places them on the carpet before Higgins, and sits as before without a word.*)

HIGGINS. (*Yawning again.*) Oh Lord! What an evening! What a crew! What a silly tomfoolery! (*He raises his shoe to unlace it, and catches sight of the slippers. He stops unlacing and looks at them as if they had appeared there of their own accord.*) Oh! theyre there, are they?

PICKERING. (*Stretching himself.*) Well, I feel a bit tired. It's been a long day. The garden party, a dinner party, and the reception! Rather too much of a good thing. But youve won your bet, Higgins. Eliza did the trick, and something to spare, eh?

HIGGINS. (*Fervently.*) Thank God it's over!

---

1. *La Fanciulla del Golden West:* opera by Puccini.

Eliza returns with a pair of large down-at-heel slippers.

(*Eliza flinches violently; but they take no notice of her; and she recovers herself and sits stonily as before.*)

PICKERING. Were you nervous at the garden party? *I* was. Eliza didnt seem a bit nervous.

HIGGINS. Oh, she wasnt nervous. I knew she'd be all right. No: it's the strain of putting the job through all these months that has told on me. It was interesting enough at first, while we were at the phonetics; but after that I got deadly sick of it. If I hadnt backed myself to do it I should have chucked the whole thing up two months ago. It was a silly notion: the whole thing has been a bore.

PICKERING. Oh, come! the garden party was frightfully exciting. My heart began beating like anything.

HIGGINS. Yes, for the first three minutes. But when I saw we were going to win hands down, I felt like a bear in a cage, hanging about doing nothing. The dinner was worse: sitting gorging there for over an hour, with nobody but a damned fool of a fashionable woman to talk to! I tell you, Pickering, never again for me. No more artificial duchesses. The whole thing has been simple purgatory.

PICKERING. Youve never been broken in properly to the social routine. (*Strolling over to the piano.*) I rather enjoy dipping into it occasionally myself: it makes me feel young again. Anyhow, it was a great success: an immense success. I was quite frightened once or twice because Eliza was doing it so well. You see, lots of real people cant do it at all: theyre such fools that they think style comes by nature to people in their position; and so they never learn. Theres always something professional about doing a thing superlatively well.

HIGGINS. Yes: thats what drives me mad: the silly people dont know their own silly business. (*Rising.*) However, it's over and done with; and now I can go to bed at last without dreading tomorrow.

(*Eliza's beauty becomes murderous.*)

PICKERING.   I think I shall turn in too. Still, it's been a great occasion: a triumph for you. Goodnight. (*He goes.*)

HIGGINS. (*Following him.*)   Goodnight. (*Over his shoulder, at the door.*) Put out the lights, Eliza; and tell Mrs. Pearce not to make coffee for me in the morning: I'll take tea. (*He goes out.*)

(*Eliza tries to control herself and feel indifferent as she rises and walks across to the hearth to switch off the lights. By the time she gets there she is on the point of screaming. She sits down in Higgins's chair and holds on hard to the arms. Finally she gives way and flings herself furiously on the floor, raging.*)

HIGGINS. (*In despairing wrath outside.*)   What the devil have I done with my slippers? (*He appears at the door.*)

ELIZA. (*Snatching up the slippers, and hurling them at him one after the other with all her force.*)   There are your slippers. And there. Take your slippers; and may you never have a day's luck with them!

HIGGINS. (*Astounded.*)   What on earth—! (*He comes to her.*) What's the matter? Get up. (*He pulls her up.*) Anything wrong?

ELIZA. (*Breathless.*)   Nothing wrong—with you. Ive won your bet for you, havnt I? Thats enough for you. *I* dont matter, I suppose.

HIGGINS.   You won my bet! You! Presumptuous insect! *I* won it. What did you throw those slippers at me for?

ELIZA.   Because I wanted to smash your face. I'd like to kill you, you selfish brute. Why didnt you leave me where you picked me out of—in the gutter? You thank God it's all over, and that now you can throw me back again there, do you? (*She crisps her fingers frantically.*)

HIGGINS. (*Looking at her in cool wonder.*)   The creature is nervous, after all.

ELIZA. (*Gives a suffocated scream of fury, and instinctively darts her nails at his face.*)!!

HIGGINS. (*Catching her wrists.*) Ah! would you? Claws in, you cat. How dare you show your temper to me? Sit down and be quiet. (*He throws her roughly into the easy-chair.*)

ELIZA. (*Crushed by superior strength and weight.*) Whats to become of me? Whats to become of me?

HIGGINS. How the devil do I know whats to become of you? What does it matter what becomes of you?

ELIZA. You dont care. I know you don't care. You wouldnt care if I was dead. I'm nothing to you—not so much as them slippers.

HIGGINS. (*Thundering.*) Those slippers.

ELIZA. (*With bitter submission.*) Those slippers. I didnt think it made any difference now.

(*A pause. Eliza hopeless and crushed. Higgens a little uneasy.*)

HIGGINS. (*In his loftiest manner.*) Why have you begun going on like this? May I ask whether you complain of your treatment here?

ELIZA. No.

HIGGINS. Has anybody behaved badly to you? Colonel Pickering? Mrs. Pearce? Any of the servants?

ELIZA. No.

HIGGINS. I presume you dont pretend that *I* have treated you badly?

ELIZA. No.

HIGGINS. I am glad to hear it. (*He moderates his tone.*) Perhaps youre tired after the strain of the day. Will you have a glass of champagne? (*He moves towards the door.*)

ELIZA. No.(*Recollecting her manners.*) Thank you.

HIGGINS. (*Good-humored again.*) This has been coming on you for some days. I suppose it was natural for you to be anxious about the garden party. But thats all over now. (*He pats her kindly on the shoulder. She writhes.*) Theres nothing more to worry about.

ELIZA. No. Nothing more for you to worry about. (*She sud-*

denly rises and gets away from him by going to the piano bench, where she sits and hides her face.) Oh God! I wish I was dead.

HIGGINS. (*Staring after her in sincere surprise.*) Why? In heaven's name, why? (*Reasonably, going to her.*) Listen to me, Eliza. All this irritation is purely subjective.

ELIZA.   I dont understand. I'm too ignorant.

HIGGINS.   It's only imagination. Low spirits and nothing else. Nobody's hurting you. Nothing's wrong. You go to bed like a good girl and sleep it off. Have a little cry and say your prayers: that will make you comfortable.

ELIZA.   I heard your prayers. "Thank God it's all over!"

HIGGINS. (*Impatiently.*)   Well, don't you thank God it's all over? Now you are free and can do whatever you like.

ELIZA. (*Pulling herself together in desperation.*)   What am I fit for? What have you left me fit for? Where am I to go? What am I to do? Whats to become of me?

HIGGINS. (*Enlightened, but not at all impressed.*)   Oh, thats whats worrying you, is it? (*He thrusts his hands into his pockets, and walks about in his usual manner, rattling the contents of his pockets, as if condescending to a trivial subject out of pure kindness.*) I shouldnt bother about it if I were you. I should imagine you wont have much difficulty in settling yourself somewhere or other, though I hadnt quite realized that you were going away. (*She looks quickly at him; he does not look at her, but examines the dessert stand on the piano and decides that he will eat an apple.*) You might marry, you know. (*He bites a large piece out of the apple and munches it noisily.*) You see, Eliza, all men are not confirmed old bachelors like me and the Colonel. Most men are the marrying sort (poor devils!); and youre not badlooking: it's quite a pleasure to look at you sometimes—not now, of course, because youre crying and looking as ugly as the very devil; but when youre all right and quite yourself, youre what I should call attractive.

That is, to the people in the marrying line, you understand. You go to bed and have a good nice rest; and then get up and look at yourself in the glass; and you wont feel so cheap.

(*Eliza again looks at him, speechless, and does not stir. The look is quite lost on him: he eats his apple with a dreamy expression of happiness, as it is quite a good one.*)

HIGGINS. (*A genial afterthought occurring to him.*) I daresay my mother could find some chap or other who would do very well.

ELIZA. We were above that at the corner of Tottenham Court Road.

HIGGINS. (*Waking up.*) What do you mean?

ELIZA. I sold flowers. I didnt sell myself. Now youve made a lady of me I'm not fit to sell anything else. I wish youd left me where you found me.

HIGGINS. (*Slinging the core of the apple decisively into the grate.*) Tosh, Eliza. Dont you insult human relations by dragging all this cant about buying and selling into it. You neednt marry the fellow if you dont like him.

ELIZA. What else am I to do?

HIGGINS. Oh, lots of thing. What about your old idea of a florist's shop? Pickering could set you up in one: he has lots of money. (*Chuckling.*) He'll have to pay for all those togs you have been wearing today; and that, with the hire of the jewellery, will make a big hole in two hundred pounds. Why, six months ago you would have thought it the millennium to have a flower shop of your own. Come! youll be all right. I must clear off to bed: I'm devilish sleepy. By the way, I came down for something: I forget what it was.

ELIZA. Your slippers.

HIGGINS. Oh yes, of course. You shied them at me. (*He picks them up, and is going out when she rises and speaks to him.*)

ELIZA.   Before you go, sir—

HIGGINS.   (*Dropping the slippers in his surprise at her calling him Sir.*)   Eh?

ELIZA.   Do my clothes belong to me or to Colonel Pickering?

HIGGINS.   (*Coming back into the room as if her question were the very climax of unreason.*)   What the devil use would they be to Pickering?

ELIZA.   He might want them for the next girl you pick up to experiment on.

HIGGINS.   (*Shocked and hurt.*)   Is that the way you feel toward us?

ELIZA.   I dont want to hear anything more about that. All I want to know is whether anything belongs to me. My own clothes were burnt.

HIGGINS.   But what does it matter? Why need you start bothering about that in the middle of the night ?

ELIZA.   I want to know what I may take with me. I dont want to be accused of stealing.

HIGGINS.   (*Now deeply wounded.*)   Stealing! You shouldnt have said that, Eliza. That shows a want of feeling.

ELIZA.   I'm sorry. I'm only a common ignorant girl; and in my station I have to be careful. There cant be any feelings between the like of you and the like of me. Please will you tell me what belongs to me and what doesnt?

HIGGINS.   (*Very sulky.*)   You may take the whole damned houseful if you like. Except the jewels. Theyre hired. Will that satisfy you? (*He turns on his heel and is about to go in extreme dudgeon.*)

ELIZA.   (*Drinking in his emotion like nectar, and nagging him to provoke a further supply.*)   Stop, please. (*She takes off her jewels.*)   Will you take these to your room and keep them safe? I dont want to run the risk of their being missing.

HIGGINS.   (*Furious.*)   Hand them over. (*She puts them into his hands.*)   If these belonged to me instead of to the jeweller, I'd ram them down your ungrateful throat. (*He perfunctorily thrusts them into his pockets, unconsciously decorating himself with the protruding ends of the chains.*)

ELIZA. (*Taking a ring off.*)   This ring isnt the jeweller's: it's the one you bought me in Brighton. I dont want it now. (*Higgins dashes the ring violently into the fireplace, and turns on her so threateningly that she crouches over the piano with her hands over her face, and exclaims.*) Dont you hit me.

HIGGINS.   Hit you! You infamous creature, how dare you accuse me of such a thing? It is you who have hit me. You have wounded me to the heart.

ELIZA. (*Thrilling with hidden joy.*)   I'm glad. Ive got a little of my own back, anyhow.

HIGGINS. (*With dignity, in his finest professional style.*)   You have caused me to lose my temper: a thing that has hardly ever happened to me before. I prefer to say nothing more tonight. I am going to bed.

ELIZA. (*Pertly.*)   Youd better leave a note for Mrs. Pearce about the coffee; for she wont be told by me.

HIGGINS. (*Formally.*)   Damn Mrs. Pearce; and damn the coffee; and damn you; and (*Wildly.*) damn my own folly in having lavished my hard-earned knowledge and the treasure of my regard and intimacy on a heartless guttersnipe. (*He goes out with impressive decorum, and spoils it by slamming the door savagely.*)

(*Eliza goes down on her knees on the hearthrug to look for the ring. When she finds it she considers for a moment what to do with it. Finally she flings it down on the dessert stand and goes upstairs in a tearing rage.*)

*   *   *   *   *   *

The furniture of Eliza's room has been increased by a big wardrobe and a sumptuous dressing table. She comes in and switches on the electric light. She goes to the wardrobe; opens it; and pulls out a walking dress, a hat, and a pair of shoes, which she throws on the bed. She takes off her evening dress and shoes; then takes a padded hanger from the wardrobe; adjusts it carefully in the evening dress; and hangs it in the wardrobe, which she shuts with a slam. She puts on her walking shoes, her walking dress, and hat. She takes her wrist watch from the dressing table and fastens it on. She pulls on her gloves; takes her vanity bag; and looks into it to see that her purse is there before hanging it on her wrist. She makes for the door. Every movement expresses her furious resolution.

She takes a last look at herself in the glass.

She suddenly puts out her tongue at herself; then leaves the room, switching off the electric light at the door.

Meanwhile, in the street outside, Freddy Eynsford Hill, lovelorn, is gazing up at the second floor, in which one of the windows is still lighted.

The light goes out.

FREDDY.   Goodnight, darling, darling, darling.

(*Eliza comes out, giving the door a considerable bang behind her.*)

ELIZA.   Whatever are you doing here?

FREDDY.   Nothing. I spend most of my nights here. It's the only place where I'm happy. Dont laugh at me, Miss Doolittle.

ELIZA.   Dont you call me Miss Doolittle, do you hear? Liza's good enough for me. (*She breaks down and grabs him by the shoulders.*) Freddy: you dont think I'm a heartless guttersnipe, do you?

FREDDY.   Oh no, no, darling: how can you imagine such a thing? You are the loveliest, dearest—

(*He loses all self-control and smothers her with kisses. She, hungry for comfort, responds. They stand there in one another's arms.*

An elderly police constable arrives.)

CONSTABLE. (*Scandalized.*) Now then! Now then!! Now then!!!

(*They release one another hastily.*)

FREDDY. Sorry, constable. Weve only just become engaged.

(*They run away.*)

The constable shakes his head, reflecting on his own courtship and on the vanity of human hopes. He moves off in the opposite direction with slow professional steps.

The flight of the lovers takes them to Cavendish Square. There they halt to consider their next move.

ELIZA. (*Out of breath.*) He didn't half give me a fright, that copper. But you answered him proper.

FREDDY. I hope I havent taken you out of your way. Where were you going?

ELIZA. To the river.

FREDDY. What for?

ELIZA. To make a hole in it.

FREDDY. (*Horrified.*) Eliza, darling. What do you mean? What's the matter?

ELIZA. Never mind. It doesnt matter now. There's nobody in the world now but you and me, is there?

FREDDY. Not a soul.

(*They indulge in another embrace, and are again surprised by a much younger constable.*)

SECOND CONSTABLE. Now then, you two! What's this? Where do you think you are? Move along here, double quick.

FREDDY. As you say, sir, double quick.

They run away again, and are in Hanover Square before they stop for another conference.

FREDDY. I had no idea the police were so devilishly prudish.

ELIZA. It's their business to hunt girls off the streets.

FREDDY. We must go somewhere. We cant wander about the streets all night.

ELIZA. Cant we? I think it'd be lovely to wander about for ever.

FREDDY. Oh, darling.

> (*They embrace again, oblivious of the arrival of a crawling taxi. It stops.*)

TAXIMAN. Can I drive you and the lady anywhere, sir?

> (*They start asunder.*)

ELIZA. Oh, Freddy, a taxi. The very thing.

FREDDY. But, damn it, I've no money.

ELIZA. I have plenty. The Colonel thinks you should never go out without ten pounds in your pocket. Listen. We'll drive about all night; and in the morning I'll call on old Mrs. Higgins and ask her what I ought to do. I'll tell you all about it in the cab. And the police wont touch us there.

FREDDY. Righto! Ripping. (*To the Taximan.*) Wimbledon Common. (*They drive off.*)

Mrs. Higgins' drawing room. She is at her writing-table as before. The parlormaid comes in.

THE PARLORMAID. (*At the door.*) Mr. Henry, maam, is downstairs with Colonel Pickering.

MRS. HIGGINS. Well, show them up.

THE PARLORMAID. Theyre using the telephone, maam. Telephoning to the police, I think.

MRS. HIGGINS. What!

THE PARLORMAID. (*Coming further in and lowering her voice.*) Mr. Henry is in a state, maam. I thought I'd better tell you.

MRS. HIGGINS. If you had told me that Mr. Henry was not in a state it would have been more surprising. Tell them to come up when theyve finished with the police. I suppose he's lost something.

THE PARLORMAID. Yes, maam. (*Going.*)

MRS. HIGGINS. Go upstairs and tell Miss Doolittle that Mr. Henry and the Colonel are here. Ask her not to come down till I send for her.

THE PARLORMAID. Yes, maam.

(*Higgins bursts in. He is, as the parlormaid has said, in a state.*)

HIGGINS. Look here, mother: heres a confounded thing!

MRS. HIGGINS. Yes, dear. Good morning. (*He checks his impatience and kisses her, while the parlormaid goes out.*) What is it?

HIGGINS. Eliza's bolted.

MRS. HIGGINS. (*Calmly continuing her writing.*) You must have frightened her.

459

HIGGINS.   Frightened her! nonsense! She was left last night, as usual, to turn out the lights and all that; and instead of going to bed she changed her clothes and went right off: her bed wasn't slept in. She came in a cab for her things before seven this morning; and that fool Mrs. Pearce let her have them without telling me a word about it. What am I to do?

MRS. HIGGINS.   Do without, I'm afraid, Henry. The girl has a perfect right to leave if she chooses.

HIGGINS.   (*Wandering distractedly across the room.*)   But I cant find anything. I dont know what appointments Ive got. I'm—(*Pickering comes in. Mrs. Higgins puts down her pen and turns away from the writing-table.*)

PICKERING.   (*Shaking hands.*)   Good morning, Mrs. Higgins. Has Henry told you? (*He sits down on the ottoman.*)

HIGGINS.   What does that ass of an inspector say? Have you offered a reward?

MRS. HIGGINS.   (*Rising in indignant amazement.*)   You dont mean to say you have set the police after Eliza.

HIGGINS.   Of course. What are the police for? What else could we do? (*He sits in the Elizabethan chair.*)

PICKERING.   The inspector made a lot of difficulties. I really think he suspected us of some improper purpose.

MRS. HIGGINS.   Well, of course he did. What right have you to go to the police and give the girl's name as if she were a thief, or a lost umbrella, or something? Really! (*She sits down again, deeply vexed.*)

HIGGINS.   But we want to find her.

PICKERING.   We cant let her go like this, you know, Mrs. Higgins. What were we to do?

MRS. HIGGINS.   You have no more sense, either of you, than two children. Why—

(*The parlormaid comes in and breaks off the conversation.*)

THE PARLORMAID.   Mr. Henry: a gentleman wants to see you

very particular. He's been sent on from Wimpole Street.

HIGGINS. Oh, bother! I cant see anyone now. Who is it?

THE PARLORMAID. A Mr. Doolittle, sir.

PICKERING. Doolittle! Do you mean the dustman?

THE PARLORMAID. Dustman! Oh no, sir: a gentleman.

HIGGINS. (*Springing up excitedly.*) By George, Pick, it's some relative of hers that she's gone to. Somebody we know nothing about. (*To the parlormaid.*) Send him up, quick!

THE PARLORMAID. Yes, sir. (*She goes.*)

HIGGINS. (*Eagerly, going to his mother.*) Genteel relatives! now we shall hear something. (*He sits down in the Chippendale chair.*)

MRS. HIGGINS. Do you know any of her people?

PICKERING. Only her father: the fellow we told you about.

THE PARLORMAID. (*Announcing.*) Mr. Doolittle. (*She withdraws.*)

(*Doolittle enters. He is resplendently dressed as for a fashionable wedding, and might, in fact, be the bridegroom. A flower in his buttonhole, a dazzling silk hat, and patent leather shoes complete the effect. He is too concerned with the business he has come on to notice Mrs. Higgins. He walks straight to Higgins, and accosts him with vehement reproach.*)

DOOLITTLE. (*Indicating his own person.*) See here! Do you see this? You done this.

HIGGINS. Done what, man?

DOOLITTLE. This, I tell you. Look at it. Look at this hat. Look at this coat.

PICKERING. Has Eliza been buying you clothes?

DOOLITTLE. Eliza! not she. Why would she buy me clothes?

MRS. HIGGINS. Good morning, Mr. Doolittle. Wont you sit down?

DOOLITTLE. (*Taken aback as he becomes conscious that he has forgotten his hostess.*) Asking your pardon, maam. (*He approaches her and shakes her proffered hand.*) Thank you. (*He sits down on the ottoman, on Pickering's right.*) I am that full of what has happened to me that I cant think of anything else.

HIGGINS. What the dickens has happened to you?

DOOLITTLE. I shouldnt mind if it had only happened to me: anything might happen to anybody and nobody to blame but Providence, as you might say. But this is something that you done to me: yes, you, Enry Iggins.

HIGGINS. Have you found Eliza?

DOOLITTLE. Have you lost her?

HIGGINS. Yes.

DOOLITTLE. You have all the luck, you have. I aint found her; but she'll find me quick enough now after what you done to me.

MRS. HIGGINS. But what has my son done to you, Mr. Doolittle?

DOOLITTLE. Done to me! Ruined me. Destroyed my happiness. Tied me up and delivered me into the hands of middle class morality.

HIGGINS. (*Rising intolerantly and standing over Doolittle.*) Youre raving. Youre drunk. Youre mad. I gave you five pounds. After that I had two conversations with you, at half-a-crown an hour. Ive never seen you since.

DOOLITTLE. Oh! Drunk am I? Mad am I? Tell me this. Did you or did you not write a letter to an old blighter in America that was giving five millions to found Moral Reform Societies all over the world, and that wanted you to invent a universal language for him?

HIGGINS. What! Ezra D. Wannafeller! He's dead. (*He sits down again carelessly.*)

DOOLITTLE. Yes: he's dead; and I'm done for. Now did you or did you not write a letter to him to say that the most original moralist at present in England, to the best of your knowledge, was Alfred Doolittle, a common dustman?

HIGGINS. Oh, after your first visit I remember making some silly joke of the kind.

DOOLITTLE. Ah! you may well call it a silly joke. It put the lid on me right enough. Just give him the chance he wanted to show that Americans is not like us: that they reckonize and respect merit in every class of life, however humble. Them words is in his blooming will, in which, Henry Higgins, thanks to your silly joking, he leaves me a share in his Pre-digested Cheese Trust worth four thousand a year on condition that I lecture for his Wannafeller Moral Reform World League as often as they ask me up to six times a year.

HIGGINS. The devil he does! Whew! (*Brightening suddenly.*) What a lark!

PICKERING. A safe thing for you, Doolittle. They wont ask you twice.

DOOLITTLE. It aint the lecturing I mind. I'll lecture them blue in the face, I will, and not turn a hair. It's making a gentleman of me that I object to. Who asked him to make a gentleman of me? I was happy. I was free. I touched pretty nigh everybody for money when I wanted it, same as I touched you, Enry Iggins. Now I am worried; tied neck and heels; and everybody touches me for money. It's a fine thing for you, says my solicitor. Is it? says I. You mean it's a good thing for you, I says. When I was a poor man and had a solicitor once when they found a pram in the dust cart, he got me off, and got shut of me and got me shut of him as quick as he could. Same with the doctors: used to shove me out of the hospital before I could hardly stand on my legs, and nothing to pay. Now they finds out that I'm not a healthy man and cant live unless they looks after me twice a day. In the house Im not let do a hand's turn for myself: somebody else must do it and touch me for it. A year ago I hadnt a relative in the world except two or three that wouldnt speak to me. Now Ive fifty, and not a decent week's wages among the lot of them. I have to live for others and not for myself: that's middle class morality. You talk of losing Eliza. Dont you be anxious: I bet she's on my doorstep by this: she that could support herself easy by selling flowers if I wasnt respectable. And the next one to touch me will be you, Enry Iggins. I'll have to learn to speak middle class language from you, instead of speaking proper English. Thats where youll come in; and I daresay thats what you done it for.

MRS. HIGGINS. But, my dear Mr. Doolittle, you need not suffer all this if you are really in earnest. Nobody can force you to accept this bequest. You can repudiate it. Isnt that so, Colonel Pickering?

PICKERING. I believe so.

DOOLITTLE. (*Softening his manner in deference to her sex.*) Thats the tragedy of it, maam. It's easy to say chuck it; but I havnt the nerve. Which of us has? We're all intimidated. Intimidated, maam: thats what we are. What is there for me if I chuck it but the workhouse in my old age? I have to dye my hair already to keep my job as a dustman. If I was one of the deserving poor, and had put by a bit, I could chuck it; but then why should I, acause the deserving poor might as well be millionaires for all the happiness they ever has. They dont know what happiness is. But I, as one of the undeserving poor, have nothing between me and the pauper's uniform but this here blasted four thousand a year that shoves me into the middle class. (Excuse the expression, maam; youd use it yourself if you had my provocation.) Theyve got you every way you turn: it's a choice between the Skilly of the workhouse and the Char Bydis[1] of the middle class; and I havnt the nerve for the workhouse. Intimidated: thats what I am. Broke. Bought up. Happier men than me will call for my dust, and touch me for their tip; and I'll look on helpless, and envy them. And thats what

---

1. *Skilly . . . Char Bydis:* mispronunciation of Scylla and Charybdis, legendary monsters of a rock and whirlpool threatening sailors. Expression is symbolic of equal evils that are difficult to avoid.

your son has brought me to. (*He is overcome by emotion.*)

MRS. HIGGINS. Well, I'm very glad youre not going to do anything foolish, Mr. Doolittle. For this solves the problem of Eliza's future. You can provide for her now.

DOOLITTLE. (*With melancholy resignation.*) Yes, maam: I'm expected to provide for everyone now, out of four thousand a year.

HIGGINS. (*Jumping up.*) Nonsense! he cant provide for her. He shant provide for her. She doesnt belong to him. I paid him five pounds for her. Doolittle: either youre an honest man or a rogue.

DOOLITTLE. (*Tolerantly.*) A little of both, Henry, like the rest of us: a little of both.

HIGGINS. Well, you took that money for the girl; and you have no right to take her as well.

MRS. HIGGINS. Henry: dont be absurd. If you want to know where Eliza is, she is upstairs.

HIGGINS. (*Amazed.*) Upstairs!!! Then I shall jolly soon fetch her downstairs. (*He makes resolutely for the door.*)

MRS. HIGGINS. (*Rising and following him.*) Be quiet, Henry. Sit down.

HIGGINS. I—

MRS. HIGGINS. Sit down, dear; and listen to me.

HIGGINS. Oh very well, very well, very well. (*He throws himself ungraciously on the ottoman, with his face towards the windows.*) But I think you might have told us this half an hour ago.

MRS. HIGGINS. Eliza came to me this morning. She told me of the brutal way you treated her.

HIGGINS. (*Bounding up again.*) What!

PICKERING. (*Rising also.*) My dear Mrs. Higgins, she's been telling you stories. We didnt treat her brutally. We hardly said a word to her; and we parted on particularly good terms. (*Turning on Higgins.*) Higgins, did you bully her after I went to bed?

HIGGINS. Just the other way about. She threw my slippers

in my face. She behaved in the most outrageous way. I never gave her the slightest provocation. The slippers came bang into my face the moment I entered the room—before I had uttered a word. And used perfectly awful language.

PICKERING. (*Astonished.*)   But why? What did we do to her?

MRS. HIGGINS.   I think I know pretty well what you did. The girl is naturally rather affectionate, I think. Isnt she, Mr. Doolittle?

DOOLITTLE.   Very tender-hearted, maam. Takes after me.

MRS. HIGGINS.   Just so. She had become attached to you both. She worked very hard for you, Henry. I dont think you quite realize what anything in the nature of brain work means to a girl of her class. Well, it seems that when the great day of trial came, and she did this wonderful thing for you without making a single mistake, you two sat there and never said a word to her, but talked together of how glad you were that it was all over and how you had been bored with the whole thing. And then you were surprised because she threw your slippers at you! *I* should have thrown the fire-irons at you.

HIGGINS.   We said nothing except that we were tired and wanted to go to bed. Did we, Pick?

PICKERING. (*Shrugging his shoulders.*)   That was all.

MRS. HIGGINS. (*Ironically.*)   Quite sure?

PICKERING.   Absolutely. Really, that was all.

MRS. HIGGINS.   You didn't thank her, or pet her, or admire her, or tell her how splendid she'd been.

HIGGINS. (*Impatiently.*)   But she knew all about that. We didn't make speeches to her, if thats what you mean.

PICKERING. (*Conscience-stricken.*)   Perhaps we were a little inconsiderate. Is she very angry?

MRS. HIGGINS. (*Returning to her place at the writing-table.*) Well, I'm afraid she wont go back to Wimpole Street, especially now that Mr. Doolittle is able to keep up the position you have thrust on her; but she says she is quite willing to meet you on friendly terms and to let bygones be by-gones.

HIGGINS. (*Furious.*)   Is she, by George? Ho!

MRS. HIGGINS.   If you promise to behave yourself, Henry, I'll ask her to come down. If not, go home; for you have taken up quite enough of my time.

HIGGINS.   Oh, all right. Very well. Pick: you behave yourself. Let us put on our best Sunday manners for this creature that we picked out of the mud. (*He flings himself sulkily into the Elizabethan chair.*)

DOOLITTLE. (*Remonstrating.*)   Now, now, Enry Iggins! Have some consideration for my feelings as a middle class man.

MRS. HIGGINS.   Remember your promise, Henry. (*She presses the bell-button on the writing-table.*) Mr. Doolittle: will you be so good as to step out on the balcony for a moment. I dont want Eliza to have the shock of your news until she has made it up with these two gentlemen. Would you mind?

DOOLITTLE.   As you wish, lady. Anything to help Henry to keep her off my hands. (*He disappears through the window.*)

(*The parlormaid answers the bell. Pickering sits down in Doolittle's place.*)

MRS. HIGGINS.   Ask Miss Doolittle to come down, please.

THE PARLORMAID.   Yes, maam. (*She goes out.*)

MRS. HIGGINS.   Now, Henry; be good.

HIGGINS.   I am behaving myself perfectly.

PICKERING.   He is doing his best, Mrs. Higgins.

(*A pause. Higgins throws back his head; stretches out his legs; and begins to whistle.*)

MRS. HIGGINS.   Henry, dearest, you dont look at all nice in that attitude.

HIGGINS. (*Pulling himself together.*)   I was not trying to look nice, mother.

MRS. HIGGINS.　It doesnt matter, dear. I only wanted to make you speak.

HIGGINS.　Why?

MRS. HIGGINS.　Because you cant speak and whistle at the same time.

(*Higgins groans. Another very trying pause.*)

HIGGINS. (*Springing up, out of patience.*)　Where the devil is that girl? Are we to wait here all day?

(*Eliza enters, sunny, self-possessed, and giving a staggeringly convincing exhibition of ease of manner. She carries a little workbasket, and is very much at home. Pickering is too much taken aback to rise.*)

ELIZA.　How do you do, Professor Higgins? Are you quite well?

HIGGINS. (*Choking.*)　Am I— (*He can say no more.*)

ELIZA.　But of course you are; you are never ill. So glad to see you again, Colonel Pickering. (*He rises hastily; and they shake hands.*) Quite chilly this morning, isnt it? (*She sits down on his left. He sits beside her.*)

HIGGINS.　Dont you dare try this game on me. I taught it to you; and it doesn't take me in. Get up and come home; and dont be a fool.

(*Eliza takes a piece of needlework from her basket, and begins to stitch it, without taking the least notice of this outburst.*)

MRS. HIGGINS.　Very nicely put, indeed, Henry. No woman could resist such an invitation.

HIGGINS.　You let her alone, mother. Let her speak for herself. You will jolly soon see whether she has an idea that I havnt put into her head or a word that I havnt put into her mouth. I tell you I have created this thing out of the squashed cabbage leaves of Covent Garden; and now she pretends to play the fine lady with me.

MRS. HIGGINS. (*Placidly.*)　Yes, dear; but youll sit down, wont you?

(*Higgins sits down again, savagely.*)

ELIZA. (*To Pickering, taking no apparent notice of Higgins, and working away deftly.*) Will you drop me altogether now that the experiment is over, Colonel Pickering?

PICKERING. Oh dont. You mustnt think of it as an experiment. It shocks me, somehow.

ELIZA. Oh, I'm only a squashed cabbage leaf—

PICKERING. (*Impulsively.*) No.

ELIZA. (*Continuing quietly.*) —but I owe so much to you that I should be very unhappy if you forgot me.

PICKERING. It's very kind of you to say so, Miss Doolittle.

ELIZA. It's not because you paid for my dresses. I know you are generous to everybody with money. But it was from you that I learned really nice manners; and that is what makes one a lady, isnt it? You see it was so very difficult for me with the example of Professor Higgins always before me. I was brought up to be just like him, unable to control myself, and using bad language on the slightest provocation. And I should never have known that ladies and gentlemen didnt behave like that if you hadnt been there.

HIGGINS. Well!!

PICKERING. Oh, thats only his way, you know. He doesnt mean it.

ELIZA. Oh, *I* didnt mean it either, when I was a flower girl. It was only my way. But you see I did it; and thats what makes the difference after all.

PICKERING. No doubt. Still, he taught you to speak; and I couldnt have done that, you know.

ELIZA. (*Trivially.*) Of course: that is his profession.

HIGGINS. Damnation!

ELIZA. (*Continuing.*) It was just like learning to dance in the fashionable way: there was nothing more than that in it. But do you know what began my real education?

PICKERING. What?

ELIZA. (*Stopping her work for a moment.*) Your calling me

Miss Doolittle that day when I first came to Wimpole Street. That was the beginning of self-respect for me. (*She resumes her stitching.*) And there were a hundred little things you never noticed, because they came naturally to you. Things about standing up and taking off your hat and opening doors—

PICKERING.   Oh, that was nothing.

ELIZA.   Yes; things that showed you thought and felt about me as if I were something better than a scullery-maid; though of course I know you would have been just the same to a scullery-maid if she had been let into the drawing room. You never took off your boots in the dining room when I was there.

PICKERING.   You mustnt mind that. Higgins takes off his boots all over the place.

ELIZA.   I know. I am not blaming him. It is his way, isnt it? But it made such a difference to me that you didnt do it. You see, really and truly, apart from the things anyone can pick up (the dressing and the proper way of speaking, and so on), the difference between a lady and a flower girl is not how she behaves, but how she's treated. I shall always be a flower girl to Professor Higgins, because he always treats me as a flower girl, and always will; but I know I can be a lady to you, because you always treat me as a lady, and always will.

MRS. HIGGINS.   Please dont grind your teeth, Henry.

PICKERING.   Well, this is really very nice of you, Miss Doolittle.

ELIZA.   I should like you to call me Eliza, now, if you would.

PICKERING.   Thank you. Eliza, of course.

ELIZA.   And I should like Professor Higgins to call me Miss Doolittle.

HIGGINS.   I'll see you damned first.

MRS. HIGGINS.   Henry! Henry!

PICKERING. (*Laughing.*) Why dont you slang back at him? Dont stand it. It would do him a lot of good.

ELIZA. I cant. I could have done it once; but now I cant go back to it. You told me, you know, that when a child is brought to a foreign country, it picks up the language in a few weeks, and forgets its own. Well, I am a child in your country. I have forgotten my own language, and can speak nothing but yours. Thats the real break-off with the corner of Tottenham Court Road. Leaving Wimpole Street finishes it.

PICKERING. (*Much alarmed.*) Oh! but youre coming back to Wimpole Street, arnt you? Youll forgive Higgins?

HIGGINS. (*Rising.*) Forgive! Will she, by George! Let her go. Let her find out how she can get on without us. She will relapse into the gutter in three weeks without me at her elbow.

(*Doolittle appears at the center window. With a look of dignified reproach at Higgins, he comes slowly and silently to his daughter, who, with her back to the window, is unconscious of his approach.*)

PICKERING. He's incorrigible, Eliza. You wont relapse, will you?

ELIZA. No: not now. Never again. I have learned my lesson. I dont believe I could utter one of the old sounds if I tried.

(*Doolittle touches her on the left shoulder. She drops her work, losing her self-possession utterly at the spectacle of her father's splendor.*) A-a-a-a-ah-ow-ooh!

HIGGINS. (*With a crow of triumph.*) Aha! Just so. A-a-a-a-ahowooh! A-a-a-a-ahowooh! A-a-a-a-ahowooh! Victory! Victory! (*He throws himself on the divan, folding his arms, and spraddling arrogantly.*)

DOOLITTLE. Can you blame the girl? Dont look at me like that, Eliza. It aint my fault. Ive come into some money.

ELIZA. You must have touched a millionaire this time, dad.

DOOLITTLE.   I have. But I'm dressed something special today. I'm going to St. George's, Hanover Square. Your stepmother is going to marry me.

ELIZA.   (*Angrily.*)   Youre going to let yourself down to marry that low common woman!

PICKERING.   (*Quietly.*)   He ought to, Eliza. (*To Doolittle.*) Why has she changed her mind?

DOOLITTLE.   (*Sadly.*)   Intimidated, Governor. Intimidated. Middle class morality claims its victim. Wont you put on your hat, Liza, and come and see me turned off?

ELIZA.   If the Colonel says I must, I—I'll (*Almost sobbing.*) I'll demean myself. And get insulted for my pains, like enough.

DOOLITTLE.   Dont be afraid: she never comes to words with anyone now, poor woman! respectability has broke all the spirit out of her.

PICKERING.   (*Squeezing Eliza's elbow gently.*)   Be kind to them, Eliza. Make the best of it.

ELIZA.   (*Forcing a little smile for him through her vexation.*) Oh well, just to show theres no ill feeling. I'll be back in a moment. (*She goes out.*)

DOOLITTLE.   (*Sitting down beside Pickering.*)   I feel uncommon nervous about the ceremony, Colonel. I wish youd come and see me through it.

PICKERING.   But youve been through it before, man. You were married to Eliza's mother.

DOOLITTLE.   Who told you that, Colonel?

PICKERING.   Well, nobody told me. But I concluded—naturally—

DOOLITTLE.   No, that aint the natural way, Colonel: it's only the middle class way. My way was always the undeserving way. But dont say nothing to Eliza. She dont know: I always had a delicacy about telling her.

PICKERING.   Quite right. We'll leave it so, if you dont mind.

DOOLITTLE. And youll come to the church, Colonel, and put me through straight?

PICKERING. With pleasure. As far as a bachelor can.

MRS. HIGGINS. May I come, Mr. Doolittle? I should be very sorry to miss your wedding.

DOOLITTLE. I should indeed be honored by your condescension, maam; and my poor old woman would take it as a tremenjous compliment. She's been very low, thinking of the happy days that are no more.

MRS. HIGGINS. (*Rising.*) I'll order the carriage and get ready. (*The men rise, except Higgins.*) I shant be more than fifteen minutes. (*As she goes to the door Eliza comes in, hatted and buttoning her gloves.*) I'm going to the church to see your father married, Eliza. You had better come in the brougham with me. Colonel Pickering can go on with the bridegroom. (*Mrs. Higgins goes out. Eliza comes to the middle of the room between the center window and the ottoman. Pickering joins her.*)

DOOLITTLE. Bridegroom. What a word! It makes a man realize his position, somehow. (*He takes up his hat and goes toward the door.*)

PICKERING. Before I go, Eliza, do forgive Higgins and come back to us.

ELIZA. I dont think dad would allow me. Would you, dad?

DOOLITTLE. (*Sad but magnanimous.*) They played you off very cunning, Eliza, them two sportsmen. If it had been only one of them, you could have nailed him. But you see, there was two; and one of them chaperoned the other, as you might say. (*To Pickering.*) It was artful of you, Colonel; but I bear no malice: I should have done the same myself. I been the victim of one woman after another all my life, and I dont grudge you two getting the better of Liza. I shant interfere. It's time for us to go, Colonel. So long, Henry. See you in St. George's, Eliza. (*He goes out.*)

PICKERING. (*Coaxing.*) Do stay with us, Eliza. (*He follows Doolittle.*)

> (*Eliza goes out on the balcony to avoid being alone with Higgins. He rises and joins her there. She immediately comes back into the room and makes for the door; but he goes along the balcony and gets his back to the door before she reaches it.*)

HIGGINS. Well, Eliza, youve had a bit of your own back, as you call it. Have you had enough? And are you going to be reasonable? Or do you want any more?

ELIZA. You want me back only to pick up your slippers and put up with your tempers and fetch and carry for you.

HIGGINS. I havnt said I wanted you back at all.

ELIZA. Oh, indeed. Then what are we talking about?

HIGGINS. About you, not about me. If you come back I shall treat you just I have always treated you. I cant change my nature; and I dont intend to change my manners. My manners are exactly the same as Colonel Pickering's.

ELIZA. Thats not true. He treats a flower girl as if she was a duchess.

HIGGINS. And I treat a duchess as if she was a flower girl.

ELIZA. I see. (*She turns away composedly, and sits on the ottoman, facing the window.*) The same to everybody.

HIGGINS. Just so.

ELIZA. Like father.

HIGGINS. (*Grinning, a little taken down.*) Without accepting the comparison at all points, Eliza, it's quite true that your father is not a snob, and that he will be quite at home in any station of life to which his eccentric destiny may call him. (*Seriously.*) The great secret, Eliza, is not having bad manners or good manners or any other particular sort of manners, but having the same manner for all human souls: in short, behaving as if you were in Heaven, where there are no third-class carriages, and one soul is as good as another.

ELIZA.   Amen. You are a born preacher.

HIGGINS. (*Irritated.*)   The question is not whether I treat you rudely, but whether you ever heard me treat anyone else better.

ELIZA. (*With sudden sincerity.*)   I dont care how you treat me. I dont mind you swearing at me. I shouldnt mind a black eye: Ive had one before this. But (*Standing up and facing him.*) I wont be passed over.

HIGGINS.   Then get out of my way; for I wont stop for you. You talk about me as if I were a motor bus.

ELIZA.   So you are a motor bus: all bounce and go, and no consideration for anyone. But I can do without you: dont think I cant.

HIGGINS.   I know you can. I told you you could.

ELIZA. (*Wounded, getting away from him to the other side of the ottoman with her face to the hearth.*)   I know you did, you brute. You wanted to get rid of me.

HIGGINS.   Liar.

ELIZA.   Thank you. (*She sits down with dignity.*)

HIGGINS.   You never asked yourself, I suppose, whether *I* could do without you.

ELIZA. (*Earnestly.*)   Dont you try to get round me. Youll have to do without me.

HIGGINS. (*Arrogant.*)   I can do without anybody. I have my own soul: my own spark of divine fire. But (*With sudden humility.*) I shall miss you, Eliza. (*He sits down near her on the ottoman.*) I have learnt something from your idiotic notions; I confess that humbly and gratefully. And I have grown accustomed to your voice and appearance. I like them, rather.

ELIZA.   Well, you have both of them on your gramophone and in your book of photographs. When you feel lonely without me, you can turn the machine on. It's got no feelings to hurt.

HIGGINS.   I cant turn your soul on. Leave me those feelings;

and you can take away the voice and the face. They are
not you.

ELIZA.   Oh, you are a devil.You can twist the heart in a girl
as easy as some could twist her arms to hurt her. Mrs. Pearce
warned me. Time and again she has wanted to leave you;
and you always got round her at the last minute. And you
dont care a bit for her. And you dont care a bit for me.

HIGGINS.   I care for life, for humanity; and you are a part of
it that has come my way and been built into my house.
What more can you or anyone ask?

ELIZA.   I wont care for anybody that doesnt care for me.

HIGGINS.   Commercial principles, Eliza. Like (*Reproducing
her Covent Garden pronunciation with professional exactness.*) s'yollin voylets [selling violets], isnt it?

ELIZA.   Dont sneer at me. It's mean to sneer at me.

HIGGINS.   I have never sneered in my life. Sneering doesnt
become either the human face or the human soul. I am expressing my righteous contempt for Commercialism. I dont
and wont trade in affection. You call me a brute because
you couldnt buy a claim on me by fetching my slippers and
finding my spectacles. You were a fool: I think a woman
fetching a man's slippers is a disgusting sight: did I ever
fetch your slippers? I think a good deal more of you for
throwing them in my face. No use slaving for me and then
saying you want to be cared for: who cares for a slave? If
you come back, come back for the sake of good fellowship;
for youll get nothing else. Youve had a thousand times as
much out of me as I have out of you; and if you dare to set
up your little dog's tricks of fetching and carrying slippers
against my creation of a Duchess Eliza, I'll slam the door in
your silly face.

ELIZA.   What did you do it for if you didnt care for me?

HIGGINS. (*Heartily.*)   Why, because it was my job.

ELIZA.   You never thought of the trouble it would make for
me.

HIGGINS. Would the world ever have been made if its maker had been afraid of making trouble? Making life means making trouble. Theres only one way of escaping trouble; and thats killing things. Cowards, you notice, are always shrieking to have troublesome people killed.

ELIZA. I'm no preacher: I dont notice things like that. I notice that you dont notice me.

HIGGINS. (*Jumping up and walking about intolerantly.*) Eliza, youre an idiot. I waste the treasures of my Miltonic mind by spreading them before you. Once for all, understand that I go my way and do my work without caring twopence what happens to either of us. I am not intimidated, like your father and your stepmother. So you can come back or go to the devil, which you please.

ELIZA. What am I to come back for?

HIGGINS. (*Bouncing up on his knees on the ottoman and leaning over it to her.*) For the fun of it. Thats why I took you on.

ELIZA. (*With averted face.*) And you may throw me out tomorrow if I dont do everything you want me to?

HIGGINS. Yes; and you may walk out tomorrow if I dont do everything you want me to.

ELIZA. And live with my stepmother?

HIGGINS. Yes, or sell flowers.

ELIZA. Oh! if I only could go back to my flower basket! I should be independent of both you and father and all the world! Why did you take my independence from me? Why did I give it up? I'm a slave now, for all my fine clothes.

HIGGINS. Not a bit. I'll adopt you as my daughter and settle money on you if you like. Or would you rather marry Pickering?

ELIZA. (*Looking fiercely round at him.*) I wouldnt marry you if you asked me; and youre nearer my age than what he is.

HIGGINS. (*Gently.*)   Than he is: not "than what he is."

ELIZA. (*Losing her temper and rising.*)   I'll talk as I like. Youre not my teacher now.

HIGGINS. (*Reflectively.*)   I dont suppose Pickering would, though. He's as confirmed an old bachelor as I am.

ELIZA.   Thats not what I want; and dont you think it. I've always had chaps enough wanting me that way. Freddy Hill writes to me twice and three times a day, sheets and sheets.

HIGGINS. (*Disagreeably surprised.*)   Damn his impudence! (*He recoils and finds himself sitting on his heels.*)

ELIZA.   He has a right to if he likes, poor lad. And he does love me.

HIGGINS. (*Getting off the ottoman.*)   You have no right to encourage him.

ELIZA.   Every girl has a right to be loved.

HIGGINS.   What! By fools like that?

ELIZA.   Freddy's not a fool. And if he's weak and poor and wants me, may be he'd make me happier than my betters that bully me and dont want me.

HIGGINS.   Can he make anything of you? Thats the point.

ELIZA.   Perhaps I could make something of him. But I never thought of us making anything of one another; and you never think of anything else. I only want to be natural.

HIGGINS.   In short, you want me to be as infatuated about you as Freddy? Is that it?

ELIZA.   No I dont. Thats not the sort of feeling I want from you. And dont you be too sure of yourself or of me. I could have been a bad girl if I'd liked. Ive seen more of some things than you, for all your learning. Girls like me can drag gentlemen down to make love to them easy enough. And they wish each other dead the next minute.

HIGGINS.   Of course they do. Then what in thunder are we quarreling about?

ELIZA. (*Much troubled.*)   I want a little kindness. I know I'm

"I know I'm a common ignorant girl, and you a
book-learned gentleman. . . ."

a common ignorant girl, and you a book-learned gentleman; but I'm not dirt under your feet. What I done (*Correcting herself.*) what I did was not for the dresses and the taxis: I did it because we were pleasant together and I come—came —to care for you; not to want you to make love to me, and not forgetting the difference between us, but more friendly like.

HIGGINS.   Well, of course. Thats just how I feel. And how Pickering feels. Eliza, youre a fool.

ELIZA.   Thats not a proper answer to give me. (*She sinks on the chair at the writing-table in tears.*)

HIGGINS.   It's all youll get until you stop being a common idiot. If youre going to be a lady, youll have to give up feeling neglected if the men you know dont spend half their time snivelling over you and the other half giving you black eyes. If you cant stand the coldness of my sort of life, and the strain of it, go back to the gutter. Work till youre more a brute than a human being; and then cuddle and squabble and drink till you fall asleep. Oh, it's a fine life, the life of the gutter. It's real: it's warm: it's violent: you can feel it through the thickest skin: you can taste it and smell it without any training or any work. Not like Science and Literature and Classical Music and Philosophy and Art. You find me cold, unfeeling, selfish, dont you? Very well; be off with you to the sort of people you like. Marry some sentimental hog or other with lots of money, and a thick pair of lips to kiss you with and a thick pair of boots to kick you with. If you cant appreciate what youve got, youd better get what you can appreciate.

ELIZA. (*Desperate.*)   Oh, you are a cruel tyrant. I cant talk to you; you turn everything against me. I'm always in the wrong. But you know very well all the time that youre nothing but a bully. You know I cant go back to the gutter, as you call it, and that I have no real friends in the world but you and the Colonel. You know well I couldnt bear to

live with a low common man after you two; and it's wicked
and cruel of you to insult me by pretending I could. You
think I must go back to Wimpole Street because I have nowhere else to go but father's. But dont you be too sure that
you have me under your feet to be trampled on and talked
down. I'll marry Freddy, I will, as soon as I'm able to support him.

HIGGINS. (*Thunderstruck.*) Freddy!!! That young fool!
That poor devil who couldnt get a job as an errand boy
even if he had the guts to try for it! Woman, do you not
understand that I have made you a consort for a king?

ELIZA. Freddy loves me; that makes him king enough for me.
I dont want him to work; he wasnt brought up to it as I
was. I'll go and be a teacher.

HIGGINS. Whatll you teach, in heaven's name?

ELIZA. What you taught me. I'll teach phonetics.

HIGGINS. Ha! ha! ha!

ELIZA. I'll offer myself as an assistant to that hairyfaced
·Hungarian.

HIGGINS. (*Rising in a fury.*) What! That imposter! That
humbug! That toadying ignoramus! Teach him my
methods! My discoveries! You take one step in his direction
and I'll wring your neck. (*He lays hands on her.*) Do you
hear?

ELIZA. (*Defiantly non-resistant.*) Wring away. What do I
care? I knew youd strike me some day. (*He lets her go,
stamping with rage at having forgotten himself, and recoils
so hastily that he stumbles back into his seat on the ottoman.*) Aha! Now I know how to deal with you. What a
fool I was not to think of it before! You cant take away the
knowledge you gave me. You said I had a finer ear than you.
And I can be civil and kind to people, which is more than
you can. Aha! (*Purposely dropping her aitches to annoy
him.*) Thats done you, Enry Iggins, it az. Now I don't care
that (*Snapping her fingers.*) for your bullying and your big

talk. I'll advertise it in the papers that your duchess is only a flower girl that you taught, and that she'll teach anybody to be a duchess just the same in six months for a thousand guineas. Oh, when I think of myself crawling under your feet and being trampled on and called names, when all the time I had only to lift up my finger to be as good as you, I could just kick myself.

HIGGINS. (*Wondering at her.*)   You damned impudent slut, you! But it's better than snivelling; better than fetching slippers and finding spectacles, isnt it? (*Rising.*) By George, Eliza, I said I'd make a woman of you; and I have. I like you like this.

ELIZA.   Yes: you turn round and make up to me now that I'm not afraid of you, and can do without you.

HIGGINS.   Of course I do, you little fool. Five minutes ago you were like a millstone round my neck. Now youre a tower of strength: a consort battleship. You and I and Pickering will be three old bachelors instead of only two men and a silly girl.

(*Mrs. Higgins returns, dressed for the wedding. Eliza instantly becomes cool and elegant.*)

MRS. HIGGINS.   The carriage is waiting, Eliza. Are you ready?

ELIZA.   Quite. Is the Professor coming?

MRS. HIGGINS.   Certainly not. He cant behave himself in church. He makes remarks out loud all the time on the clergyman's pronunciation.

ELIZA.   Then I shall not see you again, Professor. Good-by. (*She goes out the door.*)

MRS. HIGGINS. (*Coming to Higgins.*)   Good-by, dear.

HIGGINS.   Good-by, mother. (*He is about to kiss her, when he recollects something.*) Oh, by the way, Eliza, order a ham and a Stilton cheese, will you? And buy me a pair of reindeer gloves, number eights, and a tie to match that new suit of mine. You can choose the color. (*His cheerful, careless, vigorous voice shows that he is incorrigible.*)

ELIZA. (*Disdainfully.*)   Number eights are too small for you if you want them lined with lamb's wool. You have three new ties that you have forgotten in the drawer of your washstand. Colonel Pickering prefers double Gloucester to Stilton; and you dont notice the difference. I telephoned Mrs. Pearce this morning not to forget the ham. What you are to do without me I cannot imagine. (*She sweeps out.*)

MRS. HIGGINS.   I'm afraid youve spoilt that girl, Henry. I should be uneasy about you and her if she were less fond of Colonel Pickering.

HIGGINS.   Pickering! Nonsense, she's going to marry Freddy. Ha ha! Freddy! Freddy! ! Ha ha ha ha ha! ! ! ! ! (*He roars with laughter as the play ends.*)

To Enrich Your Reading

Plays present difficulties for the reader not usually encountered with novels. The playwright *tells* us very little, leaving us to infer action and characterization largely from dialogue. Since play-production problems are usually solved by the director, often in oral conference with the author, written stage directions and descriptions tend to be skimpy. Shaw, keeping in mind a reading audience, has been more generous in this regard than most playwrights. Still, the nature of the play material demands of the reader a special alertness of the eye, ear, and mind. The following questions based on the text of *Pygmalion* are intended to help you form the proper visualizations and inferences and at the same time think about their significance.

Act 1

1. What is the first impression of Freddy, as it is conveyed by his efforts to get a cab?
2. Read aloud the flower girl's remarks as she picks up her scattered flowers. How does her concern for good manners contrast with the impression she creates?
3. What conclusions do you draw about the note taker from his behavior to both the flower girl and the crowd?
4. What does the taxicab incident contribute to the impression we have of Eliza?

Act 2

5. How does Higgins' home contrast with the one in which we observed Eliza?

6. What reaction would an audience in the theater be likely to experience as Eliza comes on stage in this act? Why?

7. Why does Higgins become interested in accepting Eliza as a student?

8. What is Higgins' attitude toward Eliza, as revealed by his remarks and his conduct? How does he justify his attitude?

9. What do we learn about Higgins as Mrs. Pearce outlines details of conduct to be observed by him? How can Mrs. Pearce have come by the privilege of "laying down the law" in this way?

10. Why does Higgins call his visitor a "blackguard" (scoundrel) even before the visitor makes his appearance?

11. Why does Doolittle reject the offer of education?

12. What is Eliza's attitude toward her father? What is his toward her?

Act 3

13. How does Eliza's performance at Mrs. Higgins' "at-home" parallel Henry's in its deviations from what is appropriate? Whose lapses, in your opinion, are more serious? Why?

14. How are the guests affected by Eliza's performance? Who is most enchanted? How is Clara influenced by Eliza's speech and conduct?

15. What more do we learn of Higgins' and Pickering's involvement with Eliza? What is her role in the Wimpole Street household?

16. Why does Mrs. Higgins believe that Eliza's future is a problem? What is the reaction of Higgins and Pickering?

17. What is Higgins' attitude toward his goal of creating a different human being through speech?

18. What threat to Higgins' plan is represented by the appearance of his former student, the interpreter? How does his appearance constitute the ultimate test?

Act 4

19. How do the reactions of Eliza and Higgins differ on the

winning of the bet? With whom do you side? With whom does the author sympathize?

20. In spite of the seriousness of the "victory" discussion, several humorous instances crop up. At which do you think a theater audience would chuckle most?

21. To what extent does Higgins' response to Eliza prove his mother's characterization of him? How does Freddy's response differ from his?

22. How does Eliza respond to Freddy? Why?

23. Why does Eliza plan to return to the home of Mrs. Higgins?

Act 5

24. Why does Mr. Doolittle accost Higgins "with vehement reproach"? List the main points of Doolittle's line of reasoning.

25. How does Mrs. Higgins explain Eliza's behavior? How is the explanation received by Higgins and Pickering? How valid do you judge it to be?

26. How does Higgins defend his treatment of Eliza? How much right do you find in his defense?

27. What makes Eliza conclude that it is impossible for her to remain with Higgins and Pickering? What traits in Higgins' character and factors in his way of life seem to justify her decision?

28. At the final curtain, how does Higgins' laughter add weight to Eliza's decision to marry Freddy?

29. To what extent has Higgins proven his point and made a lady of a flower girl? How fundamentally changed is Eliza from the person we met in the first act?

Preface and Epilogue

Omitted from this volume because of space limitations are the preface and epilogue that Shaw wrote for *Pygmalion*. Although these essays are not essential to an understanding of the play, they raise a number of points that are well worth considering.

About the Preface:

1. Shaw implies that one of his purposes in writing the play was to make people aware of the existence of phoneticians, who "are among the most important people in England." In your opinion, how well is this estimate of their importance borne out in the play? How important do you think experts in the science of speech are in our own country today? Why?

2. Despite what systematic study and practice can do to improve speech, Shaw contends that an "honest and natural slum dialect is more tolerable than the attempts of phonetically untaught persons to imitate the plutocracy." What is Shaw saying here about the speech of many of the rich? Express your opinion on whether a slum dialect is truly preferable under the circumstances described.

About the Epilogue:

1. Shaw attacks the stock happy ending in which the heroine always marries the hero. He tells us that after his play ends Eliza marries Freddy, not Higgins. Which ending seems more appropriate to you, and why?

2. In defending Higgins' "bachelordom," Shaw finds reason in Higgins' strong admiration for his mother. "She sets a standard for him against which few women can struggle." How believable does this justification seem to you?

3. Shaw tells us what happens to the main characters after Eliza and Freddy marry. The newlyweds open a flower shop, which, with timely financial help from Pickering, eventually prospers. Mr. Doolittle, still subsidized, becomes extremely popular as a wit in the smartest society.

Clara, affected by Eliza's example, casts off her snobbish airs to take a position in an interesting old furniture shop. As to Higgins, Shaw tells us "it is astonishing how much Eliza still manages to meddle in the housekeeping at Wimpole Street . . . And . . . she has never got out of the habit of nagging (him) . . . He storms and bullies . . . but she stands up to him." She has a deep feeling that she is "no more to him than them slippers . . . (but) she is immensely interested in him." In your opinion, how logical is this final accounting in terms of the characters and situations as established in the play? What, if anything, would you have altered?

Style and Vocabulary

DIALOGUE

"Remember that you are a human being with a soul and the divine gift of articulate speech: that your native language is the language of Shakespear and Milton and the Bible," admonishes Henry Higgins in Act 1. Most of the characters in *Pygmalion* have an extra gift of eloquence, although not all speak in the cultured tradition upheld by Higgins. Indeed, even Higgins himself occasionally nods. ("Well, dash me if I do" is an expression one would hardly expect to find in the authorities he mentions.)

Below are snatches of dialogue uttered by characters in the play. Without referring to the text but finding clues in the idea and its manner of expression, identify the speaker, the class level of the language (upper, lower), and the sense of the italicized word in each passage. For some of the words you may have to use a dictionary; for others, such as slang expressions, you will do best to guess from context.

1. "I'm at the Carlton. Come with me now and let's have a *jaw* over some supper."

2. "Yes, you squashed cabbage leaf, you disgrace to the noble architecture of these columns, you *incarnate* insult to the English language."
3. "He's off his chump, he is. I don't want no *balmies* teaching me."
4. "I was brought up to be just like him, unable to control myself, and using bad language on the slightest *provocation*."
5. "But don't say nothing to Eliza. She don't know. I always had a *delicacy* about telling her."
6. "What! That imposter! That humbug! That *toadying* ignoramus. You take one step in his direction and I'll wring your neck."
7. "Henry: you are the life and soul of the Royal Society's soirées; but you're rather *trying* on more commonplace occasions."
8. "Undeserving poverty is my line. Taking one station of society with another, it's—it's—well, it's the only one that has any *ginger* in it, to my taste."
9. "Ha! ha! How awfully funny! . . . *Killing!*"
10. "And it's so *quaint*, and gives such a smart emphasis to things that are not in themselves very witty. I find the new small talk delightful and quite innocent."

Terms Used in Stage Directions

In column 1 below are various terms used in the stage directions of *Pygmalion*. Match them with the corresponding references in column 2. Use a dictionary or encyclopedia where needed.

Column 1	*Column 2*
1. ottoman	oratorical
2. Burne-Jones	with contempt
3. plinth	sad emotion
4. Chippendale	servant

       5. Inigo Jones   backless couch
       6. deprecation   beautiful
       7. pathos   belittlement
       8. elocutionary   column base
       9. disdainfully   prayer
      10. dudgeon   ornate furniture style
                                painter
                                anger
                                architect

Related Activities

1. Organize a dramatization of several scenes from the play. Care should be given to the selection of the right actors for the parts by holding auditions in class. Once the actors are chosen and a director approved, rehearsals should be held outside of class so that interpretations are refined and smoothness of performance insured. Following a successful classroom performance, consideration might be given to a presentation before a grade assembly.

2. Read (or listen to a recording of) the lyrics written by Alan Jay Lerner for the musical comedy adaptation of *Pygmalion, My Fair Lady* (available in book form, published by Coward-McCann). Consider to what extent these lyrics fulfill the ideas in Shaw's play. How pleased do you think Shaw would have been with the whole adaptation?

3. Read an account of Shaw's life and times in a good encyclopedia or full-length biography. (Recommended: Hesketh Pearson's *George Bernard Shaw*, and *Sixteen Self-Sketches* by Shaw himself.) Report to the class on whatever autobiographical elements you might then find in Shaw's characterization of Henry Higgins. Tell whether

you think these inclusions were deliberate or unconscious on Shaw's part.

4. In Act 3 Clara describes Eliza's strange speech, with its many social errors, as the latest in "small talk." In a short essay entitled "Small Talk," tell what small talk is and the function it serves. Give your attitude toward the small talk you have experienced. Include examples.

5. State clearly Higgins' and Eliza's views of the proper behavior of a "gentleman." Who do you think has the better point of view, and why?

6. Judging from the play itself, and from anything else you may have learned about the author, tell to what extent you think Alfred Doolittle's views on "middle class morality" reflect Shaw's opinions. What validity, if any, might these views have in modern American society?

7. "Happy is the man who can make a living by his hobby," remarks Henry Higgins. How truthful do you consider this statement to be? How have you observed its application in today's world?

THE GOLD OF TROY
The Story of Heinrich Schliemann
and The Buried Cities
of Ancient Greece

Robert Payne

▰▰

A BIOGRAPHY

The gold which the Griffins dig up consists of rock encrusted with golden drops like fiery sparks; they quarry the gold with the power of their hard beaks.

These creatures are found in India and are sacred to the Sun, having the size and strength of lions whom they excel by reason of their wings; and they can vanquish elephants and great serpents. The tiger, however, they cannot vanquish, for he excels them by his fleetness. . . .

—FLAVIUS PHILOSTRATUS
in his *Life of Apollonius of Tyana.*

ROBERT PAYNE

The Author and the Biography

There is hardly a more prolific living writer than Robert Payne. Still in his middle fifties (he was born December 4, 1911), he has written over fifty-five books under his own name and various pseudonyms. These books range through many types, including history, fiction, poetry, memoir and biography, and cover a variety of subjects. One is astonished at the vastness of interest that inspires a novel about Shakespeare (*The Roaring Boys*), memoirs of years spent in China (*Forever China* and *China Awake*), histories of ancient Greece, Rome and France, and biographies of such diverse people as Charlie Chaplin, George Gershwin, Dostoyevski, Albert Schweitzer, Lenin, and, in *The Gold of Troy*, the archeologist, Heinrich Schliemann. Equally astonishing is the high standard of writing and scholarship in works produced at what must have been breakneck speed.

One might expect that such literary industry would not leave much time for other pursuits. Yet, Robert Payne's career seems as crowded with vivid experience as the lives of many of the subjects he has characterized.

Born in Cornwall, England, of an English father and French mother, Payne spent part of his childhood in France. He early showed a strong interest in ships—derived, perhaps, from his father's family, who were shipwrights. His education was chiefly in British schools, where he was especially drawn to Latin, Greek, and mathematics and earned many scholarships. For three years he lived in South Africa, studying classics at Rondebosch and mathematics and pure science at Capetown.

When the Great Depression of the 1930's came along, Payne found work in a shipyard. He also attended Liverpool University, studying Danish, Italian, German, Russian, and Polish. Subsequently, he held a job as a British income-tax inspector for one and a half years, followed by a period of wandering in Europe. He studied at the Sorbonne (Paris) and the University of Munich, and, in his own words, "got caught up in an attempt to assassinate Hitler and visited the Spanish battlefronts for an English newspaper."

After the retreat of the Spanish Republicans, Payne became ill and went to Singapore to convalesce and to join his father, who had become head of the British naval base there. While in the East, Payne traveled through Java and Bali, and, at the outbreak of World War II, became a shipwright at the Singapore naval base. In time he served as an armaments officer in charge of camouflage. When the war spread to the Pacific, he was appointed cultural liaison officer to the British ambassador in China. The several years he spent in China gave him opportunity to attend Chinese universities. After the war, he traveled through India and visited England, France and Persia before settling in the United States, which is now his home.

These extensive travels and wide experiences have provided much of the inspiration for Payne's numerous books. His diligent scholarship, keen insight, and lively literary style are what make them a source of knowledge and delight to a growing number of readers.

The Gold of Troy, the Story of Heinrich Schliemann and the Buried Cities of Ancient Greece is one of Robert Payne's most fascinating biographies. It is fascinating on several counts: first, as a true tale of a career full of colorful events; second, as a study of a most interesting personality; third, as an archeological detective story; and, finally, as an evocation of a past civilization that has contributed mightily to our own.

The early and middle sections of the book read almost like an adventure novel. The young Heinrich Schliemann, unhappy in his childhood environment and haunted by a sense of family shame, escapes first through reading and wild dreaming, then by running away to the big city, Hamburg, in the Germany of the nineteenth century. There he begins a series of adventures that lead to a disastrous ocean voyage, trips across Europe, residence in Russia, flight to the gold fields of California, a hazardous trek across the isthmus of Panama, and other strange and exciting episodes. Through it all, he gains several fortunes, becomes a student of languages and ancient civilization, and, finally, obsessed by a passion for discovering the site of the ancient city of Troy, digs for treasure and finds it.

It is an unusual, almost baffling personality that pursues this extraordinary course. Indeed, much in Schliemann's character and actions would not pass moral muster. The reader will condemn him for his treatment of the wife of his first marriage, the ruthlessness of his business dealings, his hard uses of people in general—all stemming from a deep-rooted arrogance and, some will say, psychological disturbance. Yet there must be admiration for the energy and originality of mind that drove him in his middle years to follow his wildest dream—and, in the process, to make his great discoveries and lay the foundations of the modern science of archeology.

The sections of the book that deal with the diggings are of more than archeological interest. There is, it is true, absorbing detail about techniques and specific finds. A reader unfamiliar with the subject will find his appetite whetted. But for the pure joy of following a puzzle to its solution, few detective or treasure-hunt novels offer as much. There are daring hypotheses, real clues as well as false leads, innumerable physical and human obstacles, accidental discoveries, minor and major unravelings, and, as in the more sophisticated novels of detection, ironies at the end.

Throughout the book, but especially in the sections dealing with the findings and their significance, the author re-creates the spirit of the ancient world. In Schliemann himself he discovers something of the questing, restless nature that animated the old Greek and Trojan heroes. Moreover, in the chapter entitled *The*

Heroes, there is a brilliant discussion of the people of the Homeric period, the great leaders as well as the ordinary citizens. We learn not only how they lived but for what they lived. So directly do they and their civilization speak to us in the pages of this book that at the end we cannot but have an increased awe for whatever links their lives to ours.

DURING the seventies and eighties of the last century an old
gray-haired scholar, wearing a high collar and a sun helmet,
was to be seen wandering over the ruins of an obscure mound
in Asia Minor. He was short and wiry, with dark brown eyes,
high cheekbones, a heavy nose, and a sensual mouth; there was
something of the peasant about him, something too of the
Lübeck merchants who were his ancestors. He spoke in a
high-pitched nervous voice, dressed shabbily, walked with a
curious gliding motion, and always carried in his coat pocket
a dog-eared paperbound edition of the *Iliad* or the *Odyssey*.[1]
To the friendly inquirer he would explain that he had uncovered the ancient city of Troy and found in its walls a
secret treasure hoard of gold, which he kept securely locked
in his house in Athens. He believed that the ashes of Odysseus,
the crown jewels of the Trojan Empire, and the golden death
masks of Agamemnon and many other Greek heroes were
in his possession, and it is just possible that his claims were
justified. Until he was long past middle age he never touched
a spade, but during the last seventeen years of his life he
excavated continually. The most unscientific of archeologists,
he founded the modern science of archeology.

Luck helped him—luck, and a fierce hunger for gold. At
various times in his life he made four immense fortunes; one
fortune came from profiteering during the Crimean War,
but the greatest came from the California gold fields. And
this fortune he merely stumbled upon when he went out to
California to collect the estate of his brother who had died

1. *Iliad* . . . *Odyssey:* great epic poems by Homer (about tenth century
B.C.).

of fever. Just as some people seem to have the power of divining water, so he seemed to have some sixth sense which told him where gold was buried. He discovered the treasure of Troy when he least expected it, and he stumbled upon the treasure of Mycenae where no one else had suspected it. One day in Indianapolis, shortly after his divorce from his unloving Russian wife, he wrote to a bishop of the Greek Orthodox Church in Athens, asking the bishop to find him a wife. Once more his luck held. In all the world there was hardly another woman so understanding of his needs as the beautiful wife selected for him. Luck pursued him like a fury.

When he was born on January 6, 1822, in the parsonage of the obscure village of Neu Buckow in Mecklenburg, not far from the Polish frontier, there was no hint of the million-aire banker he was to become or the great treasures he was to unearth. Two years later his father became pastor in the village of Ankershagen, so small a place that it is rarely shown on any maps. Slavs and Teutons had once fought across the plains of Mecklenburg with their lakes and brood-ing mists, but at the beginning of the nineteenth century all Mecklenburg had become a backwater. "Stupid as a Mecklen-burger," said Berliners, but it was not true. Mecklenburgers produced few artists and few poets, but they produced food. They drank heavily, laughed hugely, cultivated their potato fields, raised beef, and amused themselves on long winter evenings by telling stories around the hearth fires. In all of Germany there were no people so deeply attached to the earth.

In later years, whenever Heinrich Schliemann remembered his childhood, he remembered the little parsonage with the cherry blossoms in the garden, the treasures reputed to be buried in the neighborhood, and the ghosts who haunted the place. One ghost lived in the little garden house under a linden tree: it was the ghost of Pastor von Rustdorf, his father's predecessor at the parsonage. On the other side of the wall, in a pond, there was a maiden who was believed to rise each midnight with a silver bowl in her hands, while less than a mile away stood the burial mound of a child buried in a golden cradle. At the center of Ankershagen stood a medieval castle with secret underground passageways. Once the castle was owned by the famous robber baron Henning von Holstein, who made war against the Duke of Mecklenburg. He offered to parley with the Duke, who marched up to Ankershagen and would have been murdered if a cowherd had not warned him in time. Henning von Holstein captured the cowherd, roasted him alive, and kicked him for good measure after broiling him. The Duke brought a larger army up against the castle, and when Henning von Holstein saw there was no escape, he hid his treasure near the crumbling round tower and killed himself. The long flat stones in the churchyard marked his grave, and every year his left leg—the one that had kicked the unfortunate cowherd—grew out of the grave like a strange flower. The sexton said he had seen the leg clothed in a black silk stocking, but none of the village boys ever saw it.

The young Heinrich grew up among these legends. He visited the castle and saw the terra-cotta[2] relief on the north wall which showed Henning von Holstein riding to war. He saw the fireplace where the cowherd had been roasted, and knew the hill where the cowherd had hidden to warn the Duke of Mecklenburg. He penetrated the underground galleries of the castle and thought he knew the entrances to the secret passageways which meandered across the whole countryside. He was fed on legends and stories of hidden treasure. In a sense, he never stirred from his native village, never so much as stepped out of his father's parsonage. To the end of his life he resembled the child with his face glued to the parsonage window, shuddering with joy as he gazed

2. *Terra-cotta:* clay used as sculptural and building material.

through the mists at the flame-lit, mysterious, and legendary world outside.

For him the ghosts were everywhere—he had only to put out his hands and touch them. It was the world of the Brothers Grimm and E. T. A. Hoffmann, with their strange fairy tales drenched in blood. The horror came unawares, at every turning in the road. There were good fairies, but there were also crab-apple women with silver cords in their hands ready to hang you on the nearest crab-apple tree. There were worse things than crab-apple women: there were strange whispers at night, lights moving about in the garden, and at any time the legless Henning von Holstein might descend from his castle. Heinrich had his own way of dealing with ghosts—he would cut his initials on trees and benches and window-panes, and somehow these boldly carved letters kept the ghosts at bay. On the great linden tree in the garden he once carved his initials in letters two feet high, and they were still there, very clear, when he examined the tree again nearly fifty years later.

Perhaps, too, he carved his name everywhere out of a need to assert himself in the crowded parsonage. There were four daughters and two sons—one other son had died the year he was born and he was baptized with the name of his dead brother. He was closest to his two sisters, Dorothea and Wilhelmine, and perhaps closest of all to his mother, a quiet woman, the daughter of a burgomaster,[3] who seems to have found little joy in her marriage with a gruff and domineering pastor. She was thirteen years younger than her husband, having married him when she was sixteen. She wore lace cuffs and played the piano, and the villagers disliked her because they thought she gave herself airs. The children adored her; her husband despised her, and showered attention on the kitchen maids. To the end of his long life—he lived to be over ninety—the pastor was a center of scandal.

3. *Burgomaster:* mayor.

Before entering theological school, the pastor had been a schoolmaster. He had a gift for teaching. He taught his children their letters and liked to show them the fine plates in his books. One day when the pastor raged against poverty, Heinrich asked why he did not dig up the silver bowl or the gold cradle. The pastor smiled. He seemed to know that he was dedicated to poverty, and no riches would ever enter the drab parsonage.

He was a man of moods, generous and close-fisted by turns, with a strange sternness which would sometimes give way to light-hearted garrulity. He told stories well. He liked playing practical jokes. He especially liked to take his children on long walks through the countryside, telling them the history of every field and hamlet, inventing everything at the spur of the moment, spinning out his stories until they became completely ludicrous and still credible; and then he would throw back his head and roar with laughter at the spectacle of his children open-mouthed in wonder. And sometimes, to keep them quiet on winter evenings, he would tell stories out of Homer until the little parsonage reeled with the thunder of the Trojan wars.

The parson knew no Greek and had never read Homer in the original, but there was nothing in the least surprising in his deep interest in the *Iliad* and *Odyssey*. All Germany was aware of Homer. Goethe and Schiller and a host of other German poets paid Homer the tribute of imitation and celebrated him to the skies. Excellent translations were available, the best and most famous being by J. H. Voss, who had spent some months of his unhappy youth as a tutor in the very castle where Henning von Holstein had roasted a cowherd. Accordingly the children in the parsonage felt a proprietary interest in the Homeric heroes and listened breathless to the stories of the war between the Achaeans and the Trojans, and it was not difficult for them to imagine the war taking place among the ruined towers and battlements of Ankershagen. In their childish imaginations Troy and Ankershagen overlapped, became part of one another; and the lives of the heroes entered their own childish lives.

At Christmas, 1829, when Heinrich was seven years old, he received as a gift from his father Ludwig Jerrer's *Illustrated History of the World*. He turned immediately to the page showing Troy in flames. In the foreground was Æneas, plumed and helmeted, wearing a corselet, striding through the smoke and flames of the doomed city, while carrying his father Anchises on his back and holding his son Ascanius by the hand. The picture fired the boy's imagination. Everything in it helped him to identify Troy with Ankershagen. The round towers, the huge castle walls, the great gateway—all these could be found at Ankershagen. But the most extraordinary thing of all was the resemblance between Æneas as depicted in the engraving and the old pastor, as we recognize him in surviving photographs. There was the same high forehead, the same enormous eyes, heavy nose, and bearded jowls. Æneas looks like a prosperous grocer, and so does the father. He is not fleeing from Troy in mortal terror. Quietly, calmly, with no backward glance, the hero emerges through the smoke, his son beside him.

When he grew older, Heinrich liked to say that this engraving was the turning point of his life, and that from the moment he set eyes on the picture he decided to excavate the buried city. He remembered turning to his father and pointing out that in spite of the fire the walls were still standing. He told the pastor that he thought Jerrer had actually seen the city.

"No, all of Troy was burned to the ground," the pastor replied. "It's just a fanciful picture."

"But Troy had walls like that—"

"Yes."

"And these walls are much too large to be destroyed by fire, so there must be something left?"

The pastor was fairly sure nothing remained, but the boy

held fast to his opinion. He told himself that one day he would make the journey to Troy and discover the walls and towers depicted so realistically in the *Illustrated History of the World.*

Fifty years later, when he told this story in an autobiographical fragment, scholars raised their eyebrows. It seemed inconceivable to them that the discoverer of Troy should be able to remember a conversation so deeply buried in the past. Schliemann answered that hardly a day passed in his mature life when he was not dreaming and planning to uncover Troy, and all his energies were directed toward the day when he would stand in triumph on the Trojan walls; and once again the scholars raised their eyebrows. It is unlikely that Schliemann was exaggerating, for the dreams of a seven-year-old child are so vast that they can encompass the whole future and dictate his journey through life.

The boy dreamed his way through school. He was seven when he fell in love with Minna Meincke, the daughter of a local farmer. Minna was his own age. She had yellow hair, blue eyes, and was pretty in a doll-like way. They met at dancing class, and thereafter they were inseparable. She enjoyed listening to Heinrich telling her stories. One day, when the whole Meincke family came on a visit to the parsonage, Heinrich vanished from sight. He had disappeared upstairs, and was sprucing himself up. Usually untidy, he appeared in the drawing room wearing his best suit, his face shining from soap and water, his hair neatly combed. The Schliemann family was thunderstruck, until they realized that Heinrich was determined to produce a good impression on Minna.

Even at the age of seven he loved Minna to distraction. He sat by her side at school, attended her at dancing class, and accompanied her on long rambles through the countryside. They haunted the castle and the cemetery, and gazed at the spot where Henning von Holstein's black-stockinged

leg had once grown through the stones. Together they examined the fireplace and the secret passageways, and interrogated everyone who could throw light on the fierce robber
baron's existence in the castle. From the sexton and the sac-
ristan they learned that at the turn of the century the leg
had appeared regularly each year, but more recently someone had taken it into his head to pluck the leg from its roots
and use the bones for knocking pears off trees. They believed
everything they were told. There was Peter Huppert, "Hopping Peter," the village tailor, who had only one eye and one
leg, but he too liked to tell stories. He told them well, and had
a prodigious memory. Like many illiterate people he could
remember everything he ever heard—he could repeat the
whole of Pastor Schliemann's last Sunday sermon, and his
recital was word perfect. One day he told them how, during
the time of Pastor von Rustdorf, he had been wondering
where the storks built their nests in winter, and so with the
help of the sexton he caught one of the storks which nested
on the parsonage barn. He fastened a strip of parchment
round its leg with a message saying the stork had spent the
summer in the village of Ankershagen in Schwerin-Mecklen-
burg, and would the finder kindly report where it had spent
the winter. The following spring the stork flew back, and
Hopping Peter said he found a strange runic message written
on parchment around the stork's foot:

> *Schwerin-Mecklenburg ist uns nicht bekannt;*
> *Das Land wo sich der Storch befand*
> *Nennt sich Sankt Johannes-Land.*

> Unknown to us is Schwerin-Mecklenburg;
> The country where the stork was found
> Is known as St. John's Land.

"We believed him," the boy wrote later, "and would have
given years of our life to know where that mysterious St.
John's Land was to be found." Perhaps, after all, St. John's

Land was only another name for Troy, that ruined and improbable land where the heroes walk unharmed through the
flames and every stork carries a mysterious message and black-
stockinged feet grow out of churchyards.

From listening to Hopping Peter the children would go to
the church, to amuse themselves by turning over the pages
of the ancient church registers, in which the names of long-
dead villagers were inscribed in heavy Gothic script in the
hands of Johann Christian von Schröder and his son Gottfriedrich. For ninety years, between 1709 and 1799, father
and son had occupied the parsonage, and Heinrich felt a
protective right over those heavy books, whose covers could
only be lifted with difficulty. And when the children wearied
of examining these parchment pages with their endless records
of births, marriages, and deaths, there was always the possibility of visiting Gottfriedrich's daughter, an old woman
eighty-four years of age, who knew all the village lore and
showed them the portraits of her ancestors. The portrait of
her mother, Olgartha Christine von Schröder, especially
pleased Heinrich because it resembled Minna.

So for nearly two years the children wandered hand in
hand through a legendary landscape, confiding their secrets
to one another, always inseparable. They swore to marry
each other and live the rest of their lives together. They
would remain in Ankershagen, because it was the only world
they knew—the high church steeple, the cherry blossoms in
the garden, the graveyard, and the great castle on the hill.
They promised faithfully they would never allow anything
to interfere with their dream.

Quite suddenly their dream came to an end, and they saw
all around them a world in ruins.

For a long time Heinrich's mother had been ailing. She
had known for many years that her husband had been
attentive to the kitchen maid. She had watched in silence
when the parson gave the girl expensive presents, jewels,

clothes and money. She had borne her husband's children and suffered his fierce temper, and she knew the maid was only waiting for her to die to become the mistress of the parsonage. The kitchen maid wore about the house the heaviest satin dresses and velvet shawls, and was not above taunting her. Two months before her last confinement, the parson's wife wrote a strange letter to her eldest daughter, thanking her for the affection she had always shown to her "forsaken mother." She went on:

In the coming days always remember that I am waging the battle of life and death. If you hear that death has prevailed, do not grieve too much, but rather rejoice that my sufferings are at an end in this, to me, so thankless world, in which patience, prayers, entreaties to God in the silence of the night, beseeching Him to change my hard lot, have not prevailed. . . . If God helps me happily to survive my time of suffering, and my life afterward becomes such that I once again find joy and happiness among men, I promise you to wear my pretty cap very often. I must now conclude, as I am in the middle of killing the pigs, and it goes so against the grain.

This letter, which seems to have been written in blood, was almost the last she wrote. A few weeks after giving birth to a son, she was dead.

The villagers knew why she died. They had long known about the affair with the kitchen maid. Now they turned against the parson in silent anger, watched him from behind their curtained windows, and hoped to make life intolerable for him. But they only succeeded in making life intolerable for his children, who were sent away to stay with relatives until the storm blew over. The kitchen maid was glad: now at last she had the parson to herself.

Heinrich was sent off to stay with an uncle who was a parson at Kalkhorst in Mecklenburg. He did not leave immediately. For some weeks, while arrangements were being made for the journey to Kalkhorst, he remained in the parsonage, and sometimes he would steal away to the house of Gottfriedrich's daughter and contemplate in stunned silence, with tears streaming down his cheeks, the portrait of Olgartha Christine von Schröder, which was so like the Minna he was no longer allowed to see. His mother's death made little impression on him. "To be separated altogether from Minna—never to behold her again—this was a thousand times more painful to me than my mother's death," he wrote later, "for I forgot my mother in my overwhelming grief for the loss of Minna. I have since undergone many great troubles in different parts of the world, but none of them caused me a thousandth part of the grief I felt at the tender age of nine years for my separation from my bride."

So he spoke in the authentic voice of grief, which he was never able to hide from others or from himself. For the rest of his life he dreamed despairingly about her. He told himself he would serve her all the days of his life, and in some mysterious way, after great hardships and many perilous journeys, he would find her again. Minna, Troy, St. John's Land—these were the names of the unavailing landscape of his dreams.

But no one can live with his grief every moment of the day, and at Kalkhorst the boy settled down to school, worked hard, and was regarded as a promising Latinist. His uncle, Friederich Schliemann, was a kindly and unobtrusive mentor. There was a bust of Homer in the school, and his professor of Latin was a certain Carl Andres from Neu Strelitz, who recognized the boy's brilliance, corrected his grammar, and saw to it that the boy wrote his Latin themes on subjects that interested him. In spite of everything that had happened, Heinrich still worshiped his father. Accordingly, as a present to his father at Christmas in 1832, he wrote a Latin essay on the Trojan wars. It was a long essay describing the principal events of the war and the adventures of Ulysses and Agamemnon, and though "not entirely faultless," it seems to have

pleased his father. The next year, when Heinrich was eleven,
it was decided to send him to the Gymnasium[4] at Neu Strelitz,
where he was placed in the third class, which meant that he
was considerably above other boys of his age in intelligence.
A pale, brilliant, unhappy youth, possessed of driving ambition, he could look forward to years of quiet study and eventually to some post in a university, perhaps at the University
of Rostock, one of the most ancient and distinguished in all
of Germany.

Within three months these dreams, too, were shattered
by his father's uncompromising determination to do as he
pleased. The village was up in arms against him. Determined
to ruin him, the villagers whispered that he had embezzled
church funds and for other reasons as well was incapable of
leading his flock. He was censured by the bishop, suspended
from the ministry, and threatened with expulsion from the
church. Since he could no longer afford to pay the school
fees at the Gymnasium, Heinrich was forced to enter the
Realschüle, the ordinary common school, where he spent the
next three years in a state of quiet and relentless misery. He
drowned himself in work. He was a good pupil and advanced
rapidly—in the spring of 1835 he had already advanced to
the first class. The blow fell the following spring, when he
learned that his father could no longer afford to pay the
relatively small sums necessary to keep him at the common
school. He must go out and earn a living, by himself, without
friends, with no hope of ever pursuing a career of letters or
entering a university.

His whole world shattered, he went blindly about the business of obtaining a menial job—anywhere, as long as it would
give him food to eat and a bed to sleep on. In the end he
decided to become an assistant in a grocer's shop in the neigh-

4. *Gymnasium:* German secondary school.

boring village of Fürstenberg, remembering perhaps that in a grocer's shop he would at least have enough to eat. He had left school just before the Easter holidays. He had decided to go to work immediately after Easter, and he was still staying at Neu Strelitz when an unhoped-for accident occurred. Visiting the house of Herr Laue, a musician of the court, he came face to face with his beloved Minna, and for a few moments he was alone with her.

Five years had passed since he had last seen her, but he recognized her instantly. She was dressed very simply in black, and the very simplicity of her dress only enhanced her beauty. She was fourteen years old, and carried herself like a grown woman. They gazed helplessly at each other, burst into tears and fell speechless into each other's arms. Several times they tried to speak, but no words came. They were still gazing at each other in the anguish of their grief and separation when Minna's parents entered the room. They were forced to separate, and it was more than five years before he saw her again, and then only for a brief moment. She came to him when he was most lonely, and most in need of her, and then vanished. To the end of his life he remembered her as she stood in the court musician's house wearing a black dress, the tears streaming down her cheeks.

Long afterward he wrote: "I was sure that Minna still loved me, and this thought fired my ambitions. From that moment I felt within me a boundless energy, and filled with an unshakable confidence in my ability to progress in the world by untiring effort and to prove myself worthy of her. And so I implored God to grant that she would not marry before I had obtained an independent position for myself."

A few days later the boy rode off to Fürstenberg, to become a servant in Herr Holtz's grocer's shop, at the beck and call of everyone who wanted herrings or a bottle of potato whiskey.

. . . 2   **THE STORM**

HE HATED the shop and everything about it. He hated old
Herr Holtz, who was as wooden as his name,[1] and he hated
his servitude and the niggardly sums of money he received.
He hated waking up at five in the morning to open the shop,
sweep the floors, dust the counters, oil Herr Holtz's boots,
and arrange the counter. Above all he hated losing Minna
and being so weary at the end of the day that it was impossible to study, impossible even to remember the lines of Virgil[2]
he had memorized at school or anything else he had ever been
taught. Outside in the sunlight boys went to school and
played leapfrog and sauntered home in the afternoon with
their satchels on their backs. In the grocer's shop it was
always dark and cold and miserable, and there were no legends
to feed his imagination, and no pictures of the ancient world
to remind him of burning Troy.

For the next five years of his life he seems to have lived
in a state of mindless abandon. Ambition gnawed at him, but
there were no prospects of wealth in sight. The village was
poor, and sometimes Herr Holtz had difficulty in making
ends meet: if they sold 12 talers worth of groceries a day,
about $8, they thought they were lucky, and their total sales
in a year hardly amounted to 3,000 talers, or $1,800. Profits
were small, hours were long, and there was no end to the
eternal drudgery.

The best hours were in the early morning when the boy
was left to himself. At eight o'clock in the morning Herr
Holtz came down and sent him off to the local distillery with
a sack of potatoes—in Mecklenberg everyone drank potato
whiskey, and Herr Holtz was the chief purveyor of it in the
obscure village of Fürstenberg. Then he would hurry back

1. *Name:* "Holtz" means wood in German.
2. *Virgil:* Latin poet (70-19 B.C.).

to stand behind the counter until eleven in the evening, re-
tailing herrings, butter, milk, salt, coffee, sugar, oil, candles,
and the inevitable potato whiskey. The shop reeked of herrings and whiskey. He was always trundling heavy casks
around the shop, counting the cases of herrings, and running
errands. There was no opportunity for study, though he
would sometimes read for a little while at night before going
to bed under the counter, his brain weary with figures, his
hands damp with herring-oil, and his clothes sprinkled with
wood shavings. He never had enough money to buy clothes,
and therefore he wore the same patched suit summer and
winter. So it went on, year in, year out, until it seemed that
all ambition was crushed in him.

Yet all this time he was dreaming of wealth, vast wealth.
The more miserable he became, the more earnestly he thought
of Minna and the day when he would be able to marry her
and provide for her. The wretched people who came to the
shop nauseated him. He would become a scholar. He would
grow rich. He would show himself to advantage in an unbelieving world. Inevitably ambition became a monstrous
growth, like Henning von Holstein's leg, clothed in black silk,
growing in the churchyard.

There were occasional interludes of contentment. One
night a drunken miller lurched into the shop, and Heinrich
watched him as he declaimed a hundred lines of Homer in
the light of the oil lamps. Heinrich was fascinated. He could
not read or understand Greek, but the rhythm of the words
struck a chord in his soul, and when the drunken miller had
recited a hundred lines, he was asked to repeat them, and
then, still not satisfied, Heinrich asked him to repeat them
a third time. He was so pleased that he gave the miller three
glasses of potato whiskey for his trouble, even though it cost
him all the money he had.

In time Heinrich came to know the drunken miller well,
and always looked forward to his coming. His name was

Hermann Niederhoffer, and he was the son of the Protestant pastor at Roebel. A twenty-four-year-old ne'er-do-well, he had been expelled from school for some misconduct or other, but not before he had learned those famous hundred lines, which he always repeated in exactly the same way, with the same flourishes and the same sweetness of tone. Heinrich wrote long afterwards that hot tears flowed down his cheeks as he listened to the words. "From that moment," he said, "I did not cease to pray to God that by His grace it might one day be permitted to me to learn Greek."

He did not imagine the incident, but he may have imagined his prayer. He was always dreaming of escape—to America, where the streets were paved with gold and a man might buy books to his heart's content. He was eighteen when he signed a contract with the land steward of a neighboring estate, which would have permitted him to make the journey to New York, if he could get together enough money to pay some of the expenses. It was 1840, with the immigrants flocking in thousands to the Western prairies. Heinrich applied to his father for a loan, but that strange secretive father was engaged in one of his innumerable love affairs and no money was forthcoming. With a heavy heart and no hope at all of ever escaping from bondage, he returned to the little grocer's shop, and he might have served behind the counter for the rest of his life if an accident had not happened.

Sometimes, when he was older, he would find himself trembling in a cold sweat when he remembered how a cask of chicory had altered the whole course of his life. It was not a very large cask, but it was heavy. He strained himself, and suddenly spat blood, and while the blood poured over the sawdust on the floor, he knew he could not go on carrying sacks of potatoes and lifting milk churns for ever. He was pale and weak-chested, and in danger of dying surrounded by packages of herrings and whale-oil candles. He decided to go to Hamburg, which was on the sea, and therefore close to America. He had saved 30 Prussian dollars, amounting to about $18. With this money and the clothes he stood in, he walked to Hamburg by way of Rostock, where he paused long enough to learn bookkeeping "on the Schwanbeck system," completing in a few days a course which normally kept a student busy for a year or a year and a half.

Even if he had wanted to return to the pitiable little village of Ankershagen, there was nothing there to attract him. His father had married a woman of the people, given her two children, separated from her and brought her back again. There were ghosts in Ankershagen, but there was something far worse than ghosts—scandal. There was no peace between his father and the new wife. They screamed at each other and fought like wildcats, and matters grew so grave that the new wife hid herself in the woodshed for fear of being murdered and the old clergyman was summoned before the court and ordered to treat her kindly or make her an allowance of 300 Reichstalers a year. All this was known at Fürstenberg and Rostock, and so Schliemann hurried off to Hamburg, a vast anonymous city where he could lose himself and forget his misery and his yearning for Minna, who still dominated his thoughts, although sometimes he found himself dreaming of his cousin, Sophie Schliemann, the daughter of the rector of Kalkhorst, who was slim and graceful and blushed easily. It was Sophie who saw him off on the coach which brought him from Rostock to Hamburg, and he was dreaming of her all the way until the five great towers of Hamburg came in sight.

The towers fascinated him—he was to be fascinated by towers for the rest of his life—and he stood outside the city spellbound by its silhouette against the September sky, saying "Hamburg! Hamburg!" over and over again. All his life he had known only small towns and villages, but here was a city with great avenues bordered by the palaces of merchant princes, with huge painted signs hanging from the second stories of the mercantile houses, and markets everywhere.

Wagons rattled along the paved streets; clocks chimed; there were carillons from the high belfries of the churches. Excited beyond measure by the magnificence of the roaring city, deafened by the noise, he forgot his own misery. He was like a sleepwalker, or a dreamer. And thinking of how he would soon make his fortune, he wrote to his sister: "Hamburg has raised me to the seventh heaven and turned me into a dreamer."

But who in Hamburg wanted to employ a youth with a weak chest who was continually spitting blood? He knew something about serving behind a counter in a grocer's shop and he possessed a precocious knowledge of double entry bookkeeping. With his sickness and his pallor he was not a very attractive youth. He was a little astonished to discover that no one wanted him. At Lindemann's grocery shop overlooking the fish market, he got a job which paid him about $36 a month, but he was dismissed eight days later. It was the last time he was ever to tend groceries, for his next job was as a bookkeeper, and this lasted only a week. He was in desperate straits, and wrote to an uncle for a loan to tide him over until Christmas. The money came by return mail with a letter so insulting that he would have sent the money back if he had not had so much need. The loan amounted to no more than ten Reichstalers. It barely kept him alive. And when Christmas came, he had abandoned Hamburg for ever.

Luck had worked for him in strange ways. The heavy cask of chicory brought salvation and suffering, and now a chance encounter with a shipbroker, who had known his mother, led him to hope he might escape from Germany altogether. The kindly shipbroker introduced him to the captain of the brig *Dorothea*, bound for La Guaira in Venezuela. There had been a time in Schliemann's youth when he had dreamed of the pampas of South America, and now he jumped at the opportunity of making the journey. His health was broken and he was penniless, with no money to buy even a blanket. Then he remembered his silver wristwatch; he sold it for three dollars and went out on a spending spree. He had spent all his money when he came on board the sailing vessel, but he had bought in a second-hand market two shirts, a coat, a pair of trousers, a mattress, and a blanket of sorts. He was to lose most of them a few days later.

He had never sailed before, and he knew nothing about ships. The *Dorothea* sailed out of Hamburg on November 28, 1841 with a fair wind. There was a crew of eighteen and three passengers: Schliemann, a joiner from Hamburg, and the joiner's son. Schliemann was seasick even in calm weather, and he was ill when the ship put in at Cuxhaven three days later. They berthed for only a short while at Cuxhaven, sailed out into the North Sea, and two days later found themselves in the path of a hurricane. The ship took on water, the pumps were manned continually, and Schliemann found himself suffering from an unappeasable hunger, which he allayed as best he could by chewing on ship's biscuits. He roped himself to a bench, set himself to learning Spanish from a Spanish grammar, and sometimes fell with a crash onto the deck. The other passengers suffered in silence in their bunks.

It was the worst weather Schliemann had ever known —the storm pouring out of the skies, the waves breaking over the sides, the ship in danger of foundering. On December 10 the gale was still raging, but the captain succeeded in maintaining his course with the help of the main top-gallant sail, the only sail he dared to use. In spite of all the efforts of the crew the ship was being blown south by evening, and hardly anyone believed the ship could survive the incessant pounding of the waves. The wild snow was falling, and sea gulls kept circling around them in great flocks—this was thought to be a bad sign. It was intensely cold with six degrees of frost, and on the afternoon of the next day the storm grew worse, with the waves piling up like mountains and then hurtling down on the ship, which seemed to be no more than a shuttlecock at the mercy of the waves. Toward evening the main top-gallant sail broke away. The storm sail was hoisted, but this too broke away. And then a strange thing happened—for a brief while the clouds parted and they all saw the blaze of the setting sun. When the clouds closed over them again, most of them thought they had seen the sun for the last time.

Schliemann was by this time too sick to worry, and he listened with an odd sense of abstraction to the joiner who was trembling with horror at the fate which awaited them. The joiner believed in dreams: he had known some terrible dreams the previous night. Then, too, the ship's cat had been whining throughout the whole day, and the captain's dog had howled. At about seven o'clock the cabin boy came down to the cabin with tea and biscuits. The boy was weeping and saying he would never bring them anything any more. A little later the captain and the second mate came to the cabin and spoke gravely to the passengers, and they were graver still when the first mate came to report he had seen two lights in the distance. The captain gave orders for the anchors to be dropped, but the anchor chains snapped like broken twine a few minutes later. By this time Schliemann had undressed and gone to bed, so completely exhausted that he was beyond fear.

Around midnight the cabin door blew open and the captain was shouting at them: "All passengers on deck! The ship's going down!" A moment later an enormous wave smashed all the portholes, flooding the cabin, and the ship lurched violently to port. Schliemann sprang out of his bunk, tried to dress, could not find his clothes, and rushed up on deck stark naked. Badly bruised, he somehow caught hold of the rigging and managed to crawl to the starboard gunwale, clutching at loose ends of rope and silently commending himself to God. He was afraid of sharks. He had seen them coming to the surface when the storm broke on them. He said his prayers and thought of his sisters, and all the time he could hear the

joiner screaming to the Virgin Mary for help. The strangest
thing of all was that the ship's bell was tolling continually. It
was like a death knell.

Naked, on the coldest night of the year, the snow falling
round him, the sky like a black cloud, he awaited his fate.
When the ship was sinking, the captain ordered the crew to
man the lifeboats. One lifeboat fell perpendicularly into the
water and vanished. The second was smashed to a pulp against
the side of the ship. There remained the small stern boat,
slung between the masts, but by this time the crew was too
frightened to do anything except climb the rigging. The ship
was waterlogged and slowly sinking. Two hours passed. At
last with a violent lurch the ship keeled over to port, and
sank. Schliemann went down with it, but soon rose to the
surface. When an empty cask floated by, he clutched at it,
his fingers curling convulsively around the rim.

So he remained for half the night, hanging between the
sky and the sea, until the first mate pulled him out of the
water and somehow got him into the stern boat, which had
been thrown free. There were fourteen people in the boat,
and no oars. They drifted until dawn, only to be thrown
up on one of the sandbanks off the island of Texel, off the
Dutch coast. The storm was dying down, and the people of
Texel were hurrying to the shore to gather all the cargo which
was drifting onto the banks. Schliemann was in great pain.
Three of his front teeth were broken, there were deep cuts
on his face and body, and his feet were swollen. All the survivors lay gasping in the sand until a friendly farmer came
along with a cart and carried them off to his farmhouse, where
a fire was kindled and they were given coffee and black bread.
For three days the survivors remained at the farmhouse, re-
cuperating from their ordeal.

Schliemann was given some wooden shoes, a pair of torn
trousers, a blanket, and a wool cap. He liked the farmer, but
what pleased him more than anything was that his sea box

with his shirts and stockings, together with his pocketbook which contained his "letters of recommendation for La Guaira procured for me by Herr Wendt," was found on the sand bank. None of the sea boxes of the other survivors floated to shore, and inevitably Schliemann was christened "Jonah."[3] A heavy cask had nearly killed him when he was a grocer's clerk at Fürstenberg; an empty cask had saved him. His luck was holding. When he took the ferryboat to the mainland, still haggard and coatless, wearing heavy wooden *sabots*,[4] with his sea box under his arm, he was amused to find himself greeted by a crowd of impudent bootblacks who, seeing him as ragged as themselves, pretended he had come to join their ranks.

But there were few things that amused him in those days. Desperate and miserable, without money, in a strange country, he realized he had survived by a miracle. He told himself he had survived the ordeal only because he had hardened himself with cold baths at Hamburg and because he had worn two pairs of under-drawers and two woolen waistcoats during the winter. He had no coat, no leather shoes, and no prospects. He refused to return to Hamburg with the other survivors, announcing that he had been inexpressibly miserable there and felt that his destiny lay in Holland.

Needing money badly, he went to the consul for Mecklenburg in Amsterdam, a certain Herr Quack, but the consul's servant, thinking he was a beggar, shut the door in his face. Schliemann rang the bell again, and when the door opened he had time to throw inside the house a short note saying he was a citizen of Mecklenburg in need of assistance. Herr Quack read the letter and sent his servant out into the bitterly cold street with two gulden, about fifty cents, for his compatriot. The servant informed Schliemann that he must count himself lucky to receive the gift, and the consul hoped it was the last he would hear from him.

3. *Jonah:* Biblical character cast up by a great fish.
4. *Sabots:* French for "wooden shoes."

Schliemann was angry. When he grew older, he would become capable of vast and volcanic rages, but now he was angry with the cool bitterness of a poor man desperately in need of assistance. He found a sailors' lodging house, kept by the Widow Graalman on the Ramskoy in Amsterdam, and when his funds were low and he could no longer pay his rent, which amounted to one gulden a day, he resorted to a ruse. He wrote to Herr Quack, saying he was ill and demanding to be taken to the hospital—it was the least the wretched consul could do for him. There was no difficulty in getting the message into the consul's house, for the widow was only too anxious to help, afraid she would have to keep and feed him until he died or recovered. The ruse was successful. He spent eight days in the hospital.

He wrote to Herr Wendt, who had befriended him in Hamburg, a detailed account of the shipwreck and his present fortunes, and by a lucky accident the letter was delivered while the shipbroker was entertaining guests at dinner. Herr Wendt read the letter aloud. Everyone sympathized with the unlucky youth, and they made a collection, which amounted to the sum of 240 gulden, a very small fortune. Herr Wendt also enclosed a letter of introduction to the consul-general for Prussia, requesting his assistance. Within a few days Schliemann was at work in the counting house of F. C. Quien and Co., as a supernumerary messenger boy. His job consisted of stamping bills of exchange and getting them cashed in the town. From that moment there was no turning back. He had found what he wanted to do, abandoned grocers' shops forever, and set his foot on the path which would lead him to a fortune.

From the beginning he saw that the only way to make a fortune was to dedicate his whole life to it. He would sharpen his wits and strip himself to the bone, surrendering himself to the task with an act of dedication so complete that he would in time find himself incapable of leading any other life. First, he reduced his expenses to a minimum. He was paid thirty-six gulden a month, and out of this eight gulden were reserved for his cheerless room in a lodging house. Second, he would waste no money on entertainment—his sole entertainment consisted of evening walks in the town to admire the shops brightly lit with gas, or wandering down to the railway station to see the trains coming in. Third, he would have nothing to do with women. This was not particularly difficult, for he found a substitute in gazing at the exquisite wax models in hairdressers' windows. There was one hairdresser who had six models of brightly colored wax, with elegant coiffures, revolving on turntables. With the passion of a poor man dedicated to making a fortune, he gazed at them with the hopeless abandonment of a suitor who knows that the fairy princess will never pay him a moment's attention, and sometimes he thought of Minna and hoped he was worthy of her. Fourth, he would acquire an education, even if it meant starting from the bottom by learning the elements of German calligraphy. In twenty lessons he learned how to write a passable German hand, and then he went on to learn Dutch and English by reading aloud, taking lessons every day, writing essays and having them corrected by a tutor. Fifth, he would train his memory, so that nothing that ever happened to him, no book he read, no figures he encountered in the ledgers, would ever pass completely from his mind. Sixth, he would spend his money only on books or on the means to advance his education.

That lonely, Spartan life left ineradicable marks on him, and he never recovered from it. He had the pride and single-mindedness of the self-taught; and if he grew bitter in his personal relationships that was the price he paid for his stern devotion to the duty of improving himself. He had no adolescence, or rather he experienced all the emotions of adolescence between the ages of nine and eleven, when he was seeing Minna every day. Now the steel was entering his soul, and with the steel went quirks of behavior, terrible rages, and titanic resolutions. Ruthlessly, dispassionately, with appalling lucidity, he mounted the steps leading to the temple of Success, and for long years the vision of Troy and even the thought of marrying Minna were to succumb to an all-consuming passion for gold.

Now every moment he could spare from the office was devoted to study—not the study of the Greek and Roman empires which were the passion of his youth, but the study of all the languages used in business. He learned English in six months by attending the English Church in Amsterdam twice every Sunday, and repeating under his breath every word spoken by the parson; and it seems never to have occurred to him that he was modeling himself on Hopping Peter, the old tailor in Ankershagen who was able to recite his father's sermons without in the least understanding what was being said. At night he read and reread *The Vicar of Wakefield* and *Ivanhoe*[5] until he knew them by heart. His brain worked best at night, and therefore he allowed himself little sleep. He grew ill and pale, and had no time for his friends; he became a kind of memory-machine, learning nouns and verbs and conjugations by rote, divorced from the ordinary world of Amsterdam all around him.

After learning English in six months, he spent the next six months learning French. At the end of the year his powers of concentration had improved so vastly that he was able to learn Dutch, Spanish, Italian, and Portuguese with astonishing rapidity, claiming that it took him no more than six weeks of concentrated study to speak and write these languages fluently. Before he came to Amsterdam he knew only German, and that only in the *Plattdeutsch*[6] of Mecklenburg, and a good smattering of Latin. Now he knew seven languages

5. *Vicar of Wakefield* . . . *Ivanhoe:* English novels by Oliver Goldsmith and Sir Walter Scott.
6. *Plattdeutsch:* "Low German" dialect.

well: he could read and write them, could draw up business reports in them, and read foreign newspapers. To accomplish this, he had stolen time from his employers and maintained a ruthless schedule, learning long lists of words even when he was running errands in the rain, or memorizing whole passages while waiting for stamps at a post office. Never for a moment did he relent. He knew that in time, if he survived the rigors of his self-composed discipline, he would come into his reward.

The reward came shortly after his twenty-second birthday, on March 1, 1844, when he stepped into the office of Herr Schröder, who headed the vast import and export business in Amsterdam. Schliemann appealed for a job, explained his qualifications—seven languages, a head for figures, and two years' experience as an errand boy—and was immediately put to the test. At first glance Herr Schröder recognized a man who might be useful to him, and within a matter of minutes Heinrich was appointed a bookkeeper at 600 gulden, and within a few weeks the salary was increased to 1,000 gulden. The kindly Herr Schröder seems to have been amused and amazed by his new bookkeeper, who bore his own Christian name and who was so very apt in his understanding of the complexities of trade. Schliemann abandoned his study of languages for a few months, and instead put his studies to use. He advanced rapidly. He soon became one of the chief correspondents in the office and was attached to the small circle surrounding Herr Schröder. When letters from Russia came to the office, Heinrich announced that he would learn Russian in a few weeks, so that he would be able to answer them.

He learned Russian in the same way he had learned English —by pitching himself head foremost at the language, without troubling about grammar, though he would sometimes permit himself a cursory examination of grammatical rules. He obtained a poor translation into Russian of Fénélon's *Les Ad-*

ventures de Télemaque, which tells in an extremely long-winded fashion the story of the son of Ulysses. He bought a dictionary and an old grammar. The first time he read the story he simply looked up all the words in the dictionary, and by dint of hammering at the text in front of him succeeded in extracting some sense from it. He had a prodigious memory, and never needed to look up the same word twice. He wanted a tutor, but none was forthcoming. He took the trouble to go to the Russian Consulate at Amsterdam and begged the vice consul to give him lessons, but the vice consul had other matters on his mind, and refused.

So he returned to his lodgings, wrote short stories and essays in uncorrected Russian, and, because he felt lonely and needed an audience for his recitations, he hired a poor student at four francs an hour to listen to him recite whole chapters of *Les Adventures de Télemaque,* which he had learned by heart. He liked to have an audience, and liked shouting the heavy and sonorous syllables of the Russian language, but the walls and floorboards were thin and the lodgers complained at these nightly exercises, and he was twice forced to change his lodgings. The method was singularly successful. At the end of six weeks he sent off his first letter in Russian, addressing it with all the proper salutations to a certain Vassily Plotnikov, the London agent of a large firm of indigo merchants in Moscow. That letter was to shape the next twenty years of his life. In time he was to acquire a huge fortune, and perhaps the largest part of it was derived from selling indigo in Russia.

In those days Amsterdam was still one of the great centers of trade in indigo, which was imported from India and the Far East. Periodically indigo auctions were held there, and Schliemann would be sent to attend the auctions. With his consuming interest in all things Russian, he sought out the Russian merchants, who were surprised to find a German in Holland talking to them in their own language. He asked about conditions in Russia, made himself agreeable to them, inquired about prospects, and spoke about leaving Amsterdam for Moscow and setting up as an importer in partnership with an established Russian firm. He even drew up a contract with a Russian importer named Zhivago, who promised to open a business agency to be called "Zhivago and Schliemann" with a capital of 60,000 silver rubles to be supplied by the Russian partner, the profits to be shared equally. Evidently he was being regarded as a man of substance, and Heinrich Schröder, while paying him well, had to contemplate the possibility that he would leave for finer pastures.

For a year and ten months Schliemann continued to live in a series of dingy lodging houses, always saving his money, spending as little as possible on himself, his only apparent vice being innumerable cups of sweetened tea—it was a pleasant vice which he permitted himself to the end of his life. Sugar gave him sudden spurts of energy, and kept him awake during the long nights of study and contemplation. And now more and more he began to write letters to his father couched in the tones of an elder brother, anxious to save the family from disaster. He was continually cajoling his father to lead a more profitable life. He showered his father with gifts—from his first savings he sent two casks of Bordeaux and a box of cigars to the old reprobate, and he continued to send gifts in an endless torrent, always accompanying them with moral maxims and admonitions to follow his son's example—and all the time he was dreaming about marrying Minna. He told himself that the years of apprenticeship were nearly over. Soon he would marry and settle down with a healthy bank account. He would become a merchant prince, modeling himself on the Brothers Schröder, his knowledge of eight languages enabling him to carry on a vast trade across the length and breadth of the earth.

Toward the end of December, 1845, he was summoned to the inner office and asked whether he would like to represent the Schröder business interests in St. Petersburg. It is possible that news of his negotiations with Zhivago had already leaked out, and the firm was anxious to retain his services at any cost, even the cost of sending him as their chief representative to the capital of Russia. Told that he would be allowed to represent all the wide-flung Schröder interests with their branch offices in Bremen, Trieste, Smyrna, Le Havre, and Rio de Janeiro, he accepted at once; and he spent his last weeks in Amsterdam interviewing the heads of other businesses and suggesting that he could act as their representative as well. He was so sure of himself and the profits he would make that he requested that no fees be paid to him until he had actually shown a profit. "I will incur no expense for you," he wrote to the head of one business, "until you are satisfied that my activities on your behalf are productive of remunerative results, and accordingly I ask you to address your letters to me in unfranked envelopes."

Just before setting out for St. Petersburg he thought of writing to his friend Herr Laue, the court musician at Neu Strelitz, to inquire about Minna and to suggest that the time had come to marry her. Then it occurred to him that it would be better to postpone the matter until he had established himself in St. Petersburg. He wrote to his father, explaining his good fortune, the result of his own relentless single-mindedness. "Such gifts," he said, "do not fall from Heaven on those who are unworthy of them." He had made few friends in Amsterdam, and he felt no greater wrench in parting from Amsterdam than he felt in parting from Hamburg. For the rest of his life he was to be a wanderer over the face of the earth.

So in a mood of profound self-satisfaction, at the age of twenty-five, only four years after being shipwrecked off the coast of Holland, he set out from Amsterdam as the chief representative of one of the greatest trading firms on earth, and sixteen days later, February 1, 1846, after an arduous journey by coach and sleigh, he arrived in St. Petersburg.

. . . 3   THE SEARCH FOR GOLD

IN THE 1840's of the last century St. Petersburg was a city
still coming to birth. Nicholas I was on the throne, a stern
square-chinned man, six feet tall, who despised his ministers
and preferred to think of himself as a cavalry officer who
had inherited the Czardom by the grace of God and was
therefore entitled to enjoy himself to the utmost. Among
his major amusements was the construction of glittering
white Italianate palaces on this bleak northern shore of the
Baltic. He held himself well, his waist tightly compressed,
as befitted a cavalry officer, and he pursued indiscriminately
all the women at his court. Nearly everyone who came into
his presence trembled, for his left eye was so much brighter
than his right that he seemed to be somehow inhuman, removed from the common preoccupations of humanity—a
trait which he shared with Alexander the Great, whose terrible eyes also made solid soldiers tremble in their shoes.

St. Petersburg in the time of Nicholas I was a city of
extremes: wide streets, a few factory buildings, innumerable
palaces, the hovels of the poor. Visitors remarked on the
absence of traffic on the streets, the emptiness of the place,
the sense of abandonment which had come over this new
city built on marshlands by Peter the Great and now rebuilt
by Nicholas I, who saw himself as the destined successor
of Peter. In winter the whole city was white, the only color
coming from the bright scarlet liveries of the royal coach-
men. At night ghosts wandered through the icy streets. While
the courtiers endured the endless frivolities of the Court, and
the serfs endured their slavery, students were already planning
to overthrow the monarchy. It was the year when Dostoevsky's[1] first novel, *Poor Folk*, appeared, and already that group

1. *Dostoevsky:* great Russian novelist (1821-1881).

of conspirators known as the Petrashevsky circle was plotting
against the Czar, with the young Dostoevsky among them.
Throughout Russia there was a gradual awakening of a feverish social consciousness: the bitterness and despair of a people
enslaved.

In all the years he spent in St. Petersburg, Schliemann
never showed any sign of being aware of the deadly poison
in the air. He told himself continually he was living in the
best of all possible worlds. For him St. Petersburg was a
good substantial city, eminently suitable for business, and
far safer than most cities. He spoke of "the beautiful and
clean houses, the fine streets and delightful climate." In his
letters the Czar becomes "the wise and most glorious emperor
Nicholas." He had no illusions about the Russian businessmen
—they were as grasping and difficult to handle as all the other
businessmen everywhere, but at least he possessed advantages
over them. He knew his trade better than most, and as the
chief representative for Schröder he was in a position to make
himself heard. Restless, energetic, ambitious, he was constantly on the move. After seven days in St. Petersburg he
drove by sleigh to Moscow, to establish connections with
firms he had been corresponding with. He was at ease in the
company of merchant princes, and was soon on intimate
terms with them.

From the moment he arrived in St. Petersburg he acted
out the part of international merchant with resounding success. He represented the Schröder interests, and six or seven
other interests as well. Even with a commission of ½ per cent,
which was all he allowed himself in those early years, he
earned 7,500 gulden during his first year, and this represented
a turnover of 1,500,000 gulden—a sum beyond his dreams
two or three years before. He achieved his success by a
meticulous attention to detail, by standing at his desk from
early morning to late in the evening, by following every clue
which would lead him to a profit, however small.

Heinrich Schliemann in St. Petersburg.

He made four separate journeys to Moscow that year, and by October things were going so well that he permitted himself a combined business and pleasure trip through Germany, France, and England, stopping off for a few hours in Amsterdam to renew acquaintance with Heinrich Schröder, for whom he felt an intense gratitude. What interested him most of all was the vast progress in industry—locomotives, bridges, factories, the telegraph, the whole of Europe surging forward into the new age of industrialism, and Russia so backward that it seemed as though he were specially selected to bring the advantages of industrialism to his adopted country. Gradually he came to regard himself as a Russian. He spoke of the Czar as "our Czar" and Russia as "my country." And while enjoying his riches, he also enjoyed his old habits of thrift. So it happened on all his travels that he would put up at the best hotels, while choosing the least expensive rooms, usually on the top floor. He had a passion for being under the roof, and perhaps it went back to those days in Amsterdam when he learned seven languages in two years in the garrets of cheap lodging houses.

He liked London, though he knew the cold chill of a typical Victorian Sunday. He wandered into the British Museum and made careful lists of the Pharaohs in their sarcophagi, and of Greek and Roman vases. He was delighted with the train which took him to Manchester, traveling so much more quickly than any other trains in Europe. At that time Manchester was the greatest industrial center in the world, a vast humming factory lit with the fires of coke furnaces and the blaze of innumerable chimneys. There he saw the giant locomotives being built for export to Germany and watched iron being cut "as easily as paper," and everything pleased him. Steamships, dockyards, iron foundries, the telegraph which could send a message from the south of England to the northernmost tip of Scotland—it was all wonderful beyond belief, and at the same time magnificently arranged by the Creator for the furtherance of trade. No one ever looked upon the industrial revolution with a less jaundiced eye.

He returned to St. Petersburg by way of Le Havre, Paris, Brussels, Cologne, Düsseldorf, Hamburg, Berlin, without pausing in Mecklenburg. There were excellent reasons for avoiding the places where he had spent his childhood. Some

time during that year he had written to Herr Laue in Neu
Strelitz and asked for the hand of Minna Meincke, only to
learn that she had married a local farmer. The marriage took
place a few weeks before he wrote his letter. The shock
nearly killed him. Sixteen years had passed since he first set
eyes on her. He told himself that through all those sixteen
years he had lived for her, and for her alone. What did it
matter to him that he was slowly acquiring a fortune, influence, and prestige, when he had no one to share them with?
So he grew sullen and embittered, nursing his grief, telling
himself that there was a kind of curse on him, but the time
would come when, with a great fortune at his command, he
would marry any Russian beauty he desired. To a man of
wealth all things were possible, even a happy marriage.

At the beginning of 1847, shortly after his return to St.
Petersburg, he was inscribed as a merchant of the First Guild.
This meant that he was now properly established, could obtain bankers' credit, and was on an equal footing with long-
established merchants. He attended the monthly meetings of
the Guild, made speeches in impeccable Russian, and was
welcomed in the Guild club. He sat at the tables of the
wealthiest people in the land. Peter Alexieff, "who is worth
100 million rubles and has a private fortune of 12 million
rubles besides," greeted him affably at the club and invited
him into his home. The prominent sugar and timber merchant
Ponomareff took a fancy to him and spoke of advancing
100,000 silver rubles if he would enter a business arrangement
with him. Then there was "my friend Zhivago, who is worth
several millions"—the man he had met by accident at the
Amsterdam auction sale, and who was therefore largely responsible for his journey to Russia—who lived in a palatial
house in Moscow and entertained him whenever he visited
the city. Zhivago was childless, but his niece Ekaterina, "an
angel of virtue and beauty," was staying with him. She was
sixteen, and completely captivating, and Zhivago himself
seemed to desire the match, for he invited Schliemann to stay

in the Moscow house for four or five months, evidently with the intention of acquiring a partner and a relative by marriage. Schliemann was a little nervous about these Moscow prospects.

He liked Ekaterina, but was unsure of himself. He wrote to his sister in Mecklenburg, begging her to make the journey to Russia—she would stay for a few weeks in St. Petersburg and then accompany him to Moscow, where she would observe the behavior of the beautiful Ekaterina. In effect, Schliemann wanted a business report on Ekaterina, just such a report as he was in the habit of receiving from his agencies abroad. What was she really like? How did she behave in the seclusion of her own apartment? Was she a person of fire and temperament? Could she cook? He wrote to his sister: "I am sure there is no lack of brides: the difficulty is to choose among a hundred would-be brides. You will help me in my choice. I myself am blind, and passion clouds my vision. I see only the virtues and never the failings of the fair sex. I have a large bath, so you can take your baths at home."

This astonishing letter proved only that Schliemann was incapable of relying on his own judgment in matters of the heart. Nothing came of the invitation to his sister, and in time he realized that no one could help him and only a miracle would provide him with a wife as adorable as Minna. So he temporized, made excursions among the daughters of the gentry and wealthier businessmen, and usually retired from the battle, hurt and confused. He was full-blooded, violently jealous, and self-opinionated. Accustomed to having his orders obeyed immediately, he found quite early in his career that the laws governing business are inappropriate in the boudoir; and in the presence of women he became more and more baffled. It was not that he lacked the social graces; it was simply that he could not trust himself, did not know exactly what he wanted, always hoped to marry a rich heiress, but could never find one who possessed the beauty, simplicity, and grace of Minna.

And while Minna still dominated his dreams, the search

for a fortune dominated his life. He had opened his own
business agency, while continuing his connections with
Schröder. He trafficked in every kind of merchandise and
took appalling risks, but never gave credit "except to merchants of the very first standing." He explained to Schröder
that he had worked exceedingly hard on their behalf, and
felt that he was now in a position to demand more than
the miserable ½ per cent which they had granted him in the
days when he was unknown. Now everyone knew him. Was
he not regarded as a man of dazzling accomplishments, with
a business which extended over the whole world? Accordingly Schröder permitted him to draw off 1 per cent of the
value of the merchandise passing through his hands, and from
that moment Schliemann knew that only a few years would
pass before he had acquired an immense fortune.

So matters progressed until the end of 1848, when for the
fifth time he made the journey by sleigh to Moscow, to spend
Christmas and the New Year with the Zhivagos. He enjoyed
the visit, but on the return journey through the snow he
suffered agonies of cold when a storm blew up, and fell ill
with influenza. He thought he was dying. For four months
he remained in bed, and as soon as he was recovered, he threw
himself so violently into his work that by June he was in a
state of collapse. The doctors put him in a dark room and
refused to let him continue with his business. He raged at the
doctors, but admitted the justice of their accusations. He was
discovering that to make a fortune a man has to live on his
nerves, in a perpetual state of intellectual fever, in a landscape where the only comfort consisted in the sight of the
gold which was always just out of his reach.

When fall came he had learned his lesson. He worked a
little less avidly, and attended more social engagements. He
gave dinner parties, served the finest wines, and surrounded
himself with merchants and their eligible daughters. All
thoughts of Ekaterina vanished when he fell hopelessly in

love with a certain Sophia, who possessed no fortune, but was thrifty and spoke three European languages fluently. He was madly in love with her. He wrote off to his father that he had found the girl of his dreams, only to write in the next letter that he had taken her to a party, where she showed unpardonable interest in a young officer, and at the sight of "giddy, stupid Sophia" behaving in this lamentable fashion, he had broken off the engagement. On the whole he was glad he had escaped from her. He would have the opportunity of cultivating a romance with the adorable Ekaterina—the Zhivagos were always asking him to visit them in Moscow. So in February 1850 he journeyed by sleigh again to Moscow, and as usual stayed with the Zhivagos. No one knows exactly what happened. Within a month he was journeying at high speed across Europe, drowning himself in business, never staying in one place for more than a few days, his letters full of sound business advice, with not a word about Ekaterina in any of them.

Like a man hounded by the police, he slipped from one hotel to another. It is possible that he thought of settling in northern England, for he spent most of the time there, visiting Edinburgh, Glasgow, Liverpool, Bangor, Chester, and London. He took notes of everything he saw, and every night wrote up his diary; the industrial progress of England continued to amaze him. At the end of a few weeks he was back again in St. Petersburg, his pockets bursting with contracts. But is is unlikely that he made these sudden journeys only for the sake of business. Most of his long journeys in those early years seem to have taken place immediately after the collapse of a love affair. These hurried and precipitous excursions abroad were in fact surrogates for the love he lacked. There were moments when he detested St. Petersburg and thought of settling down on a farm in Mecklenburg with a poor peasant girl for a bride.

But St. Petersburg summoned him. There, at least, he had

established the foundation of his fortune, and he told himself
that for a few more months he would attempt to live in that
cold northern city. He settled down to work, attended parties,
and some time in the summer of 1850 he was introduced to
a certain Ekaterina Lishin, a tall statuesque beauty, the niece
of another business acquaintance. She had a pale oval face,
dark eyes, and carried herself like a princess. Schliemann admired her, discussed the possibility of marrying her, but with
his Mecklenburg caution decided to bide his time. Since she
was extremely haughty in her manner and possessed no fortune of her own, he was a little wary of her. So the summer
passed, and fall came, and business prospered, and he still did
not know what to do with his life or the small fortune he had
already built up, largely in indigo.

He was a man who rarely committed himself. He saw the
world in harsh colors—riches, poverty; food in abundance,
starvation; life in one of the glittering capitals, or on an obscure farm. As he stood at his desk in St. Petersburg, sending
hurried messages to agents all over Europe, he was always
close to nervous prostration. Sometimes it occurred to him
that there must be easier ways to make a fortune.

Early in 1850 he received news that his younger brother
Ludwig had reached the California gold fields. For some time
Ludwig had acted as Heinrich's agent in Amsterdam. He
lacked his brother's spark of genius, but possessed an equal
amount of temperament. Headstrong, nervous, with a talent
for languages—he corresponded with his brother in French,
English, and Spanish—Ludwig also possessed a burning desire
to make a fortune. Once he thought of opening a shop and
asked Heinrich to lend him sufficient capital, and when Heinrich offered to lend him 500 talers he rejected the offer with
indignation—he had supposed his brother to be a little less
niggardly. On another occasion he wrote that he intended to
kill himself unless Heinrich brought him into the business
in St. Petersburg, and signed the letter with his own blood.

Heinrich answered at length, pointing out that it was not a small matter to introduce a partner into the complicated affairs of St. Petersburg, and he had no intention of providing for Ludwig during the long years of apprenticeship. It would take him four years to learn Russian sufficiently well to be able to use the language properly, and there was absolutely no guarantee that he had the makings of a businessman, and in particular he was lacking in the necessary driving ambition. "I myself have had to fend for myself for thirteen years without asking a penny from anyone," Heinrich wrote, and it was quite clear that he intended Ludwig to do the same.

One day in Rotterdam, while walking along the banks of a canal in a mood of desperation and anger, Ludwig on an impulse decided to sail to America. Once in New York, he became a teacher of French, and then entered business. When he had saved enough money he struck out for the California gold fields, where he became a banker, and progressed so well that he soon made a small fortune. In the infuriating manner of a younger brother who has always lived in his older brother's shadow, he wrote a long taunting letter, explaining the advantages of California over any other place on earth, and suggested that Heinrich would be well-advised to sell everything he had and come to Sacramento.

The letter must have stung Heinrich to the quick. He could hardly have failed to observe the innuendoes, the challenge, the implied superiority of the younger brother who spoke so casually of making a vast fortune in a few months. Heinrich knew that such fortunes were being made by men who did not possess a tenth of his discipline or his dedication to wealth—in a few weeks Ludwig had apparently accomplished more than Heinrich in all his years as a businessman. Ludwig's final jibe was the most painful: he promised to take full financial care of his sisters and hoped to send Heinrich "a fat remittance" in the fall.

The remittance never came. Instead, there came a clipping

from a Sacramento newspaper announcing that "on May 25, 1850, Mr. Louis Schliemann, of German nationality, lately of New York, died from typhus in Sacramento City, at the age of 25 years." The news reached Heinrich in the middle of August. Together with the clipping came a brief covering letter which said little more than that Ludwig had left a large estate.

For the rest of the year Heinrich continued to supervise his business, uncertain what was demanded of him. He had a profound horror of death, and his brother's death shook him. So that grief would not fall too heavily on his sisters, he wrote them a strange letter, saying that he had seen his brother lying dead in a dream. "I, who have not wept for twenty years, a man who is never shaken by things of this kind, found myself weeping continually for three days, and all because of a dream." A few days later he wrote that Ludwig had died in Sacramento and left a large fortune.

By the end of the year he had made his decision. Out of a sense of brotherly duty he would go to the gold fields and make a fortune, following in his brother's footsteps. He would start business with the money left by his brother, and grow rich far more rapidly than in St. Petersburg. He would build a proper gravestone for his brother's tomb, and remain in America for the rest of his life. Nothing held him: there were no attachments in St. Petersburg close enough to keep him there, though he still admired Ekaterina Lishin and sometimes it crossed his mind that he might return to Russia and marry her, but only if he possessed a fortune so large it would dazzle her. In all his life he had never stayed very long in one place. He had thought he would be able to strike deep roots in St. Petersburg, but it was all a mistake. He decided to begin his life again, and once more he was a wanderer on the face of the earth.

On December 10, 1850, he gave his last dinner to his friends, the merchants Melin and Lishin, and said farewell to St.

Petersburg. The Neva was frozen over, and an icy wind blew across St. Isaac's Square. His friends accompanied him to the post office, where the sleighs set out for the long journey to Germany; and as he passed the gleaming white Winter Palace, the Admiralty, and the equestrian statue of Peter the Great, he saluted them as though he never expected to see them again. At that moment he could not have guessed what misadventures would come to him before he stood by his brother's grave at the other end of the world.

As usual, he kept a diary. Very often during his travels the diary reads like an extended timetable. He notes the times of the trains, where he stayed, how much he paid for his room on the sixth floor, how much money he exchanged at the bank, and the names of the businessmen who met with his approval. One wonders what satisfaction he derived from those endless pages which announce the names of the railway stations he passed through. He wrote on December 15, 1850:

By 7 o'clock in the morning we breakfasted at Elbing, at 11 o'clock we passed Marienburg and at 4 o'clock P.M. we went at Dierschau on a large floating bridge over the Vistula. On the 18th Decbr. at noon we arrived at Woldenberg, where we got a bad dinner and at 1 o'clock we started by the railroad over Stargard to Stettin, where we arrived at 5½ o'clock P.M. At 6½ o'clock we started again by rail and arrived at 9½ o'clock at night in Berlin.

Mercifully, he does not always write like this. The diary of his journey to America, which he wrote in English, contains some of his best writing. It was not intended for publication, or to be read by any eyes but his own, but it was written carefully, and sometimes there is a direct, tortured honesty in his story which enables us to share his experiences. When the diary opens, he is still the businessman with a consuming interest in acquiring the fortune he had promised himself. He goes about his affairs pompously, doing the right things

at the right moment, very sure of himself. By the time the
diary ends, the raw edges of human experience have shaken
him to the depths: storm, tempest, and sickness have laid
him low. He has looked into the face of horror, and become
a man.

No one who turns to the opening pages of the diary is
likely to believe that he is about to read a human document
comparable with Conrad's *Heart of Darkness*.[2] Schliemann
arrived in Amsterdam, called on B. H. Schröder and Co.,
acquired letters of introduction to agencies and banks in
America, and conducted himself as a proper businessman.
On December 23, a Sunday, he arrived in London and took
up lodgings "with Mr. Keizar, the Royal Hotel, Blackfriars
Bridge." On Christmas Eve he discounted the bills on London
he had brought with him from St. Petersburg and sold his
gold to the Bank of England, and in the afternoon visited the
Crystal Palace, which delighted him—it was only one more
illustration of England's undoubted advances in industrializa-
tion. He attended services at Westminster Abbey on Christmas Day. It seems to have been a lonely Christmas. He notes
in his diary that on December 26 he saw "the celebrated
tragedian 'Macredy,' who played for the last time before retiring from the stage." This is a puzzling entry, for Macready
spent the entire Christmas holiday with his family at Sher-
borne and did not retire from the stage until two months
later, the gala performance at the Prince's Theatre occurring
in an atmosphere of wild excitement, with Dickens and Bul-
wer-Lytton in the audience, on February 26, 1851. On the
day following the imaginary performance he took the train to
Liverpool, staying as he always did in the huge square Adelphi
Hotel, which must have reminded him of the heavy-set hotels
of Germany. Then he arranged for his passage to New York,
paid £35 for passage, sauntered around Liverpool, and went

2. *Heart of Darkness:* novel by Joseph Conrad, British writer (1857-1924).

to bed. He did not know it, but very soon the mask of the imperturbable businessman—that mask which he liked most to show the world—would be torn to shreds.

The S.S. *Atlantic,* 3,000 tons, on which he sailed for New York the following day, was one of the fastest ocean-going steamers of the time. They were eight days out from Liverpool when they struck a storm. A huge wave smashed the port wheel with such force that the main shaft broke, and the ship was thrown to the mercy of the waves. Both engines were disabled. They were in mid-Atlantic, 1,800 miles from Liverpool and 1,400 miles from New York. With a strong westerly gale blowing, the captain decided to make for the American coast, and put up a mainsail and maintopsail, hoping to be blown across the ocean. Schliemann noted in his diary that "the sails looked like handkerchiefs" and none of the passengers approved of the captain's desire to make his way against the prevailing winds—it would be better to return to England. There were long debates. It was pointed out to the captain that the ship would almost certainly capsize if he continued to fight against the storm: it would be much safer if he turned round and sailed to the nearest port. In the excitement of the storm seasickness miraculously stopped, and Schliemann discovered to his surprise that he was in good heart, and even a little amused by the behavior of the famous ocean-going steamer which sailed home under her pathetic sails.

Sixteen days later the ship put in at Queenstown, and soon Schliemann was making his way back to Liverpool by way of Dublin, where he heard that there was some outstanding business in Amsterdam to be attended to. He hurried off, but he was back again in Liverpool on February 1, ready to sail to New York on the S.S. *Africa.* This time the journey was uneventful.

He liked New York—"a very regularly built, nice, clean town with many elegant and even colossal buildings"—

though he felt it did not compare with the European capitals. He found little to admire in New York women, and noted in his diary that "at the age of 22 they look just as old and worn out as they are beautiful and symmetrical at 16 and 18." He complained of their tendency to be amusing and frivolous. Also, he disliked the railroads, and commented sternly after a trip to Philadelphia: "The American railroads are merely laid out with the design to make money, and not the least notice is taken as to convenience and accommodations for passengers." Later he invested huge sums in American railroads.

In Washington he called on President Fillmore. "I made my introduction by stating my great desire to see this beautiful country of the West," he wrote in his journal, "and to make the acquaintance of the great men who govern it." Soon after attending a *soirée*[3] at the White House, he hurried off by ship to the Isthmus of Panama, at that time the most direct route to the Far West. There was no Panama Railroad. Prospectors journeyed by mule train across the Isthmus, where yellow fever was prevalent and there were bandits in the surrounding jungles. Schliemann went armed with a revolver and a long dagger. He saw alligators in the Chagres River and butterflies as large as pigeons. It was the first time he had ever set foot in the tropics, and he paid the tribute of his grudging admiration to the natives:

The Isthmus of Panama is an immense Eden in which the descendants of Adam and Eve seem to have retained the manners and customs of their primitive forefathers; for they go quite naked, and live upon the fruit which the splendid tropical vegetation puts around them in magnificent abundance. Their chief characteristic is a horrible laziness, which does not permit them to occupy themselves with anything; they cannot find themselves happier than lying in their hammocks and eating and drinking. They are very fantastic.

3. *Soirée:* party (French).

Fantastic or not, he feared them—and not only for their laziness. The bones of many prospectors, killed by these Indians, littered the mule trail. He was no happier when he reached Panama City and discovered that the Spanish inhabitants suffered from the same laziness, and in addition possessed the vices he attributed to the young women of New York. "The characteristic of the Spaniard in this country," he wrote sententiously, "is a great inclination for the frivolous and amusing, a great laziness, and a great lightness of character." It did not occur to him that in a tropical climate vast ambitions are sometimes at the mercy of the weather.

But though he detested everything in Panama, he was curiously content. The journey was nearly over, and the prospect of acquiring gold in California pleased him. Because he had to wait several days for a ship, he amused himself by visiting the old city of Panama, destroyed by Morgan and his pirates and now half overgrown with jungle. It was the first time he had paid any attention to ruins since leaving Ankershagen, and though he showed no particular excitement—what puzzled him most of all was how the roots of trees became embedded in the ancient walls—this visit to the old city must be accounted his first archeological exploration. He noted that the guide was stupid, and seemed to know nothing at all about the ruins, and the whole journey was a waste of time.

He sailed for California on March 15, 1851, on the S.S. *Oregon*, and hated every moment of the journey. He complained bitterly about the food: no ice, no fresh meat, only salt pork and corned beef. He liked to take his baths in seawater, but the ship's servants were curiously uncooperative. A week after leaving Panama the ship put in at Acapulco, and his intense distrust of the Spaniards was exchanged for a still more intense distrust of the Mexicans—they were all false, ignorant and arrogant, and Acapulco itself was nothing but a huddle of huts "like an African village." Nor did he have anything good to say about the port of San Diego, which he dismissed as a small village with a few wooden houses around a bay thick with yellow seaweed. Hating the earth and his fellow passengers, he took to reading about astronomy and spent long hours at night gazing at the stars. He might have exploded altogether with ill temper if they had not arrived quickly at the Golden Gate. San Francisco delighted him, but he had no time to waste. He was off immediately to Sacramento, in search of his brother's grave.

Sacramento was still in its infancy, and as he went about that strange clapboard town which owed its existence to the neighboring gold fields, he had the same feeling which came to him with surprising force when he visited St. Petersburg for the first time: here was undreamed-of wealth for the asking. But he noted, too, that the number of graves in the cemetery exceeded the total population of the town. He found his brother's grave. There was no marker, and so he gave $50 to a local undertaker for "a beautiful marble tombstone." He asked about the fortune his brother had left, and learned that Ludwig's partner had absconded with it. He made some inquiries about whether the police would be able to trace the partner, but came to the conclusion that nothing would be gained by an attempt to pursue him. The fortune had vanished into thin air.

When Ludwig arrived in Sacramento in July, 1849, the whole town consisted of exactly one frame building and a few huts. In two years it had mushroomed into a city of 16,000 inhabitants, and was likely to continue expanding at the same pace. Schliemann liked the town, and in his customary fashion set about exploring its potentialities by making trips into the surrounding areas. He visited Sutterville and the Yuba River gold fields and Nevada City, which he described as "a small and extremely nasty place in the midst of a pine forest." He was always searching for people who shared his interest in languages, and he was delighted on a journey through the Sonoma Valley to encounter a certain Professor Reeger, who

spoke English, French, German, Italian, Portuguese, and
Dutch; and it pleased him to sit up half the night with a
stranger who could slip from one language to another with
his own ease.

Though Sacramento pleased and intoxicated him, he was
still undecided about his future. He lent a little money on
short-term mortgages, but otherwise showed no particular
desire to take root there. He had often thought of making a
prolonged journey to the Far East, and it occurred to him
during moments of weakness that he might return to Germany
by way of the Pacific, taking a boat from San Francisco and
visiting all the ports of China, India, and Egypt, and then
taking a train through Italy. But these moments of weakness
passed, and as the excitement of being in a strange country
wore away, he began to think seriously once more of the
fortune which was only waiting for him to gather in his
hands. So April and May passed in a preliminary reconnais-
sance, and June found him once more in San Francisco in
conferences with the agents of Messrs. Rothschild and other
businessmen, while he prepared to set himself up as a buyer of
gold dust, with headquarters at the corner of J and Front
Streets in Sacramento.

He was attending these conferences on June 4, 1851, and
had retired to his hotel room after an exhausting day, when
the whole city burst into flame. That was the night of the
famous San Francisco fire, and Schliemann in his downtown
hotel was caught in the middle of it. Awakened by the clang-
ing of fire bells, he dressed hurriedly and ran out into the
street. A gale was blowing and fanning the flames. For a few
moments he watched the houses all round him melting in the
flames, and then he found himself hurrying up Telegraph
Hill. "The roaring of the storm, the cracking of the gunpowder, the cracking of the falling stone walls, the cries of
the people and the wonderful spectacle of an immense city
burning in the dark night all joined to make this catastrophe

awful in the extreme." So he wrote the next day, the flames still dazzling his eyes. There was a rumor that foreign incendiaries were responsible for the conflagration, and Schliemann reports casually that many foreigners, especially Frenchmen, were murdered by the people of San Francisco on suspicion of setting the fire. He was amazed by the coolness of the Americans who went about rebuilding their city while the ashes were still hot and the flames were still burning. He spent the whole night on Telegraph Hill, and in the morning set out for Sacramento.

Because he was afraid of fire, he leased an office in the only fireproof stone-and-iron building in Sacramento, and because he was afraid of theft he bought a huge iron safe and stood over it from six in the morning to ten at night, working himself and his two assistants, one Spanish, the other American, to the bone. Prospectors were flocking to California from all over the world, and so in a single day he would find himself speaking all the eight languages he knew. There were some languages he did not know, including the Kanaka spoken by the natives of the Sandwich Islands who had mysteriously appeared in Sacramento. During his rare moments of leisure he inspected the Californian Indians. They were a small copper-red people, extremely dirty, and suffered from disease. "They lived," he said, "like ants in their heaps of earth."

He had dreamed of a fortune, and now within a few months a fortune was within his grasp. There were days when 180 pounds weight of gold passed through his hands. His wealth increased from week to week, until he became almost afraid of it, and like his assistants he went about armed with a Colt revolver. He wrote later that he felt no particular fear of the rascals he met in the course of business: he could always outwit them. But he repeats himself too much, and boasts a little too often of his expertness: there were days when he seems to have lived in mortal terror of the gold which came so easily into his hands. And sometimes he remembered that he might die of typhus, like his brother, and there would be nothing to show for those long hours spent at his desk.

He had reason to be afraid, for in October he was lying on his back, vomiting and raving like a madman, his body covered with yellow spots, while the doctor fed him with quinine and calomel, which were the usual medicines against yellow fever. In his absence his clerks carried on the business, thieving to their hearts' content. When he returned to his desk the fear came back again. In a revealing letter to a friend in San Francisco he described the misery and loneliness which goes with acquiring a fortune:

I had a *very hard time* here during the week, and never a slave worked harder than I did.

But that is all nothing to the danger of sleeping the night alone with so immense accounts of gold in cash. I always spend the night in a feverish horror and loaded pistols in *both* hands. The noise of a mouse or a rat struck me with terror;—I could eat only once a day viz: at 6½ at night, and other wants of nature I was forced to forget entirely. In one word: it was a most awful time.

He had hardly recovered from one bout of fever when he caught the fever again. In January 1852 he went to recuperate in the Santa Clara Valley, a sick man, drained of energy, worried beyond measure because his doctor had told him he had the same constitution as his brother and was likely to die in the same way. Yet he knew his strength, and possessed a driving compulsion to acquire a fortune before he left Sacramento, and he was back again at his desk at the beginning of February. Once more he rose at five in the morning, took his place behind his desk, weighed gold dust, wrote out banker's drafts and talked to prospectors in eight languages—a stiff, unsmiling, punctilious man, with a curiously shrill voice and the air of a scholar resolved to solve the mystery of wealth and harness it to his own purposes, though he was still unsure what these purposes were. He called himself an American, spoke of "our gold fields" and "our cemetery," and sometimes thought of settling in America for the rest of his life. More often he found himself dreaming about a farm in Germany, though he must have known he possessed no skill as a farmer. He had put Russia behind him. Sitting over his horde of gold, he lived a life of quiet desperation, at odds with himself, certain of only one thing: he must make his fortune, or perish.

He very nearly perished at the end of March, when the fever came again and once more his body was covered with yellow spots. He had given his clerks instructions—as soon as he showed himself incompetent to carry on his business, they were to wrap him in a blanket and send him by steamer to San Francisco. Seven days later, on April 7, he had made his resolution. Miraculously recovered, he visited the Rothschild bank in San Francisco and arranged for the transfer of his assets and the liquidation of his business. He had made his fortune. Others had made larger fortunes from the California gold mines, but few had made them so quickly, or at so little risk. In the course of nine months he had amassed $400,000. He was not in the least staggered by his staggering good fortune. It seemed to him that this was no more than his due reward, earned by remorseless attention to detail and a consuming passion for hard work. He was to learn during the following weeks that the gods sometimes punish those to whom they have shown excessive favors.

He admired the Americans, but found them curiously uncouth, their manners reprehensible, and their women unattractive. Accordingly, he now decided to spend the rest of his life among the Russians, whose social graces he respected and whose women showed the proper seriousness he demanded. His fortune would enable him to lead a life of baronial magnificence in Moscow or St. Petersburg. He decided to return to Russia in style, paying $600 for a stateroom in the steamer taking him from San Francisco to Panama. He would cross the Isthmus, take a ship to New York, and then make his way in a leisurely fashion to Russia.

The first warning from the gods came in the Gulf of Tehuantepec, seven days out from San Francisco. The ship was caught in a typhoon, and nearly foundered. The second warning came in Panama City, when an attempt was made to steal his luggage—he sat over it grimly with a Colt revolver in one hand and a dagger in the other. A few miles of the Panama Railroad had been laid, but thereafter the journey across the Isthmus was along the mule trail.

He had chosen the worst season of the year for his journey. It rained continually. They were abandoned by their guides. They had no food, and were forced to live on iguana lizards, which they ate raw. They were attacked by scorpions and rattlesnakes. It was a landscape of nightmare and terror. He suffered excruciating pain from a wound in his leg, which became gangrenous. There were no bandages, no medicines. For fourteen days they pushed forward along the forest trail, their clothes sticking to their skins, in danger of attack from the Indians, without maps, without any reason to believe they would ever reach Colon. They shot monkeys, skinned them, and ate the flesh, and quarreled violently among themselves. Some died of dysentery, others of yellow fever, and their bodies were left beside the trail for the jungle animals to feed on. And still the rain came down, a bitter cold rain which sucked their energy and gave them the appearance of drowned men wandering at the bottom of the sea.

For Schliemann the most terrible thing of all was that he trusted no one and therefore could not afford to sleep. With his dagger and revolver he stood guard continually over his luggage: the gold bars, the drafts on Rothschild, the letters of introduction to merchant princes all over Europe. He was a man who rarely wrote vividly of his own emotions, but sometimes emotion comes through. So it was when he described the storm off Texel, and so it is again in a short paragraph he permitted himself when describing the agonies of the journey across the Isthmus:

We became so familiarized with death that it lost for us all its terror, that we began to like it and to look upon it as a lingering of our sufferings. Thus came that we laughed and amused ourselves at the convulsions of the dying and that crimes were perpetrated among us; *crimes so terrible!* that now at a later date I cannot think of it without cold and trembling horror.

He never revealed what crimes were committed, or whether he himself committed them. In later years, whenever he wrote about his life, he always passed quickly over the years he spent in America, and he never again referred to his journey across the Isthmus of Panama. He did everything he could to forget those terrible fourteen days, and became more merciless and demanding of himself and of others. His sisters had always complained of his coldness, the air of indifference which he showed to the world; now he was to become colder, harder, sterner, and more than ever in love with wealth. In a strange way he was becoming more and more like the Greek heroes who slumbered in the depths of his imagination, for they too had laughed and amused themselves at the convulsions of the dying, and like him had pursued wealth avidly, with barbaric abandonment.

So he made his way back to Europe, pausing only long enough in New York to have his wound bandaged, and in London to have the gangrene burned out with *lapis infernalis*, and then he was back in Mecklenburg for a few weeks, renewing old acquaintances and flaunting his wealth, giving expensive presents to his uncle, his father, and his sisters. He had abandoned the idea of settling down on a farm. He would have a mansion of his own, or at least a large apartment, and marry a Russian girl of good family, and perhaps in time he would be elevated to the Russian nobility. He was thirty; he had made his fortune; and he feared no one. As he rode back in the sleigh to St. Petersburg, he counted himself the most fortunate man in the world. He had only to lift his finger, and everything he had ever dreamed of during his poverty-stricken days in Fürstenburg and Amsterdam—books, wine, women, servants, houses—would all be given to him in double measure. He did not know, and could not guess, that for seventeen long years his wealth was to taste like ashes in his mouth.

. . . 4   THE MERCHANT PRINCE

OUTWARDLY he was a man of the world, the very type of the successful business executive, with his gold-rimmed spectacles and long coat with an astrakhan collar. He wore his mustache *à la Tartare,* carried an ebony cane, and possessed his own carriage. His vast apartment on one of the best streets of St. Petersburg consisted of two salons, seven bedrooms, five other rooms, a kitchen, stables, cellars, and a coach house. The best available wines were in the cellars and three of the most expensive horses were in the coach house. Princes and merchants clamored for invitations to the house of the adventurous businessman who was believed to have made a vast fortune in the California gold fields. He had an air of authority. He was cultivated and well-mannered. He spent money lavishly—had he not spent a thousand rubles to furnish a single guest room? In St. Petersburg he was regarded as the most fortunate of men, the most desirable of acquaintances, a man in line to become president of the Chamber of Commerce.

The inward man, however, bore very little resemblance to the image he showed to the world. Fires blazed in him, and passion drove him almost insane. Above all he wanted a wife and children, and with all the women in Russia to choose from, he had to choose a cold virago who married him only for his money, taunted him continually, and lived out her life as though she were waiting for him to die so that she could inherit his fortune. Again and again in letters to his father and sisters he complains in a tone of bewilderment against the horror of being married to a woman who despised him.

Perhaps it was unavoidable. Perhaps he was so full of his

wealth that no woman would have married him on his own merits. Ekaterina Lishin had refused him before, when he was already a wealthy merchant. Now that he was wealthy beyond the dreams of avarice, she accepted him. He called on her the day after he reached St. Petersburg and continued to call on her during the following weeks. He told himself he was in love with her, and would always love her. She possessed all the virtues: she was good, kind, simple, attentive. She held herself well, and was equally at home in her own salon and at the receptions given by wealthy merchants. He adored her, and promised to do everything to make her happy. On the day of his marriage, October 12, 1852, he wrote to his family:

Today I became the happy husband of Catherine Lyschin, who is a Russian lady of great accomplishment of body and mind. My wife is a very good, simple, clever and sensible girl, and I love and respect her more with every passing day. Because I am so happily married, I have decided to make St. Petersburg my home for the rest of my life.

No one ever entered upon a marriage with such high hopes, or regretted them so quickly. Within a few weeks he was writing to his sisters that his marriage was a mistake and he was being driven to the verge of madness. He had hoped for warmth from his wife, but received only implacable coldness. "There are some phlegmatic people," he wrote, "whose passions glow with a gentle, almost imperceptible flame, but in me passion becomes a consuming fire when obstacles prevent me from obtaining the objects of my desire. I know that intense desire and hopeless passion can drive a man to madness. . . ."

He was so shocked that he wrote a series of confidential letters to his friends, begging for advice and consolation. Little consolation was forthcoming. A friend in Amsterdam urged him to remember that even if Ekaterina had married him without love, at least by the very fact of marrying him she had sacrificed herself for him. She was perhaps not wholly bad. Probably she was only terrified by his parsimony, and if he was more generous to her, she might return his affections in time. His sisters wrote in the same strain, pointing out without malice that his own forbidding coldness might be the cause of the coldness in his wife. He must learn to be human, to be warm, to give himself to others. But there was no school where he could learn the art of being human, and so he plunged voraciously into the world of business. In this world he was master, and knew exactly how to behave and what was expected of him.

By instinct he was a gambler. Returning to Russia he put his entire fortune into indigo, and he controlled the market. His headquarters were in St. Petersburg, but a few weeks after his marriage he established a branch office in Moscow, placing his friend Alexei Matveiev in charge of it. He still worked twelve and sometimes fourteen hours a day. He saw little of his wife, preferring to stay in his office or to travel around Russia rather than face her temper. He showed no interest in the arts. Work was his opium: he drugged himself steadily, compulsively, and without any enjoyment except the enjoyment which came to him when he sent copies of the *Kronstadt Shipping Journal* to his father. The *Journal* gave the names of incoming and outgoing vessels, the owners and consignees, and likely as not there would be a long list of vessels filled with indigo and consigned to the firm of H. Schliemann and Co. There were thirty-three incoming vessels and three outgoing vessels shown against his name in the report for 1853, but this was only part of the story. Thousands of freight wagons were bringing consignments to him from Königsberg and Memel. He wrote to his father that his cash turnover amounted to a million silver rubles a month, and there was no end to it—fortune piled on fortune, gold on gold, and he was still no nearer the happiness he yearned for. And just as previously he had dreamed of ending his days on a farm in Mecklenburg, so now there would come to him the thought of returning to America and buying a farm there. "I believe I would enjoy country life," he wrote to a friend in America, "and I am sure I would find plenty to occupy me in the cultivation and development of my land."

He had none of the instincts of a farmer, who waits patiently for the seed to flower. He was always in a hurry, always working at a breath-taking pace, angry if there were any moments in the day when he was not actively concerned with business. About this time he wrote a revealing letter to his father, saying: "I cannot follow your well-meant advice to retire from business and devote myself to a quiet life. I was so accustomed to living a life of intense activity that inactivity, even under the most favorable circumstances, would drive me into an insane asylum." He was close to madness, and knew it, a strange sallow-featured high-strung genius of finance who sometimes broke into screams of rage and whose letters to his agents all over the world were often written in tones of demoniac fury, because his orders were not instantly obeyed. The dream of an escape to America pursued him during the early years of his marriage.

But for a man to dream of America while living in Russia in the middle years of the last century was to invite disaster. America was as legendary as Atlantis, a place of perfect freedom, where men never suffered from the infuriating attentions of the bureaucracy. In *Crime and Punishment* Dostoevsky tells the story of Svidrigailov, who had always dreamed of going to America. We see Svidrigailov wandering through the dirty yellow fog of St. Petersburg on a winter day, making his way along the wooden pavements covered with slippery mud. Suddenly through the fog there looms up a strange little man muffled in a gray soldier's cloak, with a brass Achilles helmet, evidently the guard outside one of the great official buildings. Svidrigailov and Achilles glare at each other.

"You've got no business to be here," says Achilles.

"Well, good morning to you—that's true," says Svidrigailov.

"Then explain yourself."

"I'm going away."

"Where to?"

"To America."

"To America, eh?"

Svidrigailov draws out his revolver and cocks it. Achilles
raises his eyebrows.

"You mustn't do things like that here," Achilles says.
"What sort of joke are you playing?"

"It's all right—"

"I assure you it is not all right!"

"Oh, there's no harm done," Svidrigailov says. "This is
just as good a place as any other. If they ask you any questions,
tell them I was going to America."

Svidrigailov puts the revolver to his right temple.

"You shouldn't do it," Achilles protests. "This isn't the
right place at all."

Then Svidrigailov pulls the trigger.

Such was Dostoevsky's story written only a few years
later, and though Schliemann showed no interest in Russian
literature or the strange upheavals in the spiritual atmosphere
of Russia, he was inescapably involved in the Russian temper,
and perhaps all the more involved because he believed himself
so detached. Like the Russians he felt the terrible yearning
for the freedom of America, which he had known for a few
months in California, and like them he possessed a revulsion
from freedom and contempt for American ways. Those
dreams of America, which enter so casually in his letters, had
the stuff of tragedy in them.

Meanwhile business held him. Half-mad with anxiety, hating his wife, at odds with his agents, he found security in
attending to his ledgers. The richer he became, the less use
he had for his riches. Yet business was the air he breathed,
and his Pole Star. Whatever he looked upon must be turned

to profit—there was no other law. At rare intervals he permitted himself the solace of writing letters to his father and sisters, presenting them with moral maxims and encouraging them to live in the utmost sobriety. His letters must have set their teeth on edge, but they always thanked him for the small sums of money he sent. He wrote to his father:

By today's post I have forwarded instructions for 500 talers to be credited to your account. I have high hopes that you will use this sum in establishing yourself at your new address in Danzig in the manner befitting the father of Heinrich Schliemann.

In placing this sum at your disposal I must however insist that in future you keep a respectable manservant and a respectable maid, while preserving a decent standard of cleanliness in your house. I expect your plates, dishes, cups, knives and forks to be shining and clean, and the floorboards should be scrubbed three times a week, and you will have food on your table befitting a person of your station in life.

The 500 talers he sent his father were a pittance compared with the money he was making. Wherever he turned, luck pursued him. He heard that the Czar was about to issue a new legal code, and it occurred to him immediately that the code would be printed on paper of fine texture and distributed in thousands of copies. Accordingly, he made a corner in the best available paper, offered to sell it to the government, and his offer was accepted. He branched off in a hundred different directions, and always made money.

Occasionally there were moments of tension. In the fall of 1854 he was returning to Russia after attending the indigo auctions in Amsterdam. The Crimean War[1] had broken out. The Russian ports were being blockaded, and all merchandise intended for St. Petersburg had to be shipped through Königsberg and Memel, then forwarded overland. Hundreds of chests of indigo and huge quantities of other goods had been shipped by his Amsterdam agent to Memel. He arrived at

1. *Crimean War:* war between Britain and Russia for control of Crimean Peninsula.

Königsberg on October 3, and as usual put up at a hotel near the Green Gate. The next morning he looked out of the window, and saw, as he had seen many times before, the words written in large gold letters on the gate-tower:

Vultus fortunae variatur imagine lunae:
Crescit, decrescit, constans persistere nescit.

The face of fortune varies as the image of the moon,
Waxes and wanes, and knows not how to remain constant.

For some reason the words with their ominous warning threw him into a panic. Years before he had mentioned this strange inscription to his father, and sometimes his father had quoted them back at him. This time, however, the words came to him with surprising force. He was sure something terrible had happened. He rode off to Tilsit, and then to Memel, and learned on the stagecoach that large areas of Memel had burned to the ground during the night. Smoke drifted over the city, and the ruined warehouses were still smoldering when he arrived. Almost insane at the thought of losing those hundreds of chests of indigo, convinced that he was ruined, he sought out his agent, who simply pointed at the smoking ruins and shrugged his shoulders.

Schliemann panicked easily. Whenever he suffered losses, he thought he was on the verge of bankruptcy. He told himself that he would have to start again from the beginning, and in his confused state of mind began to make plans: he would write to the Schröders and beg them for credit, sell his houses and estates, live at the bare minimum of subsistence. He had done all this before, and triumphed. He told himself he had lost everything, and would return immediately to St. Petersburg and attempt to put his affairs in order. All that day he trembled in an agony of hysterical misery, too sick at heart to think of anything else except his loss.

He was moaning about his loss to the people standing around the stagecoach that evening, as he was about to continue the journey to St. Petersburg, when someone tapped him on the shoulder. The stranger introduced himself as the chief clerk of Meyer & Co., Schliemann's agents in Memel, and said none of his chests of indigo had been lost. The warehouses were full when the ships put in at Memel, and some wooden storehouses had been hastily erected at a distance from them. The flames had not touched the storehouses. Schliemann was so overwhelmed by his good fortune that he remained speechless for some minutes. Once again, so it seemed to him, divine providence had saved him when he was in desperate straits. The only one saved from the general ruin, he saw the finger of God pointing at him and he exulted like a child.

There was no need to hurry on to St. Petersburg. Instead, he stayed at Memel and superintended the sale of his goods at a vast profit, turning his money over again and again, and closing deals on terms which sometimes astounded him. He had the Midas touch, and no objection to playing the part of a war profiteer—he sold indigo and other dyes, but he also embarked on trade in saltpeter, sulphur, and lead, to be used for gunpowder and bullets. He had made one fortune in the California gold fields, and he made another in the Crimean War. By the end of 1855 he was worth $1,000,000.

In other respects, too, fortune smiled on him. For the first time he was enjoying happy relations at home. His greatly increased wealth made Ekaterina more amenable and more loving, and that year she presented him with a child, who was called Sergey. For a few brief months he was overwhelmed with gratitude toward his wife. He bought an estate near the summer residence of the Czar at Peterhof, gave his wife jewelry, and promised to let her have a holiday in the south of France. At odd moments during 1854 he had learned Polish and Swedish. This *annus mirabilis*,[2] which gave him a second fortune and a son, was to be crowned with one further gift—the gift of the Greek language, which he had

2. *Annus mirabilis:* marvelous year (Latin).

always hesitated to learn because he was afraid he would fall completely under its spell.

Ever since he had heard the drunken miller reciting a hundred lines of Homer in the grocer's shop at Fürstenberg, he had told himself he would learn Greek. He had suffered agonies of misery when he was forced to leave the Gymnasium at Neu Strelitz just when he was about to enter the Greek class. Over the years he had acquired a library of books concerned with Homer and the Greek heroes in a multitude of languages, but he deliberately avoided books written in Greek for fear that he would set everything aside until he could recite whole books of Homer by heart. Now at last he could afford to permit himself this supreme luxury. But characteristically he did not allow Greek to interfere overmuch with his business.

For six days a week he worked at his office, but on Sundays he shut himself up in his study, sometimes alone, sometimes with a teacher, and after six Sundays of prodigious mental activity he was able to compose long, complex sentences in ancient Greek, and soon he was writing in modern Greek as well. The fountain burst forth. He was overwhelmed by the beauty and clarity of this language, which was even more glorious than he had anticipated. He was so delighted that he wrote to his former teacher at Neu Strelitz, enclosing a résumé of his whole life in the language spoken by Homer, insisting that even in his darkest moments he had been "uplifted by holy hexameters and the music of Sophocles." "I am intoxicated by this language," he wrote. "I must go to Greece, and live there! It surprises me that a language can be so noble! I do not know what others think, but it seems to me there must be a great future for Greece, and the day cannot be far distant when the Hellenic flag will fly over Sancta Sophia![3] And what amazes me more than anything else is that the Greeks, after three centuries of

3. *Sancta Sophia:* church in Istanbul, Turkey (then Constantinople).

Turkish domination, still preserve their national language intact."

As always, his enthusiasms ran wild. Not content with reading Sophocles in the original, he must translate Sophocles into modern Greek. He must read everything that Plato wrote, every speech spoken by Demosthenes. He filled notebook after notebook with lists of words, sentences, conversations with himself, and long monologues. At night in an inn in Nizhni Novgorod, he sat down and described in classical Greek the impression produced upon him by the famous fair. Then he went on to unburden his soul, writing a list of his own faults: his nervousness, his absurd addiction to money, the ruthlessness which he was the first to recognize, his strange desire to escape—to Mecklenburg, to America, even to the equatorial regions, where perhaps he might become like the natives who cared nothing for money, so long as there were bananas and oranges growing on the trees. All his most secret thoughts were written in Greek, a language so beautiful that he believed to the end of his life that it was spoken by the gods. But instead of calming his spirit, the Greek language only made him more wildly excited. He lived for those Sundays and those other days when, to escape from his wife, he traveled over Russia, from one fair to another, always with a traveling case filled with Greek books.

These Greek notes, written in thirty-five notebooks over a period of two years, contain his most revealing comments on himself. Here the stern moralist gives way to the Rabelaisian[4] commentator, who was not above taking a pretty woman on his knee when he was traveling by stagecoach, or exchanging risqué stories with other businessmen at the great summer fair at Nizhni Novgorod, which he attended year after year. In St. Petersburg he was the man of property, sharp-tongued, with a shrill voice and a consuming ambition to make

4. *Rabelaisian:* broadly humorous, as in the writings of Rabelais (1490-1553).

more and more money. At Nizhni Novgorod he became human again, got drunk and behaved like all the other merchants who kicked over the traces at the fair.

Increasingly, as time passed, he saw the world through Greek eyes. He became a fanatic champion of Greek claims to Constantinople, an attitude not calculated to endear him to the Russians, who also claimed Constantinople. For some months he searched for a Russian-speaking Greek, saying that nothing would please him more than to have a Greek in his employ. He found a tutor named Theokletos Vimpos, a priest of the Greek Orthodox Church who was studying in St. Petersburg. Vimpos was a warm friendly man who spoke Greek with the purest of Athenian accents. The tutor was one of the few who could penetrate Schliemann's reserve, and soon the iron-hard casing began to crack. With the help of Vimpos, and a few other scholars who attended the Sunday *soirées* given in the vast apartment, he began to abandon the idea of escaping to some remote part of the world. He told himself he was inescapably European, and as soon as possible he would abandon his business and devote himself to a life of scholarship.

So the weeks passed, while he fought within himself the war of his own opposing natures. He was like a weathercock: one moment he was telling himself he dared not leave his business, the next he was swearing by the almighty gods of Greece that his life was senseless and miserable, and he was the living example of a vile miser—no, it would be best altogether to slip out of St. Petersburg and study in one of the great university towns in Germany. But would he be accepted there? He possessed no degrees, no formal training. Then where? At such moments of doubt and indecision, he would find himself backsliding again—he would have a farm and devote the remainder of his life to scientific pursuits. In July 1856 he wrote to a friend that he was searching for a farm along the Rhine, but only a few weeks before he had

written to another friend that he was determined to see the
world, because he had seen so little of it, and he was beginning to think that he might make a career for himself as a
writer.

The truth was that he did not know his own mind, or
what he wanted, or what direction to pursue. In spite of
some losses and a few bad debts he had made a second fortune
out of the war, and he was aware of a mounting sense of
guilt. He wrote in his Greek notebooks: "I am, I know, mean
and avaricious. I shall have to give up being so mercenary. All
through the war I thought of nothing but money." This was
true, but he could hardly remember a time when he was not
thinking of money. He hated himself, and approved of himself, and went about his business, hoping that the solution
would come from somewhere outside himself, and none came,
and so he fed his own misery.

He made plans to retire in 1857, but the financial panic
which settled over Europe during the closing months of the
year caught him just at the moment when he was about to
abandon his business. He had, as usual, overextended himself.
There were bills outstanding on London, Paris, Hamburg, and
Amsterdam totaling 3,000,000 talers. Acting for himself, all
his capital invested in trade, he saw himself ruined again.
Foreign firms went bankrupt. His hair turned gray, and he
was almost out of his wits with worry, trying to keep afloat.
By juggling figures, by taking enormous risks, by superintending every aspect of his business, even the least important, he
succeeded in keeping his business going. Actually, he had
never been in any great danger. Yet the horror of that winter
affected him deeply, and for months afterward hot tears
would spring to his eyes as he remembered how he had kept
awake through the long nights, pitting his financial skill
against the skill of European bankers.

By the spring of 1858, when he realized that there was no
longer any need for panic, with his fortune as secure as ever,

he had decided the time had come to visit Greece. His relations with his wife had never been worse: they stared at one another coldly across the dining table and hardly exchanged ten words in a week. He had however begotten another child. When summer came, he decided he could bear her presence no longer and set out alone on a long journey of exploration through all the countries he had wanted to see, promising himself he would pay special attention to Athens and Ithaca, the island of Odysseus. Not Troy, but Mount Aetios on Ithaca, where Odysseus kept his palace, was the object of his dreams, perhaps because he saw himself as a wanderer like his hero, searching for a home.

First he went to Sweden and Denmark, having learned Swedish and Danish in 1854 for business purposes, but he stayed in these countries only a few days—they had little to teach him. Then he paid a brief visit to his father in Germany, and he was off to Italy. He was a little afraid of going straight to Greece, and decided upon delaying tactics. He would see what Egypt had to offer him before throwing himself with heart and soul upon the land which entranced him more than any other. As an ordinary tourist he sailed down the Nile on a *dahabiyeh*[5] as far as the Second Cataract, learning Arabic during the journey. From Cairo he went by caravan to Jerusalem by way of the rose-red rock city of Petra, but he found little to interest him in Jerusalem, and soon by way of Smyrna and the islands of the Cyclades he was making his way to Athens. In later years he liked to remember that at some period during this journey he disguised himself as a bedouin and penetrated the holy city of Mecca. But he makes no mention of the visit to Mecca in his voluminous diaries, and seems to have imagined the entire journey.

But he did not imagine Athens. He put up at the best

5. *Dahabiyeh:* river boat.

hotel, climbed the Acropolis, and was supremely content. Athens was everything he had hoped for. That bright and glittering city possessed the power to hold his ghosts at bay. Through letters of introduction from Theokletos Vimpos he was able to meet Greek scholars, who complimented him on his perfect pronunciation and listened approvingly when he explained that he intended to spend some months on the island of Ithaca and perhaps compose a book on it. They offered him more letters of introduction.

He was about to leave for the island when he received a telegram from St. Petersburg announcing that he was being sued in the High Court by a businessman who had failed during the crisis of 1857, but instead of paying the sums due to Schliemann had decided to sue on the grounds that he had been defrauded. Schliemann was suffering from a fever. He sent telegrams to St. Petersburg asking whether the suit could be postponed, but the court permitted no delay. His career as an amateur archeologist came to an abrupt end as he hurried back to St. Petersburg, exchanging Greece for the miseries of an intolerable marriage and a court trial. For five more years he was to remain in Russia, safeguarding his fortune.

He won the trial; he won another child from Ekaterina; he won a third fortune; and he lost himself. He lost, too, his interest in languages, and Greece frightened him. To reach Athens he had made a long roundabout tour, as though not daring to confront the ultimate vision until he had steeled himself to the enchantments of other countries and other landscapes. Now, when he spoke about journeying abroad, he never mentioned Greece—he would go to China or South America. For nearly ten years the palace of Odysseus slept.

He was the businessman again, proud, imperious, sending off scathing messages to his agents, who bore with him only because he paid promptly and was regarded as one of the greatest importers in the world. In a delirium of high finance, he began to extend himself still further. Olive oil and indigo had been his staples; now he embarked on cotton and tea on a large scale. He quarreled with everyone. He quarreled with Ekaterina on the upbringing and education of his children. Sergey was turning into a bright boy, the apple of his father's eye. The second and third children were girls. Natalya was born in 1858, and Nadezhda—the word means "hope"—was born three years later, the year when he made his most far-reaching deals. His business prospered. In 1862-63, in spite of insurrections in Poland which threw trading in Russia out of kilter, his net annual profit on indigo alone was $40,000,000, with 6 per cent interest on the capital. This third fortune was the largest of all, and with this safely invested he could no longer pretend he would ever be in danger of penury.

He was always making final decisions which were never final. Now he decided he would settle down in Dresden with his wife and children, and live the life of a moneyed businessman in retirement, with properties and investments scattered all over the earth. He bought a house in Dresden, and then sent urgent messages to his wife to join him. She refused to come. He threatened to return to St. Petersburg. "With the aid of the police and my own arms," he wrote, "I shall take my darlings away from my own home so that I can give them here in Dresden the German education which their mother denies them." So he wrote to a high government official, and he seems to have been surprised when he discovered that his demands were listened to without sympathy. His wife called him a tyrant, a despot, and a libertine, and he was all these. A graying unattractive millionaire, with a high domed forehead and watery brown eyes which lit up only when he was talking about money, he represented all that was most repugnant in Russian society. No one knew, or guessed, that this lost and bedeviled man would find himself in the end.

He did not find himself easily. Many years were to pass before he found the clue to himself. He did not know that to accomplish any act of any worth a man must submit himself to a higher authority, must submit completely and with awful humility, casting aside all the goods of this earth except those which assist him in the act of perfect submission. He knew indigo and cotton, olive oil and tea, and how much they were worth on the world's markets, but he had not even learned the beginner's steps in the art of living. So he wandered about in the quicksands, miserably aware that he was generally detested, with no close friends, a stranger to himself, hating himself, the prey of strange fancies. "How is it," he asked himself, "that I who have made three fortunes am so miserably unhappy?"

A heavy sum of money was owed to him by a certain Stefan Solovieff, and as soon as this money was paid in the winter of 1863, he decided to leave Russia. He sold his business, settled some money on his wife and children, and vowed he would never return. He had not the least idea what he would do. He seems to have gone traveling simply to drown his miseries, without plan, in a state of bewilderment. At odd moments it occurred to him to write impressions of his journeys, but he had no high opinion of his own writings. "All my scribblings collapse like a house without foundations," he wrote once, and in the same letter he speaks of himself as "one who will never remain anything else but a dabbler in scholarly pursuits." In his journey which took him round the world, he remained the dabbler, making his elegant, precise comments on the world as he found it. He was still a dilettante.

In April, 1864 he was in Tunis, gazing open-mouthed at the ruins of Carthage. He made another trip to Egypt, and then went on to India, where his talent for languages failed him—he took no interest in learning Urdu or any of the Indian languages. He visited Ceylon, Madras, Calcutta, Benares, Agra, Lucknow, Delhi, and made his way to the foot-hills of the Himalayas. The heat and the noise of India frightened him, but Singapore pleased him and he was delighted with the short side trip he made to Java, before going on to China. It had been a long leisurely tour. He had high hopes for China. There at least were great scholars and men held learning in high repute.

Most of the time he was miserable in China. He complained of the food, the accommodations, the dust, the smells; and he especially hated traveling in the little two-wheeled carts. In his diary he mentions with approval only one person he met in China—the expatriate Englishman, Robert Thomas, who had been a missionary, but lost his faith and became a humble interpreter attached to the customs house at Cheefu. Schliemann liked him because he was a man who knew nine languages, speaking fluently in Russian, Swedish, German, French, Spanish, Portuguese, Italian, Japanese, and Chinese. Thomas learned these languages by writing out words and sentences and making stories from them. It was a method close to Schliemann's heart, and as he describes the impression produced by "this most humble and intelligent man," there is a touch of envy, a salute to an astonishing intellect, and a sense of his own righteousness. It seemed to Schliemann that Thomas could have bettered himself if he had only applied himself more actively to making a fortune.

Soon he was on his way to Peking, which he reached on April 30, 1865, after an uncomfortable journey by two-wheeled cart from Tientsin. He hated every moment of the journey. He could neither sit nor stand in the cart, and made most of the journey sitting astride the lead pole. It was evening when he reached Peking, and he was out of temper. He admired the huge stone walls surrounding the city, but once inside he was filled with horror. There were no hotels. He found lodgings in a Buddhist monastery, where he was asked to pay 12 francs for a room, but after prolonged bargaining he succeeded in reducing the cost to 6 francs. Everything about the room displeased him—the *k'ang,* the raised brick bed of northern China, the floor which had turned to mud because the monks had sprinkled water on it, the stools and the little tables. There were ten large scrolls hanging on the walls of the room, and for some reason it occurred to him to make careful measurements of them. They were covered with precise Chinese calligraphy, and he says in his diary that the scrolls contained extracts from the Confucian classics—an unlikely decoration for a Buddhist monastery.

But if he hated the room, he hated the lack of service more. He asked for food, but the monks assured him there was no food to be obtained. He slept soundly, exhausted by hunger, and at five in the morning he was awakened by his servant Atchon, who brought him a bowl of dirty yellow rice, a teapot filled with green tea, and a tea cup. Schliemann was almost out of his wits with horror. He could not eat rice without salt, and he could not drink tea without milk and sugar. He looked at the tea and came to the conclusion that the most ill-paid workman in Europe would have rejected it out of hand. Milk and sugar being unobtainable, he sent Atchon out to get rice salt, and being unable to maneuver the chopsticks he succeeded in finishing the rice by picking it out of the bowl with his fingers. Barbarous people! He wondered how they could live without knives and forks, milk and sugar!

At six o'clock he sent his servant out to procure horses, and he spent the day wandering through the most beautiful city on earth, hating everything he saw: the beggars, the rag-pickers, the decapitated heads on the execution ground, the idiotic funeral ceremonies, the whole Forbidden City, which seemed, from his vantage point on one of the towers on the wall surrounding the city, to be crumbling into powder because "the imbecile Manchus"[6] had not the sense to keep up appearances. He visited temples and swore under his breath at the priests who allowed the painted gods to crumble away. He observed that the silk gowns worn by the gods were all threadbare, and the paper windows were torn, and the temples themselves were being eaten away by climbing vines.

The young Empress Tzu Hsi was on the throne, and the Taiping Rebellion was still being fought in the Yangtze Valley, but his diary reveals not the slightest trace of any interest in the vast changes which were occurring in China. He spent only one day in Peking. Characteristically, he saw Peking as though it were already a buried city waiting to be excavated, and drew an astonishing portrait which agrees with no other account by contemporary chroniclers:

Here and there I found the remains of white granite paving stones, and everywhere the ruins of ancient sewers, and the mutilated cornices of columns and pieces of sculpture half buried in the mud; and there were many magnificent granite bridges, but half of them were in ruins, so that it was impossible to pass over them—one had to make a detour. And all this debris of paving stones, these ruins of drains and columns and sculptures and bridges—all this only shows that Peking, now inhabited by a degenerate and bestial race, was once peopled by a great and inventive nation. Once there were magnificent clean streets with paving stones, great houses and splendid palaces, but now there were only hideous and dirty houses and the roads are more like vast sewers than the highways of a great capital.

So he raged, growing angrier every minute, while the rain fell, and his horse stumbled through the mud. He spent the whole day from six in the morning to seven at night riding through the desolate streets. He stored his observations in his capacious mind, made deductions from them, related them

6. *Manchus:* Chinese emperors.

to one another, came to conclusions—and nearly all his conclusions were wrong. There never had been paved streets in Peking, nor stone sewers, and the "mutilated cornices" were probably carved tiles blown down by the wind. In all of Peking there were no granite bridges. He thought the shining palaces of the Forbidden City were in ruins, when they were merely invisible behind a green flood of summer trees. He had no understanding of, and no sympathy for, the Chinese addiction to shabby exteriors, to hide the exquisitely decorative interiors. It never occurred to him to blame the weather or his own weariness, or to ask questions; so he went on to the end, performing miracles of improvisation on the theme of the ruined city slowly sinking into the mud—if he had come on another day the dust would have been gold and all the yellow tiles would have been laughing in the sun.

His observations on Peking are instructive, for they show the manner of man he was: in love with ruins, seeing them even when they were not there, hasty in judgment, and not unusually inquisitive. A few years later, when engaged in excavating Troy, he would improvise theories in the same reckless way.

He was not thinking of Troy when he came to Peking. He was thinking of a far greater ruin stretching over hundreds of miles of mountain and desert—the Great Wall of China. Since childhood he had dreamed of climbing along one of the parapets of the Great Wall, and the long journey to China was only the preparation for the journey to the Great Wall. There, if anywhere, he told himself, he would find the secret of the ancient creative life which had long ago vanished from the earth. Accordingly, the next day, he set out with his servant and made his way to Kou-pa-kou, close to the Great Wall on the frontiers of Manchuria, which he reached two days later. He was in good heart. The sun was shining and he amused himself by wearing an Arab turban around his head, which attracted the attention of the villagers along the way, and he was delighted at the thought of coming into the presence of that majestic wall which wanders grotesquely along its irregular course for 1,400 miles. Everyone laughed when Atchon explained that his master had come all the way from Europe to see the wall—it was a great joke, and Schliemann beamed, happy to be in the presence of these wonderful clear-eyed, generous people on the frontier, so different from the degenerates of Peking.

The sun was hot on his face and he was exhausted by the journey, but the wall tempted him. He called for volunteers, but even Atchon refused to climb up the jagged foothills. Schliemann decided to climb alone. According to his diary, it was a hard and dangerous expedition, which he would not have attempted if he had not been so overwhelmed by the sight of that gleaming wall wandering across the mountains until it vanished into the distance. He brought his measuring scale with him, and once he reached the wall he measured the size of the bricks—they were 67 centimeters long, 25 centimeters high, and 17 centimeters thick. He measured the height of the walls—they were 20 to 30 feet high, and the distance between the watch-towers was about 300 feet. He was sure the bricks dated from the Han Dynasty, about 200 B.C., although in fact they date from the Ming Dynasty, about 1400 A.D. He was almost delirious with joy after scrambling up to the top of the wall and seeing the foothills in the distance.

He remained in the tower most of the afternoon. It was not enough to have reached the wall; he wanted time to enjoy the spectacle of the small and shadowy world below him. He remembered everything he had read about the heroic defenders of the wall, who fought off invasions of the barbarians from Central Asia; and he remembered all the other great vistas he had seen in Java and from the Sierra Nevada. At last, when it was growing dark, he carefully detached a brick from the wall and with a piece of string succeeded in strapping it to his back; then he went slithering down the slope on his stomach. This was the first serious work of excavation he had performed, and he was understandably proud when he discovered that the brick was intact when he reached Kou-pa-kou. Thirsty, he shouted for water, and the peasants came hurrying up to him with bowls of water, and when he showed them the brick, they laughed at the thought of all the trouble he had been to to secure a solitary brick. "I am sure," he wrote later, "these generous and kindly people, who answered my call for water, have never smoked opium."

Some days later he wrote up his diary, describing at length everything that had happened on the journey. Nothing in the world, he said, had so moved him as the sight of the wall, now crumbling, once the bastion of China. In words of elation and triumph he describes his emotions as he gazed from his solitary tower at the world below, and if he exaggerates his own prowess in mountain-climbing—for he claims to have scaled the Himalayas and the summits of the Sierra Nevada —there is no doubt of the validity of the emotion. Here, for the first time, the merchant prince surrenders to the ardent archeologist:

Standing on the volcanoes of Java and on the summits of the Sierra Nevada in California, on the high mountains of the Himalayas and the great plateaux of the Cordilleras in South America, I have gazed on magnificent vistas, but never on one so magnificent as this. I was astonished and stupefied, filled with admiration and enthusiasm, and I could not accustom myself to this miraculous wall, which had always excited me even in my earliest childhood. I saw it now before my eyes a hundred times more glorious than I had seen it in my imagination. The more I gazed at this immense wall with its formidable crenellated towers seeking always the crests of the highest mountains, the more it seemed to me to be the work of a fabulous race of antediluvian giants.

I knew that the wall was built about 220 B.C., but even so I could not bring myself to understand how mortal hands had built it: how it was possible for them to transport and put in place on those great jagged rocks those huge blocks of granite and the myriads of bricks. It occurred to me that the bricks must have been baked in the valley immediately below the wall. But to build such a wall, holding at bay so many invasions of the enemy in the north, needed the strength of Hercules himself.

Today the Great Wall lies abandoned and neglected, and instead of soldiers in the crenellated towers there are only pigeons peacefully making their nests, and the harmless lizards multiply among the yellow flowers and violets which announce the coming of spring. No one can deny that this is the greatest work ever accomplished by the hand of man, now to become the funeral monument of an age long since departed from this earth.

When Schliemann wrote these words, he was not yet certain what he intended to do with his life. The vision of Troy was still remote, and though he claimed afterward that not a day had passed since his childhood when he did not think of uncovering the buried city, it is likely that the discovery of Troy came about as the result of a slow process of crystallization. At about this time he was writing to friends, saying that it was always his ambition once he had secured a large fortune to set himself up as a writer. He would leave Russia and settle somewhere in Europe and cultivate his fellow writers—he could think of no more agreeable occupation. It is possible that the journey to the Far East was simply the preliminary to his life as a writer, for many of the writers of his day entered upon their careers with accounts of their travels in strange countries. This diary, so carefully composed, the descriptive passages modeled closely on those of Ernest Renan,[7] seems to have been intended as his first offering in the market place. He possessed the gift of tongues; he had always admired writers; he had never yet failed to achieve his ambitions. Yet already in the opening pages of his first book, written at the age of forty-three, he was announcing the theme which dominated the last years of his life—crum-

7. *Ernest Renan:* French writer (1823-1892).

bling ruins, cyclopean walls, the endless pageant of the buried past. What is surprising is that he should have announced the theme first in Peking and in a remote corner of China close to the Great Wall.

Once he had stood on the Great Wall, China lost all interest for him. He describes his journeys briefly and desultorily, with the air of a visitor amused by the strange customs of the barbarians. For some reason he paid particular attention to the bound feet of the women. "I have closely examined their feet many times," he says, "and I have not read any reports by European writers which describe accurately how they are bound." Thereupon he explains exactly how the three toes are forced back under the soles of the foot and how the peculiar waddling walk is accomplished. He is equally amused when he discusses the Chinese theater—the brocaded gowns, the high falsetto voices of the male performers, the strange masks and still stranger gestures. He seems to have been glad when the time came to leave China for Japan.

He was intoxicated with Japan, and all his best writing in the book he later wrote concerns the carefree days he spent there, though it rained most of the time and there were no friendly Englishmen like Robert Thomas to act as interpreter. He was on his own, enjoying himself. He attended *kabuki* plays, visited the public baths, admired the friendliness and silk kimonos of Japanese women, and was on the best of terms with ambassadors. He liked the little inns where he stayed, the continual bowing, the air of gentle decorum which met him everywhere. To him Japan was delightful and mysterious, hardly credible, like a fairy tale, and he wrote about his brief experiences there leisurely, without haste, as though trying to recall the savor of every moment.

He arrived by luck during one of those brief periods of peace between the Mikado and the Shogunate.[8] Only twelve years before Commodore Perry had sailed up the Bay of Yedo

8. *Shogunate:* military governors of Japan.

and presented his demands to the Emperor of Japan, without suspecting that there were two Emperors, and only the year before the combined British, French, American and Dutch fleets had bombarded Shimonoseki in retaliation against the actions of a local princeling, the Daimyo of Choshu, who repeatedly fired on foreign ships from his batteries along the coast. But Schliemann had no interest in contemporary history. Japan unfolded before him like a pageant, and he was delighted when he saw the colorful procession of the Shogun passing along the great imperial road called the Tokaido. He took careful notes of the gaudy uniforms worn in that brilliant and barbaric procession:

First came the coolies carrying heavy luggage on bamboo poles, then a troop of soldiers in long white or blue blouses, black or dark blue trousers fastened at the ankles, blue socks, straw sandals and lacquered bamboo hats, with knapsacks on their backs, and carrying bows and quivers, swords and rifles. Their officers wore fine yellow calico, with sky-blue or white coats reaching to their knees and these were decorated with little touches of color as a sign of nobility. They wore blue trousers tied to the ankles, blue socks, straw sandals and lacquered black hats, and they carried two swords and a fan at their belts. Their horses were without iron shoes; instead they wore straw sandals.

After the officers came more coolies carrying luggage, and then came the higher officers on horseback with red hieroglyphics on the back of their long white gowns, and then came two troops of lancers—then two pieces of artillery—then two more troops of infantry—then coolies carrying great lacquered chests—then lancers dressed in white, blue and red—then once again came dignitaries on horseback wearing white robes with red hieroglyphics—then a troop of soldiers in large white jackets followed by stableboys leading four horses caparisoned with black hangings and four magnificent *norimono* (sedan chairs) black-lacquered, and behind these a standard in the shape of a fleur-de-lys in gilded metal.

At last there came the Shogun riding a beautiful brown horse without iron shoes, but with straw sandals like all the other horses. His Majesty seemed to be about 20 years old, with a fine face, his complexion rather dark. He wore a white gown embroidered in gold, and a hat which was gilded and lacquered. Two swords hung from his belt, and about twenty great dignitaries in white gowns rode beside him.

Never again was Schliemann to show such a passionate and feminine interest in the colors of things, and to write so accurately and delicately. He was so delighted by the procession that he returned the following day on horseback to look upon the scene where the procession had passed, and was surprised to find, not far from where he had been standing, three mangled corpses lying in the dusty road, so mutilated that it was impossible to tell whether they were soldiers or peasants. There they lay, sprawled out, terrible in their silent misery, and he could make nothing of it. The long and glittering procession of the Shogun, accompanied by nearly two thousand soldiers and retainers, had passed before his eyes, and he had not suspected that they marched over three mangled corpses.

Returning to Yokohoma, he made delicate inquiries. Had they been killed by orders of the slender, dark-featured Shogun, a sick man who was to die a year later? Why had they been left there? Why had they been trampled in the dust? At last he received an explanation which satisfied him. It appeared that no one at all was allowed to cross the road when the Shogun was setting out on a journey. Heralds were usually sent on ahead to clear the road. But it happened that a peasant had wandered inadvertently across the road just when the advance guard came up. An officer told one of his soldiers to hack the peasant to pieces, but the soldier refused. Thereupon the officer brought his heavy sword down on the soldier's head and then turned his attention to the peasant, who was soon killed. At that moment a senior officer rode up, and thinking the officer had gone mad, he bayoneted the officer who had already killed two men. So there they lay, a peasant, a soldier, and an officer of the Shogun's army, and the whole procession had passed over them. As Schliemann tells the story, we are aware of the authentic *frisson*, the quick barbaric horror of the thing, but he wastes no words.

From Yokohoma he went to Yedo, where he admired the great fortress-like bastions, the palaces, and the crowded streets. Yet from his account Yedo made no great impression on him—it was simply one more city on his itinerary, to be marked off after a few days' visit. By early September he was weary of Japan and ready to commit his impressions to paper, and so he boarded a small English ship called *The Queen of the Avon* and set off across the Pacific for San Francisco. With time on his hands, he wrote an account of his travels through China and Japan, a small book of 221 pages, which he published in Paris two years later under the title *Le Chine et le Japon au temps présent*. It was his first book, and he was very proud of it, but it is of no particular value except for the light it throws on the author. The last entry in the book is a cry of triumph so disguised that it is meaningless unless we know his relationship to his wife.

A few days out from Japan, he calculated that he had reached the opposite end of the earth from St. Petersburg, and he noted: "On 7 September between 10.45 and 11 o'clock in the morning we passed latitude 43°9′ and longitude 149° 42′27″ west—the antipodes of St. Petersburg." Apparently he did not trouble to consult the ship's captain. The calculation is inaccurate, and he was not as he thought at the other end of the earth from St. Petersburg.

Still the wanderer, still without a home, he stayed only a few days in San Francisco and took ship to Nicaragua. He had no intention of making the trip through Panama again, and instead crossed Nicaragua and went on to Havana, where he bought some property. He stayed there a few weeks, and

then decided that Mexico City might be worth a visit, but
everything he saw in Mexico City discouraged him. At last,
in the spring of 1866, he found himself in Paris with an apartment overlooking the Seine and the Cathedral of Nôtre Dame
at the foot of the Place St. Michel. At the age of forty-four,
he had decided what he wanted to be: he would become a
philologist, a student of languages, going to classes at the
Sorbonne,[9] and in the intervals between attending lectures he
would publish his book on China and Japan.

He had made three fortunes, visited half the countries in
the world, had three children by an unloving wife, learned
twelve or thirteen languages, collected a vast library, but
even now, grown gray and weary, he had no idea what he
would do with his life.

. . . 5   THE SEARCH FOR TROY

FRANCE in the sixties of the last century was a country which
had surrendered to the bourgeoisie. Napoleon III was on the
throne—a sick and stammering Emperor who rarely knew
where he was going, and hardly cared. Around the Emperor
and the beautiful Empress Eugénie an elegant court gathered,
remote from the people and strangely sterile. In those years
all France seemed to be sleepwalking. The most prosperous
and intelligent people in Europe were moving slowly towards
the disaster of Sedan.[1]

Schliemann, studying at the Sorbonne, was perfectly at
home in the France of the Second Empire. Wealthy, he could
indulge his whims, eat in the fashionable restaurants, and consort with the aristocracy. A scholar, he could seek the com-
panionship of other scholars. A businessman with huge in-

9. *Sorbonne:* university in Paris.

1. *Sedan:* scene of battle in Franco-Prussian War (1870) which led to
downfall of the French Empire.

vestments in America, Cuba, Germany, and Russia, he could amuse himself by buying and selling property in Paris, thus proving to himself that he had lost none of the instincts of a merchant. He bought some houses in the Bois de Boulogne, and sometimes he would complain about the cost of plumbing and refurnishing the houses for his tenants. Why a multi-millionaire should have troubled to become a house agent, spending his time in long discussions on wallpaper, is only one more of the insoluble problems presented by that lonely and embittered man, who came to France in the expectation of being able to reap the fruits of his wealth and discovered only that he was regarded as one of the least prepossessing students at the Sorbonne, a man who seemed to go through the motions of life without any deep-rooted interests in living. There was no gusto in him. Like many men who retire from business, he discovered that retirement solved none of his problems.

As usual, he went about his life methodically: so many hours for study, so many for business, so many for amusement. He attended theaters and the races, and was welcomed in the salons of the great ladies. He met Ernest Renan, who seems to have accepted his fawning admiration with reserve, answering his letters politely but without enthusiasm. Since Paris is the spiritual home of all wanderers, he found solace in the city, but no sense of direction, and sometimes he longed for the bitter winds of St. Petersburg.

Above all, he longed for his children. He seethed with rage at the thought of Ekaterina keeping guard over them. He told her he intended to reopen his house in Dresden and welcome her with open arms. He would provide her with every luxury she desired—carriages, horses, jewelry, dresses from the most expensive *couturiers* in Paris—if only she would share her life with him. "I have become a true Parisian," he wrote, "and so when I come to Dresden our life will be pure happiness."

It never occurred to him that she refused to leave St. Petersburg because she could not bear the sight of him. In letter after letter he attempted to dazzle her with the inducements of his prodigal wealth, and on the rare occasions when she troubled to reply to his letters, she showed herself to be in complete mastery of the situation. She would not come, she would not offer herself to his embraces, and she would never permit the children out of her sight. He answered that if she came to him, he would make no demands on her. He loved her, and it was enough if he could only set eyes on her. He let his apartment on the Place St. Michel and bought a magnificent town house on the Bois de Boulogne, spending 40,000 francs on the furnishings, and promised her she could travel between his palatial residences in St. Petersburg, Dresden, and Paris as she pleased—they were all hers, and he had bought them only for her enjoyment.

When these inducements failed, he threatened to cut off her allowance and that of the children. "You have brought it upon yourself by your unreasoning and insane behavior," he wrote. "You yourself are responsible for the fact that the children are being disinherited. I swear to you that I have finally disinherited them. You have attained your ends. This is the last letter I shall ever write to you in this life."

There were many more letters. He pleaded, cajoled, demanded that she see the error of her ways, wept endless tears; and never realized that his letters only reinforced her decision to live her life apart from him. He told her that with one stroke of the pen he had canceled the inheritance amounting to a million francs each which he had set aside for his children, "even though I would joyfully have given my life to each and all of them." Ekaterina remained unmoved. She had rich relatives, the house in St. Petersburg, and the large sums he had settled on her. Gray and balding, looking older than his years, Schliemann continued to wear the disguise of a middle-aged student at the Sorbonne.

Though he had promised to abandon business many times, he never succeeded in keeping his promise. He read the financial pages of the London *Times* every day, and continually studied the money market. When he read that American politicians were clamoring to pay off certain bonds with paper money, he realized that the operation would involve thousands of millions of dollars, the value of gold would increase sharply, and the issue of paper money would in effect form a repudiation of the bonds. He had large American holdings. Afraid that his holdings would depreciate, he decided to visit America.

He sailed for New York early in 1868, and as soon as he reached Washington, he called upon the Secretary of the Treasury, who explained that the American Government had no intention of repudiating the bonds. A little later he called on President Andrew Johnson, as previously he had called on President Fillmore. "Johnson is quite a simple man, about fifty-five years old," Schliemann wrote later to a German friend. "I told him I had come to pay my respects, and said I was pleased with his latest message to Congress concerning Cuba. He told me that Cuba had great leanings towards the United States, and the time will soon come when the States will absorb the island." It is unlikely that the President would have committed himself in this way to a total stranger. Yet he was genuinely pleased with his conversations in Washington—he felt that his land holdings in Cuba were more secure than ever, and he was understandably gratified to learn that the bonds would not be repudiated.

He liked Washington, but New York no longer attracted him. On his previous visit he had admired the huge buildings, the broad streets, the air of frantic hurry and good fellowship he found everywhere. This time he examined New York through the eyes of a Parisian and saw only narrow ill-lit streets and confusion everywhere, the whole city still reeling from the effects of the Civil War. Like most Europeans he sympathized with the fate of the Southern States. "Today they are being treated like a conquered territory," he wrote. "They are under martial law, without political representation, without money, banks, or means of defending themselves."

At the same time he became passionately interested in the Negroes, visited their schools and listened to their spirituals, filling his diaries with long dissertations on their virtues. Then, just as suddenly, he lost interest in them. His consuming passion became the study of the American railway system. He rode on all the lines which reached out to the Great Lakes. Previously he found the American railways rather less than efficient. Now, after a thorough inspection, he was delighted with them. He noted that they were all paying a 10 per cent dividend.

He noted other things: the price of indigo, the amount of grain exported, statistics about the development of Chicago during the past thirty years, the size of buildings in Indianapolis, the value of timber at the current market rates. He was feeling his way back into the world of business, which he had never for a moment completely abandoned. Indianapolis pleased him. He came to know many of the businessmen and important politicians, and sometimes the talk would turn to the divorce laws of the State of Indiana, then undergoing revision.

Schliemann was not an American citizen, though he sometimes claimed to have become a citizen while he was in California, when that state entered the Union. But in fact he had not claimed citizenship, and to divorce his wife according to the state law of Indiana he would first have to become a citizen. This he knew, and accordingly with the help of his friends, who were not above stretching the law a little, he made arrangements for becoming a citizen the following year. He bought a house in Indianapolis and an interest in a starch business there. He was in good humor, looking forward to the time when he would be free of Ekaterina for ever.

Throughout this winter journey to America he was in a gay mood. He had ridden on the railroads with the feeling of a director. He had made a number of profitable investments. He had met everyone in the government he cared to meet except General Grant (who for some unexplained reason refused to see him), but everyone else was impressed by the intelligent, incisive merchant, who had made **three** fortunes and seemed on the verge of making a fourth.

Outwardly debonair, he was seething with misery and loneliness within. Gaiety crackles in his notebooks, but his letters to St. Petersburg and Germany tell a different story. He did not want to divorce Ekaterina. He told himself he was being forced to it, and he constantly sent her imploring letters, accusing himself, admitting his faults, promising to be more generous in future. On January 6, which was Christmas Day in Russia, he was alone in a Washington hotel room, close to tears and dreaming about his three children, the Christmas tree, the presents, the happy laughter. He was utterly miserable. He had sent no presents, because he was estranged from their mother, but now he was sorry. In his weariness and anger he told himself it would be worth $100,000 in American money to be among them. It was beyond everything, that he should be unable to share their joys and sorrows. Worse still, the next day was his forty-sixth birthday, and there was no one to share it with him. So he wandered about Washington like a ghost, not daring to tell his secrets to others, wearing his loneliness like a garment.

Sometimes the calm exterior he liked to show to the world cracked wide open. A friend had given him a letter of introduction to the Prussian Ambassador in Washington, and Schliemann presented himself at the embassy. The Ambassador, Baron von Gerolt, welcomed him and asked his business. Schliemann replied that he was paying a courtesy call, and began talking about his life in Paris and the fortune he had made in St. Petersburg. Suddenly the Ambassador roared with anger, and shouted: "Well, why don't you go and call on the French Ambassador—or the Russian? The Russians don't have so many people here, but there are a lot of Germans, and I have no time——" Schliemann marched out of the embassy in a raging temper, and when he left New York for France in February, his last letter written just before the ship sailed consisted of an insulting diatribe addressed to the Prussian, reminding him of the bleak reception he had given him, repeating every word the Ambassador had spoken, remembering every detail of the agony. His pride wounded, Schliemann flung a final taunt at the Ambassador: "I beg to inform Your Excellency that your insufferable treatment of me forms the only unpleasant recollection of my recent tour. I shall remember America as a place where everyone is highly cultured, charming and well-mannered—everyone except yourself!"

Then he was in Paris again, the chestnut trees in bloom and the war clouds looming on the horizon. He attended lectures at the Sorbonne and resumed his study of philology, went to the theater, amused himself by buying more houses and acting the part of landlord—he wrote voluminously on the subject of gas burners and water closets—and it was not long before it occurred to him that he was being bored to death. The compass needle was still revolving frantically. He had no direction. There was nothing of any importance worth doing. Would he spend his life buying enamel baths and mirrors for his tenants?

Suddenly, in the middle of that restless spring, two things happened which changed the course of his life. They seem to have occurred simultaneously, shortly after his return to Paris. He attended some lectures on archeology at the Sorbonne, and he received a letter from his cousin Sophie Schliemann. She was a spinster, nearly fifty, and she wrote him an impassioned declaration of love. He answered coldly that he remembered the days they had spent together at Kalkhorst, but he had not the least intention of gallivanting with an elderly woman who had once refused to embrace him, or even to give him her arm. Injuries he had suffered when he was fourteen, thirty-three years ago, awoke in him; and he dismissed her in the same tone with which he dismissed the Prussian Ambassador. She had suggested timidly that she would love to travel with him. "Of course," he wrote to her, "I would think myself fortunate to travel with an experienced woman of the world, but to travel with a saint, and one far more suited to the cloister than the stage of this great world —this I would regard as the most tedious thing in the world!"

Sophie Schliemann, his childhood playmate, never received the letter, for she died on the day it was written.

When he heard of her death some days later, he flew into a passion of grief. In Washington he had told himself he would give vast sums of money to share Christmas with his children. Now he told himself he would have done everything possible to save the life of his devoted cousin. The most famous doctors from Hamburg and Berlin would have hurried to her bedside. He himself would have watched over her, and perhaps by his very ardor saved her life. "There was nothing calculating, nothing sensual, in the love I possessed for this pure, true-hearted and angelic being. The love I had for her was purely platonic, of the most sublime sympathy." He asked for a photograph of Sophie's coffin, and raged because the letter was unstamped and addressed incorrectly, with the result that it was delayed. He told his sisters that he would have given a fortune to travel ten times round the world with her. If only he had known, he would have devoted the remaining years of his life to her. He accused himself of the utmost ingratitude because she had sent him a lock of her hair shortly before he left for America, and he

had thrown it carelessly in his trunk. He retrieved it, and
spoke of placing the hair in a gold case set with diamonds,
which he would carry over his heart. "I shall do this as long
as I live, for her beautiful hair has become the most sacred
treasure of my life."

The death of Sophie Schliemann struck him where he was
most vulnerable. He had loved her briefly and then dismissed
her from his mind, but she was one of the few who had ever
been close to him. She was the only girl beside Minna Meincke
who had loved him for his own sake. Gay and impetuous, she
was one of those girls who at the age of eleven or twelve
look as though they will settle down quite early in their lives
to a happy marriage, but instead choose to become spinsters.
At long intervals in his life he had thought fondly about her.
Just before his marriage to Ekaterina, he had written to his
sisters, asking about her, hinting that he was thinking seriously
of marrying her. But that was fifteen years ago, and he had
no very clear impression of her. Quite suddenly she died, and
just as suddenly she returned from the grave to haunt him.

He was a man without faith in religion, or any hope of
an after-life. He believed that man was the measure of all
things: with industry and acumen any man could make a
fortune and enjoy the good things of the earth. But now
he found that the old shibboleths were wanting. His grief
over the death of Sophie was exaggerated and raw with self-
pity; but there was a real despair in the hurried letters he
wrote off to Germany, asking for details of how she died,
a portrait of her, anything which would help him to remember her living. He learned with horror that she had spent
the last six months of her life in penury. Then his misery
knew no bounds, as he realized that with a small fraction of
his fortune he could have eased her last days. The proud man,
homo superbus,[2] was compelled to examine his own motives.
Why was he living? Why was he unhappy? Why was he

2. *Homo superbus:* Latin for "superb man."

always wandering around the world like a homeless beggar, friendless and alone, with no children around him, with no wife to comfort him? There must be some God somewhere, some hope of peace in the world.

Then there came to him, in that intolerable spring, the memory of Homer which had enchanted his childhood—not the *Iliad* with its tale of Troy besieged, but the *Odyssey*, the story of a wanderer who returns at last to his own home. He would go to Ithaca, where Odysseus found his Penelope in his own mountain stronghold high above the Ionian Sea. He would stand there, and somehow, by some miracle still unknown, he too would find his Penelope and there would be an end to his wandering.

Schliemann always gave the impression of a man of decision, who knew exactly where he wanted to go. He had a look of determination. He could add up sums at a prodigious pace, and make decisions on financial matters quickly, suddenly, with an intuitive grasp of complex dealings in merchandise. But in all other matters he was slow and halting, unsure of himself, pathetically aware of his own weaknesses. Nearly all the major turning points of his life came about as a result of forces over which he had no control. He did not go to Greece because he believed in his own powers as an archeologist. He went because he was haunted by the ghost of Sophie Schliemann, because his wife refused him, and because at long last he had found a divinity so infinitely superior to him that it was no longer possible to withhold his entire devotion.

In his distress he turned to Homer, who had reigned over his childhood, and it did not surprise him that what he had been searching for had been close to him from the very beginning. The name of his god was Homer—not Homer the poet, nor Homer the master of a complex language which provided excuses for philological excursions, nor Homer regarded as the father of the Attic dramatists. What he yearned for was Homer the creator of a world so valid, so entrancing, and so truthful that a man could live in it and hold his head high.

When he made his way to Greece in the early summer of 1868 he had already decided to become an archeologist. He would unearth the towering castle on Mount Aetios, or "eagle's cliff," which Odysseus entered disguised as a beggar in rags on his return from his long wanderings.

To reach Ithaca, he went to Rome and Naples, and took ship to Corfu. He spent only a day on Corfu, the ancient Corcyra, which was perhaps Homer's island of Scheria, the abode of the Phæacians, where King Alcinoüs had his splendid palace and his beautiful daughter Nausicaä entertained Odysseus. He could find no trace of Alcinoüs' palace, but he found the legendary stream where Nausicaä had washed her clothes and played with her handmaidens, and after swimming naked in the stream he sought out the place where Odysseus had been hiding in the bushes. It pleased him to stand naked where the naked Odysseus had stood.

The next day he took a steamboat to Cephalonia, the largest of the Ionian islands, but its ancient capital had been destroyed by the Romans, and he found little to interest him there. Soon he had crossed the little strip of sea which separates Cephalonia from Ithaca. He had been a little dubious about the Homeric antecedents of the other islands, but in Ithaca everything reminded him of Homer. "Every hill, every stone, every stream, every olive grove reminded me of Homer," he wrote, "and so I found myself with a single leap hurled across a hundred generations into the glittering age of Greek knighthood."

From the moment he stepped foot on Ithaca he was like a man enchanted. He must go everywhere and see everything. In spite of the heat—the thermometer stood at 120°— he was deliriously happy. There were no hotels, but he found lodgings with two elderly spinsters. He met a miller with a donkey who offered to take him round the island, which was shaped like a figure eight with a thin craggy isthmus: on the isthmus, according to legend, was Odysseus' castle.

The miller, whose name was Panagis Asproieraka, knew all the legends of Odysseus and pleased Schliemann by reciting them at great length. Sometimes Schliemann would interrupt and ask: "Is that the harbor of Phorkys? Where is the grotto of the nymphs? Where is the field of Laertes?" But the miller was too full of his stories to answer these questions, and Schliemann commented wearily: "The roads were long, but so were the miller's stories." Yet he liked the miller, and they got on famously together. He approved, too, of the villagers—hard-grained peasants with a natural nobility about them, neighborly and industrious, with honest eyes, worthy of their great ancestor Odysseus. Above all, he enjoyed the prospect of uncovering the palace, and so, after two days of exploration, he organized an expedition up Mount Aetios.

It was a small and inexpensive expedition, consisting of four workmen and a donkey. Because it was the hottest time of the year, they had orders to set out at five o'clock in the morning. Schliemann would wake at four o'clock, bathe in the sea, then drink a cup of black coffee and spend the next two hours climbing up the mountainside. Once there, he could look out over the wine-dark sea at the mountains of the Peloponnesus, and sometimes it seemed to him that he could see the whole of Greece.

The first day he found nothing of any importance, but the day was saved when a peasant came and offered him an ancient vase and a silver coin from Corinth with the head of Minerva on one side, a horse on the other. The next day he had the workmen pulling up the brushwood inside the circuit wall, and he set them to digging in the northeast corner. It flashed through his mind that here, on this very spot, Odysseus might have built his marriage chamber—that chamber of stone built around a long-leafed olive tree, which had been made into a bed.

The workmen went on digging, but they found nothing until three hours later, when they came upon the foundation stones of a building 3 meters wide by 4.75 meters long and Schliemann was wild with excitement. He thought he had found the foundations of the marriage chamber. Then he found a semicircular stone covered with earth, carefully lifted it and continued digging. Four inches below the surface his pickax struck a delicate vase and smashed it to fragments. A little while later he found twenty more vases, some standing upright, others on their sides, and all of them containing ashes. He was sure they were human ashes. Then he found a sacrificial knife 6 inches long, a clay goddess holding two flutes to her mouth, and some animal bones.

There were no inscriptions, but his enthusiasm was now boundless and he turned to the workmen and told them that one of these funerary urns might very well contain the ashes of Odysseus. He wrote in his diary: "I believe these urns to be older than the oldest urns from Cumæ in the Museum at Naples, and it is quite possible that they contain the ashes of Odysseus and Penelope, or their descendants." The last words were perhaps a sop to his own incredulity.

He had made his first discovery, and his appetite for archeology was now whetted. For the first time he had stood on sacred soil and seen the mysterious past gazing up at him from the earth. Instead of a marriage chamber he had found the ashes of the dead; and he was overwhelmed with gratitude. Unfortunately this first easy success led him to believe in his innate ability as an archeologist, and all his subsequent diggings followed the same plan. There was always a "northeast corner." Intuitively, holding Homer in his hand, he would choose a spot where he thought there was some likelihood of treasure, and then he would order the workmen to dig. Only in rare cases could he explain why he had chosen the place. He worked by instinct and enthusiasm, feeling his way into the past, with result that he spent most of the re-

maining years of his life in fruitless digging. Twice he discovered great treasuries of gold, but these were the exceptions.

As the result of his first morning's digging he had twenty
urns, a clay goddess, and a knife. In his excitement he forgot
the heat and his raging thirst. Noon came. They had eaten
nothing since the early morning. He decided it was time to
break the fast, and wandered a little way from the summit to
the shelter of an olive tree between the double walls. It struck
him that perhaps here, on that very spot, Odysseus shed tears
when he saw the dog Argus, which died of joy to see him
home again. And then other thoughts occurred to him. Perhaps near here, or not very far away, the swineherd Eumæus
had spoken the terrible words: "All-seeing Zeus takes away
half the worth of a man when he becomes a slave." It is odd
that, with so much of the *Odyssey* to choose from, he should
have remembered these particular passages—slavery and the
triumphant return, the two poles of his mind.

After a lunch of bread and wine, the workmen enjoyed
their siesta while Schliemann resumed digging. He remembered afterward that the wine of Ithaca was three times
stronger than Bordeaux, and he was a little drunk; but he
found nothing more that day, and nothing the next. He made
inquiries. He learned from these villagers with long memories
that a certain Captain Guitara had discovered golden earrings
and bracelets in 1811 and 1814, but no one knew where these
treasures were. On the "Field of Laertes" he recited for them
the last book of the *Odyssey*, translating the words into their
own dialect.

The peasants clustered around him, surprised and delighted
to see a foreigner who knew their legends so well that he
could recite them from memory. As Schliemann recounts the
story, it was almost the greatest moment of his stay in Ithaca:

Their enthusiasm had no bounds, as they listened to the me-
lodious language of Homer—the language spoken by their glori-

ous ancestors 3,000 years ago. They heard of the terrible sufferings which the old King Laertes endured in the very place where
we were all assembled, and they heard too of his great joy when
he found again after twenty years the son he had thought dead.
All eyes were bathed in tears, and as I concluded the song, men,
women and children came up to me and embraced me, saying:
"You have given us a great pleasure! We thank you a thousand
times over!" Then they bore me in triumph to their town.

A few days later, having made no more discoveries, he
sailed for Corinth, a lamentable place where there were no
hotels and once more he had to pass a night in a dark bug-
infested inn. He was up early the next morning, swam for
half an hour in the sea, found a guide, a donkey, and two
soldiers for escort, and made his way south to Mycenae,
which made no deep impression on him, though he measured
the walls and admired the Lion Gate.

He had left his guide and the escort in the village of Char-
vati, and when he returned in the afternoon he found them
fast asleep: to wake them he had to squirt water on their faces.
He told them he wanted to proceed to Argos, but they told
him it would be quite impossible to reach Argos that evening. "I had no desire to stay in this village, the poorest and
dirtiest I ever saw in Greece—no spring water, no bread, no
food, only some brackish rain water." By cajoling the guide
and giving the soldiers small presents, he was able to continue
the journey and reached Argos. Perhaps because he was
exhausted by the long ride, the heat, and the miserable inn,
he had little to say about the place, though he noted that it
had been "the greatest and most powerful city in ancient
Greece, famous for the love of its inhabitants for the fine arts,
especially music." This reads like Baedeker,[3] and is not very
convincing. He is more illuminating when he discusses the
rich, sweet wines of Argos—he found them *ausgezeichnet*.[4]

3. *Baedeker:* popular tourist guidebook.
4. *Ausgezeichnet:* excellent (German).

The next afternoon he wandered off to Tiryns, the great
fortress stronghold with its immense walls, but he was not
particularly attracted to it, and the two pages devoted to
Tiryns in his journal are concerned with philological questions. Weary of ruins, and still more weary of his escort, he
walked alone to Nauplia, glad to be once more by the seashore, where it was cooler and there was no need to ride
about on a donkey without a saddle. In later years he was to
make great discoveries at Mycenae and Tiryns, but his first
glimpse of them was disappointing.

Nauplia refreshed his spirit. Here was a hotel, good food,
a rest from wandering. And here, while he was waiting for a
ship to take him to the island of Hydra, a strange incident
occurred. During the afternoon he was walking in the main
street when he saw five men shuffling through the dust with
chains round their legs. They were evidently prisoners on
leave of absence from the local prison. One of these prisoners,
seeing that Schliemann was carrying some books, approached
him and asked to borrow a book or a newspaper. The man
was a heavy-set dignified peasant, with handsome features,
and Schliemann immediately gave him a book. The prisoner
expressed his gratitude and examined the book carefully, holding it upside down. Puzzled, Schliemann said: "Can you
read?" "Not a word," the prisoner answered, "but I shall
soon learn." The other prisoners came up. Asked why they
were wearing leg chains, they explained that they were good
peasants from the hills, had been arrested without cause, and
were suffering from the perfidy of the police. They spoke
gently and bravely, and Schliemann approved of their devotion to reading. He learned later that they were all murderers,
and would soon be executed.

A few days later he sailed to Athens, where he renewed
his acquaintance with Theokletos Vimpos, the man who
taught him Greek in St. Petersburg. Vimpos was now Bishop
of Mantinea and a professor at the University of Athens. For

a few days they were inseparable, and then in August Schliemann set out for Troy by way of Constantinople. The Russian consul obtained a guide and two horses for him.

As he wandered over the plain of Troy he was in high spirits. It was soft rolling land; there were clumps of spruce and oak; the water was sweet and the air was like wine. At Bunarbashi, long believed to be the site of Troy, he found a huddle of small houses inhabited by Turks and Albanian Greeks. The walls were black with mosquitoes, the people were poverty-stricken. When he asked for milk to slake his thirst, it was given to him in a jug which had not, he thought, been cleaned out for ten years. The impertinence of the villagers and the stupidity of the guides annoyed him, but he was pleased to see the storks flapping their wings on the roofs of the houses, because they reminded him of Ankershagen. He wrote in his journal: "Storks are very useful—they eat snakes and frogs."

He had dreamed of a Troy of white marble, majestic and permanent, gleaming in an eternal noonday of the imagination. At Bunarbashi he found only filth, rubbish heaps, miasmas rising from the surrounding marshlands. He was not inclined to look favorably on Bunarbashi, ten miles from the sea. Homer speaks of the Achaeans making seven or eight journeys a day from the seashore to the site of Troy. Schliemann felt sure that the hill of Hissarlik at the western end of the valley was a more likely site. This was an opinion he shared with Charles Maclaren, an English scholar who wrote *A Dissertation on the Topography of Troy* in 1822. Frank Calvert, an Englishman who acted as American vice-consul at the Dardanelles, shared the same view. He owned half the hill. With the Austrian consul, Von Hahn, he had done some preliminary digging. Convinced that he had found the site of Troy, he wrote a report on his finds in the *Archeological Journal* and invited the British Museum to begin large-scale excavations. On the eastern slope of the hill Calvert had discovered the remains of a palace or a temple formed of great blocks of hewn stone. He wanted the British to have the honor of discovering Troy, but nothing came of his proposals. He was convinced that he had discovered Troy, while his brother Frederick, who owned a $5,000-acre estate near Bunarbashi, was equally sure he had discovered Troy near his vineyards. Frank Calvert had already begun his excavations with two ditches dug across the hill. Schliemann simply followed in his footsteps.

As Schliemann concentrated on Hissarlik, everything began to fall into place. The approaches, the shape and size of the hill, even the evidence from the pathetic ditches dug by Calvert proved that Hissarlik was Troy. To find the ruins of Priam's palace, all that was needed was to remove the top crust of the hill. As he imagined it, the citadel was on the hill, while all around it stretched the wide-flung city, as Athens lies below the Acropolis. There would be ruins buried in the earth all around the hill, while the hill itself would contain the marble palaces, the treasures, and the bones of the heroes. On August 21, less than two weeks later, he was back in Constantinople, busily discussing his theories with Frank Calvert.

He was in a mood for quick action. Vast plans, sudden resolves, furious onslaughts against the hill—he would enter into battle at once with the ghosts of the past. Calvert, whose mind moved more slowly, was a little amused by Schliemann's wild enthusiasm. A calm, quiet man, he suggested that it was already late in the season for digging, and it might be better to wait for the following spring. There would have to be careful preparations, a *firman* permitting the excavations from the Turkish government, among other things. Calvert generously promised not to stand in the way. Half the hill belonged to him; he could, if he had wished, have bargained with Schliemann, but it seems never to have occurred to him. In all his dealings with the vice-consul, Schliemann seems to have been a little dazzled by the Englishman who assisted him at every opportunity, asked for nothing, and behaved in all matters unlike the merchants who always demanded the best possible terms. Without Calvert's help there would have been no discoveries at Troy.

Troy had become Schliemann's obsession, but there was one other matter preying on his mind—his forthcoming divorce from Ekaterina. Friends in Indianapolis had promised him a divorce in the following spring. Accordingly he proposed to be in America in the spring, and as soon as the divorce papers were signed, he would return to Troy. Meanwhile he decided to spend the fall and winter in his apartment in the Place St. Michel, writing an account of his six-week tour through Greece.

The book, which he called *Ithaka, der Peloponnes und Troja*, falls between many stools. The antiquarian, the philologist, the archeologist, the historian, the businessman, and the excited child quarrel among themselves. There are whole pages and even chapters which read like the dreariest doctoral dissertation, but here and there the spark shines through. The gods, who endowed him with wealth and intuition and the knowledge of many languages, unfortunately gave him no sense of style. Too often he writes like a banker. His schoolmaster at Neu Strelitz had described him as "a diligent worker, but often lacking clarity of thought." There is little clarity in the book, and only too many signs of diligence in the long philological discussions. But occasionally ideas bubble up from the remote depths of his capacious mind.

He makes no attempt to conceal himself: his desire for glory, his acquisitiveness, his unsmiling contempt for nearly everyone he meets, and his rejoicing whenever he encounters another wealthy banker in his travels. When he describes how he recited the twenty-fourth book of the *Odyssey* to the worshiping peasants of Ithaca, it is almost impossible to believe that it happened in exactly that way. Yet it is easy to believe that he possessed genuine sympathy for the shackled prisoners he met in Nauplia. He was a man at odds with himself, and the book shows it. He parades his knowledge, quotes the authorities who bolster his arguments and neglects sometimes those who oppose him, and runs every philological conundrum to the ground. Where Homer and Strabo conflict, he pours scorn on Strabo; and setting himself up as the champion of Homer, he ascribes intolerable prejudice to anyone who would dare to find the least topographical inaccuracy in his cherished poet. His fundamentalist belief in the divinity of Homer emerges clearly from this book, together with the fundamentalist's combative temper.

This book, so oddly put together from his journals and scraps of philological learning, was to be his passport to fame. He wrote it hurriedly in English, then translated it into German and sent it off to his Leipzig publisher, who printed 750 copies at the author's expense. How deeply he regarded his role as author can be seen from the letter he wrote at the beginning of November to his thirteen-year-old son Sergey:

> I have been laboring day and night over my archeological work, for I really have the hope of achieving some small reputation as an author. I am a member of the Geographic and Archeological Society here, and I read them some thirty pages of the book—it gives me great joy to tell you that my remarks were greeted with enthusiasm.
>
> If this book is successful, I will spend the rest of my life writing books, for I cannot imagine a more interesting career than the writing of serious books. Writing, one is always so happy and content and at peace with oneself, and then when a writer emerges again into society he has so many thousands of things to say—the fruit of his long researches and meditations—and so he can amuse everyone. And everyone looks up to writers and welcomes them, and even though I am only an apprentice at the game, I have ten times as many friends as I want. . . .

In fact he had almost no intimate friends, and nearly all his letters contain concealing pleas, little despairing cries, for friendship and understanding. Greece had warmed him, but he was still a remote, faintly intimidating figure, who took offense easily, cared little for the feelings of others, and possessed a ludicrously high opinion of himself. Ernest Renan was the lion of Paris society, and Schliemann hoped fervently to follow in his footsteps, without possessing any of Renan's grace and ease. As his letter to his son indicates, he knew little enough about the burdens and rewards of authorship.

Above all, Schliemann was driven by the desire to be honored and respected; the rewards which the world offers to dignitaries meant a good deal to him. Nothing would please him more than to be addressed as "Herr Doktor," and one of his chief reasons for staying in Paris was the doctorate he hoped to obtain from the Sorbonne. Unfortunately, the curriculum at the Sorbonne was so arranged that he was unable to see himself as anything more than an occasional student, and so he applied to the University of Rostock. Asked what thesis he proposed to submit, he suggested an account of his career written in classical Greek. This extraordinary dissertation—perhaps the most astonishing in the annals of the university—was accepted. Schliemann wrote his history of himself, received his doctorate, and was always annoyed if he was not addressed by his title.

So November and December passed, while he wrote his brief autobiography and his book on Ithaca, the Peloponnesus, and Troy. Meanwhile his enthusiasm for excavating the hill at Hissarlik was waning. Alone in his Paris apartment, with the cold winter fog creeping up from the Seine, he was no longer the wild enthusiast he had been. It would be an expensive undertaking, and might take years, many years. Also, he knew nothing about the arts of excavation. How does one go about it? How many workmen would he need to employ? How much would it cost? How does one protect oneself against bandits? What kind of hat does an excavator wear?

All these problems, and many more, were troubling him when he wrote to Frank Calvert toward the end of December, 1868, enclosing a list of nineteen questions and requesting an immediate answer. In these questions, which are reproduced here as he wrote them, we see the tentative beginnings of the work which was to engross him for the remaining years of his life:

1 When is the best time to begin the work?
2 Is it not advisable to begin as early as possible in Spring?
3 I am very susceptible to fever; is there much apprehension of same in Spring?
4 What medicines have I to take with me?
5 Must I take a servant with me? or can I get a very trustworthy one in Athens? Probably it is better to have a faithful Greek who speaks Turkish.
6 Have I to take a tent and iron bedstead and pillow with me from Marseilles? for all the houses in the plain of Troy are infested with vermin.
7 Please give me an exact statement of *all the implements* of whatever kind and of *all the necessaries* which you advise me to take with me.
8 Do I require pistols, dagger and rifle?
9 Is there no obstacle on the part of the landowners to excavate the artificial hill?
10 Can I get labourers enough, where and at what wages?
11 How many can I employ? Is it better to take Greek(s) or Turks?
12 In how much time do you think I can dig away the artificial mountain?
13 At what cost?
14 You suggested to dig first a tunnel! But I am sure this is not practical, for if the hill really consists of ruins of ancient temples and walls, the cyclopean stones will impede the tunnel being made.
15 What has led you to conclude that the hill is artificial?
16 You indicate the dimensions as 700 feet square; a Frenchman would understand you 26½ feet long and as much in

breadth; but I think you mean 700 feet long and the same in breadth, which—in the French mode of calculating, would make 490,000 square feet. But in my book I have stated the length and breadth with 233 metres, which would make about 54,000 square metres.

17 What is the height of the artificial mount to be taken away?
18 I think the best plan is to take a credit on Constantinople banker, who adds to it a firm in the Dardanelles so that I am not bothered and can take out at the Dardanelles what I require.
19 What sort of a hat is best against scorching sun?

This long list should be read carefully, for it shows his hesitations, his hopes, his fears, and his curiously wayward approach to the whole subject of excavations. He seems to be appalled by the enormity of the task before him, and astonishingly ignorant. Frank Calvert replied immediately in a sensible letter full of cautious advice and gentle remonstrance. He had studied archeology and read widely in the works of Layard, who discovered Nineveh,[5] and he explained exactly how the trenches should be dug and the best season for digging—between early spring and summer—and where laborers could be obtained, and how much they should be paid.

As for Hissarlik: "Part of the artificial hill is my property and as I have already informed you, you have my consent to clean it out." He promised to use his influence with the other proprietor to permit the excavation of the whole hill, and expected no serious difficulties. Knowing Schliemann's predilection for tea, he pointed out that few luxuries were obtainable in the Dardanelles, and though there was coffee and sugar in abundance, he had better bring tea leaves with him. He corrected Schliemann's mathematics, explained there was no real need for pistols and daggers—those romantic implements were not so dependable as guns—and he suggested that Schliemann would be wise to rent one of the houses

5. *Nineveh:* ancient Assyrian city.

in the village of Ciplak, whitewashing it and destroying the
vermin with insect powder. Finally he suggested that the
best hat to wear against the heat of the sun was a white muslin
turban, like those worn by the Turks.

Still contemplating Calvert's letter, Schliemann went off
for a holiday in Germany, visiting Fürstenberg where he
had been a grocer's assistant, and Rostock, for the presentation of his doctorate. His book was in the hands of his
publishers, and there was little at this stage that he could do
to prosecute the excavation of Troy, especially since his
presence was needed in Indianapolis. So off he went to
America. He hoped to get the divorce immediately, but
there were inevitable delays. He had suggested important
alterations in the laws, but these were rejected by the state
legislature. Weary of hotel life, he bought a house in the
fashionable district of Indianapolis and settled down to await
the final decree. He filled his house with servants and a cook,
employed five lawyers, and amused himself while fighting the
case by writing long letters to acquaintances all over the
world. On April 14 he wrote to Calvert, saying he feared he
would be unable to obtain the divorce before June: consequently digging would have to be abandoned until the spring
of the following year.

On the same day he wrote to Renan a strange little letter,
half in English and half in French, describing an incident he
had observed in New York concerning an eight-year-old
merchant who was selling books on a streetcar. The boy
went down the streetcar shouting: "Two cents each for the
books!" Then he whispered to each of the passengers in
turn: "But *you* shall have three for five cents!" Afterward
he went around the streetcar again, picking up the books or
taking money, and Schliemann talked to the boy, who said
his father had died the year before, leaving a sick wife and
six children, and so the boy was trying to support the family.
Schliemann was impressed and gave him a dollar, but the

gift was rejected. "I will not take your money unless you accept sixty books from me," the boy said, drawing himself up to his full height. "I am a merchant, not a beggar!" Schliemann was deeply impressed, took the sixty books, and made a little speech. "May this dollar," he said, "be the foundation stone to your earthly fortune, my boy! May you one day become a great banker, the pride and glory of this great country, which, with such characters as yours, is bound to eclipse all the empires emblazoned in history!"

There is nothing improbable in the story, with its troubling reference to "a great banker, the pride and glory of this great country," but one would like to know what Renan thought of this typical Horatio Alger story. Unfortunately there are no records of Renan's reply.

In his usual way Schliemann kept himself busy in Indianapolis. His starch factory was progressing well. He studied the money market, wrote lengthy reports about business to Schröder, polished up his Arabic—he wrote a short treatise on *The Arabian Nights Entertainment*—and sent to the Convention of American Philologists meeting in Poughkeepsie a lengthy dissertation on the art of learning languages quickly. Troy was temporarily forgotten; he was writing enthusiastic letters on the subject of the Northwest Passage and the discovery of the North Pole, and promising to give financial assistance to prospective explorers. And while the divorce was still under study, he was preparing in the most extraordinary way to find a bride to replace Ekaterina.

He had decided upon a Greek bride, because he liked the sound of the language, especially when spoken by women. But how to find one? He could, of course, return to Greece, make inquiries, and search diligently for a suitable wife, but an easier way occurred to him. In February, as soon as the unbound sheets of his book on his Greek travels arrived, he sent two copies to his friend Theokletos Vimpos: one copy was for Vimpos himself, the other for the library of the University of Athens. He enclosed a check for 100 francs drawn on Paris to pay for the binding, adding that if there was any money left over, it might be spent for the benefit of the poor of Athens.

Then, abruptly, he turned to the subject which absorbed him completely. Would Vimpos please send him the portrait of a Greek girl—any girl, so long as she was beautiful. He would especially like one of those portraits which hang in the windows of photographers' shops; and with this photograph in his letter case, Schliemann was sure to be immune from the danger of marrying a Frenchwoman, for everyone knows that French women are dangerous. He began the letter hesitantly, almost reluctantly. Half way through, he felt in a mood to make his supreme request—would Vimpos please choose a bride for him. Her qualifications? She should be poor, beautiful, an enthusiast for Homer, dark-haired, well educated, and the possessor of a good and loving heart. The ideal was Vimpos' sister, but she was already married. Perhaps he could find an orphan, daughter of a scholar, compelled to earn her living as a governess. Schliemann concludes his letter by saying that there was no one in the world except Vimpos to whom he could entrust the secrets of his heart, and he encloses another 100 francs for the poor of Athens.

Vimpos was not in the least outraged by the letter. He went about Athens, collected photographs of desirable young Athenian girls, and sent them to Indianapolis. Among these photographs was one of Sophia Engastromenos, a pretty dark-haired girl with a delicate oval face, large eyes, and thick curving eyebrows. It was the face of a girl of quite unusual beauty, very serious but capable of lighting up with quick childish smiles. Schliemann had twelve copies of her photograph made, and sent one off to his father with a brief note saying he knew he would be happy with her, but he had decided not to marry her unless she was enthusiastic about learning. If all went well, he would go to Athens in July, marry her and then bring her to Germany.

He did not reach Athens in July because the divorce pro-

ceedings were held up. He had nothing to fear. He had
become an American citizen in March, and it was therefore
only a question of waiting patiently for the time when the
papers were signed. At last, toward the end of July, his
divorce was granted. He hurried to New York and took
the first available ship across the Atlantic. He was still not
sure whether he would marry Sophia, for he wrote to a
friend from the ship: "Thank God, there are great possibilities
of choice in Greece, and the girls there are as beautiful as
the pyramids of Egypt." It is unlikely that Sophia would
have been pleased to be compared with a pyramid.

He arrived in Greece in August on the eve of the Feast of
St. Meletius, the patron saint of the little church near the
country villa of the Engastromenos family at Colonus, slightly
more than a mile northwest of Athens. Colonus was the birth-
place of Sophocles and the scene of the mysterious disappearance of Oedipus—"White Colonus," says Sophocles, "fed
by heaven's dews, the place where the clear-voiced night-
ingales sing amidst the wine-dark ivy." There was no place
more auspicious. The moment Schliemann reached the little
town he found himself looking upon the celebration of an
ancient rite, for the girls were carrying garlands to the church.

Sophia was not an orphan, nor was her family particularly
poor, nor had she ever been a governess. Her father was a
draper, with a shop and town house in Athens, a solid handsome man who won the cross in the War of Independence.
Sophia was in the church, standing on a stool and hanging up
garlands when Schliemann arrived at the house in the company of Theokletos Vimpos. In the church there was the cry:
"The German has come!" He had not been expected so early
in the day. Sophia jumped off her stool and hurried into the
house to change her dress. The whole family was there—
father, mother, sisters, brothers, cousins—and they were all
sitting round the table, gazing at the strange German with
the sad smile and the gold-rimmed spectacles, nearly bald,
with a heavy gold watch-chain hanging over his waistcoat.

At last Sophia came into the room, wearing a white dress, with ribbons in her hair, very demure. Wine and cakes were being served. Sophia sat down at the table with her eyes lowered. Schliemann was talking about his travels all over the world in impeccable Greek. Suddenly he turned to Sophia and asked her three questions. The first question was: "Would you like to go on a long journey?" Sophia answered that she would. The second question was: "When did the Emperor Hadrian visit Athens?" Sophia gave the exact date. The third question was: "Can you recite passages of Homer by heart?" Sophia could and did. The examination had been passed with flying colors.

During the next three days Schliemann haunted the country villa. He spent his days there, retiring to his hotel only in the evening. Sophia knew she was being watched closely, but she showed no nervousness. She played with her sisters and cousins, helped to prepare the table, and sometimes vanished into the cellar where they kept their casks of oil, butter, and olives. There were so many relatives in the house that Schliemann had to slip a message into her hands to see her privately.

Once when they were alone, he said abruptly: "Why do you want to marry me?"

"Because my parents told me you were a rich man," Sophia answered simply.

Schliemann was hurt to the quick and strode off in anger to his hotel. He had thought the girl possessed a natural nobility, and she had answered like a slave. He wrote on his hotel notepaper:

I am deeply pained, Miss Sophia, at the answer you have given me—one worthy of a slave, and all the more strange because it comes from an educated young woman. I myself am a simple, honorable, home-loving man. If ever we were married, it would be so that we could excavate together and share our common love for Homer.

The day after tomorrow I shall leave for Naples, and perhaps we shall never meet again. But if you should ever need a friend, remember your devoted

HEINRICH SCHLIEMANN
Doctor of Philosophy,
Place St. Michel, 6, Paris

This letter, with its confusions and self-appraisals unresolved, was written in white-hot anger and dispatched by hotel messenger. Sophia was overwhelmed. While the whole family insisted that she compose a letter to allay the German's wrath, and called in one of her uncles, a government official, to help her, she seems to have known exactly what to do. The letter she wrote shows no evidence of any assistance. She wrote on cheap notepaper hurriedly bought from a local store:

Dear Herr Heinrich: I am so sorry you are going away. You must not be angry with what I said this afternoon. I thought that was how young girls should speak. My parents and I will be very happy if you will come and see us again tomorrow.

Schliemann was relieved, but determined to punish her. He wrote more letters and received more letters in exchange, until he felt assured of her affection. It was as though he could not trust himself to confront her. Six days passed before he relented, and then only because the seventeen-year-old girl wrote in her round careful handwriting a proposal of marriage, and against such a proposal he was defenseless. He had arrived in Athens late in August, and on September 24 they were married.

Schliemann wore a frock coat, Sophia wore a white dress and bridal veil wreathed with flowers from Colonus, and all her relatives attended in Greek national costume. Then there was a feast which lasted late into the evening, and that night the bride and groom drove to Piraeus, the port of Athens, and waited until three o'clock in the morning before they could board the ship for Naples. Sophia insisted on bringing

Heinrich Schliemann in middle age.

her dolls with her, and Schliemann was in no mood to argue. She had won her first victory, and she was to win all the others.

Beautiful and childlike, moving with an easy grace which she never lost even in old age, Sophia dominated him by appearing never to dominate him. She loved him to distraction, with the violence of the young in love with the old, yet never completely understanding him. Reserved and cold even in the presence of his intimate friends, he loved her passionately, delighting in her quick changes of mood, her laughter, and her profound seriousness, which was always like the seriousness of a child. During the honeymoon he wrote: "She has a kind of divine reverence for her husband."

It was true; but the words should not be allowed to stand alone, for he too possessed a kind of divine reverence for this wife, who had been given to him so unexpectedly and against all odds. To the end of his life he worshiped her; and though they quarreled, and sometimes the old habits of intolerance were renewed in him, her own quiet gaiety was proof against his pride, his self-esteem, his overweening vanity. In her company he was warm and gentle. The miracle had been accomplished; and sometimes he would find himself looking at her with the expression of a man bewildered by his own good fortune.

It was a strange honeymoon. Naples, Pompeii, Florence, Munich—always the hurried journeys through the museums, with Schliemann delivering in his high-pitched voice a running commentary on all the works of art, until Sophia could have cried out in agony, and loved him all the more for it. People stopped and stared at the elderly professor—he was forty-seven, but looked ten years older—and his young wife, both so serious, so intent upon the study of art. In the evenings he would ask her to recite two hundred lines of Homer, and often she would fall asleep before she was finished. She had awakened the pedagogue in him.

He was determined to mold her closer to his heart's desire, and he insisted that she become a linguist—she would learn German and French, one language a year, and surely that was not demanding too much from her! Then he took her to Paris and installed her in the vast apartment overlooking the Seine and the Cathedral of Nôtre Dame. It was a cold winter. She missed her relatives. Her husband dressed her in the latest fashions and made her wear a chignon, but when some Greek girls came to visit her, she tossed the chignon away, got down on her knees and showed them her dolls.

She hated Paris—the fog coming over the Seine, the cold,

the dampness, the knife-edge winds blowing up the Place St. Michel. She was bored by the society he cultivated, the visits to the Geographical Society, the continual talk about Troy, Mycenae, and the islands of the Greek archipelago, where hitherto unknown treasures might be buried. Schliemann's mind moved like the intricate mechanism of a watch, never still, for he was still searching for a theater of operations and was desperate for the opportunity to prove himself.

By the end of January he was restless again, planning to return to Troy, but about this time he learned of the death of his daughter Nadezhda and was prostrated with grief. Once again he was haunted by ghosts. He accused himself of complicity in her death: he would have done everything in the world to save her, the best doctors would have been sent to her bedside, why had he not been informed before? It was a familiar story: the millionaire caught in the toils of grief, telling himself he would have fought against death itself with his gold, if only he had been given the opportunity. He thought of rushing to St. Petersburg to comfort his remaining children, and might have done so if Sophia had not fallen ill.

She grew pale and listless, but the doctors could find nothing wrong with her. She was studying too hard—he had decided she should learn German and French simultaneously, and could not understand why she was so slow. Sometimes he took her to the circus, where she enjoyed herself, but more often she was taken to the theater. Sitting upright in a box, wearing diamonds, listening to speeches she could barely understand, she was bored to tears. When she fell ill, the doctors could find nothing wrong—perhaps it was no more than the fever of homesickness.

In the middle of February, with Sophia no more than a ghost of herself, suffering from unaccountable fits of weeping, Schliemann decided to take her to Athens and make his way to Troy. Calvert had promised to obtain a *firman* to permit the excavations from the Turkish government, but no *firman* had arrived. On board the steamer *Niemen* bound from Marseilles to Piraeus he wrote to Calvert on February 17, 1870, with his usual impatience:

Please inform me by the first opportunity whether you have got now the firman, for in that case I would like to commence the excavations at Hissarlik at once. I think the early season can be *no* impediment to do so, for the weather is warm and delightful here and it can hardly be different in the Troad. I would wish to begin work at once, the more so since I have later on other important things to attend to.

Thus, if you have got the firman, please give me once more a list of the implements and instruments required, for in the hurry with which we left Paris I have forgotten to copy same from your letter of last winter . . .

When Schliemann reached Athens, there was no *firman* awaiting him. He had thought of making some excavations at Mycenae, but a party of seven Englishmen had been killed by bandits not many months ago, and the Greek government frowned on archeologists who wandered alone into the interior. In despair, Schliemann decided to pass the time until the *firman* arrived by sailing in a sailboat among the islands of the Ægean Sea.

It was an unhappy adventure. He knew nothing about sailing boats, and the Greek sailor who accompanied him seems to have been incompetent. He visited Delos, where Apollo was born, and Paros, famous for its marble quarries, and Naxos, which was sacred to Bacchus, but he was most attracted to the small island of Thera (Santorino). He reached Thera after drifting for four days in a storm, living on bread and water. It was the most southerly of the small islands scattered about the Ægean Sea, and had an important history: from this island in 631 B.C. the Greeks had sailed to colonize the rich province of Cyrene in Africa. It was a volcanic island, and Schliemann was delighted with the strange cliffs formed of layers of lava in different colors—red, black, yellow,

white and brown. These cliffs, seven hundred feet high, were "a terrifying and awesome spectacle." He liked the islanders and was able to buy from them some recently discovered Stone Age vases found under three layers of lava, and then he made his way back to Athens, hopping from one island to another.

In the past his good fortune was sometimes announced beforehand by a great thunderstorm. So it had been when his ship foundered off the island of Texel; and then again in mid-Atlantic the thunder of Zeus roared overhead and not long afterwards he made a fortune in California. So now, returning to Athens, he may have believed that the four-day storm which hurled his small sailing ship onto the shores of the island of Thera was a sign of the good fortune waiting for him in Troy. No *firman* had arrived from Constantinople, but there was nothing to prevent him from visiting the Troad; nothing to prevent him from employing workmen; nothing to prevent him from wielding a pickax. Alone, without help, leaving Sophia behind in Athens, he decided to take Troy by storm.

. . . 6 THE GOLD OF TROY

WHEN Schliemann came to Troy, he was traveling a well-trodden road. Other and greater men had worshiped at those crumbling altars, overgrown with thorny scrub and decaying trees. There was no mystery—or only a little mystery—about the site. For generation upon generation men had wandered along the inhospitable Phrygian coast to seek refreshment among the broken towers and moldered stones of the city where Helen was kept captive and the ten-year war was fought.

Xerxes, King of Persia and most of the world, had paused there, if we can believe Herodotus,[1] during his march through

---

1. *Herodotus:* Greek historian of the fifth century, B.C., author of *The Persian Wars.*

Asia Minor on his way to Greece. He climbed up to the citadel, sought out the knowledgeable inhabitants of the place, and listened to their stories of the siege. Then he sacrificed a thousand oxen to the Trojan Athena and ordered his priests to pour libations of wine to the spirits of the great men of old. That night all the Persian troops who had gathered there felt a ghostly dread coming out of the earth, but they could put no name to it.

For the Persians and for others Troy was a place of strange terrors, of mingled myths and nightmares. Like all battle-fields it was haunted by ghosts screaming for vengeance. Xerxes called himself the avenger of the crime. According to the Persians, it was the fall of Troy which made them the hereditary enemies of the Greeks.

But when the Greeks came to Troy, they saw it as the place where they had triumphed over Asia. So when Alexander crossed the Hellespont on his way to make war on Persia, he ran oiled and naked around the tomb of Achilles on the promontory of Sigeum, and donned some of the arms preserved in the Temple of Athena, and made grandiose plans for embellishing the city.

Julius Caesar, hunting Pompey over land and sea, arrived on the Rhoetian promontory and wandered about the ruins of the city burned forty years before by a Roman expeditionary force. All he found was the enveloping forest, rotting oak thickets growing over the palaces of kings and the temples of gods. He was crossing a stream which meandered through the sand when someone said: "This is the famous river Xanthus!" He stepped on a patch of grass, and someone cried: "This is where they brought Hector's body! Be careful not to offend his ghost!" And when he came to a pile of loose stones, someone plucked his sleeve and said: "Do you not see the altar of Hercaean Jupiter?"

Caesar had seen nothing, only ruins and the surrounding darkness, but he knew he had come to a sacred place, and feared the ghosts. So he hastily erected an altar of turf, burned incense on it, and prayed to the gods who guarded these sacred ashes, asking prosperity for himself and vowing to rebuild the shattered walls until they gleamed and sparkled as before. And then remembering Pompey, he hurried off to Egypt, so impatient to kill his enemy that he sailed past all the wealthy cities of Asia and did not pause until he reached Alexandria.

Madmen and emperors came to Troy. The mad Caracalla paid tribute at the shrines. Hopelessly lost among delusions of grandeur, he imagined he was Achilles, as in Macedonia he imagined he was Alexander the Great. He remembered that Achilles had been grief-stricken by the death of his beloved friend Patroclus; so he poisoned his favorite freed-man Festus in order that he should have someone to grieve over, and ordered a great funeral pyre to be built, and himself slaughtered the sacrificial animals and lifted the body onto it and set the pyre alight. Then he sprinkled wine on the flames and called upon the winds to celebrate the death of his friend. Herodian, who tells the story, adds that in his grief he tried to cut off a lock of his hair to throw into the fire, but as he was very bald-headed, he was laughed at. Afterward he remembered that Alexander had run naked round the tomb of Achilles, and nothing would satisfy him but he must do the same.

And after Caracalla came others—the endless procession of tourists determined to set foot on the sacred soil while on their way to Persia or Jerusalem. The Emperor Julian visited Novum Ilium in 124 A.D. and gave fresh burial to the bones of Ajax. The young emperor, who laughed when the Christians worshiped the bones of martyrs, worshiped devotedly at the shrine of Ajax. Two hundred years later the Emperor Constantine decided to build a new capital of the Roman Empire in the East, and thought of establishing it in Troy before finally deciding upon Byzantium. Then for a few more years the Trojans secretly offered sacrifices at the ancient altars, but with the coming of the Christian emperors the city lost its importance.

For fifteen hundred years it had guarded the approaches to the Dardanelles. Now grass grew in the streets, the walls of temples and palaces collapsed, and soon there was nothing but a huge mound of thistles and grass. The Anglo-Saxon chronicler Saewulf, who passed close by the shores of the Troad about 1100 A.D., says the ruins of Troy were scattered over many miles; and two hundred years later Sir John Mandeville, that mysterious traveler who may never have visited the East, says that nothing remained, for Troy was completely destroyed.

Though destroyed, Troy remained. No other city except Jerusalem had such power to kindle the imaginations of men. Virgil and Homer kept it alive during the Renaissance; and Italian scholars dreamed of the day when they too could walk along the roads where Achilles strode, "as high as a mountain." The English, like the Romans, sometimes thought they were the descendants of the Trojans, claiming that the original name of London was Troynovant, the "New Troy." In the *chansons de geste* Troy was a living city, all the more luminous because it was a city of the imagination.

In 1870 there seem to have been only two people—Frank Calvert and Heinrich Schliemann—who believed firmly that Troy was a real city; that its walls, its palaces, even the furniture and literature of the Trojans, lay buried in the mound at Hissarlik. Charles Maclaren, the brilliant archeologist, who had proved to his own satisfaction as far back as 1822 that Troy was to be found at Hissarlik, was dead; the consensus of scholars was that Troy was at Bunarbashi, and few people believed that anything would be gained by excavations at Hissarlik.

Frank Calvert had neither the money nor the inclination to make a complete excavation of the mound. The eastern part of the mound belonged to him, the western part belonged to two Turks living at Koum-Kale.

Schliemann was convinced that the more important discoveries would be made in the western part, overlooking the sea. Characteristically he decided to attack the part belonging to the Turks, leaving for some future occasion the exploration of the part belonging to Calvert. He said later: "I was so sure of finding great buildings, and then too I hoped they would pardon my audacity when they saw the treasure —*j'espèrais qu'ils me pardonneraient mon audace à la vue de ces trésors.*" From the very beginning his eye was on the buried treasure.

On April 9 he dug the first trench with the help of ten Turkish laborers from the nearby village of Remkoi. The workmen were paid 10 piasters a day. Schliemann stood over them with a pistol in his belt, a riding whip in his hand. The first spadeful of earth was dug on the northwest corner of the hill at a place which roughly corresponded in Schliemann's mind to the position of the Scaean Gate. After an hour's digging, 2 feet below the surface the workmen came upon the remains of a wall. Schliemann was excited. The workmen worked hard, and by sunset they had uncovered the foundations of a building 60 feet long and 40 feet wide.

The next day, with eleven more workmen, he began digging at the southeast and southwest corners of the building which was slowly emerging before his eyes. At last the flagstones were revealed. They were covered with 2 feet of earth and detritus formed through the ages—sheep dung, the remains of plants, and atmospheric dust. There were no potsherds; only this thick coating of earth. Then he dug below the flagstones and found exactly what he had expected to find: cinders, calcined matter, evidence of fire. There was so much burned matter and it was arranged in such an orderly manner that he came to the conclusion that altogether ten wooden houses had perished in the flames before the last stone house was built on their ruins. Among the cinders he found a coin, bearing on one side the image of Emperor Commodus and on the other the image of Hector, the son of Priam, the great general who commanded the Trojan forces. In Schliemann's eyes the coin, which bore the inscription *Hector Ilieon* ("Hector of Troy") was the most auspicious sign of all.

For two days, Schliemann dug around this building, but on the third day, fearing that the Turkish proprietors might arrive at any moment, and in haste to discover more profit- able remains, he started on two long trenches, one from east to west, and another running due north. By slicing across the top of the mound he hoped to form a general picture of the buried city, just as a man drawing lines at right angles across a small village and examining all the objects en- countered in the path of these lines might reasonably be able to form a rough sketch of the entire village. Somewhere these lines would cut through the main street, the mayor's office, the post office, the fire-engine shed.

Schliemann's plan was perfectly sound, but he had hardly begun these new excavations when the Turks arrived, to discover a small army of excavators on their land. Schliemann explained through an interpreter that he was doing work of scientific importance, that he wanted nothing for himself, and that he was honoring Turkey by his presence. Alarmed and baffled, the Turks argued that he had no right to be there, and asked him to leave. Schliemann took them over the prop- erty, cajoling, pleading, making long speeches about his dis- coveries which would soon be hailed by archeologists all over the world—he had already discovered part of the wall of the temple of Pallas Athena, innumerable bones, tiles, boars' teeth, signs of conflagration.

The Turks were more interested in the heavy blocks of stone he had unearthed. They intended to build a stone bridge over the Simois, and these blocks exactly suited their purpose. They agreed to let Schliemann continue digging the two long trenches on condition they were allowed to use the stone for the bridge. He paid them forty francs, and they went off smiling.

Throughout his life as an excavator Schliemann had the habit of giving heroic names to his discoveries. He had found an immense wall, and instantly named it the temple of Pallas Athena. A little while later, while digging deeper in the north trench, he discovered below twenty-two layers of cinders the terra-cotta bust of a woman, and instantly named it the bust of Helen of Troy. Supremely self-assured, never hesitating to make grandiose claims, he rarely permitted himself the luxury of the slightest doubt. But sometimes doubts crept in.

The more he thought of his encounter with the Turks the more convinced he was that he was at the mercy of forces beyond his control. By paying them forty francs and promising them the use of the stone for the bridge, he had obtained a temporary truce. But what if the truce were broken? What if the Turks insisted on their rights? He had tried to bargain for the land, but the price they demanded was exorbitant. They had demanded the use of the stones for their miserable bridge—it was the worst kind of sacrilege. How to deal with them? How to obtain full rights over the land? He was still debating these questions when, on the afternoon of April 21, the Turks returned, said they now had enough stones for their bridge, and ordered him to stop digging.

Schliemann had no weapons against this ultimatum. He could not fight them on their level, but he could fight them on other levels; and that night, in a mood that curiously mingled resignation, despair, and vast hopes for the future, he wrote off a series of letters outlining what he had done and the problems he faced to friends in Germany, France, Athens, and Constantinople. To a powerful friend in Germany he wrote:

I have uncovered the ruins of palaces and temples on walls of much older buildings, and at the depth of 15 feet I came upon vast walls six feet thick and of most wonderful construction. 7½ feet lower down I found that these same walls rested upon other walls 8½ feet thick. These must be the walls of the Palace of Priam or the Temple of Athene.

Unfortunately there has been continual unpleasantness with the two Turks who own the land, and they will probably make me put an end to my work tomorrow. Meanwhile I intend to go to all possible lengths to buy the land, and shall not rest until I have uncovered the Palace of Priam.

For the moment there was nothing he could do. Bowing to the inevitable, he paid off his workmen and returned to Athens, where he hoped to receive permission to dig in the ruins of Mycenae. He would spend a few weeks in Mycenae, and then, with the *firman* from the Turkish government and the mound of Hissarlik in his possession, he would resume digging in the Troad.

Everywhere he turned there were obstacles. The Greeks refused to allow him to dig at Mycenae, claiming that the surrounding territory was infested with bandits. Frank Calvert had only just recovered from a serious illness and was in no condition to assist him. Sophia was still ill. Schliemann wrote an account of his ten-day adventure in the Troad for the *Kölnische Zeitung*, openly admitting that he had excavated the mound without the permission of the owners, and he was surprised when he learned that the Turkish authorities had read the account and disapproved of his activities. There was nothing for him to do but bide his time in Athens.

He hated his inactivity. He could not understand why Frank Calvert was so unhelpful. He offered to pay £100 for the land owned by the two Turks, adding tactlessly that if Calvert could buy it cheaper the difference would be his own profit. To Schliemann it was all very simple: once the land was in his possession the excavations could go on, and he was perfectly prepared to spend three months every year for five years cleaning the rubbish away from the palaces buried in the mound.

The weeks passed, with Schliemann oppressed by the misery of frustration. He bombarded Frank Calvert with letters, begging him to intercede with the Turkish government, waiting as always "with immense anxiety your kind information on this head," but there was little Calvert could do—little he had inclination to do. The Turks were outraged, in no mood to offer assistance to a man who dug huge trenches across Turkish property.

Summer came. It was too hot for digging on the plain of Troy, and Schliemann set out for Paris and the cultivated conversation he missed in Athens. He had big investments in property—more than 200 people lived in the buildings he owned—and it pleased him to look over his property from time to time. One day in the middle of June when Paris was empty, he received a letter from Sergey in St. Petersburg. The boy said he was not progressing well at school.

Schliemann replied in French in a letter so filled with frigid boasting that he gives the impression of a man on the verge of insanity. He wrote:

It was very sad to hear you have not been progressing. In this life one must progress continually, otherwise one becomes discouraged. Try then to follow the example of your father who, in all the positions he has occupied, has always proved how much a man can accomplish provided he has a fierce energy. I performed miracles during the four years 1842-1846 in Amsterdam. I did what no one else has ever done and no one else could ever do. Then I became a merchant in St Petersburg, and no merchant was ever so accomplished or so prudent. Then I became a traveler, but not an ordinary traveler—I was a traveler *par excellence*. No other merchant in St Petersburg has ever written a scientific work, but I wrote one which was translated into four languages, a book which became the object of universal admiration. Today I am an archeologist, and all Europe and America are dazzled by my discovery of the ancient city of Troy—that Troy which the archeologists of all countries have searched for in vain for two thousand years . . .

I did what no one else has ever done and no one else could ever do. . . . These boasts arose from weakness. They are cries of despair, uttered in loneliness and misery, as he sought in vain for the purposes of his own life. He had hoped to lay bare the legendary city of Troy, but two obscure Turkish peasants whose sheepfolds lay across the mound of Hissarlik had simply ordered him off their property, as though he were a common trespasser. They had no right to do it! He, Schliemann, had unearthed the buried city, that city which was his by right of discovery. Had he not promised to spend a hundred thousand francs on the excavation, for the sole purpose of enlightening the scholars of the world? He possessed property all over the world. Then why should a small hill in a corner of Asia Minor be refused to him? Why had these Turks in baggy trousers defiled his city by removing the sacred stones to build a bridge? Just before leaving Hissarlik these same peasants had demanded £100 for the damage he had caused, but this, of course, he refused to pay.

On July 19, 1870, Napoleon III declared war on Prussia, and Schliemann was still in Paris, burning with resentment against those two peasants who by this time had probably forgotten his existence. He wrote to Frank Calvert from Boulogne-sur-mer, where he fled shortly after the declaration of war, begging him to see that no stones were removed from the palace walls he had unearthed—surely there must be some way to prevent those peasants from destroying a work which had survived for thirty centuries?

At the end of August he wrote to Safvet Pasha, the Turkish Minister of Public Instruction, a long, imploring letter, saying that he had never hoped to find any treasure. No, this was not the reason why he had dug at Hissarlik. On the contrary, he had acted out of "the pure and disinterested love of science," with only one desire—to prove that the city of Troy lay beneath the mound. He enclosed a copy of *Ithaka, der Peloponnes und Troja*. He threw himself on the mercy of the Turkish government. Surely they would realize the importance of his researches. Surely they would not blame him for having made, in the wild enthusiasm for Homer which overcame him when he found himself at Hissarlik, a few unimportant excavations which nevertheless proved the existence of Priam's palace and the great wall surrounding the city.

"I worked in rainstorms as though it were summer. I thought I had lunched and dined when I had eaten nothing all day, and every little piece of pottery which I brought to light was for me another page of history!" He begged His Excellency's pardon for having acted high-handedly, and offered to wait upon His Excellency at any time, if only there was some slight hope that the excavations might be allowed to continue. There was no reply. The inscrutable Safvet Pasha confronted the inscrutable Schliemann across the whole length of Europe, and neither gave an inch.

If Schliemann had not written this outrageous letter with its pious sentiments and florid appeals to "our common mother Science, to whom both of us owe our lives, which both of us adore with the same enthusiasm," the story of the discovery of Troy might have been very different. The letter, for all its denials, convinced Safvet Pasha that Schliemann was looking for buried treasure, and when Schliemann arrived in Constantinople at last in December, the minister greeted him affably, promised him every kind of assistance, proclaimed his total belief in the blessings of science, and did everything he could to prevent the excavations from continuing. Schliemann was left with the impression that it was only a matter of a few days before he would be in full possession of Hissarlik, with a *firman* from the Turkish government permitting him to excavate to his heart's content.

While waiting in Constantinople, his mind absorbed by the approaching fall of Paris and the problem of obtaining title to the mound at Hissarlik—with great difficulty Frank Calvert had obtained from the two Turks a verbal promise that they would sell their land for 1,000 francs—Schliemann received a letter from his wife full of dejection and despair. He could be cruel to those he loved. He answered that she had no reason to despair. If she would only count her blessings —her husband who worshiped her, her position in life, her house in Athens and all the good simple people who were devoted to her, while in France two million men, women, and children were dying of starvation, with enemy shells falling on their defenseless houses, with not a crust of bread to eat, and not a stick of firewood to warm them. If she would only think about more important matters! He had visited Safvet Pasha. He had been greeted cordially. The long-wished-for *firman* had been promised, and in a few days would be safely in his hands. He would go to Hissarlik in a few days, buy the land, and then he would have to return briefly to Paris, but she should not think of the dangers of the journey. He went on:

You should fall straightway on your knees and thank God for all the blessings He has showered on you, and you should ask His pardon for permitting yourself in these days of strain to forget the bounty He has poured over you.

You forget, too, that I have learned Turkish during my involuntary stay here. I have been studying the language for the past eighteen days, and I assure you I speak and write it fluently, and already I have a vocabulary of 6,000 words.

A week passed. There was still no word from Safvet Pasha. On January 8, 1871, Schliemann wrote a formal request for permission to continue the excavations. Ten days later he was summoned to the Ministry of Public Instruction. There he learned that Safvet Pasha had telegraphed the governor of the Dardanelles granting permission for the excavations to continue and at the same time ordering that the land be bought *on behalf of the ministry*.

Schliemann was violently angry. "I told him in the plainest language what I thought of his odious and contemptible conduct." He explained that for two and a half years he had done everything possible to acquire title to the land. He had been actuated by the purest scientific principles. All he had ever wanted to do was to prove that the Trojan War was no fable, that Troy had actually existed, but it was a question of cutting through a whole mountain at enormous expense, and it was intolerable that he should not be allowed to possess that little spit of land, which he was perfectly prepared to pay for.

An Englishman, the director of the National Museum, was present at the interview, and Safvet Pasha seems to have been confused and ashamed by the outburst. He did his best to calm Schliemann by saying that everything was perfectly in order. Of course there was nothing to prevent him from going to Hissarlik and buying the land and continuing his excavations "as long as he submitted to the regulations of the Ottoman Empire concerning any treasures which are discovered."

At this new turn in the discussion, Schliemann overflowed with gratitude. He evidently assumed that he had been granted everything he asked for. He thanked the minister cordially, and promised to mention the minister's name in his forthcoming book on his excavations at Troy. It is possible, and very likely, that Schliemann had completely failed to understand what the minister was saying. It is also possible that he deliberately misinterpreted the minister's words. He had shouted and threatened. In the Turkish fashion Safvet Pasha had attempted to quiet him, saying that Schliemann was a man of good sense, and of course everything was possible to him. Among these face-saving gestures and hesitant smiles, Schliemann appears to have detected approval and genuine sympathy, and it never seems to have occurred to him that he was being politely dismissed. To the end of his life he maintained that at the meeting on January 18 he received a verbal promise which gave him full authority to buy the land and continue the excavations.

Three days later, in the pouring rain, he reached Koum-Kale, a little village on the Trojan plain. He was soaked to the skin and exhausted by the journey. There he learned that the minister had telegraphed orders for the purchase of the land on January 10, and title to the land was transferred to the minister two days later. At once Schliemann demanded to be taken into the presence of the Governor of the Dardanelles. He asked whether the minister had countermanded the order. "No, the order stands," the Governor replied. Feeling betrayed, in a raging temper, Schliemann returned to Athens.

If the Turks thought they had seen the last of him, they were mistaken.

Schliemann was a man who rarely changed his ideas. He had long ago convinced himself that the land belonged to him by right of conquest. Had he not left his irrefutable mark on it? Then, too, he had learned that the minister had paid 600 francs for the land, while he himself was prepared to offer 1,000 francs. Surely the land should go to the highest bidder! If they were refusing to give him the land, it was because they held science in disrepute, because they were barbarians, because they feared his towering eminence as an archeologist, whose fame resounded through Europe—he was prepared to use all arguments, on all levels, in order to outwit them. Like a blustering child, he was prepared to strike back in all directions.

His first attack took the form of a long letter to Wayne MacVeagh, the American Ambassador to the Sublime Porte, begging for the Ambassador's intervention and enclosing 4,000 piasters—3,000 piasters to pay for the land, and 1,000 piasters for the Ambassador's trouble. In this letter Schliemann de-

scribes his interview with Safvet Pasha, painting himself as
a knight in shining armor and the minister as an incompetent
fool who had forgotten to countermand an order after promising to do so. He wrote:

What is certain is that His Excellency Safvet Pasha gave me
the field at Hissarlik and authorized me to travel to Hissarlik
and purchase it formally, and therefore it follows that if his
word is sacred the place belongs to me at the price of 3,000
piastres, which he paid for it. I am therefore taking the liberty
of enclosing 4,000 piastres with the request that you pay 3,000
to His Excellency, and I would beg you to accept the remaining
1,000 for the costs attendant upon this petition. He knows that
everything I have stated is true, and he will not for a moment
hesitate in agreeing with my demands.

This is not a question of a commercial transaction. It is a
question of resolving the most important of all historical problems, and every step you take in this affair will be applauded
by the entire civilized world.

There was method in Schliemann's madness. There were
to be many more letters to officials in Constantinople. He
would show himself in all his disguises: gentle, severe,
charming, intolerant of all opposition. Little by little he
would break down all opposition, and in the end his will
would prevail.

Meanwhile there were more urgent matters to attend to.
That winter Paris was ringed around by the heavy guns of
the army of the Crown Prince of Prussia. Schliemann was
concerned about the fate of his property. He had a deep
affection for his apartment on the Place St. Michel, which
contained his library and a small collection of archeological
treasures from the Far East, Ithaca, and Thera, and among
them was the vase containing the ashes of Odysseus. There
was nothing for it but to return to Paris.

Armed with a letter of introduction from the Prussian
Ambassador in Athens, he left hurriedly for Munich, acquired more letters of introduction, went on to Strasbourg

where he interviewed Count Bismark-Bohlen, the governor-general, and then to Versailles where he attempted to acquire from the hands of Bismarck himself a safe-conduct into the besieged city. But Bismarck and President Jules Favre, who had already concluded a form of armistice, had agreed that no one should enter Paris until peace was restored.

Characteristically Schliemann regarded all laws which impeded his progress, even martial laws, as intolerable abuses of freedom. For five francs he bought a false passport written out in the name of the postmaster Klein of Lagny. Schliemann was forty-nine, but looked sixty; the photograph on the passport showed a man about thirty years old. Inevitably, as he made his way through the German lines, he was regarded with suspicion. Three times he was detained for examination. He said later that he might have been put up against a wall and shot, but he remembered the German mania for titles, and by addressing every lieutenant as general and every simple soldier as full colonel, he succeeded by flattery in passing through the lines unscathed.

News reaching Athens suggested that Paris was in ruins, but it was not so. As he walked around the city, Schliemann discovered that all the familiar buildings were still standing— the Pantheon, the church of St. Sulpice, the Sorbonne were untouched. His apartment at 6 Place St. Michel, and the house he owned next door, were exactly as he had left them. Tears rolled down his cheeks when he entered his library— "such tears as would have sprung to my eyes if I had come into the presence of a child resurrected from the dead." Oddly enough, the house at 5 Place St. Michel had received a direct hit, and he found himself thinking of that day when all the warehouses except his own at Memel had been destroyed in the flames. Once more a divine purpose had protected him. It was spring, and the chestnut trees were in flower, and Paris on the eve of the Commune[2] was as beautiful

2. *Commune:* insurrectionary government that held control of Paris from March 18 to May 28, 1871.

as ever. He wrote to his friend Gottschalk, a businessman in Würtemberg:

By day the face of Paris has changed so very little. There are just as many people on the streets as before: only there are few carriages, because most of the horses have been eaten. It is at night that Paris is sad, the only light in the streets coming from miserable oil-lamps. Because there is no gaslight the theaters are open during the day. All the museums and libraries except the Sorbonne are still closed. To my great delight the College of France opens its doors tomorrow. Among the hundreds of untruths I heard about Paris there is the one that the trees every-where—in the streets, in the gardens of the Tuileries, in the Parc Monceau and the Champs Elysées—have been cut down. Let me assure you that not a single tree has been cut, and you may wander through the Bois de Boulogne for days before coming upon any trees cut down, and these are usually near the for-tifications . . .

When the Communards were in possession of Paris, Schlie-mann was still there. He had faith in France, and little faith in Germany under the monarchy—he agreed with Victor Hugo[3] that Germany would become a republic in time, and that she had power to invade other countries was of very little interest, since she would herself be invaded in her turn. He passed the time quietly in his study, contemplating the war from a distance.

He wrote to Frank Calvert suggesting that something might be gained by a meeting between Safvet Pasha, the American Ambassador, and himself—surely the opportunity must not be allowed to lose itself in the chancelries of the Sublime Porte. He remembered that treasure had been found at Hissarlik, and this not far from the place where he had dug his first trench. The treasure, which consisted of 1,200 large silver medals of the period of Antiochus the Great, was per-haps one of the factors which weighed heavily with the min-

3. *Victor Hugo:* French writer (1802-1885).

ister. In that case Schliemann would demonstrate his pure disinterestedness. He offered to give all the gold and silver treasure he discovered to the minister, and every coin. He offered to permit two watchmen from the ministry on the site of the excavations. Only one thing he refused: he would not dig unless he was given title to the land:

I will even give him double the value of the precious metals I may find, for I have no other object in view than to solve the mighty problem of Troy's real site and am ready to sacrifice for its excavation years of my life and a vast amount of money, but the field must be my property and as long as this is not the case I will never think of commencing the excavations, for if I dig on Government ground I shall be exposed to everlasting vexations and trouble . . .

Never previously had he promised to surrender all the treasure he discovered to the ministry and in addition pay double the value of the precious metals. He was speaking like one possessed of illimitable largesse, who cared nothing for the treasure once it was dug out of the earth, but in fact he was still determined to seize the treasure, and keep it. Against the duplicity of the Turks he was prepared to employ the greater duplicity of a skilled merchant, and the cunning of Odysseus.

In those days he thought often of Odysseus. In a sense he had modeled himself from childhood on that cunning wanderer. Sophia was pregnant, and he had already settled the name he would give to his unborn son—Odysseus.

Paris was in the hands of the Communards. Undaunted, Schliemann simply walked through the German lines with his false passport. He reached Athens in May, in time for the birth of his child. He had always imagined it would be a boy. Instead it was a girl, and he called her Andromache after the beautiful wife of Hector.

In June, a month after the birth of Andromache, he hurried

to Constantinople and presented a new offer to Safvet Pasha. This memorandum reveals the temper of the man—his Odysseus-like cunning, his highly developed sense of his own importance, and that quality which the Jews call *chutzpa,* which is neither nerve nor gall, but the finest flower of these. He denied that he had any hope of finding treasure; this, indeed, was the last thing on his mind. If, however, any treasure was dug up, he offered solemnly to divide it between himself and the Turkish government. He made no claim on the land, and asked only that he be provided, in the name of the Grand Vizier, with the protection which would be afforded to any foreigner in a remote part of Turkey. He wrote:

I have the honor to submit to Your Excellency a proposition which is very close to my heart concerning excavations I hope to undertake in the Troad, near the Dardanelles, with the aim of determining, if possible, the true site of the palace of King Priam.

I have already made some small excavations at Hissarlik, and I believe I have found the palace which formed part of the ancient city of Troy. The difficulties I there encountered on the part of the two proprietors have been happily resolved now that Your Excellency has bought the property.

I do not expect, Your Excellency, to find any treasure there. Such hopes vanish in the light of the far-distant epoch we are dealing with. My task, then, will be limited to archeological tests based upon the writings of Homer. If by chance it should happen that I come upon ancient objects of value which would be of interest to the Imperial Museum, I would be happy to divide them, one half for the Museum, the other half for my collection, to remunerate me for the expenses I have undertaken. The equitable division of the treasures should take place in the presence of a representative of the said Museum, and I should be permitted to take my share out of the country.

I am not asking Your Excellency for any financial assistance in making these excavations, for I myself shall assume the entire financial burden. However, I request Your Excellency to fur-

nish me, as soon as possible, with a *firman* from His Highness
the Grand Vizier addressed to His Excellency the Governor of
the Dardanelles, so that I may be protected during my researches
and excavations, and the same protection shall be given to the
historic buildings brought to light as a result of my work.

This letter, written with the help of Wayne MacVeagh,
the American Ambassador, and John Brown, the sympathetic
and learned Secretary to the Embassy, resolved all the outstanding problems. Shrewdness and guile lay concealed within
it; poison was mingled with honey; and Schliemann himself
had no intention of keeping to the letter of the agreement.
But now at last there was a face-saving agreement which
satisfied both parties to the dispute.

Schliemann was in London on August 12, 1871, when a
sealed package arrived from the American Embassy in Constantinople. The package contained the *firman*. The same
day, anxious to start digging, Schliemann wrote to Frank
Calvert, saying that he hoped to start work at the end of
September: "Pray, write me to Athens whether *the fever
are then over* and what the average weather is in the Dardanelles in October."

Once more there were delays. On September 27 he arrived
with his wife in the Dardanelles, only to learn that there was
some doubt about the wording of the *firman:* it was not clear
whether it referred to the hill at Hissarlik, and no permit had
reached the local authorities from Achmed Pasha, the governor of the Dardanelles. Also, the *firman* as written ordered
him "to respect the walls of the ancient and celebrated city,"
and he wondered what would happen if he broke through
any of the cyclopean walls.

He had already established his headquarters in the village
of Ciplak. Everything was ready. He had chosen his foreman, the workmen had been hired, wheelbarrows and baskets
had been assembled, spades, picks and axes were being un-
bundled—all that remained was to break through the last vesti-

ges of red tape. He sent an urgent message to Brown, followed it with another three days later, and at last, on Wednesday, October 11, he was able for the first time to attack the hill with the full protection of the Turkish government. Beside him as he worked was a Turkish official, Georgios Sarkis, an Armenian by birth, a former second secretary of the Chancery of Justice of the Dardanelles, "the eyes and ears of the government," to act as a perpetual watchdog and to see that no treasure was taken from the earth without the Turkish government being aware of it.

Schliemann had brought only eight wheelbarrows from France, and accordingly he started work the first day with eight workmen. The next day, seeing that work was progressing rapidly, he employed thirty-five, and on the following day he employed seventy-four. He paid each workman 9 piasters. The wages were paid out by Nicholas Zaphyros Jannakis, a colorful Greek who entered Schliemann's service shortly after his marriage. Jannakis, who came from the village of Remkoi and knew all the local dialects, acted as bodyguard, cook, cashier, and general factotum. Schliemann trusted him implicitly and always called him by his proper name, though it was his invariable custom to give his other servants names out of Greek mythology. Wherever Schliemann was, Jannakis was sure to be somewhere near; and whenever there was some local official to be bribed, Schliemann would leave it to Jannakis, who paid out the bribe money from the gold coins he always carried in his belt.

The rains came, and they were still working. As usual, Schliemann was in a hurry; he hoped to uncover the whole of Priam's palace in six weeks. Even in the rain the workmen worked from six in the morning to six at night. There was a thirty-minute rest for breakfast at nine o'clock in the morning, and an hour and a half for lunch in the early afternoon. No one was allowed to smoke except during meals—Schliemann had a theory that smoking reduced a man's energy and powers of concentration. He was a hard task-master as he superintended the digging, cursing the rains and the interminable Greek feast-days which held up operations. Three times in the course of a month there were such heavy storms that digging had to be abandoned; on those days he wrote out his reports.

But there was little to report: a few coins and calcined bones, huge walls, and some strange oblong objects which seemed to belong to a period long before the Homeric Age. On the morning of October 30 he began to dig up hundreds of these objects—lance heads of green stone, curious objects shaped like fiery mountains, and oblongs of hard black diorite, some striped with white and all of them beautifully polished. Among these were boars' tusks and boars' teeth.

He could make nothing of this. It was the last thing he expected to find. And day by day these objects were being unearthed. He began to find little clay models which resembled owls, and it occurred to him that they might represent the owl sacred to Pallas Athena. Homer spoke of "owl-faced Athena," but since Athena was the protectress of Athens, scholars assumed that the term meant that her eyes had the brightness of owls' eyes and she could see in the dark. He had hoped to find treasure, the painted walls of a palace, perhaps a great funeral chamber; instead there were these little black glistening oblongs, painted owls, and tiles with an owl's head sketched on them, and here and there traces of molten copper.

Most puzzling of all were the terra-cotta shapes which resembled small spinning tops, or *carrousels*, sometimes with two holes bored into them, which he found at a depth of ten feet. What in heaven's name were they doing in the palace of Priam?

All of his discoveries that winter puzzled him. Owls, of course, were sacred to Athena and appeared on Athenian coins, but these owls seemed to derive from an age beyond

history. He thought he had discovered some relics from the
Stone Age, and wrote off a discouraging letter to James
Calvert, the brother of Frank Calvert, begging for advice.
Calvert replied that there was nothing peculiarly astonishing
in these finds. The Greeks made no painted pottery until
the sixth or seventh century, and such abstract shapes had
been found before. "You must not be discouraged by the
supposition that you are working in a barbarous period," he
wrote. "Go ahead!"

So, more puzzled than ever, Schliemann continued to dig,
finding more and more oblongs and spinning tops, which
strangely resembled the shapes of the funeral mounds dotted
over the plain of Troy. He found obsidian knife blades so
sharp they might have been used for razors and small terra-
cotta boat-like objects which reminded him of the canoes he
had seen in India. Perhaps all these objects derived from India.
He was convinced that the oblongs had some remote connection with Vedic India. But there were also faint inscriptions
which seemed to be Egyptian, and here and there he came
upon clay tiles with swastikas cut into them, and these puzzled
him as much as the *carrousels*.

He went on working. On November 16 he was excavating
one of the walls formed of huge blocks of wrought and un-
wrought stone, and for three hours sixty-five workmen were
engaged in clearing a single door sill with block and tackle.
They were still at work on the wall the next day. November
18 was a Greek holiday, when the workmen refused to work,
and Schliemann occupied his time writing up his journal. He
was a man who rarely expressed himself with humility, but
he was so puzzled by the obsidian knives, the spinning tops,
the oblongs, the swastikas, and the occasional spidery inscriptions that he entered a general plea for assistance in elucidating
his finds. It was his custom to send copies of his journal to
scholars abroad, and in his characteristic fashion he invited
those "who desire further enlightenment in these matters to

write to me at my address in Athens, where I shall be spending the winter."

The bitter north wind was sweeping across the plain of Troy. Huddled in his greatcoat and wearing a sun helmet, he decided to superintend the excavations until the last possible moment. But on November 24, after two days of violent storm, he abandoned all operations and returned to Athens, where he spent part of his enforced holiday assembling notes for a treatise on the swastika. Unlike the Nazi swastika, the true swastika moves from right to left, and there is hardly any place in the world where it has not been found. They are seen on ancient Chinese carvings, on the pulpit of St. Ambrose in Milan, on a Celtic funeral urn found in Norfolk, England, and in the *Ramayana* the ships of King Rama bore it on their prows. He carefully assembled a vast number of references to swastikas and seems to have contemplated a book on the subject, but he was still engrossed by the thought of uncovering Priam's palace and refused to wander from his appointed path, and so the book was left unfinished.

Much of his time was spent in rewriting his journal, which appeared in five installments in the *Augsburger Allgemeine Zeitung*, later reprinted in his book *Troianische Altertümer* (Trojan Antiquities). Ernst Curtius, the distinguished Hellenist, after reading the early reports, pronounced against Hissarlik in favor of Bunarbashi, and Schliemann roared with anger. He admitted that the lower city of Troy probably extended along the valley and perhaps reached as far as Bunarbashi, but only a fool would assume that the palaces were anywhere else but at Hissarlik.

In spite of the oblongs and the *carrousels* he was still convinced that he had discovered the ancient city. Great scholars like Ernest Renan, Max Müller, and Longperier might believe that Troy was a completely imaginary city, but for himself he was convinced of its reality. In March, 1872, just before setting out for his fourth expedition to Troy, he wrote from Athens: "I have an unshakable faith in Homer. If I succeed in bringing to light the palace of Priam, the acropolis of ancient Troy, my discoveries will produce an immense sensation all over the world, and admirers of Homer will come in their hundreds of thousands to admire the sacred relics of those historical times." That they did not come in their hundreds of thousands was no fault of Schliemann's.

He embarked on his fourth attempt in good heart. From Schröder's in London he received a present of sixty wheelbarrows and a large number of excellent English spades and pickaxes. With his wife he returned to the Dardanelles at the end of March and resumed digging on April 5.

There was the usual trouble with the workmen. There were so many rainstorms and so many Greek festivals that in the first two weeks he obtained only eight days' work from them. Some days he employed 100 workmen, other days 126, and he calculated that he was employing an average of 120 at a cost of 300 francs a day. Three weeks after digging began, most of the workmen mutinied when he found them smoking and ordered them to stop. Worse still, the few workmen who remained at work were being stoned by the rest.

Schliemann acted promptly. He dismissed almost his entire work gang and spent the night rounding up replacements so successfully that he had 120 new workmen working for him the next day. Because work was progressing slowly, he increased the workday by an hour. Work now started at five in the morning and ended at six in the evening. Yet he was still plagued by the unaccountable and baleful influence of the Church—during the Greek Easter no work was done for six days. He tried to bribe the men back to work, threatened them with obscure punishments, taunted them with laziness, and got nowhere. There were still no great discoveries. Occasionally there were moods of black despair, when he felt like a man committed to the task of honeycombing a mountain to no purpose.

In May there were more feast days. Once again he attempted to bribe the workmen with higher wages, but they only answered: "If we work, the saint will strike us." On those days he sometimes visited the workmen and prescribed remedies for their diseases. The local doctors were usually Greek priests, whose prevailing remedy was the bleeding cup. Schliemann had a horror of blood and of bleeding, and he especially detested the bleeding of children—one could always tell when children had been bled repeatedly because there were deep wrinkles around their lips. For himself, he thought the sovereign remedy was salt water, and wrote: "I never bleed anyone, and prescribe sea bathing for almost all diseases."

One day a girl covered with ulcers was brought to him. The whole of her left eye was ulcerated; she suffered from fits of coughing and could hardly walk. His remedy was a dose of castor oil, frequent sea baths, and some simple exercises to expand her chest. Two weeks after receiving the prescription, she made the three hours' journey from her village to Schliemann's camp at Hissarlik, threw herself down at his feet and kissed his shoes. She told him she had regained her appetite after her first bath in the sea. There was no hope for her left eye, but most of her ulcers were cured, and for years afterwards he liked to tell the story of the girl from the village of Neo-Chori who had been cured by sea water.

Summer came. The heat roared out of the sky, and the nights were thunderous with the croaking of frogs in the marshes. It was the time when small brown vipers, thin as whips and very dangerous, scuttled out of the ruins. Schliemann learned that the villagers drank a concoction of snakeweed found on the Trojan plain, and for safety's sake he followed their example.

But he was not a man who played for safety. He was always taking risks. He cut deep trenches across the mound, and was surprised when the walls sometimes collapsed and his workmen were buried under the rubble—by a miracle no one was ever seriously injured. He was always climbing about the excavations with the agility of a monkey. He labored all day, and worked on his notes through the night.

Yet he knew nothing about scientific archeology, a science which was then in its infancy. Emile Burnouf, the director of the French School at Athens, had to reprimand him for his carelessness. It was not enough to dig oblongs and *car-rousels* and broken pieces of pottery out of the ground: the exact positions must be recorded, the date, the time, the circumstances, all these must be entered into the day book. "You must take care to report these things accurately," he warned, "or else you will never be able to come to definite conclusions on your wonderful discoveries. *Tenez bien compte de cela!*"[4] Those last words suggest an impatient schoolmaster. Schliemann was an obedient pupil. He took far greater care of his records, labeled everything, and came to realize at last that accurate records were almost the most important part of the excavation.

And still very little was coming to light. Huge walls, occasional marble slabs with long dedicatory texts, all very late, and a few huge jars and some delicate black pottery— this was almost the sum of his discoveries. Of King Priam, Prince Hector, and Achilles there was no sign.

Suddenly on June 18, 1872, he discovered a monumental relief of Apollo riding the four horses of the Sun. Though small, it was a brilliant work—the horses modeled lightly but with great skill and vigor, the god crowned with a spiked diadem with ten long rays and ten shorter ones, his golden hair flowing free. It was a late rendering, perhaps Ptolemaic, but Schliemann was immensely pleased with it and immediately set about smuggling it out of the country with the help of Frank Calvert, on whose part of the mound it was discovered. Then for years it graced the garden of Schliemann's house in Athens.

4. *Tenez . . . cela:* "keep track of that!" (French).

As summer advanced and still there was no sign of Homeric Troy, his moods of black despair returned. At enormous expense he had cleared a large terrace on the northern slope, and revealed a stone tower; but increasingly doubts entered his mind. The work was easier now, for the British Consul at Constantinople had sent him 10 handcarts and 20 more wheelbarrows and he had a whole armory of digging implements—6 horse carts, 108 spades, 103 pickaxes, 24 iron levers —but though the work was easier, Schliemann himself was losing hope.

He paid his workmen five centimes for anything they dis-

Apollo riding his chariot, found by Schliemann at Troy.

covered, and came to the conclusion that they were forging
clay goddesses and *carrousels*. The workmen feared him and
showed little liking for him. Though he had an excellent
memory, he could never remember their names. They reminded him of people he had seen in the past, and he gave
them new names—this one was "doctor," that one "the monk,"
another "the dervish," another "the schoolmaster," because
he reminded him of a schoolmaster he had known in Germany.

That summer for the first time Schliemann complained of
weariness and sickness. The old fire was burning low. He
began to talk of surrendering his *firman* to a well-endowed
archeological society or to a foreign government, and spoke
bitterly about the drain on his resources. For days on end
there were dust storms, so that the workmen could hardly
see. The wind, driving down from the north, exhausted them.
In July came "the pestilential miasma," which in Schliemann's
view arose from the decomposition of millions of dead frogs,
and with the miasma came fear. He feared the snakes which
fell from the rafters of the house he had built on one of the
cliffs of Hissarlik; he feared scorpions; he feared the workmen.

Sometimes he would wander off to a neighboring village
and forget his loneliness in conversation with a Greek shop-
keeper, Constantinos Colobos, who was born without feet,
but who had learned Italian and French and could recite
pages of the *Iliad* by heart. He enjoyed his discussions with
the old man, but there were few other relaxations in that
"lonely and miserable wilderness." On August 4, when he
was already suffering from marsh fever and was about to
give up for the summer, he found his first treasure.

At first sight the treasure was not calculated to throw
him into ecstasies. It consisted of three gold earrings and
a gold dress pin. Nearby was a skeleton. He pronounced it
the skeleton of a young woman, and was sure she died during
the burning of Troy. "The color of the bones," he wrote,

"The Great Tower of Ilium" seen from the southeast
during excavations at Troy.

"leaves no doubt that the lady was overtaken by fire and burned alive."

He worked on, hoping more treasure would come to light, but though he found some more oblongs and "a very pretty bird's egg made of fine marble," there were no more important discoveries. There had been no rain for four months. For days on end the mound of Hissarlik was hidden by clouds of dust. Suddenly there were thunderstorms and the whole mound seemed to turn into mud. He gave orders to abandon the excavations for the season, and with his wife he returned to Athens. He was a sick man. His three foremen, his bodyguard, and his wife were all suffering from fever.

In Athens he recovered his health, and he was well enough a month later to pay a brief visit to the Troad with a photographer. Burnouf had asked to see a plan of the palace of Priam, and noticing some inaccuracies had suggested that a better plan could be drawn with the help of photographs.

When Schliemann reached Hissarlik he found that the watchman was calmly selling huge stones from the walls to the villagers. Some of the stones went to build houses in the Turkish village of Ciplak, others to build a belfry in the Christian village of Yeni Shehr. Schliemann was almost out of his wits with anger. He dismissed the watchman and had another installed in his place. He insisted that the new watchman be armed with a musket. With the photographs and new plans he returned in triumph to Athens.

As usual, Schliemann was planning to do a hundred things at once. When he felt discouraged by the excavations at Troy, he would remember the other places which had not yet felt the excavator's spade. He wrote to the Greek government a memorandum in which he offered to excavate both Mycenae and Olympia at his own expense, provided that he could keep the finds until his death when they would become the property of the Greek nation, and he offered to leave 200,000 francs to build a museum which would bear his name. The offer was rejected, and he began to talk wistfully of abandoning Athens for ever and living in Paris.

But Troy held him. When he heard that his *firman* from the Turkish government had been canceled on the grounds that he had exported nearly all his finds, he became still more attached to Troy, and bombarded all his acquaintances in high places to intervene with the Turkish government. As soon as he received unofficial permission to continue his excavations, he was back at Hissarlik. He told friends he proposed to start digging on March 1, but he was already at work on January 31. The ice-cold north wind was blowing. He caught a cold. There were more thunderstorms and a plague of church festivals. In March an unexpected enemy appeared in the shape of a merchant from Smyrna who engaged 150 villagers to dig up licorice roots, paying them 12 to 23 piasters a day—a sum considerably above that which Schliemann was paying. Schliemann cursed, but there was nothing he could do. He wrote in his journal:

March 15, 1873. The nights are cold, and the thermometer frequently falls to freezing point in the morning, but during the day the sun is beginning to be oppressively warm, the thermometer frequently reading as high as 72°. The leaves are beginning to burst on the trees, and the Trojan plain is covered with spring flowers. For the last fortnight we have heard the croaking of millions of frogs in the surrounding marshes, and during the last eight days the storks have returned. The misery of life in this wilderness is increased by the innumerable owls who build their nests in the holes in the walls I have excavated: there is something mysterious and horrible in their screeching; it is unbearable, especially at night.

He had built a small stone house and a wooden house on the cliff. The stone house, built in the autumn of 1871, had 2-foot thick walls which could keep out the bitter cold winds, but he decided to give this house to his foremen, who had not enough blankets. Schliemann himself occupied the wooden house. The wind penetrated the cracks in the walls. One night toward the end of March he awoke at three o'clock to find the room full of dense smoke and one wall already in flames. In one corner of the bedroom there was a stone fireplace resting on wooden boards, and evidently a spark had ignited the wood. The north wind was blowing fiercely. Shouting to Sophia to run out of the building, he threw water from a bath onto the burning wall, and later the foremen, who had been awakened, helped to put out the flames with earth.

In a quarter of an hour it was all over, but for days afterward he shivered at the thought of how he had been within an inch of losing his books, papers, and antiquities, and how if he had slept only a few moments longer Sophia might have perished. And once again in his journal he complained of weariness, the hopeless fight against the perpetual north wind, the huge cost of employing an army of workers—he was still employing 160 workmen—and the church feasts which reduced him to abject misery, for he was sure he was on the eve of important discoveries. He found some delicate pottery, a copper lance head, more *carrousels*, all shattered and worth nothing.

In April the wind dropped, and the whole plain was covered with yellow buttercups. Now the workmen slept in the open under the cloudless skies. Schliemann was calmer than ever. He seems to have had a strange premonition that he was close to a great discovery. On April 16, he found a paved street and nine enormous earthenware jars as tall as a man. Such jars had never come to light before, though similar jars would be found later in Cnossus. In May he was hot on the trail. He uncovered two gates 20 feet apart, which he immediately named the Scaean Gate, and the large building behind the gates he called Priam's palace. There were more vases with owls' heads and vast amounts of rubble.

He was content. He had found what he had hoped to find,

the long years of labor nearly at an end. He announced that he was preparing to publish his discoveries—there would be 200 plates and 3,500 engravings. True, Hissarlik was a small mound, and people would say that Homer never envisaged a small city when he spoke of Troy; but the wide gate, the palace walls, the cyclopean breastworks, the innumerable pieces of black pottery, the great jars, and the thousands of artifacts proved that Schliemann had discovered the citadel of Troy. His joy was short-lived. Sophia heard that her father was dying. She hurried off to Athens, only to learn that he was already dead. From his house on the cliffs of Hissarlik, Schliemann wrote the gentlest of all his letters:

Comfort yourself, my dearest, with the thought that after a short while we shall all join your wonderful father. Comfort yourself with the thought of our dear daughter, who needs her mother and will never have any joy in life without her. Comfort yourself with the thought that your tears will never bring your father back to life, and that good, courageous man—far from the sorrows and cares of this life—is now enjoying the purest happiness beyond the grave, and is therefore happier than we who remain behind to weep and lament him. If you cannot master your grief, then come back to me by the first steamboat and I will do everything I can to assuage your grief. There can be no excavations without you. With tears of joy I pray you will soon come back to me.

A few days later Sophia hurried back to him. She knew where she was wanted. He was lonely without her. She was the emblem of all his success in life, and when he wrote that there could be no excavations without her, he meant that he could not excavate in good heart or with hope of success unless she was by his side.

Summer was coming on, the buttercups were dying, and soon the whole plain would have the burned-out black appearance which came with summer. Schliemann was folding up his tent. He wrote to his son Sergey that he would bring

the excavations to an end in the middle of June and then take
his wife and daughter to some bathing place in Central Europe
for a much-needed rest. He was pleased with his four months'
work. He had discovered the walls of Troy and the site of
the palace, excavated 250,000 meters of earth, and obtained
enough antiquities to furnish a whole museum.

The letter to Sergey was written on May 30. On the same
day he wrote to Frederick Calvert, who had an estate at
Thymbria near Bunarbashi only a few hours' walk away,
a letter of a different temper altogether. It was a letter written
in fear and trembling, smuggled past the guards at night. In
all his life Schliemann never wrote a more dramatic letter
nor one so intimately connected with his fondest hopes and
dreams:

I am sorry to inform you that I am closely watched, and expect that the Turkish watchman, who is angry at me, I do not
know for what reason, will search my house tomorrow. I,
therefore, take the liberty to deposit with you 6 baskets and a
bag, begging you will kindly lock them up, and not allow by
any means the Turks to touch them.

In the six baskets and the bag was the golden treasure of
Troy.

In his published writings Schliemann never revealed the
exact date on which the treasure was discovered. We know
the hour and the place—it was about seven in the morning,
and the place was a deep cut below the circuit wall close to
Priam's Palace. He may have discovered the treasure on May
30, the day he wrote his hurried note to Frederick Calvert,
or a few days earlier.* On May 31 he wrote in his journal his

---

* In *Troya*, which he published ten years later, Schliemann says "the
treasure was found at the end of May, 1873." This is the only definite
statement he ever made about the date of the discovery. Emil Ludwig, in
Schliemann of Troy: The Story of a Goldseeker, says the discovery was
made "on a morning in the middle of June, one day before the termination
of the work," but this is clearly wrong. (*Payne's note.*)

first account of the treasure, adding that he had not yet had time to examine his finds or even count them—by this time they were out of his possession and safely in the hands of Frederick Calvert.

From three separate accounts written at different times, it is possible to piece together the story of his discovery. It was one of those hot May days, with the whole plain smoking with bright yellow dust. Eight days previously he had discovered a large silver vase with a small silver beaker inside it. Not far away he found a copper helmet; the helmet itself was shattered, but the characteristic horns (oblongs) were intact. For days he worked on, hoping to find more treasure.

He was sure there must be more treasure nearby. Accordingly, he divided his workmen into many groups and sent them digging in different places on the mound. By scattering them and losing them in the long trenches and corridors which honeycombed the mound, he felt sure that if he discovered any large cache he would be able to smuggle it unobserved to his own house on the cliffs. In particular, he was anxious that the Turkish representative on the scene, Amin Effendi, should not be present when he discovered the treasure.

Schliemann, his wife, and a handful of workmen were digging along the circuit wall close to the Scaean Gate when Schliemann suddenly noticed at a depth of 28 feet "a container or implement of copper of remarkable design." Peering through the dust and rubble he was able to make out that the container was about 3 feet long and 18 inches high, and that there were two-helmet-shaped objects on top of it, and something which resembled a large candlestick. The container was broken, and he could see some silver vessels inside it. Above all this were some reddish and brown calcined ruins from 4 to 5 feet thick, as hard as stone, and above this again were the huge fortification walls, 5 feet broad and 20 feet high.

He had found treasure, and now there was the question

of preserving it from the cupidity of the Turks. None of the workmen had noticed it. Sophia was beside him, and he turned to her and said: "You must go at once and shout *'paidos!'* "

Paidos was a Greek word meaning "rest period."

Sophia had not yet seen the treasure, and was puzzled at the thought of ordering a rest period so early.

"Now, at seven o'clock?" she asked.

"Yes—now! Tell them it is my birthday, and I have only just remembered it! Tell them they will get their wages today without working. See that they go to their villages, and see that the overseer does not come here. Hurry and shout: *'Paidos!'* "

Sophia did as she was told. It was her task to call out the rest periods, and so she climbed up the rickety ladders which led to the platform. Soon the workmen were drifting away, pleased at the opportunity of an unexpected holiday, and a little troubled, because there had been no such holidays before. Amin Effendi was especially puzzled, because he was usually well-informed about holidays.

When Sophia returned all the workmen had gone, and Schliemann was attempting to dig the treasure out with a pocket knife. The fortification wall, composed of earth, rubble, and heavy stones, was threatening to fall, but at the sight of so much treasure he lost his fears. He turned again to Sophia and said: "Quick, bring me your big shawl!"

Once again Sophia had to make the journey up the step-ladder to the upper platform and to the house. She returned with an enormous scarlet shawl, heavily embroidered, such as Greek women wear on feast days. The treasure was poured into the shawl, and together they carried it back to the house.

As soon as the door was locked, the treasure was spread out on the rough wooden table. Many of the pieces had been packed into one another. Such treasures gleam freshly behind glass cases in museums, pale yellow, with a curious lifelessness,

Schliemann's own photograph of the treasure shortly
after its discovery.

but when they were found they had a wonderful glowing reddish color. The treasure consisted of a copper shield, a copper cauldron, a silver vase and another of copper, a gold bottle, 2 gold cups, and a small electrum cup. There was a silver goblet, 3 great silver vases, 7 double-edged copper daggers, 6 silver knife blades, and 13 copper lance heads. At the bottom of the largest silver vase there were 2 gold diadems, a fillet, 4 gold eardrops, 56 gold earrings and 8,750 gold rings and buttons, most of them very small.

The most astonishing were the diadems, one of them consisting of ninety chains, forming an elaborate gold headdress with leaf- and flower-pendants and long tassels hanging down at the sides. Persian and Roman diadems were simply jeweled bands worn round the head; the Trojan diadems were formed of innumerable gold rings entirely covering the forehead. Nothing like them had been seen before, and none have been discovered since.

Trembling with excitement, Schliemann held them up to the light and then placed them on Sophia's forehead. To the end of his life he seems to have thought they were the diadems of a queen, though they are more likely to have been those of a king. He heaped necklaces around her neck and put the gold rings on her fingers, until she shone with barbaric splendor. At last, after so many years, the obscure son of a Mecklenburg clergyman was standing in the place of kings before a woman arrayed like a queen.

He was sure he had found the treasure of King Priam, hidden secretly in the wall when Troy was already in flames. At the last moment, he thought, they had been stowed away in a wooden box, and there was no time even to remove the key. What he thought to be the key was later shown to be a copper chisel, and there was no evidence that the treasure was ever enclosed in a box.

Much was, and remains, mysterious about the finds. The gold vessels were of superb workmanship, but the tiaras,

Sophia Schliemann

Wearing the diadem of Troy.

Shortly after her marriage.

wonderfully impressive at first sight, proved to be of primitive workmanship, built up with coils of wire and thin gold
sheeting. None of the rings was engraved. The beautifully
modeled gold sauceboat was a masterpiece of design, but why
should it have been found among knife blades, arrowheads,
and strange little terra-cotta idols? Not only gold and silver
had been stored in the wall. There were some crudely carved
ivory and shaft-hole hammer axes of semi-precious stone, but
there was also a little lead figurine of a woman with a swastika
scratched on her. Idol worship and barbarism went hand in
hand with artistic refinement. Was this the Troy of Homer,
or of some earlier, more barbaric age?

Schliemann was perfectly certain that he had unearthed
treasure belonging to Priam, and in the following weeks he
liked to speak ironically about how he had found "the treasure
of King Priam, that mythical king, of a mythical city, who
lived in a mythical heroic age." It was his way of saying that
the discovery of the treasure had proved that Priam was real,
and the city was real, and the heroic age was supremely un-
mythical. The gold was there to prove that Troy was real.

He was a man tormented by gold, and never more tormented than when he found himself in possession of the gold
and was afraid of being discovered. He had not completely
succeeded in hiding his discovery. Rumors were flying across
the Trojan plain. Amin Effendi called at the house, and said
angrily he was sure something was being kept from him. The
watchman demanded permission to search the house. In the
name of the Sultan he ordered Schliemann to open all his
chests, even the wardrobes. Schliemann's only reply was to
throw him out of the house.

That night, or the next night, the treasure was taken to
Frederick Calvert's house at Thymbria and a few days later
smuggled out of the country.

For a few more days Schliemann peered and probed at
the foot of the wall, but no more treasure was discovered.
On June 17 the excavations were abruptly terminated. The

workmen were paid their wages, and a priest came to bless
the desolate mound, now riddled with corridors and trenches
like a battlefield. Announcing that he would return to Athens
and never set foot on Troy again, he left quietly, taking with
him only a few of the objects he had gathered, for the rest
had been sent on ahead. On June 19 he was in Athens, and
that day he set about writing the first of the long series of
letters in which he celebrated his discovery.

He was on fire with enthusiasm and excitement. He had
made "the greatest discovery of our age, the one which all
men have been looking forward to." For the first time this
strange man who boasted continually had cause for boasting. Against hope, against reason, against all the evidence
he had discovered Troy. *Ubi Troia fuit*.[5] He had only to
hold up the shimmering golden diadems, and who would
dare to disbelieve him?

But the gold treasure remained a liability, and the habit
of secrecy, which he had fostered so carefully at Hissarlik,
was not easily put aside. While he was writing to all the
learned societies in Europe that he had discovered the treasure—the letters sometimes read like proclamations—he was
busily arranging to bury the treasure in the earth. Sophia's
relatives were brought into the conspiracy. All over Greece
strange objects wrapped in straw were being concealed
in stables, barns, and farmyards. A wickerwork basket was
dispatched to an uncle living in Eleusis. The treasure itself
vanished shortly after Schliemann weighed and described
minutely each object. Neither the Greek nor the Turkish governments would be able to lay hands on it.

Schliemann remained in Athens when Sophia went off
to Ischia, for a long deserved holiday; and some weeks
later a trusted servant was sent to tell her by word of
mouth where each object had been buried.

Schliemann was caught on the horns of a dilemma. He

5. *Ubi Troia fuit*: "where Troy was" (Latin).

wanted fame, which is impermanent, and the treasure, which was the most permanent of all things. The treasure was a weapon he could use against governments, particularly the Greek government. He had only to announce that he would bequeath this treasure to any one of three or four governments, and he knew he would be received with open arms and allowed all the facilities he needed for excavations. As soon as he returned from Hissarlik, he quarreled with the Greek government. He let it be known that he possessed the treasure and would give it to Greece, but they must give him full permission to excavate at Mycenae and Olympia. They had refused his offer before. They refused again, apparently because they were afraid of trouble with Turkey.

Trouble came in August when the Turks had had time to make a few elementary inquiries and to read the dispatches which Schliemann had sent to the *Augsburger Allgemeine Zeitung*. Schliemann learned that Amin Effendi was to be punished because he had failed to keep close watch on the excavations. Punishments of officials in the Ottoman Empire sometimes ended fatally, and once again Schliemann found himself on the horns of a dilemma. He would not return the treasure. He would not return to Turkey to intercede for the official. But at least he could write a letter "in the name of humanity and of sacred justice," pointing out that Amin Effendi was completely innocent:

If he was unable to keep watch over everything that happened, that was because there were always five works of excavation proceeding at any one time, and by heaven, no one has yet been born who can multiply himself five times and keep watch over five works simultaneously.

I found the treasure while Amin Effendi was working on another part of the mound altogether, and if you had seen the despair written on the poor man's face when he learned from other workmen about the treasure, and if you had seen his tearing rage when he came rushing into my room, ordering me to open all my chests and wardrobes in the name of the Sultan, you would have had pity for him.

No one ever watched over my excavations more relentlessly than Amin Effendi, but a man must be an archeologist himself before he can survey the work of one excavation, and his only fault was that he was not an archeologist. . . .

It is not a convincing letter. There are hesitations and ambiguities, such as might come to a man defending himself when he knows he is in the wrong. In his one-sided fashion Schliemann argued that when his *firman* was revoked, he was left free to do as he pleased. "The Turkish government," he wrote, "broke our written contract in the fullest sense of the word, and I was released from every obligation."

But the Turkish government had permitted him to continue his excavations and no doubt expected from him its fair share of the objects he removed from the earth. Schliemann's instinct was to regard any agreement with governments as though they were commercial agreements. The Turks asked him privately to send a part of the treasure as a token offering to the Imperial Museum in Constantinople. Schliemann answered that he would send nothing, and in the same letter requested permission to return to Troy and dig for three more months, promising that everything he discovered in those three months would be given to the Museum.

Once again, as so often in the past, Schliemann found himself riding a storm. His weapons were guile, cunning, patience, loquaciousness. He could, and would, use every trick of the market place to preserve his gains. Dissatisfied by the attitude of the Greek government, he began to think of immigrating to Italy. Palermo and Naples were both excellent sites for an archeologist, and he was soon making tentative approaches to Italian museum officials: he would build a museum to house his treasures, provided he was given a free hand to dig as he pleased.

Meanwhile his fame was increasing. Gladstone, the British Prime Minister, heard of his discoveries and was impressed by them. Max Müller, the distinguished orientalist, wrote an article on them. In Germany the battle between the defenders and the opponents of Schliemann was already launched. Through the fall and early winter Schliemann completed his book *Troianische Altertümer,* which consisted largely of his Trojan journals interspersed with photographs. Simultaneously he made a French translation, and sent both copies to his publishers.

With the book finished, he was restless again. The right to excavate in Olympia had been officially granted to the Prussian government. He was outraged, but there was nothing he could do about it. He decided to make a preliminary survey of Mycenae. There, if anywhere, he thought he would be able to repeat his successes at Troy.

With his contempt for governments and permits, he embarked on the expedition secretly with Sophia, informing no one. He engaged workmen on the spot and in five days dug thirty-four small trenches on the acropolis, discovering only a few unimportant pieces of shattered pottery. Long ago, in his book *Ithaka, der Peloponnes und Troia,* he had stated his belief that there were graves dating from the heroic age within the citadel wall at Mycenae, and the most important result of this brief visit was to reinforce his belief. He suspected the existence of a mortuary dome chamber near the famous Lion Gate, and still another one a little further away. He could not explain why he was so sure the tomb chambers were there, and he seems to have sensed them, as he sensed the presence of gold at Troy. He spoke of digging a single shaft just beyond the Lion Gate. This shaft, he thought, would reveal the mausoleum of the Kings of Mycenae—Thyestes, Agamemnon, and all the others. Already he possessed the ashes of Odysseus and the treasure of Priam; the discovery of the royal graves at Mycenae would crown his career.

Unfortunately he had no business to be in Mycenae at all, and as soon as the Greek government heard that he was digging there, orders were sent by telegram to the prefect of Argolis to prevent him from putting a spade to the earth. This telegram was followed by two more. The first said that everything Schliemann had dug from the ground must be confiscated, and the second said that his luggage must be examined.

These tasks were entrusted to the police chief at Nauplia, who visited the house where the Schliemanns were staying, discussed the matter calmly over coffee, and was shown a basketful of broken pottery. It was the opinion of the police chief that such potsherds could be found in any village lane and in all ancient cities, and wrote to his superiors: "I found nothing of importance, and so I let it pass."

When Schliemann returned to Athens he found the government up in arms against him. He had been an object of suspicion ever since his discoveries at Troy. The police chief, the prefect of Argolis, and the mayor of Mycenae had shown themselves incompetent. "By their actions," wrote the Minister of Education, "they have proved that the soil of Greece is defenseless, and any unauthorized person can do as he pleases with it, in complete disregard of the laws."

Schliemann, who had discovered nothing of any real worth, simply bided his time. He had fallen in love with Mycenae. As soon as a favorable opportunity occurred, he would send a memorandum to the Greek government, offering to dig at Mycenae at his own expense, giving everything he found to the government, reserving for himself only the right to report and describe his finds. The favorable opportunity occurred two months later; and the same minister who had characterized him as a thief and an enemy of Greece solemnly signed the agreement.

He had decided to start digging at Mycenae on April 21,

and he was making arrangements for the journey when the Turks instituted proceedings against him for half of the treasure. The trial, which was fought through the upper and lower courts, lasted a year, and exhausted his patience. He had to remain in Athens. By court order, policemen came to his house and searched for the treasure, and found no trace of it. He refused to say where the treasure was hidden, he refused to answer the questions of the prosecutor, he refused to make a settlement. He was determined to fight the Turks to the bitter end, and at the same time he sent a stream of messages to Constantinople, demanding the right to continue his excavations at Hissarlik, as though there were no quarrel between them.

In that strange year from April, 1874 to April, 1875, perhaps the strangest he ever lived through, he quarreled with everyone. He quarreled with the police, who dogged his footsteps. He quarreled with his own lawyers. He quarreled with the Greek government, and he quarreled with his critics. In Germany particularly doubts were being cast on the value of his discoveries at Hissarlik, and he replied to these criticisms with unaccustomed acerbity. Why had the Prussian government been given the concession to dig at Olympia? He was outraged. Had he not offered to dig there at his own expense—those words which are repeated in so many of his letters—and give everything he found to the Greeks? He appealed over the heads of his ministers to King George of Greece. "I have come to Greece for the sole purpose of serving science," he wrote, "and I brought with me *my own honorably acquired fortune*." He underlined the last words, as though an honorably acquired fortune was itself a passport to royal protection.

To placate the government and to put himself in good standing with the Athenians, he offered to remove at his own expense the Venetian Tower, built in the Middle Ages on the Acropolis. The tower spoiled the view. No one liked it, but no one had troubled to remove it. The tower was

80 feet high, and the Venetians had built it out of slabs of marble from the Acropolis, and now the owls had their nests in it. How better could he serve Greece than by demolishing an eyesore? He estimated that it would cost £465 to pull down the tower, and when the Greek government accepted his offer, he was delighted. Then for many days he stood on the Acropolis, superintending the destruction of the old tower, as pleased with himself as if he were excavating for gold.

When the courts adjourned for the summer, he slipped out of Athens and made a quick tour of northern Greece, visiting Orchomenos, where he made some excavations six years later. He was so convinced of the importance of that ancient city that he offered to finance an exploration to be undertaken by the Greek Archeological Society. Then he was in Athens again, fighting critics and lawyers, demanding from the Greeks the right to excavate at Olympia, from Safvet Pasha the right to return to Troy, from the King the right to speak in the name of science and to excavate where he pleased. It was a year of patient improvisation, of somber reflections, and of sudden sallies against his enemies, and when it was over he was exhausted. The trial aged and embittered him, and once more he began to speak of abandoning Greece forever and settling in southern Italy.

At last the long trial came to an end. Schliemann had played his cards skillfully. The Greek judges found in favor of the Turks and ordered him to pay an indemnity of 50,000 francs. Since he valued the treasure of Priam at a million francs, he had in effect won the trial. As a gesture of friendship he sent five times the amount of the indemnity to the Imperial Museum at Constantinople. He also sent seven large vases and four sacks filled with stone implements.

Having won his victory, he was in a mood to enjoy his growing fame. Gladstone[6] had written him an affectionate

6. *Gladstone:* William Gladstone (1809-1898), British statesman and prime minister.

letter of greeting, and his warmest admirers were in England. Accordingly he set out for England in the summer of 1875, taking Sophia and Andromache with him. He stopped in Paris to address the Geographical Society, but he made so many vast claims that his speech was greeted coldly; and when it was over, no one came up to congratulate him, and there were no flocks of visitors at his house on the Place St. Michel.

In London he was lionized. Gladstone eulogized him. All through July he was being wined and dined in the best circles. He had installed Sophia and Andromache in Brighton, and complained that he was only able to tear himself away from London once or twice a week to visit her. From London he wrote to Gauthiot, the secretary of the French Geographical Society:

Here the meetings of the learned societies are crowded when I address them, everyone applauds me, and everything I say is published. The Court demands my presence, and all the foreign princes and princesses send me invitations and listen to my remarks with interest—everyone wants to have the name of the discoverer of Homeric Troy in their autograph books. Soon I shall be leaving this charming society, where everyone heaps honors on me and offers me much kindness, to return to Paris— where I was regarded as a traitor!

He spent only a few hours in Paris. The Queen of Holland invited him to The Hague. There was a reception in his honor, attended by all the dignitaries of the Kingdom. The Queen gave him a private audience, and for long hours he pored over the Egyptian objects in the Leyden Museum in her company. He had two excellent reasons for admiring the Queen: she had a passion for archeology, and she spoke seven languages fluently. He wrote to Felix Ravaisson, the Conservator of the Louvre:

Her Majesty is always inviting me for breakfast, lunch and dinner. She has read much, and is gifted with a quite extraordinary memory. I believe I could even persuade her to do some excavations in Asia Minor, the Greek Archipelago or in Italy, but of course I shall limit myself to advising her and not take part in them.

Then he went off to Copenhagen for a week of prowling round the museums, happy to discover among the Stone Age weapons some curious similarities with those he discovered in Troy. He went to Rostock to deliver yet another speech on his excavations. The Italians welcomed him on his return. He announced that he intended to settle in Naples for the rest of his life. He spent some weeks at Alba Longa, where some funeral urns had been excavated recently, but it was not a promising ground. He had no better luck on the island of Motyë off the west coast of Sicily, where there was once a Carthaginian settlement; and though he examined the ruins at Segente and made some preliminary diggings, he found nothing to warrant a prolonged stay. At the end of October he was writing: "I do not know where to turn. For Troy it is too soon, and if I return to Greece I shall have to fight their continual explosions of jealousy."

All his fame had come from Troy. Abruptly leaving Naples at the beginning of December, he made his way to Constantinople, interviewed Safvet Pasha in the Ministry of Public Instruction, and demanded a new *firman*. Safvet Pasha was dubious. He promised, however, to use his good offices, on condition that Schliemann faithfully keep to his promise of offering everything he discovered to the Imperial Museum.

In April, 1876 the *firman* was sent to him, but by this time he was engrossed in the thought of uncovering the royal graves of Mycenae. He knew how to time his excavations. "For Troy it is too soon. . . ." He wrote up his reports on the small and scattered excavations he had made the previous year—there was only a handful of Carthaginian arrowheads to show for the weeks he had spent at Motyë—and immersed himself in the study of Mycenae.

More and more Mycenae attracted him. He could not

have Olympia, and he had discovered all he could reasonably hope to discover at Hissarlik. There remained Mycenae, which the ancients believed to have been founded by Perseus, the son of Danaë and Zeus, who appeared to her in a shower of gold. There, if anywhere, he would find treasure.

. . . 7   **THE GOLDEN MASKS**

IN SCHLIEMANN'S DAY the traveler approaching Mycenae in summer saw the plain of Argos all yellow and white with stubble and dust, and the once-great fortress city was no more than a rubble of stones on one of the foothills, guarding the pass between two mountains nearly 2,500 feet high. These blue and barren mountains have something threatening about them—ponderous and sharp-edged, with power in their heavy outcrops and huge boulders. The mountains still threaten and the wolves still howl in the foothills, but much has changed. Today the plain is well-cultivated, there are good roads through it, orchards flower between tobacco and cotton fields, and there is barley in the foothills. Still, even today, Mycenae is a menacing place as it lies huddled in the shadow of the bleak hills, commanding all approaches.

Mycenae is an ideal site for a city dominating the plain of Argos and the sheltered bay of Nauplia 9 miles to the south, and appears to have been inhabited from prehistoric times. Here about 1700 B.C. a powerful king built gigantic ramparts around an early Bronze Age city and erected a new palace. No one knows the name of the king, or where he came from. The entrance to the city was a paved highway flanked by two bastions. Deep within the bastions there stood, and still stands, a great Lion Gate of massive and imposing construction, once closed by a double wooden door, with an enormous lintel crowned by a relief of two lionesses face to face. Once through the Lion Gate and beyond the

**The Lion Gate at Mycenae at the time of
Schliemann's excavations.**

walls which are 16 feet thick, the visitor comes upon a circular terrace. In Schliemann's day this was covered with
rubble and the detritus of the ages, and beyond this lay
the tumbled ruins of palaces and private houses, all weather-
worn and covered with lichens. On the slopes of the ridges
and in the surrounding valley lay the ruins of the lower
city. This windswept hilltop was a wild and desolate place,
rarely visited except by plunderers. For centuries nothing

had changed. In the second century A.D. Pausanias[1] visited
the place and found the same bare wilderness and pasture-
land interspersed with slopes and precipitous cliffs. It was
even then a ruin lost in the corner of the plain, dark and
ominous and crumbling away.

Once it was a large and prosperous city with broad
streets, carriage roads, and shining pathways. A powerful
king ruled from the citadel, armies poured through the
Lion Gate, and there were great treasuries of gold. Both
Homer and Sophocles speak of Mycenae as being "rich in
gold." Pausanias says the city was founded by Perseus, who
gave it its name either because he lost his scabbard cap
(*mykes*) there, or because he found mushrooms (*mykes*)
at a spring which later came to be called the Perseia. In
fact no one knows the origin of the city's name. Schliemann
thought it must come from *mykithmos* ("bellowing") since
the plain of Argolis was renowned for its oxen. It was a
guess, as good as any others, and he did not insist upon it.

The dynasty founded by Perseus was peaceful, but the
following dynasty, founded by Atreus, was soaked in tragedy.
When Atreus learned that his wife had been seduced by his
brother Thyestes, he killed two of his brother's sons and
placed their flesh before the father at a banquet. Told that
he had eaten his sons' flesh, Thyestes vomited what he had
eaten, overturned the table and ran off, calling down curses
upon all the descendants of Atreus.

The curse uttered by Thyestes had indeed a fatal power.
While Agamemnon, son of Atreus, was fighting at Troy,
Aegisthus, the child of Thyestes, made love to Clytemnestra,
the wife of Agamemnon. The guilty lovers waited for the
coming of Agamemnon. They sent a watchman to the seashore, to signal the coming of the ships laden with captives
from Troy. Across the plain an unsuspecting Agamemnon
rode in his chariot at the head of his armies. When he reached

---

1. *Pausanias:* Greek travel writer.

Mycenae a banquet was served, and at the banquet or in a nearby bath he was murdered by his wife and her lover.

Agamemnon dead, the curse still hung heavily over the house of Atreus:

> . . . and sang within the bloody wood
> Where Agamemnon cried aloud,
> And let their liquid siftings fall
> Upon that stiff dishonored shroud.

So T. S. Eliot[2] and the Greek dramatists depict those times when a curse was like a physical thing, palpable in the midnight air, continuing for ever like ripples when a stone is flung in a pool. Agamemnon's death did not put an end to the curse. His children, Orestes and Electra, murdered Clytemnestra and her lover Aegisthus. Orestes came to the throne, and with him the curse which had devoured the family of Atreus may have lost its power.

Homer, Aeschylus, Sophocles, Euripides all tell the story of the murder of Agamemnon. For the Greeks the fall of Troy and the fall of the house of Atreus were the great heroic tragedies on which their spirits fed. They regarded Mycenae and Troy as equally sacred: both were places haunted by the presence of great heroes. Having uncovered Troy, Schliemann was simply following the logical path when he turned his attention to Mycenae. In Troy he had found the treasure near the main gate leading into the city. He had the feeling that at Mycenae, too, he would find treasure near the main gate.

He had few clues to work on. There were legends and traditions, but few of them were clear and some were misleading. The most authoritative statement about the tombs of the heroes was made by Pausanias:

In the ruins of Mycenae is a fountain called Perseia and the

---

2. *T. S. Eliot:* contemporary English poet.

underground buildings of Atreus and his sons, where their treasure is buried. There is the tomb of Atreus and there are also tombs of those whom Aegisthus murdered on their return from Troy after entertaining them at a banquet. There is the tomb of Agamemnon and that of his charioteer Eurymedon, and of Electra, and one of Teledamus and Pelops—for they say Cassandra gave birth to these twins and while they were still infants Aegisthus killed them with their parents. Clytemnestra and Aegisthus were buried a little outside the wall, because they were thought unworthy of burial within it, where Agamemnon lies and those who were killed together with him.

Schliemann, who had read all the available books and plays about Mycenae, pondered these words, learned them by heart, and came to regard them with the same reverence with which he regarded the words of Homer. When Pausanias wrote, 1,300 years had passed since the fall of Troy. Pausanias was simply recording local traditions. Schliemann was inclined to accept these traditions for the same reason that he accepted the traditions concerning Henning von Holstein. He had implicit faith in stories about buried treasure.

The more Schliemann pondered the words of Pausanias, the more he became convinced that previous commentators were in error. According to them, the tomb of Clytemnestra lay outside the city walls, while the tombs of Atreus and Agamemnon and those who died with him lay inside the city walls. But it occurred to Schliemann that even in the time of Pausanias the city walls had been reduced to rubble. He argued that Pausanias meant that the tomb of Agamemnon was to be found inside the walls of the Acropolis, not the city walls which could be traced across the surrounding countryside. With this belief, and fortified by the knowledge that the treasure of Troy had been found near the main gate, he set to work in August, 1876, with sixty-three workmen in the neighborhood of the Lion Gate.

This time he was not allowed to work alone. Three officials from the Greek Archeological Society watched every movement he made.

Schliemann had always hated being watched, and he especially hated the presence of the officials. Beyond the gate huge stones blocked the passageway. He set his workmen to removing the stones. The officials objected. Schliemann replied that they were interfering with his plans. As usual, he had divided his workmen into groups and hoped to confuse the officials by working on several projects at once. In the relentless heat, with huge clouds of dust pouring over the ruined city, Schliemann's temper was easily roused, and the officials usually brought their complaints to Sophia, who did her best to quiet them, not always with success. As the work went on, and more workmen were employed, and Schliemann threatened to level more walls, they objected to Schliemann's highhanded operations more violently. Stamatakes, the chief representative of the Greek Archeological Society on the spot, wrote to Athens:

He is eagerly demolishing everything Roman and Greek in sight, in order to lay bare the cyclopean walls. Whenever we find Greek or Roman vases, he looks at them in disgust, and when these fragments are put in his hands, he lets them fall to the ground. He treats me as though I were a barbarian. If the Ministry is not satisfied with me, I beg to be recalled, for I remain here at the expense of my health. After spending the whole day until 9 P.M. with him at the excavations, I sit up with him until 2 A.M., entering up the finds. I allow him to take some things which he wants to study to his own rooms. For all these kindnesses which are permitted to him, Schliemann expressed himself to the Mayor as very well satisfied.

The government, however, had taken note of Schliemann's methods at Troy and was determined not to be caught napping. Stamatakes was instructed to see that (a) no walls were pulled down, (b) the excavations should no longer take place over several areas, but should be concentrated at one place at any given time, and (c) the number of workmen should be limited to a reasonably manageable figure. Stamatakes himself would be held responsible for any infringement of these regulations.

The new rules were easier to announce than to enforce. Accompanied by the prefect of Nauplia, Stamatakes delivered the message to Schliemann. They approached him hesitantly and took pains to speak with an almost excessive politeness. Schliemann completely lost his temper. He appealed to the prefect to have Stamatakes dismissed. He said it was intolerable that he should have to work with such a man. Stamatakes said something about carrying on "according to the law and the agreement you have signed." Schliemann answered hotly that it was not a matter of agreements. No one else understood what needed to be done, and he was being plagued by absurd officials, who were completely unaware of his, Schliemann's, sacred duty to reveal an ancient civilization buried deep in the earth. He would employ every device of modern science to protect and preserve this ancient civilization, but it was necessary for him to work in perfect freedom. Away with the officials!

While Schliemann blazed with anger, and Sophia remained in the shadows, the prefect of Nauplia solemnly read out the dispatch he had received from Athens. The tall, slender Stamatakes confronted the small and wiry Schliemann: the responsible official who owed a duty to Athens, and the archeologist who owed a duty only to the past. The air was electric. Schliemann's face had turned bright red, as it always did when he was angry, and he was muttering to himself. The workmen had stopped working. Occasionally there would come from one of them, a stout, heavily-built buffoon who had been elected mayor of the local village, an ironical remark uttered in a stage whisper. All the time the prefect of Nauplia continued to read out the edict.

At last, the reading over, Schliemann turned on his heels, barked out an order to the workmen to continue digging, and paid no more attention to the officials. The workmen obeyed him, but slowly, with no heart in the work, frightened by the bright glare in his eyes. And that evening Schliemann wrote one more of a long series of letters to the minister, and not trusting the post office to deliver it, he asked Sophia to leave the next day for Athens. She would deliver the letter herself to the minister, and await his reply.

So the work went on, with Schliemann and Stamatakes at each other's throats. There were brief reconciliations, fervent declarations of affection, sudden bouts of hatred. Schliemann had refined the art of employing delaying tactics. His letter to the minister was a masterpiece of subterfuge, in which he proclaimed his undying love for Greece, his dedication to archeology, and his belief that the minister's dispatch to the prefect of Nauplia was written in a moment of aberration. He added that he no longer possessed the least desire to excavate in a country where he was treated with such contumely.

The Greek and Turkish governments possessed large files full of similar letters. They recognized his tactical skill, and were in a position to take his threats seriously: if he wished to leave Greece, they would do nothing to prevent him. But Sophia had no desire to leave Greece, and she was an accomplished actress, always at his side, employing all her charm and all her wiles to defeat the adversary. Soon Stamatakes, usually so reserved and scholarly, was referring to the slight Athenian girl as "that inhuman monster." He recognized that she had a full share in organizing the careful plans by which Schliemann maintained full liberty of action in spite of orders from the government.

While Schliemann was threatening to leave for America, Stamatakes was threatening to resign. He spoke of the intolerable burdens that were laid upon him, the unbelievable

rudeness of Schliemann, his obstinacy, his cunning, his devilish habit of making life insufferable for everyone around him.
Sophia bided her time. Whenever the air grew thick with
threats and counter-threats, she would watch her opportunity,
and then at a moment chosen by herself she would enter the
fray and speak a few calming words. In the body of a girl
there was the mind of a mature woman. Schliemann, who
rarely gave credit to others, was unstinting in his admiration
of her cunning. Was she not Penelope, and was he not
Odysseus?

The work went on, but nothing of great moment was
being discovered. Curiously, they found no Roman or Byzantine coins, like those found at Troy. Below the ruins of
the Hellenic city they found splendid archaic vases painted
with geometric patterns and terra-cotta goblets bearing a
strange resemblance to Bordeaux wine glasses. There were
the usual clay figurines of goddesses painted bright red. There
were knives, buttons, clay animals, arrowheads not unlike
those he had excavated at Motyë, hundreds of *carrousels*
made of a beautiful blue stone, combs, needles, shattered fragments of crystal. There were millstones and hatchets, and
pieces of bones which Schliemann believed to be parts of
Mycenaean musical instruments. It was beginning to look as
though he was fated to repeat the same experience he had
suffered at Troy—innumerable *carrousels*, innumerable oblongs, innumerable little clay goddesses, nothing of very
much significance.

At last in the fourth or fifth week the workmen digging
south of the Lion Gate came upon two tombstones, each
about 4 feet high, made of sandstone and bearing designs in
relief in a technique resembling primitive wood-carving. One
showed a hunter in a chariot pursuing deer with a hunting dog
running beside the chariot wheels. The other showed another
chariot with the horse led by a naked soldier armed with a
broadsword.

Schliemann thought he saw some resemblance between the

style of carving on the tombstones and the style of the famous lions on the Lion Gate. He noted that the tails of the horses, dog, and deer were unusually thick and long, and though the chariots were only briefly sketched in, he came to the conclusion that they faithfully reflected the chariots used in the time of the Trojan wars. A few more fragments of tombstones appeared in the following days. A still more important discovery was a solitary gold button. With gold and tombstones, Schliemann felt he was hot on the scent.

He had found the tombstones within the great circular space beyond the Lion Gate, and as he continued to work there he became increasingly puzzled by what he discovered. All around the circle he found stone slabs arranged to form a nearly continuous ring of benches. This suggested that the circle represented the open-air meeting place where the nobility would be summoned by heralds to listen to proclamations; and perhaps too it served as a dance floor and a place where the poets celebrated their kings. Orators would stand there; prizes would be given there; and here too the sacred symbols of power would be periodically shown to the people.

These places were holy ground and were usually connected with the dead heroes, and sometimes the tombs of kings would lie beneath the stones. Such a place was called the *agora*, and though holy, was used as a market place. Euripides in the *Electra* speaks of the people of Mycenae being called "to the *agora* to see the wonderful lamb with the golden fleece," the golden lamb being a symbol of royalty. Pausanias said that the heroic tombs were within the *agora* of Megara. Pindar, too, speaks of the heroes being buried in the *agora* on the island of Thera. Schliemann began to believe that the tombs of the heroes would be found within that ring of stone.

For some reason which he never made clear, he did not at once begin to excavate within the circle. South of the circle lay a gigantic house with seven large windowless rooms; and thinking this was the royal palace, he decided to excavate here in earnest. The early finds were disappointing: the inevitable *carrousels* of blue stone, the inevitable hatchets and axes, the inevitable scraps of painted pottery. The great discovery was a vase some 12 inches high, on which an ancient artist had depicted a procession of soldiers marching off to war. They are painted dark red on a light yellow ground. Here for the first time we see the equipment of the soldiers who fought in the wars before Troy, and what is surprising is the liveliness of these quickly sketched portraits and their curious air of modernity. They march out of an ancient past, but we would recognize them if they came into the room.

It is worth while to pause and study these soldiers, for it is likely that the Homeric heroes wore a garb similar to theirs. They wear horned helmets with plumes fluttering from the crests. Similar horned helmets appear on Egyptian reliefs representing battles between the Egyptians and "the people from the lands of the sea." They carry long spears to which wine bottles are attached, and heavy semi-circular shields. They wear small breastplates like gorgets over their coats of mail, which are fastened at the waist by a belt, perhaps of metal. The coats of mail reach only to their thighs, which are protected by tassels, probably of mail. They wear stockings, which may also have been of mail, though Schliemann was inclined to believe they were made of cloth. On the paintings the helmets are dotted over with white points, and Schliemann suggested that the artist intended to represent the luster of bronze. It is more likely that the helmets were made of leather and dotted with metallic spikes such as are found on a small fragment of another warrior vase which Schliemann discovered a few days later.

Schliemann was puzzled by the horns (oblongs) on the helmets. "It is altogether inexplicable to me what they can have been used for," he wrote, "and there is no word in Homer which might be interpreted so as to indicate their existence on a Homeric helmet." For once Schliemann was caught napping, for Homer refers to them clearly enough

in the third book of the *Iliad* in the description of the duel
between Menelaus and Paris: "Menelaus drew his silver-
mounted sword, swung it backward, brought it down on
the horn of the enemy's helmet, and then the sword broke
into pieces and dropped from his hand." The purpose of the
horn was to receive the blow of a sword, but there may
have been other purposes: to avert the evil eye, to reinforce
the warrior's virility, and to give him the feeling that he had
an extra eye. There were two-horned and four-horned helmets, and sometimes the oblongs were curved like goats'
horns.

But though these curved and pointed horns provide an
important clue to the bearing of the soldiers as they march
away from the slim-waisted woman waving to them on the
left, there are more important clues. The plumes seem to be
feathers, not horsehair. The thick belt corresponds to the
Homeric *mitre*, a broad band of metal which protected the
lower abdomen. We know that Homeric leggings were sometimes provided with silver ankle clasps, and ankle clasps seem
to be indicated here. Even the long noses, large eyes, and
neatly trimmed beards are what we might expect. These
soldiers are related to those who fought hundreds of years
later against the Persians, and they march with the same
dancing step. In the most extraordinary way this broken vase
illustrates the ancient history of Greece.

So the months passed, and of worthwhile discoveries there
were only the four fragments of tombstones found on the
agora and the warrior vase. With about 125 workmen Schliemann had worked from morning to dusk under the scorching
sun. Clouds of hot dust roared across Mycenae. His eyes were
inflamed, his temper was short, and he was continually fighting the officials, who were more interested, he thought, in
leaving everything *in situ*[3] than in uncovering the past.

Visitors came, but there was little to show them except

3. *In situ:* "in place" (Latin).

potsherds and beads and painted figurines. The Emperor of
Brazil, Dom Pedro II, rode up from Corinth to examine the
excavations. Schliemann was delighted to have so distinguished a visitor, and gave him a great dinner in the underground tomb called the Treasury of Atreus, which had long
been known and therefore offered little prospect for excavation. Schliemann spoke of discovering treasure. He would
repeat at Mycenae his famous discoveries at Troy. The Emperor smiled. He had been warned by the Greeks of Schliemann's boasts. He expressed interest in the tombstones, and
was a model of politeness. Handsome, skeptical and unassuming, the Emperor astonished Schliemann by his knowledge of
archeology, praised him highly, and spoke of "the invaluable
contributions you are making to the understanding of ancient
civilizations."

Flattered, Schliemann presented the Emperor with pieces
of painted pottery; and he was a little surprised a few days
after the Emperor's departure to learn that Police-captain
Leonidas Leonardos, who had carefully watched over the
Emperor's safety during his visit, had received the miserable
sum of forty francs as an imperial gift to be distributed among
the police force. The police were saying that the captain had
received a thousand francs and embezzled all except forty.
There was an inquiry, and the captain was dismissed from
his post.

Schliemann, who knew the man well, was outraged. He
telegraphed to the prime minister in Athens, without effect.
Learning that Dom Pedro was in Cairo, Schliemann telegraphed the Emperor:

When you left Nauplia, Your Majesty gave 40 francs to Police-
captain Leonidas Leonardos to distribute among the police. In
order to slander this worthy man, the mayor of Nauplia maintains
that he received 1,000 francs from Your Majesty. Leonardos has
meanwhile been dismissed from his post, and I am having the
greatest difficulty in saving him from prison. As I have known

him for many years and regard him as a most honest man, I beg Your Majesty in the name of sacred truth and humanity to telegraph to me the exact amount you gave the Police-captain.

Dom Pedro was a weak man, but he could be generous on occasion. He telegraphed that he had in fact given the Police-captain forty francs, and soon to Schliemann's delight Leonidas Leonardos was reinstated.

Summer came to an end, and the rains came beating down on the *agora*, turning the rubble into mud. The work went on. About the middle of October Schliemann was digging deep in the *agora* when he came across a tomb 20 feet long and 10 feet broad cut out of the slope of the naked rock. Robbers must have plundered the tomb, for he found only some stone slabs and a scattering of gold buttons and ivory horns, which may have been decorations for the mortuary chamber. Then he dug a little further south toward the center of the circle, and at a depth of 15 feet he reached a layer of pebbles. Below this lay three bodies thickly covered with clay and what seemed to be the ashes of a funeral pyre. Through the clay came the glint of gold.

With the treasure in sight and the government officials peering over his shoulder, Schliemann once more knew the powerful agitation which came over him when he discovered the treasure of Troy, and once more he turned to Sophia for assistance. He was too nervous and too excited to uncover the bones himself. Sophia curled down in the hollow and stripped the clay off the bodies with a small pocketknife.

There were five golden diadems with each body. Five golden crosses with the arms shaped like laurel leaves lay on one body, five on the second, and four on the third. These diadems were unlike the elaborate gold-chain diadems found at Troy; they were made from thin sheets of gold hammered with decorative circles and bosses. Where the diadems of Troy showed extreme sophistication, even though the design was simple, the Mycenaean diadems were curiously unassum-

ing, and their simplicity was disarming, suggesting the raw
nakedness of power.

Scattered about the shaft grave were small obsidian knives,
fragments of painted vases, and a silver cup. Schliemann
thought he saw evidence of fire and afterward spoke at considerable length of how the bodies must have been burned
or roasted. He thought the pebbles at the bottom of the tomb
somehow provided ventilation for the funeral pyres, and it
was his belief, shared later by Dörpfeld, that it was the
Mycenaean custom to roast the flesh off the bones. He could

One of the gold crowns from the shaft graves at Mycenae.

make out the shapes of the skeletons, but they had suffered
from moisture and soon crumbled. The treasure of Mycenae
now consisted of fifteen diadems and fourteen golden crosses.

Schliemann now decided to explore the side of the grave
circle furthest away from the Lion Gate. At a depth of 9
feet he found some skeletons and near them were obsidian
knives, but there was no treasure. He was a little puzzled, but

went on digging. If the first grave was disappointing, and the second gave up only a handful of treasure, the third treasure which he came upon after digging only a little way below the skeletons showed a dazzling and unexpected richness of ornament. Here was God's plenty, the whole chamber crammed with objects of gold which shone with a reddish luster.

By this time most of the workmen had been sent away, and a ring of soldiers guarded the treasure chambers. Once more Sophia curled herself among the skeletons and the gold, carefully removing the soil which still covered the royal tombs. She worked patiently and slowly, afraid of destroying the delicately chased patterns on the thin sheets of gold. As in the second grave there were three bodies; one of them wore a gold crown with more than thirty gold leaves surmounting it. These leaves were lightly fixed to the crown, and they must have trembled and shimmered when the king wore it. There were eight more diadems, and six more crosses of gold, some of them double crosses and very ornate. There were gold necklaces and goblets and vases and wine jars, some with golden lids attached by fine gold wires. There was a golden flower on a silver stalk. There were shining spheres of rock crystal which may have been the pommels of royal swords.

But the most surprising discovery was an enormous number of stamped golden disks—he counted over seven hundred of them in this tomb chamber alone. Some were shaped like leaves, others like butterflies, octopuses, stars, and sunflowers, and there were some with purely geometrical designs. Schliemann came to the conclusion that they were miniature copies of shields, but it is more likely that they were symbols of the enduring life which the dead were expected to lead throughout their underground existence.

Together with the gold disks were a large number of gold plaques, rarely more than an inch across and not unlike the miniature gold plaques which have been found during excavations in Persia dating from the time of Cyrus and Xerxes. With extraordinary liveliness the artist has modeled a strip of gold foil into the shape of lions, griffins, cuttlefish, deer, eagles, and swans. These, too, were perhaps ornaments sewed onto the robes of the dead.

Schliemann thought he had found in the third grave three skeletons of women, and he pointed to the smallness of the bones and of the teeth, but it is just as likely that they were men, a king and two princes arrayed in their panoply. A dagger was found among the bones; and two scepters of silver plated with gold.

With the third grave opened, Schliemann set about excavating the rest of the *agora*. Wondering where to dig next, he remembered being struck by the appearance of the dark soil to the west of the third grave. The soil was almost black, markedly different from the soil elsewhere in the *agora*. He dug down to a depth of 15 feet, but found only potsherds. Nine feet further down he discovered what he thought to be a circular altar 4 feet high with a round opening, reminiscent of a well. He felt sure it was an altar raised in honor of the dead heroes who must be buried below, and perhaps gifts were poured through this altar for the dead. The royal graves of Sumeria have clay funnels through which offerings are poured, but they had not been excavated in Schliemann's time and as usual he was forced to rely on his own guesses. The altar still puzzles scholars, but Schliemann's original guess was right. He dug a further 3 feet below the altar and found another tomb filled with treasure. There were five bodies smothered in gold and jewels. Three of them wore masks of gold, and near the head of the fourth lay a strange twisted mask in the shape of a lion's head, which at first Schliemann thought to be a helmet.

Of these four masks one was so crumpled that it had almost lost the shape of human features. By gazing at it for some minutes, Schliemann thought he could make out a youthful face with a high forehead, a long Greek nose, and a small mouth with thin lips. This mask possesses no character. But two of these golden masks are the glory of the fourth grave. They possess power and authority, and a terrible beauty. Death is marked on them, but there is no hint of repose in those awesome features. In character they are completely unlike the serene masks painted on wood which appear on the coffins of the Egyptian pharaohs, and evidently they serve a different purpose. The artist has not attempted to depict them as they were in life, for they wear the unmistakable signs of death. Schliemann thought they were portraits. "There cannot be the slightest doubt that every one of them represents the likeness of the deceased," he wrote. "Had it not been so, all the masks would have represented the same ideal type."

But if they are portraits they are so simplified that they have almost entirely lost those features by which they would be recognized in life. They are reduced almost to abstractions. In one the hollowness of death is conveyed by two bulbous eyes which appear to be bursting out of the face, and in the other the heavily ridged forehead and the tightness of the compressed lips suggest the agony of death. Like the gold masks of Peru, which are extraordinarily similar, they represent not so much portraits of dead men as portraits of death, sculptured and molded by an artist who has transferred to a thin sheet of gold his own terror before the sight of a decaying corpse. An unearthly beauty shines through the masks. We see these kings or princes as they were many hours after their deaths, through the eyes of an artist who made no attempt to reveal them exactly as they were, for otherwise he would have shown them in greater detail and with a more human aspect. Almost they are godlike. It seems to have been the artist's intention to suggest the divinity in the dead rulers, who carried into the grave the mysterious power they exercised during their lives. These masks can be interpreted as portraits of kings at the moment of dissolution when they became gods.

One looks at these masks with awe and a sense of failure.

All through Western history artists have grappled with death and attempted to depict it, but rarely with the success of these unknown artists at Mycenae. Here, at the very beginning of our civilization, death is depicted fearlessly, with immense power and simplicity.

Yet no one knows the precise purpose served by these masks. Neither Homer nor any other Greek writer refers to death masks of any kind. We know that the masks were wrapped round the faces of the dead, and perforations near the flattened ears show how they were held in place by means of threads. Unfortunately the skulls of the five bodies were in such a state of decomposition that none of them could be saved, and we do not know their exact position when they were found. We have the masks; we have all the jewelry scattered around the bodies; but we know too little about archaic Greece to be able to envisage the scene when the bodies were laid in their rock tombs.

When Schliemann first discovered the lion mask, it was flat and broken, and some small pieces appeared to be missing. Assuming it was a helmet, he laid it aside. Later he examined it more closely, made out the lion's eyes, ears, and muzzle, and pronounced that it was a mask and therefore worn over the face. Later kings wore lion's heads as helmets with the muzzles resting on their foreheads, as we see on the coins of Alexander the Great. It is possible that the lion mask was a helmet after all.

Even Schliemann was baffled by the wealth of treasure in the fourth grave. The masks formed only a small part of the treasure. Two of the bodies wore golden breastplates, another wore a crown with dancing leaves, and there were eleven massive gold goblets. One of these had two delicate doves chased on the handles, exactly like Nestor's gold wine cup in the *Iliad*, which was "studded with gold pins and decorated with two golden doves." There were ornamental golden brooches, and golden pins. There were minute double-

The Cup of Nestor from Mycenae.

headed battle-axes in gold less than an inch across. There were 12 enormous buttons covered with gold plate, and more than 400 round pieces of gold which may have been coins, and more than 150 gold disks. There was a lively cuttlefish in gold. There were 10 golden plates which may have served as sword handles. There were copper cauldrons, and bronze swords like rapiers, very narrow. There was a cow's head of silver with flaring horns of gold which must have been, like so many other things found in the tomb, a sacred emblem of the tribe. Amid this vast heap of gold the most surprising discovery was a large number of oyster shells, and some oysters which had never been opened.

The fourth shaft grave at Mycenae contained more treasure than he had discovered at Troy, but Schliemann was in no mood to stop. While he was still excavating this tomb, he began to dig directly north of it. Here he found his fifth and last grave, which gave every evidence of having been rifled: there was only one body in it, which quickly crumbled to powder. In the grave he found a gold diadem, a gold drinking-cup, a green vase and a few terra-cotta fragments.

Work on the first grave had stopped when the grave filled with mud. After weeks of bright weather the mud had dried, and he spent his last days at Mycenae carefully reexamining the first tomb. He had found it empty. By digging further he found three bodies squeezed within the inner walls. They had evidently been pushed away to make room for other bodies, but all traces of these were lost. With the bodies he found a small remnant of treasure. Two wore gold masks, and one of them still had flesh adhering to the skull. Squashed flat by the weight of debris, and without a nose, it possessed recognizable features, and Schliemann was excited beyond measure because he thought he recognized the face of Agamemnon.

It was the round face of a man about thirty-five years old, who retained all his teeth in a perfect state of preservation. He wore a large gold breastplate, and golden leaves distributed over his forehead, chest, and thighs. A flattened mask lay over the face. Schliemann raised the mask to his lips and kissed it. Then he sent off a telegram to the minister in Athens:

In last tomb three bodies one without ornament have telegraphed Nauplia for painter to preserve features dead man with round face resembling picture of Agamemnon I formed long ago.

From all over the plain of Argos people came to view the body of an ancient hero whose face was so miraculously preserved. A painter was summoned from Nauplia to sketch it, and for two days Schliemann watched over it in a fever of anxiety, afraid lest the face would crumble into powder before it could be embalmed. Then a druggist from Argos arrived on the scene. He poured a solution over it, which rendered it hard, and shortly afterward the body was taken in triumph to Athens.

The treasure found in the first tomb could not compare with the great heaps of massive gold found in the fourth; only a small scattering had been left there by the grave-robbers. But there were gold cups and breastplates and bronze swords with golden handles—altogether Schliemann counted eighty swords, most of them wafer-thin. There were twelve gold plaques, some of them representing stags being pursued by lions. There was a battle-ax and a gold sword tassel, and long ribbons of gold were found laced over the body of one of the heroes. But the most glorious discovery was a mask even more beautiful than those he had discovered previously.

This last mask, almost the last thing Schliemann discovered at Mycenae, possesses a perfection lacking in the others. They spoke of death powerfully and were of the earth, earthy; this one speaks with a pure and serene majesty, and with no less power. Once again we are confronted not with a portrait but with an image or *ikon* of death: no human face peers up at us. Where the other masks show the heroes at the moment of dissolution, this mask shows the hero at the moment after he has become a god. There is no trace of earth's fevers, only of benignity. The large eyes are closed, the eyelids clearly marked, and the thin lips are pursed in a mysterious smile. There is a hint of a beard, and the eyebrows are heavily incised and curl upward in imitation of the flaring mustaches; but the total effect of eyebrows and mustaches and smile is to give a curious depth to the face, as though it were seen immensely magnified at the end of a long corridor, beckoning. It is a face to be compared with the great mosaics of Christ at Daphne, Cefalù, and Palermo, and belongs among the most superb achievements of ancient art.

The diadems of Troy, the crowns of Mycenae, and all the heaps of massive gold treasure speak of a people still rude and barbarous. The Warrior Vase tells us how they went to war. The gold trinkets found in the tombs tell us how they decorated themselves on exalted occasions. But only this mask tells us of the deep reverence they paid to their gods.

Now the work was done, and as Schliemann gazed around the *agora* which resembled a crumbled honeycomb after so many shafts had been dug into it, he expected to find no more treasures. He had found five royal graves and thought he had looked on the faces of Agamemnon, Clytemnestra, and the others who had taken part in that heroic tragedy. One day

The Beautiful Mask.

toward the end of November he sent off a telegram to the King of the Hellenes:

With extreme joy I announce to Your Majesty that I have discovered the tombs which tradition, echoed by Pausanias, has designated as the sepulchres of Agamemnon, Cassandra, Eurymedon and all their companions who were killed while partaking of a meal with Clytemnestra and her lover Aegisthus. They were surrounded with a double circle of stone slabs, which would not have been erected unless they were great personages. In the tombs I found immense treasures of the most ancient objects of pure gold.

These treasures alone will fill a great museum, the most wonderful in the world, and for centuries to come thousands of foreigners will flock to Greece to see them. I work only for the pure love of science, and accordingly I have no claim on these treasures. I give them intact and with a lively enthusiasm to Greece. God grant that these treasures may become the cornerstone of an immense national wealth.

He was disappointed with the reply written by the King's secretary. It was a very brief reply. He was thanked for his important discoveries, his zeal, and his love for science. The King added the pious hope that further excavations would be crowned with a similar success.

For the first time Schliemann returned from his excavations empty-handed. Everything he discovered in Mycenae became the property of the Greek government. The hated Stamatakes, so long a thorn in his side, was already making announcements about the discoveries. In horror Schliemann dispatched a telegram to the government: "Forbid publication by Stamatakes. Not the Government, but I, have the right."

Once more he was pitting himself against governments. The town of Nauplia intervened in the dispute with the demand that all the treasure should be housed there—it would be good for the town, and was not Nauplia the logical proprietor? Schliemann raged in his tent. He wrote off telegrams to all the learned societies and contemplated the huge collection of photographs he had assembled during the excavations and wrote up his notes and diaries. As usual the Germans were inclined to laugh at his claims, the French showed little interest, and only the English shared his enthusiasm.

He spent the winter in Athens. One day in January he sent one of the assistants he had employed at Mycenae to make a detailed drawing of the *agora* for his records. This assistant, Vasilios Drosinos, was a young engineer who had worked with him in the tomb-chambers. Recognizing near a partly excavated house south of the *agora* some roughly carved stones which resembled the stones in the tomb-chamber, Drosinos discussed the matter with Stamatakes, who had returned to Mycenae that day. A workman with a pickax was brought to the spot. With the first or second blow of the ax a gold cup came to light, and in less than half an hour there was a small treasure consisting of four gold cups, all of them with delicate dogs' head handles, one plain undecorated cup, a number of rings fashioned out of gold wire, and two gold signets. One of these signets showed some animal heads and ears of corn, all jumbled together, and no one has ever been able to understand what it was intended to convey. The other signet was a masterpiece.

We know it now as the Signet of the Mother Goddess, and like the gold mask found in the first tomb it hints at an unexpected depth of religious feeling among the Mycenaeans. A ceremony is being performed, the simplest of all ceremonies—an offering to the goddess. There are no temples, no altars, no veils, no rituals. In silence they make their offerings, and the artist seems to have caught the actors in the ceremony at a moment which is at once very casual and filled with significance.

The goddess sits beneath the sacred tree with flowers in her hair and more flowers in her hands, receiving a tribute of flowers from two women of noble aspect, who may be priestesses. One of the handmaidens of the goddess stands before her, introducing these worshipers, while another handmaiden is climbing a small cairn of stones, plucking the sacred fruit from the tree and offering it to her divine mistress. All wear the flounced richly embroidered doubleskirts which were characteristic of Mycenaean culture during the heroic age. Like the Mother Goddess they wear flowers and ornaments in their hair.

Between the first of the worshipers and the goddess stand two double axes, the smaller superimposed upon the other; these axes perhaps represent earthly and spiritual power. And beyond this strange emblem of power there floats a presiding genius who is helmeted and holds a spear and hides behind a shield shaped like a figure "8"—the first representation of an armed goddess known to us. Above this scene the sun shines in full splendor beside the crescent moon: it is at once noonday and the depth of night.

But what is most remarkable about the signet is the quiet composure and serenity of these people partaking in the offering. Such a signet could not have been carved except at a time of great self-assurance. The signet is extremely small, hardly more than an inch across, but the artist has poured into it the accumulated knowledge of centuries of religious meditation. The power of the heavens flows down in rings of light, and power wells up from the goddess as she reposes in the sacred grove. In the attitudes of the priestesses there is no humility; they come to her as though by right, gravely, making their offerings out of affection for the goddess, towering over her, with none of the servitude which can be seen in the Egyptian paintings showing the offerings to the gods. A very human dignity informs them. Bathed in the light of the sun and moon, they stand and move according to their own volition.

We cannot hope to understand the full meaning of the

signet. We do not know, for example, what meaning can be attached to the six strange objects which decorate the side facing the tree. They may be golden masks, skulls, helmets, sacred flowers, or they may simply be decorations to balance the tree with its heavy fruit. No one knows what kind of tree is being represented. Schliemann, studying the signet from photographs he obtained with difficulty from Stamatakes, pronounced that they were pineapples or perhaps breadfruit, such as he had seen in Central America. He thought the women wore vizors, and was puzzled by their masculine features; and he noted that the curved parallel bands of their skirts mirrored the crescent shapes which are to be seen everywhere in the signet. For some reason he thought that the waving lines beneath the sun and moon represented the sea, though it is more likely that they represent rings of heavenly light or the Milky Way.

In the *Iliad* Homer describes how Hephaestus made for Achilles a great shield with five panels, the first representing "the earth, the sky and the sea, the indefatigable sun, the moon at the full and all the constellations," and when Schliemann first saw the signet with Sophia at his side, he exclaimed: "It must have been seen by Homer when he described all the wonders which Hephaestus wrought on the shield of Achilles." It was one of his greater griefs that he had not discovered the signet, but he took comfort in the thought that it might have lain undiscovered if he had not sent his surveyor to Mycenae.

The work at Mycenae was over. Schliemann never returned there, feeling that his work was done. He wrote a book about his finds in eight weeks, and then set about translating it into French and English; and then he wrote to Gladstone, begging for the honor of an introduction to the work from the Grand Old Man of English politics. Gladstone, an excellent Homeric scholar, was reluctant to undertake such a task, fearing that his commendation would be misinterpreted. During the summer Schliemann visited London, bringing with him the treasure of Troy, which was exhibited in the South Kensington Museum. Gladstone was not quite convinced that this was the treasure of Troy, but he was impressed by Schliemann's learning and finally wrote a rambling introduction which covers nearly forty pages.

Gladstone was particularly struck by the Signet of the Mother Goddess and debated with himself whether the six strange objects on the side were stars or lions' heads, and suggested that the waving band below the sun and moon represented mother-earth, "with its uneven surface of land and its rippling sea." He was inclined to believe that the body found in the first grave belonged to Agamemnon. The fact that the features had been preserved suggested that the body had been embalmed, and this would only apply to a very eminent personage. The *Iliäd* relates that Agamemnon was always accompanied by two priestly heralds, and the heralds were no doubt the two other bodies found in the tomb.

Schliemann gloried in the attentions he received in London. He dined with Gladstone, and sent off a flood of telegrams to Sophia, who was ill in Athens. He could never tolerate her absence for long, and at last when the members of the Royal Archeological Society asked her to address them she came post-haste from Athens and stood beside her husband on the platform, telling the story of how for twenty-five days she had knelt among the tombs, carefully scraping off thin layers of clay from the bodies of the ancient kings and queens of Mycenae. She spoke very simply in English, and received an ovation. Schliemann smiled approvingly. He had written her speech, and was delighted because she recited it without faltering, and still more delighted because she was carrying his son, born later that year. Long ago he had chosen the name he would give to his son—Agamemnon.

Fame exacts its penalties, and not the least of them is the

temptation to rest on one's laurels. For eighteen months Schliemann basked in his growing fame, and it was not until the summer of 1878 that he put a spade into the earth again.

Still looking for treasure, he thought he might find it in Ithaca in the great palace of Odysseus. He spent two weeks in July excavating among the immense walls at the top of Mount Aetios, but though he found the ruins of 190 houses, he found little else of value, and abandoned the excavations.

Troy summoned him—Troy where he had encountered so many defeats from the Turkish government, and so much success. Once again he was employing all his resources to obtain a *firman*. This time he was not alone, for Gladstone was sympathetic to renewed excavations at Troy and the full weight of his influence was felt in Constantinople, where Austen Layard, the discoverer of Nineveh, had become British Ambassador. The Turks granted a *firman*, but took care to send a special commissioner and ten policemen to Hissarlik to superintend the excavations.

It was Schliemann's sixth journey to Hissarlik. He began work in September, and for nearly two months nothing of value was discovered. But his luck was holding. On October 21, 1878, in the presence of some officers from a British warship, he discovered, northeast of the Palace of Priam, not far from the place where he had found the first Trojan treasure, a small hoard consisting of 20 gold earrings, a number of gold spiral rings, 2 heavy bracelets of electrum, 11 silver earrings, and 158 silver rings and a large number of gold beads. A few days later he found a still smaller treasure consisting of gold bars and pellets of gold, a gold bracelet and a silver dagger. Work stopped on November 26. This time Schliemann was allowed to keep only a third of the treasure he found; the rest went to the Imperial Museum in Constantinople.

His luck, which had been holding so well, lasted into the following spring, when digging was resumed with the assist-

ance of Emile Burnouf and Rudolf Virchow. Schliemann
arrived in Troy in February. His plan was to uncover the
town wall of Troy and to make a complete map of Homeric
Troy. In April he discovered two small pockets of treasure consisting of gold disks, chains, earrings, and bracelets.
He never found any more treasure again. Homer had mentioned that there were three towns rich in gold—Troy,
Mycenae, and Orchomenos, once a great city in Boeotia. The
following year Schliemann hoped to crown his achievements
with the gold treasure of Orchomenos, but though he excavated the beehive tombs and mapped the walls of the
ancient city, the results were disappointing.

The years of luck were over. For the last ten years of
his life he was to be a wanderer on the face of the earth,
always hoping to come upon traces of gold, searching for it
relentlessly, as though driven by some inner force, and never
finding it. The old magic had gone. He had the eagerness
of a child and the passion of an adolescent, but his skin
was leathery and he was growing old. He must find roots
somewhere, and so at last, having made his peace with Athens,
he decided to build a house worthy of himself in the heart
of the city.

Characteristically, he designed the house himself on the
model of the palaces he had uncovered in Troy and Mycenae.
He called it *Iliou Melathron,* or "the palace of Troy." It
stands on the Boulevard de l'Université at the foot of
Mount Lycabettus, overlooking the royal stables. It is a
huge house, cold and chilling, with marble steps and mosaic
floors on which are depicted the gold cups and vases he
discovered at Troy. Along the walls run friezes with classical landscapes and paintings of the Greek heroes with appropriate Homeric quotations.

On the lower floors he displayed his treasure. Upstairs
was his private study, with the notice on the door: "All who
do not study geometry, remain outside." The study was

crammed with books. Here were some of the more precious objects he had gathered. On the walls were fading views of New York and Indianapolis, two cities which he especially admired. For whole days he would sit there in a heavily upholstered armchair studying the Greek classics, while the smaller chair beside him was piled high with the stock exchange lists which came every morning from Paris, London, and Berlin. Telegraph forms were always at hand. He was still a businessman, and some hours every day had to be spent on superintending his financial dealings which extended over the whole world.

In his house he behaved as tyrannically as any Homeric prince. His word was law. All messages were sent to him in classical Greek, and Greek was the language employed exclusively at table. He renamed all his servants. The porter was Bellerophon, the footman Telamon, Andromache's governess was Danaë, Agamemnon's nurse was Polyxena, and the old gardener was called Calchas, after the soothsayer whose curses open the *Iliad*. Because the ancient Greeks employed little furniture, he did the same; and there were only a few chairs and sofas tucked away in the corners of the bare, draughty rooms. He refused to have curtains, because it was unthinkable that Achilles would ever stay in a curtained house. The ruins of Pompeii had always had a peculiar fascination for him, and so in this great house patterned on the palaces of ancient Greece, he built a ballroom patterned on the villas of ancient Pompeii, with a delicate blue and white frieze of putti encircling the wall. The putti were modeled on people he had known and encountered in his travels. Among them was a portrait of Schliemann in horn-rimmed spectacles.

On the flat roof of the house, facing the four corners of the sky, were twenty-four marble gods. Zeus, Aphrodite, Apollo, Athena, and all the other gods stood there, protecting and encouraging him during the declining years of his life.

. . . 8   THE HEROES

DURING the last thirty-four years of his life, Schliemann
read the *Iliad* avidly. It was his bible, the book he consulted
at all hours of the day, the fountainhead of nearly all the
thoughts that ever occurred to him, and no single part of it
was to be preferred to any other. In his library were all the
available editions, many in folio and bound in heavy mo-
rocco, but there were also cheap paperbound Tauchnitz editions which he carried on his travels and annotated heavily.
Once when a correspondent wrote that he found the *Iliad*
full of difficulties, Schliemann replied that on the contrary
he found it as clear and pellucid as the Castalian springs,
there were simply no difficulties, and anyone in his right
mind could read it as he reads a modern novel. For Schliemann both the *Iliad* and the *Odyssey* were holy writ, blessed
by the gods, written with a nobility and elegance almost
beyond the range of human accomplishment. In these books,
if a man sat down to read them attentively, he would find
all the fruitfulness and joy, and all the tragedy of man
displayed. Here was the perfect story told by the perfect
poet, and beyond this it was unnecessary to go.

More than once Schliemann protested that it was impossible to make any choice between the parts of the *Iliad*. On
one occasion, however, he broke his own rule. He said the
most splendid passage of all is in the third book: the account
of Helen arising from her embroidery—she had been weaving
a kind of tapestry showing the Trojans and Achaeans at one
anothers' throats—and making her way to the Scaean Gate,
where on one of the gate-towers overlooking the plain Priam
and the elders of the city have congregated "like cicadas
perched on trees chirping merrily."

News has come that there will be no more war. Instead
Menelaus and Paris, her husband and her abductor, will
fight a duel, and her fate will be determined by the issue of

the duel. Veiled in white, accompanied by her handmaidens, she approaches the tower. The elders lower their voices as they see her coming, astonished by her beauty, and happy that a solution to the long conflict is in sight. Priam beckons her to his side, points to the enemy, and asks: "Who is that man, taller by a head than the rest, with a majestic air about him?"

She answers that it is Agamemnon, her husband's elder brother. Then Priam points to a smaller deep-chested man, who has left his armor lying on the ground, and she answers: "That is Odysseus." There is a third man, eminently tall and handsome, and she says: "That is Ajax." Then she recognizes Idomeneus, the King of Crete, the gentlest of Agamemnon's captains, but she cannot see either Castor or Polydeuces, her two brothers, one a famous horse tamer, the other a renowned boxer. She gazes after them, and in her silence there is all the desolation of grief, for she knows nothing of what has happened to them but suspects the worst; and Homer comments:

> The fruitful earth had laid them already on her lap,
> Far away in Lacedaemon, the land they loved.

There are seven or eight other passages in Homer where grief enters just as nakedly. Grief—grief over the lot of man—is the major theme of the story. At the very beginning Homer proclaims that his subject is the wrath of Achilles, the havoc he will create, leading to the deaths of so many good men. An explosive death-dealing force is let loose, and we watch with bated breath as he destroys everything in his path, quarrels with everyone around him, and never rests until he has not only destroyed his appointed enemy but outraged the corpse of Hector and mangled it beyond recognition, so that at last when he surrenders the body to King Priam, there is nothing human or godlike left in the appearance of the young hero—Hector is no more than a squashed fly.

Achilles is the hero, but he is a hero in love with death; and those who listened to the story were a people in love with life. They marveled at the destructiveness of the gods, who had made the earth so beautiful and filled it with so much tragic irony. The flashing armor, the bold glances, the supple bodies of men, the dancing and the gold—all end in tears. In a sense, the *Iliad* is no more than a long litany on the tragic deaths of young heroes.

All through the *Iliad* there rings the cry of suffering. Why must these things happen? Why are the Greeks determined to destroy? What pleasure do they derive from it? From the beginning we know that Hector must be dragged by the heels around the walls of Troy, and that Achilles will triumph, and that Helen in her white and shining robes will pass wraith-like through the story, always beautiful and unattainable, a ghost who lives in horror of her own beauty. For a ghost men waged this war, and for a ghost they perish. Men must die, women must weep, blood must be spilled, and it is all in vain. A grim irrational fate broods over everything.

That life was vain and therefore senseless was something Homer knew only too well. Homer knew fighting. He did not fight in the Trojan wars, but he knew the excitement of small skirmishes and what bodies looked like when they lay on the ground. He knew poverty and starvation, for otherwise he would not have taken such enjoyment in describing banquets and the embroidered raiments of heroic men. Tradition says he was blind, and this accords with his constant reference to the brightness of things; and that he was an islander from one of the islands of the Ægean, and this accords with his curious detachment, for his sympathies are neither with the Greeks nor with the Trojans, but only with the individual human beings who are caught up in the senseless war.

Three figures stand out in massive grandeur: the turbulent

Achilles, the cunning Odysseus who assumes many of the
characteristics of Achilles in the last terrible chapters of the
Odyssey, and the doomed Hector, who remains the private
hero of the epic, as Achilles is the public hero. Nearly all
the tender and intimate passages concern Hector. Almost
he is Hamlet.[1] He is the man caught in the web, waiting
impatiently for his own doom, dissembling, hoping for a
way of escape, falling into dreams and out of them, remembering his childhood, more aware than anyone else of the
evanescence of life and the terrible responsibilities he carries.
He is speaking to his wife on the eve of a disastrous battle:

The day will come, my soul knows it is coming,
When our holy Troy will go down into ruins,
Troy and the brave King and the King's people with him.
And I am not moved so much by the grief of the Trojans—
Grief will come—Hecuba's grief, and the grief of my father,
The grief of so many good men, lying
In the bloody dust under the feet of our enemies.
I think of my death, and then your grief hurts me:
And I am grieved at the thought of you being carried away
    weeping
By the bronze-coated enemy into certain slavery.
They will set you to work over somebody's loom in Argos
Or carrying a pitcher in a remote village somewhere,
And always against your will, because you're a captive.
Seeing you weeping, they will say:
"Look, the wife of Hector, the great captain
Of the horsemen of Troy, in the days when they fought for their
    city."
Hearing them, your grief will become greater,
For having no man like me to free you from slavery.
O let me be dead and let the earth be heaped over me
Before I hear you weeping or how you were enslaved.

So he spoke, the shining one, and stretched his arms to his son,

---

1. *Hamlet:* hero of the great play by William Shakespeare (1603).

But the boy cried out to his nurse with the beautiful girdle—
Frightened by the glint of steel and the horsehair crest of the
     helmet.
Suddenly both the father and mother were laughing,
And the shining Hector put his helmet away,
Set it shimmering on the ground, and threw out his hands
To his beloved son, kissing him and rocking him in his arms.

No one could have written such scenes of intolerable
poignancy without being overwhelmed with affection for
the character he had created. There is a sense in which the
Iliad is Hector's *apologia*. He speaks throughout, and it is
his voice, now shouting defiance, now trembling with anger,
now calm and composed, which speaks most distinctly.
"These things happened," he says. "This doom was brought
on us. We fought back, and we extracted from every passing moment the little joy that was left to us." It is a curiously modern answer, and as we read Homer, we find ourselves continually confronting a curiously modern world.

We know Achilles only too well. He represents the violently anarchic monster in the human soul. He kills for the
pure joy of killing, contemptuous of danger, certain only
of the blessedness of destruction. To say he is ruthless and
vengeful is to underestimate his terrible sobriety. He kills
aimlessly, as huntsmen kill. He is without any sense of guilt,
and cares nothing for the old or the very young. When he
falls upon the child Lycaon, shouting: "Death to all!"
and makes fun of the child who is pleading for his life, he
is just as amused as when he fights with Hector, knowing
that the gods will protect his own life. When Odysseus
says to Eumaeus in the *Odyssey:* "My delight was in ships,
fighting, javelins and arrows—things that make men shudder
to think about," we hear once again the authentic voice of
Achilles. The nihilist asks for no pardon. He despises the
world, and is content to surrender all his privileges for
the pleasure of destroying the world. Achilles did not take

part in the Trojan war to rescue Helen: he went because
he wanted to kill and because he wanted to see all Troy
reduced to ashes and flame.

As we know Achilles, so we know Odysseus, "the cunning artificer," the man who cares very little for the gods,
but relies on his own rude strength. He is the Good Soldier
Schweik[2] elevated to general's rank, an excellent soldier, and
the rankest amateur as a sailor, for how otherwise would he
have taken so long to make the comparatively short journey from the Dardanelles to Ithaca?

Best of all do we know Hector. He is the disenchanted
one, for whom no magic wand is ever waved, Hamlet and
the Prince d'Aquitaine, the last of his race. Hector wears
the face of our own time. He defies augury. He will do
everything humanly possible to escape his fate, but he knows
that it is inescapable. He will behave at all times with exquisite nobility, but he knows that honor will never win any
wars. As Homer says, he has the look of nightfall on his
face. "None but the gods could meet and hold him as he
sprang through the gate." So in the end he is stabbed in
the throat, stripped of his armor, and dragged through the
dust, because the gods have aided his enemy and forsaken
him, and all this was known to him from the very beginning.

In every age men have read Homer, but never has he been
read so widely or attentively as in the present age; and for
good reason. He holds the mirror up to nature. The world
he describes is the world of today, for little has changed in
the thirty centuries since the burning of Troy. The fires
burn; the besieged make their desperate sorties; everywhere
the cries of the doomed can be heard. We are all Trojans;
and Homer, the blind wanderer among ancient islands, describes our present plight with excessive brightness. It is
not that he was a prophet: it is simply that no one else has

2. *Schweik:* character in a novel by Jaroslav Hasek (1883-1923), Czech
writer.

ever described the human condition with such starkness and majesty.

When Schliemann went in search of Troy, he was searching for the fountainhead of Western civilization. He, too, possessed the modern temper. Restless, feverish, moving among shadows, he possessed many of the vices of the Victorians, but he also possessed to a quite extraordinary degree the determination to break through the trappings of the cluttered civilization which surrounded him. Because he had no roots, he must search for roots even in the most ancient past, in places where there are no signposts and men must walk warily.

He had a typically modern irreverence toward scholars who are content to weave their theories without observing the evidence. He must find the evidence and bring it to light and prove incontestably that Homer existed and wrote about battles still warm in the memories of men. When he went beyond this and attempted to prove that he had looked upon the face of Agamemnon dead and hung Helen's diadem on his wife's forehead, he was greeted with derisive laughter, but it is at least possible that his claim was justified. His greatest merit was that he clothed the more shadowy statements of Homer in flesh and gave them more substance than they ever possessed before. He discovered no writing except a few scratched fragments in Troy, but all his discoveries were in the nature of a Homeric poem suddenly unearthed and laid before an unbelieving world. He found the fountainhead, and beyond this there was no need to go.

To this day we do not know what happened at Troy, and why the battle was fought. We do not know whether Homer ever visited the Troad, but the story of the fall of Troy comes to us with so much authentic detail that it is no longer possible to doubt the essential outline. Homer reshaped his heroes, magnifying and distorting them for his own purposes, as a poet will. His own sympathies were deeply involved in his portrait of Hector. He believed that the war was fought over the abduction of Helen by Paris, and the modern scholars who assert that it must have been fought for the control of the Dardanelles forget that wars often start senselessly for causes remote from economics.

Herodotus provides an ironic commentary to the Homeric story. Egyptian priests told him that the war was completely senseless, for neither Helen nor Paris was in Troy when the Greeks attacked—they had escaped to Memphis, the capital of Egypt, where they were arrested by orders of Pharaoh. Paris was interrogated and asked to explain the presence of the beautiful Helen by his side. His explanation failed to satisfy Pharaoh and he was therefore banished from the country. Shortly afterward Menelaus, Helen's lawful husband, came to Memphis, claimed her, and returned with her to Greece.

Here is Herodotus' account of the mysterious origin of the war:

I asked the priests whether there was any truth in the Greek story of what happened at Troy, and in reply they gave me some information which (they said) came directly from the lips of Menelaus. According to the priests the Greeks sent a great force in support of Menelaus' cause when they learned of the abduction of Helen. As soon as they landed and established themselves on Trojan soil, they sent ambassadors—Menelaus was one of them—to the city. When they were received within the walls, they demanded the restoration of Helen together with the treasure which Paris had stolen, and they asked too for an indemnity. The Trojans answered that neither Helen nor the treasure were in their possession: she had fled to Egypt, where she was being detained by the Egyptian King. It was the greatest injustice that they should be punished for something over which they had no control.

The Trojans always held fast to this answer, and they were always prepared to swear an oath that this is exactly what happened.

The Greeks however regarded this as a perfectly frivolous

answer. They laid siege to the city, and continued to fight until it fell; but no trace of Helen was found, and in defeat the Trojans told the same story they had told at the beginning. When the Greeks at last realized that the story was true, they sent Menelaus to Proteus (the Pharaoh) in Egypt. He sailed along the river to Memphis, and after he had given a true account of what happened, he was most hospitably entertained and Helen was restored to him with all his other possessions. Helen was none the worse for her adventures.

Though Menelaus received generous treatment at the hands of the Egyptians, he himself proved no friend of Egypt. When about to leave the country, he was delayed by contrary winds for many weeks. To change the course of the winds, he seized two young Egyptian children and sacrificed them to the gods. When this terrible crime became known, the friendship of the Egyptians was turned to hatred. Menelaus was pursued, but succeeded in escaping with his ships to Libya. What happened to him afterwards none of the Egyptians could say.

Such was Herodotus' account of a Trojan war fought over shadows, and it is not altogether unsupported by some strange references in the Homeric poems to a journey by Paris to Sidon in Phoenicia and another by Menelaus to Egypt. With all his admiration for Homer, Herodotus found it difficult to believe that Priam was mad enough to sacrifice Troy and all the Trojans simply in order that Paris might possess Helen. "I do not believe," he wrote, "that even if Priam himself had been married to her, he would have failed to surrender her to bring this succession of calamities to an end." No one, not even Herodotus, knew what had happened. Only one thing is certain: it was a war so senseless that it beggars the imagination, and at the same time it was no more senseless than any other war.

But while we can never be certain about the causes of the Trojan War, we know a great deal about the men who fought in it. No Trojan graveyards have been found; and the graves of Mycenae belong to a time before the war was fought. But

we know those soldiers well: Homer and the evidence of
the excavations speak with the same voice. There was little
change between the time of the unknown kings found at
Mycenae and the time of the Trojan War: the appearances
of people, their social customs, their way of fighting and
tilling the soil and worshiping their gods. We know what
they wore and how they decorated themselves, and what
they ate. If we saw them walking towards us across a field,
we would recognize them instantly.

They wore their hair long, and bound it with gold and
silver threads. In summer the men wore sleeved cloaks reaching to the knees; in winter they wore great capes, and these
capes also served as bed-coverings. They delighted in ornamental belts, earrings, necklaces, jeweled diadems, and ribbons; they wore gloves and furs. Priestesses and rich women
were attired in long embroidered skirts with panels of various
colors, and sometimes the skirts were divided, as we see
them on the Signet of the Great Mother or in the remnants
of a frieze found in Tiryns. Warriors wore helmets made
of rings of boars' tusks, like the helmet Meriones lent to
Odysseus, and the curved tusks found in Mycenaean graves
correspond perfectly to the description given by Homer.
Everything we know about their skill in ornament suggests
an extreme sophistication.

They had chairs and tables, but no plates; food was eaten
off the table, which was afterward washed with sponges.
They ate meat: mutton, goat's flesh, pork, and more rarely
beef. These animals were domesticated. Fowl were kept in
their farmyards, and geese wandered in and out of their
houses. Game included deer, wild boar, wild goats, rabbits,
and wolves. They ate fish, and especially delighted in oysters.
They grew wheat, barley, millet, beans, peas, and lentils,
and cultivated vines and olive trees. They sweetened their
wine with honey, and enjoyed the fruit of their orchards;
in the garden of Alcinoüs there were pears, apples, figs, and

pomegranates. Children ate meat, marrow, relishes, fat, and wine, but there seems to have been no milk. They regarded cheese as a common dish enjoyed by even the poorest. There were no cats—the cat appeared in Greece about the sixth century B.C.—but they had hunting dogs and watchdogs.

It was a simple and primitive society, organized around the sacred persons of their kings. There was almost no industrial organization, and no coinage. Each community was fiercely proud and hostile to all other communities, yet capable at times of forming leagues of friendship and peace with them. As Walter Leaf observed long ago, "their organizations were not yet strong enough to hold in subjection the grown bodies of men." Of all people living today they resembled most the Balinese, those proud and vivid people whose lives are spent in unremitting toil, in harmony with the gods and the seasons, under the rule of cultivated and despotic rajahs.

The Trojans worshiped the gods and the spirits of the dead, but their worship was joyous. They knew no fasting or atonement, no sense of guilt, no doom descending from a crime committed long ago in a garden. They were young and fresh, living in an elemental sunlit world, the sap still new in their veins; and divinity was all around them. It did not perturb them overmuch that the gods possessed a rank and order of their own: Apollo, the lord of the silver bow, was "the mightiest of the gods," but so was Zeus. For them the gods were almost mortal, and men almost divine; and the greatest triumph of man was to enter the realm of the gods. A mortal Diomedes might wound the goddess Aphrodite. Gods walked in the market place, and they too were vulnerable, shuddering before "the dark realm of death."

Most of all they loved brightness and feared the dark. For them divinity was almost within men's grasp, a thing as light as air, as palpable as flesh, resembling the glimmering flames of campfires at night, the gleam of bronze, the shining

of olive trees, the faces of people. Achilles recognizes the
goddess Athena by "her mighty flaming glance." The signs
of divinity were the double ax, the wheeling swastika, the
little clay figurines of the Mother Goddess and those strange
carrousels, usually of blue stone, which seem to have sym-
bolized the mysterious beginnings of things. Every little
stream possessed its attendant nymphs, and every thunder
clap was a word from a hidden god. Rivers, sea foam, mountains, trees, all living things partook of divinity, but all
divinity failed at the gate of death. The gods were humbled
by death; men feared it with an unappeasable fear; all the
heavens shuddered at it. Death was an error marked upon the
face of the world: from death they recoiled with bated breath
and shuddering horror. Nothing is so remarkable in Homer as
the special quality of their fear of death—that fear which is
also a kind of pride. Hating and fearing death, they were
still capable of regarding it with laughter and derision and
flashing eyes.

According to Homer the Trojans and Achaeans burned
their dead; like the Balinese they danced around the funeral
pyres. Patroclus was placed on a pyre, and there were con-
sumed with him not only sheep and oxen, horses and dogs,
but also twelve young Trojans. But this was a very special
ceremony, ordered by the ferocious Achilles in honor of his
dead friend, and it is unlikely that it was often repeated.
Achilles abused the corpse of Hector for twelve days until
Apollo restrained him, and this too must have happened very
exceptionally. All the evidence we have suggests that the
Homeric Greeks regarded the dead with grave reverence.

Scholars have remarked that the Homeric descriptions of
funeral pyres have nothing in common with the grave
chambers found at Mycenae. They have said repeatedly that
Mycenaean burial customs point to a civilization far earlier
than the Trojan War; and it is true that the shaft-graves
heaped with gold antedate the Trojan War by many cen-

turies. But gold is flame. Homer says that the spirits of the
dead can only be admitted to the realm of the dead after
burning. Yet it is perfectly possible to conceive that a gold
mask was itself a kind of flame. The kings of Mycenae wear
gold masks; Patroclus wears a raiment of flame; and to the
Greeks these may have been no more than variants of the
same custom.

Like nearly all the great epics, like the *Æneid*, *Beowulf*,
The Song of Roland and *Paradise Lost*, the *Iliad* is the story
of a defeat endured heroically in an evil time. Good men
perish, the evil profit, but the verdict of the gods is not based
upon the good or evil deeds men perform; and the gods are
indifferent to men's fate. To the gods what is ultimate and
significant is man's raw courage, the majesty he wraps
around himself as he treads the path of danger, defying the
gods to do their worst. The highest virtue of man is his
audacity, which makes him most god-like; then his tenderness, which makes him most human. So Odysseus says in the
Iliad: "Praise me not much, neither blame me, but let us go
forward; for the night is far spent and the dawn is near."

Between those two worlds of the utmost audacity and
the most eloquent tenderness Homer moves with enviable
ease, reflecting a world where men were still innocent, and a
pure fire burned in their veins, before they became intimidated by guilt and terror and the endless repetition of tragedy.
They stand foursquare to the winds, simple and sensuous,
before history began. Writing in old age and two hundred
years after the events he described, he may have painted them
brighter and more enchanting than they were, mingling the
stories handed down over the years with memories of his
own youth.

He had an old man's serenity, an old man's love for the
ardors of youth. With his own eyes he had seen such a murder as he described in the last books of the *Odyssey*, the
bodies of the suitors lying on the floor and the maidservants

hanged in the courtyard. He had seen a young chieftain killed and dragged still bleeding behind a chariot around the walls of a ruined city. He had heard the old men hushing their voices "like the chattering of swallows" when a beautiful woman passed by. He had been wounded, and loved a woman as beautiful as Helen, and sat in the tents of kings when the captured women were portioned out among the victors. He had seen all this, but it all happened a long time ago; and so he wandered from town to town, telling these stories and playing on his lyre, and the same stories were told by his disciples; and in time they were written down.

Generations passed; the stories changed a little, but the unquenchable voice never died. It was so powerful and eloquent a voice that the shapes and colors of an entire civilization were carried with it, and nothing like this has ever happened since. The civilization Homer portrayed was so rich, so beautiful, so filled with sensuous majesty that men came to believe it wore the aspect of a dream. Then Schliemann came along and staggered the world by showing that it was a waking dream: it had all happened in the sunlight of the Ionian seas.

. . . 9 THE LAST YEARS

As THE YEARS passed Schliemann showed little sign of change. He had been inflexible in youth, and in old age he was just as inflexible, just as demanding. He still spoke in a gruff clipped voice and carried himself like a man afraid of unbending. All his life he had maintained a vast correspondence, writing his letters and books while standing at a high desk; and he had never employed a secretary. Even though he was wealthy and famous and possessed a palace worthy of him, he still saw no reason for employing a secretary and continued to write his letters in longhand, jumping from one language to another according to his mood.

His wealth increased. He kept a close watch on the stock market and the houses he owned in Paris, Berlin, and Athens; he confessed that if a house stood empty, it cost him two sleepless nights. Occasionally there were small signs of change. In the past he enjoyed dressing shabbily; now he began to pay a little more attention to his clothes, his body linen, and his hats. He had one oddity: there was always a red silk handkerchief hanging from his coat pocket, perhaps in memory of the red shawl in which Sophia had gathered the Trojan treasure. In company he was quiet, rarely communicative, and he disliked discussions about his excavations, but he was affable to the lower classes. Ambition still drove him, and he still lusted after gold. In all this he was recognizably the same man who had been washed ashore on the island of Texel with a burning ambition to make good in the world.

He was always in a hurry, always restless. He had an acute perception of the passing of time, and hated wasting any of it. He marked out the work of the day—so many hours for correspondence, so many hours for reading, so many hours for studying the stock market. In summer he would rise sharply at three o'clock in the morning and then ride to the Bay of Phaleron for a bath, taking his wife with him. He still thought that sea bathing cured all the ills of the flesh, and he was constantly celebrating the medicinal properties of salt water. As he grew older, he became even more Spartan in his habits. He was sixty-four when he had a cyst cut out of his lip without an anesthetic. A few months earlier, when he fell from his horse and splinters from his spectacles were driven into his cheeks, he did not trouble to send for a doctor, but patiently waited for the splinters to come out of their own accord.

He did not know that his constant bathing in the sea was slowly killing him. In November, 1877, about the time that Gladstone was writing the famous preface to *Mycenae*, he complained for the first time of deafness and illness. Sea water entering his ears caused inflammations and burning headaches. For the remaining thirteen years of his life he suffered intermittently from earaches and headaches, and sometimes he looked like a man frozen with horror at the thought of all the pain he had to bear.

Troy, which had given him his greatest claim to fame, still summoned him. In *Ilios,* which he published in 1879, he presented a complete account of his excavations at Hissarlik, adding a lengthy autobiographical fragment, correcting some of his earlier theories, and bringing the account of his discoveries up to date.

But there were problems which still troubled him. Was Hissarlik Troy? Was it possible that the vast city described by Homer was represented by this small mound? He calculated that this city on a mound could have held only five thousand inhabitants with an army of five hundred soldiers. Then where were the sixty-two vast and palatial rooms described by Homer? The citadel at Troy was even smaller than the citadel at Mycenae, where for a while he believed he had disinterred Agamemnon, Clytemnestra, and all the court of the golden Atridae.

The more he thought of Hissarlik, the more he was plagued by doubts. Perhaps, after all, Troy was only a figment of Homer's imagination. He wrote to his publisher Brockhaus: "The only remaining question is whether Troy really existed or was a product of the poet's imagination. If it existed, then Hissarlik must and will be universally accepted as the true site of Troy." But this was begging the question, and he knew it. To the end of his life he was to continue his excavations at Troy in the hope that some fragment of ancient writing or another hoard of treasure would somehow prove beyond doubt that Hissarlik was Homer's Troy. Like a ghost haunting the scenes of his youthful exploits, he returned again and again to the honeycombed mound which had fascinated him ever since he first set eyes on it on a summer day in 1868.

Up to this time all his knowledge of the Troad consisted of Hissarlik, Bunarbashi, the valley of the Scamander and the small villages on its banks. Now he decided to go further afield, to see whether the surrounding countryside would throw light on the problem. In May, 1881, he made a long journey by horseback across the Troad. It was a curiously uneventful journey and he learned little, but he did succeed in climbing Mount Ida, from where the gods once looked down on the battles below. Homer said Mount Ida was "the mother of wild beasts," but Schliemann saw no living creature on it except the cuckoo, which is common all over the Troad. On one spur of the mountain he found the solitary tomb of an unknown herdsman, and on another spur he came upon a slab of marble which he believed to be the remains of the throne of Zeus.

The throne was filled with blue hyacinths and violets. Hissarlik lay far below. It was about the size of a coat button, and he wondered how Zeus could distinguish the movements of the armies so far away. Characteristically, Schliemann announced that it was quite certain that Homer had also stood on the summit of Mount Ida. It was as though he dared never stand where Homer had never trod.

That year he did a little desultory digging at Hissarlik, but the problem which chiefly occupied his attention was the disposal of his Trojan treasure. At various times he had thought of offering it to Greece, Italy, France, and England. There was a brief period when he considered selling the jewels to Russia, and for some weeks he maintained a confused correspondence with an agent in Russia, who was promised a fair commission if the treasures were bought by the Hermitage Museum. In fact Schliemann had no very great desire to sell the treasure, which was beyond price— what price can one pay for the Sistine Chapel?[1] It was in the character of the man to hesitate continually, while he

---

1. *Sistine Chapel:* chapel in the Vatican decorated by Michelangelo.

waited upon events. At the end of 1878 he wrote to a Berlin merchant, saying he would never leave it to Berlin, a city which had never shown any appreciation of his work. He did not know that less than six months later a sprig of flowering blackthorn would profoundly affect the disposal of the treasure. In the end it would come to Berlin, because a friend plucked the blackthorn and presented it to him.

In all of Schliemann's life he made exactly two friends. One was Wilhelm Dörpfeld, a young archeologist sent out by the Prussian government to work on the excavations at Olympia. The other was Rudolf Virchow, the famous pathologist. Virchow was everything that Schliemann was not. He was calm, methodical, tactful, relentlessly logical, indifferent to money, and even more indifferent to fame. He was one of those people who are able to scatter their energies in a hundred different directions and still maintain a sense of quiet orderliness in their existence. Schliemann envied him, cherished his friendship, continually pestered him with medical questions, and asked his advice on such different matters as the proper clothes to wear at a reception and the proper formula for baby food.

On one occasion after a visit to Hanai-Tepe near Troy, Schliemann heard that Virchow was considering the publication of a report on his finds. Schliemann telegraphed immediately: "Publish nothing about Hanai-Tepe, else friendship and love for Germany both perish!"

In the spring of 1879, during a pause in digging at Hissarlik, Schliemann suggested an excursion along the banks of the Scamander. Virchow was delighted to have the opportunity of accompanying Schliemann on a brief tour along the valley. They came to the foothills of Mount Ida. Schliemann was unusually silent, immersed in his own thoughts; and when Virchow asked him what was the matter, he answered gruffly that he was concerned about so many things that it would be unreasonable to demand a full accounting of them.

A little while later, when they were resting in the shade of a blackthorn tree, Virchow asked him again what was tormenting him. Schliemann mentioned that he was preoccupied with the thought of what would happen to the treasure after his death. Suddenly Virchow plucked a sprig of flowering blackthorn, handed it to Schliemann and said quietly: "A nosegay from Ankershagen!"

Virchow could never afterwards understand why he said these words. They came unbidden. He observed the sudden change in his friend's features: it was as though a great weight had fallen from him.

"Yes, a nosegay from Ankershagen," Schliemann said, and then without exchanging any more words they both knew that the decision had been made.

Some hours later, when they were returning from the excursion, Virchow said casually: "Of course they should go to the German nation. They will be cared for, and you will be honored for giving them. It is all very simple. With your permission, I shall speak to Prince Bismarck about it."

Schliemann nodded. The answer to the question which had plagued him for seven years was suddenly revealed. Now at long last, on a spring day, gazing at the sprig of blackthorn, which reminded him of the great masses of flowers in the garden at Ankershagen, he made his decision.

When he thought about the matter coldly, he always remembered that the two countries where he had been most at home and where he was treated with the greatest kindness were England and the United States; but his whole life revolved around the possession of the treasure, and to give the treasure away meant the offering up of his whole life in a sacrifice, and where else could he turn but to his native land? The treasure was to be a crown laid upon the village of Ankershagen, even though it would be housed in Berlin in a great museum bearing his name.

All through the summer and autumn Virchow worked

quietly and efficiently at the task. He was afraid Schliemann would change his mind, and he knew he had to arrange everything quickly, neatly, in a fashion which would soothe Schliemann's feelings, always liable to be hurt by imagined slights. In a long series of letters he explained that a gift of such magnitude must be carefully prepared. The full effect of such an outstanding gift, one which would redound eternally to the credit of Schliemann, would only be felt if the negotiations were carried on at the highest levels. He pleaded for time. He interviewed everybody—once he was kept waiting for two hours in Prince Bismarck's anteroom, and thought the time well spent, for the German Chancellor was on fire with the idea of having the treasure on permanent exhibition in Berlin and was prepared to go to extreme lengths to honor the discoverer of the treasure. "What honor does Dr. Schliemann want?" Prince Bismarck asked; and on this subject Virchow was prepared to be evasive, merely remarking that Schliemann was a man who thirsted for recognition and sought eagerly for every kind of tribute, provided that it came from the most exalted circles.

As usual Schliemann temporized. He had always fought against governments, and now he was determined to exact the best possible terms from the German government. He complained that by offering the treasure to Germany he had alienated himself from Great Britain, America, France, and Italy. Henceforth he would be compelled to live only in Greece and Germany. Privately, to Virchow, he suggested his terms. They were: a special letter of commendation from the Kaiser, the order of *Pour le mérite*, the highest private order the Kaiser could bestow, the honorary citizenship of Berlin, membership in the Prussian Academy of Sciences, and the museum containing the treasure must bear his name in perpetuity. He hinted that he would not be displeased with a title, but did not insist upon it. He did not receive the *Pour le mérite*, but Virchow almost singlehandedly succeeded in arranging that all the other demands were met. Only Sophia was alarmed by the progress of the negotiations. She insisted that the treasure belonged to Greece, but she was no match for her husband when he was determined upon a course of conduct, and her fury was appeased when she saw her own name in the letter of commendation written in the Kaiser's own hand.

At last, in December 1880, the treasure, which had been on exhibition in London, was crated and sent to Berlin. Six months later Schliemann attended the royal reception in Berlin, where the treasure was solemnly handed over "to the German nation in perpetual possession and inalienable custody." It was housed in a wing of the Völkerkunde-museum, and Schliemann's name was written in bright golden letters above the doors. At the reception Crown Prince Wilhelm, later Kaiser Wilhelm II, escorted Sophia to the banquet. It was July 7, 1881. Sophia was twenty-eight, and her husband was six months short of his sixtieth birthday.

The treasure remained in Berlin until the end of the Second World War. When the war broke out, it was hidden in a secret bunker excavated deep below the Berlin Zoo. In the spring of 1945 Russian troops discovered it and sent it back through the lines. Today only the Russians know where it is.

On that July day in Berlin Schliemann reached the pinnacle of his fame. The Kaiser, the Kaiserin, the Princes and Princesses of the Court paid tribute to him, but in his view this was the least of the honors he received. The greatest was the honorary citizenship of Berlin, which had been bestowed on only two people before: Prince Bismarck and Count Helmuth von Moltke, the two men chiefly responsible for the resurgence of Germany. The boy who had glued his face to the window of an obscure parsonage, shuddering with joy as he viewed the legendary world outside, saw the world of legend come to life. Had he not summoned into his presence the most ancient kings, and a living king as well? Looking back on his life, filled with so many heroic deeds and so much accomplishment, he was content.

Still, there was much to be done. Troy was never far from his thoughts, and he hoped before he died to discover the tombs of the Trojan kings and to make a detailed map of all the cities built on the mound of Troy, where he had found his greatest happiness.

At last, after careful preparations, on March 1, 1882, he paid his ninth visit to Hissarlik and resumed digging. Fourteen years had passed since his first visit. He was once again in good humor, with no headaches or earaches. When he first visited the place he had only the most primitive implements and was almost without supplies. This time he came royally provided. Messrs. Schröder of London sent him as a gift large supplies of Chicago corned beef, peaches, English cheese, and ox tongue. There were also 240 bottles of pale ale, and Schliemann drank all of them in the course of five months, announcing that "pale ale is the best medicine ever discovered for constipation, from which I have suffered for the past thirty years."

There was the inevitable trouble with the Turks, who dispatched a certain Bedder Edin Effendi from the Ministry of Public Instruction to see that Schliemann kept to the letter of his agreement with the Turkish government. He was a monster of officiousness, who examined minutely everything that passed through the hands of Schliemann or Dörpfeld, his capable assistant, and caused no end of trouble.

Dörpfeld imported surveying instruments. Bedder Edin Effendi examined the instruments and pronounced that they must have been designed for taking measurements of the small fortress at Koum Kale, five miles from Hissarlik. Dörpfeld argued, but to no avail. The matter was reported to Said Pasha, the Grand Master of Artillery at Constantinople, and orders came back that the surveying instruments must on no account be used. More trouble came when the Turk saw Dörpfeld and Schliemann taking notes. He thought they were drawing up plans of the crumbling fort; they were ordered to commit nothing to writing, otherwise they would be sent in irons to Constantinople. Schliemann shrugged his shoulders. He had a magnificent memory, and no one could prevent him from making mental notes.

On his ninth visit Schliemann lived very much as he had lived during his first. Every morning he rose before sunrise, rode to the Hellespont and took his sea bath as the sun was coming up. On these expeditions he was always accompanied by three guards armed with flintlocks. By day he worked with 150 workmen, wearing a battered sun helmet, enormous spectacles, and a greatcoat, with a red silk handkerchief dangling from his pocket. As before his factotum, bodyguard, and chief paymaster was Zaphyros Jannakis, who also served as a storekeeper, selling bread, tobacco, and brandy to the workmen at enormous profit.

The winter had been dry, and in July the Scamander dried up completely, and all that spring there were no flowers in the plain. In June the locusts came, and Bedder Edin Effendi, growing more officious than ever, began to make still more unreasonable demands. At the end of July Schliemann decided he could bear the presence of the Turkish official no longer, and put an end to the excavations, but not before sending an urgent telegram to Prince Bismarck, demanding protection from the Turks. Nothing came of the telegram, and little was accomplished at Troy, though Dörpfeld succeeded in making an excellent map of the various cities which had once stood on the mound. No treasure was found, only a small cache of bronze and copper objects; and these were of little value.

The next year Schliemann published *Troja*, the third of his books on the excavations at Troy, bringing the story up to date. It is the least rewarding of all his books, and consists very largely of a catalogue of his unimportant finds during the excavations of 1881 and 1882. His luck was running out. Gold no longer rose out of the earth at the touch of his magic wand. For the remaining years of his life he was to wander restlessly after treasure, only to find potsherds.

Years before there had been a period when he embarked on a large number of sporadic projects in Italy and Sicily. There were always the arrowheads of Motyë to remind him that success came at rare intervals. He thought of excavating at Thera, where he was once shipwrecked, and at Cythera, where Aphrodite rose from the sea-foam, and at Pylos on the western shore of the Peloponnesus, the scene of a great battle described by Thucydides. At a lucky moment his mind turned toward the island of Crete, still under Turkish domination. There in 1878 a merchant of Candia bearing the legendary name of Minos Kalokairinos had made some excavations on a hill called Kephala Tselempe, the traditional site of the ancient city of Cnossus. Schliemann made inquiries about the finds and thought seriously of transferring his activities to Crete. If he had dug at Cnossus he might have made the great discoveries which Sir Arthur Evans made many years later. But in those days Crete seemed a less likely prospect for the archeologist than the mainland of Greece.

Perhaps there were too many places to choose from, too many ruins beckoning him. As we see him during these last years, he seems to be hesitating, for the first time unsure of himself. He decided to dig close at hand, at Marathon near Athens, where there was a small and famous mound. Tradition, supported by Pausanias, said the bodies of 192 Athenians who fell in battle against the Persians were buried there. In February, 1884, Schliemann obtained permission to excavate the mound. It was the work of only a few days. He dug a trench through it, but found no trace of the Athenian dead. He hoped to find spears, swords, helmets, breastplates, all the trappings of warriors. All he found were a few potsherds and some evidence that the mound was raised in archaic times, before the Persians set foot on Greece.

There remained Tiryns, the great citadel on the plain of Argos, which he had visited during his first tour through Greece, and excavated for a few brief weeks before the long summer and autumn which saw the discovery of the golden masks of Mycenae.

Tiryns was old when Mycenae was young. Hercules was born there. Zeus visited the city in the shape of a shower of gold and had a child by Danaë, imprisoned there in a brazen tower. Of this union was born Perseus, the legendary hero of the Argives, who cut off the head of Medusa. Even the ancient Greeks regarded Tiryns with awe, and Pausanias cried: "Why should we trouble to go to see the Pyramids when we have this?"

On March 14, 1884, a few weeks after the unsuccessful excavations at Marathon, Schliemann arrived in Nauplia to superintend the work. He was accompanied by Wilhelm Dörpfeld, on whom a large share of the work would fall. This time, too, there were vast quantities of supplies sent by Messrs. Schröder from London: Chicago corned beef,

Tiryns at the time of Schliemann's excavations.

peaches, the best English pale ale. He employed 70 workmen,
and used 40 English wheelbarrows, 20 large iron crowbars,
50 pickaxes, 25 large axes, and a windlass. Never before had
he planned an expedition so scientifically. Schliemann and
Dörpfeld divided their responsibilities between them. Schliemann would indicate where he wanted walls torn down and
digging to begin, while Dörpfeld would act as surveyor, consulting engineer, mapmaker, and principal contractor. In
effect Schliemann was in charge of pottery and treasure, and
Dörpfeld in charge of the buildings.

They lived at Nauplia. There every morning, according
to his custom, Schliemann rose before sunrise and was carried out to sea in a rowboat just as the sun was coming up.
Far from land he would jump overboard, swim for ten minutes, climb back on the boat by pulling himself up over the
rudder, and shortly afterwards he would be making the
twenty-five minute journey to Tiryns on horseback. At eight
o'clock there would be the first pause, when all the workmen
gathered in the shade of the great stone galleries and had
breakfast. At sunset the work ended, and Schliemann would
ride back with Dörpfeld to Nauplia.

They worked until June. During the very first summer
the workmen laid bare the whole floor plan of a Homeric
palace. The great fortress stood on a limestone crag projecting over a swampy plain. The galleries, vaulted with huge
blocks, had served for generations as sheepfolds, and in some
places the stone had been rubbed smooth by the sheep.
Pausanias had seen these cyclopean walls and proclaimed
that a mule team would have been unable to remove even
the smallest of the stones; and though, in Tiryns as in Mycenae, Schliemann was disposed to believe every word written
by Pausanias, it pleased him to discover that there were
many small stones which could be lifted easily by the workmen.

He went to Tiryns again the next summer, and discovered a brilliant fresco showing a boy leaping over the back

of a tawny bull, portions of a geometric frieze, and innumerable *carrousels* of blue stones. He found obsidian knives
and arrowheads, but the only gold which came to light
was in the form of a gold ax half an inch wide.

Schliemann's book *Tiryns*, published in 1886, was almost
as disappointing as his last book on Troy. He contented
himself with describing the objects found in the debris,
leaving to Dörpfeld the task of discussing the great palaces
they unearthed. Many of the terra-cotta vases were exquisitely fashioned, in a style which showed great advances
on the vases discovered at Troy and Mycenae; but it was
the huge bull with the curving horns which astonished the
world. Such bulls were to be found later in Cnossus, and
it is possible that the bull at Tiryns was painted by a
Minoan artist. But Minoan influence on the mainland of
Greece was still largely unsuspected. Schliemann believed
that the citadels at Mycenae and Tiryns were built and inhabited by Phoenicians, who flooded Greece and the islands
of the Ægean and Ionian Seas at a remote prehistoric age,
until they were expelled by the Dorian invaders about
1100 B.C.

Among the theories which Schliemann clung to throughout his life was the gradual decay of heroism. It seemed to
him that heroism was concentrated in a quite extraordinary
degree in the great heroes of archaic Greece, and never since
then had it flowered with the same intensity. Great men
had walked the earth at Troy and Mycenae; and from that
day to this the world had suffered at the hands of lesser men.
There were however occasional exceptions to the rule.
Schliemann was inclined to believe that Czar Alexander II,
murdered by Nihilists in St. Petersburg in March 1881, belonged to the ranks of the authentic heroes. A still more
shining example was General Gordon[2] whose fortunes in
the Sudan he followed with avid interest.

2. *General Gordon:* Charles George Gordon, British nineteenth-century
soldier, served gallantly in the Crimea, China, and Egypt.

Schliemann and Gordon illuminate one another. They had much in common: daring, unyielding faith in themselves, a strange intimacy with the hidden things of the earth. Trusting in Homer and Pausanias, Schliemann uncovered the buried cities of Troy, Mycenae, and Tiryns. Trusting in the inspired words of the Bible, Gordon wandered over the Holy Land and believed he had discovered the exact sites of Golgotha, Gibeon, and the Garden of Eden. Both were solitaries, who confined their reading only to those works which seemed to be directly inspired. They were both haunted by dreams, ill at ease in their own civilization, seeing themselves as figures in an ancient and irrecoverable past. When Gordon wanted to examine the future, he opened the Bible at random and saw the future written clearly before his eyes. For the same reason Schliemann was constantly consulting his Homer. They were men who would have understood each other.

From Athens Schliemann looked out across the Mediterranean to Khartoum, where the real hero of the age—the man closest to Hector in his time—was being surrounded by the wild and pitiless army of the Mahdi. Relief supplies had been cut off. Food was low, and ammunition was running out. Gordon was urged to sandbag the palace windows, and refused. Instead he ordered a lantern with twenty-four candles to be placed in one of the windows, and declared: "When God was portioning out fear, it came to my turn, and there was no fear left to give me. Go, tell all the people of Khartoum that Gordon fears nothing."

On the night of February 3, 1885, the Mahdi and his dervishes approached the palace. By sunrise they were pouring through the town. Gordon was waiting for them on the palace steps. Sword in hand, he fought magnificently, flew at the enemy, and died amid a heap of corpses at the foot of the steps. When his head was cut off, wrapped in a cloth, and presented to the Mahdi, orders were given for it to be hung from a tree and for days the hawks wheeled around the bloody head.

For Schliemann it was a nightmare. Of all living men he admired Gordon most. Everyone, even Queen Victoria, believed Gordon met his death as the result of the inexplicable folly of Gladstone, who failed to send reinforcements in time. Schliemann knew Gladstone well. Had not Gladstone written the long preface to *Mycenae*, and invited him to dinner at 10 Downing Street?[3] Trembling with indignation, Schliemann removed the signed photograph of Gladstone which stood in his study. He debated what to do with it: whether to hurl it on the stone floor or tear it to pieces. He decided to be more cautious, and with typical Mecklenburger cunning punished Gladstone by installing the photograph in the lavatory.

More and more during those last years he grew convinced that the most rewarding discoveries would be made in Crete. Thera, Cythera, and Pylos would have to wait. His enthusiasm for Crete was shared by Dörpfeld. Accordingly, in 1886, they visited Cnossus together and examined the site. There were long interviews with the owner, a Turk whose business sense was at least the equal of Schliemann's. They debated endlessly over cups of Turkish coffee, and came to no conclusion. The Turk was asking $16,000 for the field, an excessive price. Schliemann was infuriated. He had already obtained from the Turkish governor of the island a *firman* permitting him to excavate provided he obtained the consent of the owner; and this consent was being withheld. He was still hopeful that he would be able to wear down the opposition when he returned to Athens.

He thought of returning to Troy, made long-range plans for the excavations in Crete, debated with himself whether to inspect his houses in Paris or to make another tour of

3. *10 Downing Street:* residence of the British prime minister.

Ithaca, and did nothing. As he grew older and wearier, he disappeared more into himself, reading Homer all day and half the night, as though Homer had become a drug, the only thing that could keep him sane. He still wrote interminable letters, sometimes beginning the letter in one language and continuing in another and concluding in still a third; but the handwriting was becoming cramped, and increasingly he wrote in the tones of one of the Trojan heroes hurling abuse at the Achaeans below. Those tremendous invocations which once poured from the mouths of Homeric heroes look curiously out of place when written by a small graying man who resembled a timid professor.

Yet there was nothing timid in Schliemann as age caught up with him. He raged interminably at those lesser men, the charlatans who refused to credit him with great discoveries, or worse still, paid him only a grudging tribute. There was, for example, a certain Captain Böttischer who wrote a monograph explaining that Hissarlik was a huge fire necropolis, probably Persian in origin. Schliemann expended reams of paper in an attempt to demolish the farcical theory. It was his custom to roar like a wounded lion at the slightest slight. The Grand Duke of Mecklenburg had never acknowledged a dedication. Schliemann sent a telegram—he had a passion for telegrams, and half of them were like explosives, and the other half resembled pages torn out of reports of meetings of boards of directors. The Grand Duke permitted himself the luxury of striking a gold medal in Schliemann's honor, and then there was peace again.

For months on end he put archeology aside. Instead of Schliemann the world-renowned archeologist, there was Schliemann the businessman, traveling all over the world to see that his property and investments were safe. He had large estates in Cuba, and so he made a hurried trip to Havana. He had property in Madrid and Berlin, and rushed off to inspect them and to address conferences in defense of his theories of the origin of Troy. He enjoyed money for the power it gave him to travel anywhere on earth at a moment's notice.

Physically he was changing. With his taut, weatherbeaten skin, enormous forehead like an onion, and sad, wispy mustache, he was coming to resemble a mummy. Earaches drove him nearly mad, and sometimes his lips twitched. He made little jerking movements with his hands, stuttered in all the languages he knew, and now more and more it became necessary for him to keep to a strict regimen. He was up early, took a bath in the sea, enjoyed a breakfast of three eggs and a cup of weak tea, read the newspapers and the stock-exchange reports and attended to his correspondence. Then it was time to read three hundred lines of Homer, Sophocles, or Euripides—he rarely read Plato and seems never to have bothered with Aristotle. Then lunch and a brief walk and more study, and usually in the evening there were visitors. At ten he was in bed, but he suffered from insomnia and sometimes read through the night.

As he grew older, he paid particular attention to his dreams, always analyzing them carefully; and he was profoundly worried if Sophia dreamed of crows, beanstalks, or visitors from abroad. Homer spoke with the authentic voice of ancient gods, and so did dreams, and so did gold. In those years when he seemed to be slowly slipping away from the world, there were few other pleasures.

As the flesh withered, and the earache grew worse, and the cold winds of Europe made him shiver, he decided to spend his remaining winters in the south. Egypt attracted him. He had read widely in the reports of the French and English archeologists who had been excavating in Egypt for three generations. None of them possessed his genius, none of them had discovered great treasures of gold, and he suspected that they knew very little about the science of excavation. He permitted himself the thought that he might amuse himself with a little digging in Egypt.

As 1886 was coming to an end, he decided to spend three

months in a leisurely progress down the Nile, alone except
for a secretary and a heap of books in Greek and Arabic. It
was an expensive undertaking. He hired a magnificent roomy
dahabiyeh, luxuriously furnished with all the conveniences
known to that time, at a cost of about $4,000. Sometimes
as he sailed up the Nile past Theban ruins and Ptolemaic
temples, he would order a halt and come ashore and wander
through a village market place. He liked talking in Arabic
to the villagers, and he liked to offer them simple salves for
their sores. To one Egyptian girl suffering from paralysis
and a swelling in the shoulder, he ordered a twice daily bath
in the Nile and the application of linseed and hot herbs to
the shoulder, with what result no one knows. He detested
the Mohammedan sailors on the boat, who were dirty and
disloyal and continually falling on their knees to pray in the
direction of Mecca. He liked the Nubians with their dark
gleaming sculptured faces, the only people he had ever met
who looked like heroes.

He intended to sail as far as Wadi Halfa, that small frontier
post which marked the southern boundary of the Khedive's
dominion. He dug occasionally, thought a good deal about
Cleopatra, took soundings of the depth of the Nile, and
studied cloud formations, calculating the next day's weather
by the direction of the higher clouds. He recorded the temperature every day, as he always did, and copied occasional
inscriptions, and paced up and down the deck, restless but
strangely quiet, happiest of all when he was reading Homer
and all the annoyances of Egypt were temporarily forgotten.

It annoyed him that the British military authorities in
Cairo had shown no special interest in his presence, and he
was inclined to sympathize with the native Egyptians against
their conquerors. When he reached Assouan, he sent his
secretary on shore to announce his arrival to the native officials. They had not heard of him, and were in no mood to
offer him any special honors. The secretary returned empty-

handed. Astonished that his fame had not penetrated the offices of the Egyptian bureaucrats in Assouan, Schliemann fretted and fumed, and swore he would not come ashore unless a welcoming party came to greet him.

That winter Assouan was crowded with tourists, who brought their lunch off the Nile steamers and went grubbing in the sand for beads. Thousands of amateur archeologists haunted the place, but there were also a number of young dedicated archeologists. Among them was E. A. Wallis Budge, then comparatively unknown, making his first mission to Egypt on behalf of the British Museum. He was a thickset, keen, uncomplicated man, and his chief task at the time was to acquire for the Museum some early Mohammedan dome-tombs inscribed with Kufic inscriptions, for Assouan had been a place of pilgrimage in the early years following the Hegira.[4]

As soon as he heard that Schliemann had been slighted, he decided to do what he could to make amends. He rounded up two of his friends and got a boatman to row them over to the *dahabiyeh*. A butler greeted them and led them to a large saloon in the stern of the ship. Coffee was served, cigarettes were lit, and soon Schliemann was being invited by the three Englishmen to inspect the newly excavated Mohammedan tombs. And then an extraordinary thing happened. Schliemann drew himself up very stiffly, and showed that he had not the least desire to see their work.

"It is very kind of you to be so amiable," he said. "I should like to place my archeological science at your disposal and explain to you the tombs, but I have not the time as I am going to Wadi Halfa!"

There was a moment's silence, and then without another word Schliemann reached for the paperbound copy of the *Iliad* in the Greek text, which he had been reading until

4. *Hegira:* Mohammed's flight from Mecca, 622 A.D.

disturbed by the Englishmen. He had simply laid the book
face downward on a cushion while talking to them, preparing to take it up again at the first opportunity. The Englishmen were appalled, and Major Plunkett, who had accompanied Wallis Budge, asked permission "in a sweetly soft
voice" to withdraw. Permission was granted, and they returned to Assouan with the curious feeling that they had set
eyes on the world's most famous archeologist and everything
they saw disturbed them.*

Such conduct was unusual, and perhaps due to the recur-
rent headaches which made the last years of his life so miserable. We have another glimpse of Schliemann from another
English archeologist the following year. Once again Schliemann was sailing down the Nile, this time accompanied by
Rudolf Virchow. He was in better spirits. The earache no
longer troubled him. He tramped for hours through the
columns of Karnak and inspected the vast labyrinth which
Flinders Petrie had mapped out the previous year.

Petrie was a young archeologist, and Schliemann was impressed by his painstaking excavations on the site of the labyrinth, once the greatest building in the world, with its twelve
immense courts and three thousand rooms, half of them underground. As Petrie describes him, Schliemann was "short,
round-headed, round-faced, round-hatted, great round-gog-
gle-eyed, spectacled, cheeriest of beings, dogmatic, but always
ready for facts." Virchow was less agreeable—"a calm, sweet-
faced man with a beautiful grey beard, who nevertheless tried
to make mischief for my work."† This is the last thumbnail
sketch we have of Schliemann; and the story of the remaining years of his life must be pieced out from his letters and
from the funeral orations pronounced at his death.

* E. A. Wallis Budge, *By Nile and Tigris*. London, John Murray, 1920,
p. 109. (Payne's note.)

† Sir Flinders Petrie, *Seventy Years of Archeology*. London, Sampson
Low, Marston. 1931, p. 83. (Payne's note).

There were only three more years left to him; years of frustration and disappointment, with no great accomplishments to satisfy his desire for fame. In 1888 he worked for a short while on the island of Cythera, where Aphrodite first appeared among men, and uncovered her temple in the Byzantine chapel of Hagios Cosmas. He sent off a long telegram to the London *Times* announcing that he had made a discovery of the first magnitude, only comparable to his discoveries at Hissarlik and Mycenae, but he must have known that he was aiming too high. In the same year he made excavations at Pylos and on the island of Sphacteria, where he laid bare the old fortifications which according to Thucydides[5] were discovered and used by the Spartans in 425 B.C. No doubt these were important finds, but they could not compare with his two greatest exploits. He wanted another triumph, and dreamed of uncovering the royal city of Cnossus. "I would like to end my life's labors with one great work—the prehistoric palace of the Kings of Cnossus," he wrote on January 1, 1889, but he seems to have guessed that this triumph would be refused to him.

Ever since March, 1883, when he first applied for the right to excavate at Cnossus, he had met with repeated refusals from the owners of the land. He had visited Crete and sent his agents there, to no avail. Now in the spring of 1889 he decided to make one last effort to buy the land. He went with Dörpfeld and was prepared to pay a high price. The man who claimed to own Kephala Tselempe wanted 100,000 francs, the price to include the 2,500 olive trees that grew there. Schliemann countered with an offer of 40,000 francs. Finally it was agreed that he could purchase the land for 50,000 francs. At the last moment before signing the contract Schliemann decided to count the olive trees. There were only 888. He flew into a temper, and announced

5. *Thucydides:* Greek historian (460-400 B.C.).

that he could not sign a contract with a man who lied about the number of trees he possessed.

Dörpfeld, who was not prepared to allow the negotiations to be sabotaged so easily, thought there was still hope. He made inquiries and discovered that Hadjidakis, the man who claimed to own the hill, actually owned only one-third. Negotiations were renewed with the owner of the remaining two-thirds, and these were concluded successfully. Another contract was drawn up, and Schliemann promised that one-third of the treasure would be given to the owners. All that was necessary was to get Hadjidakis' signature to the contract. The Turk refused. There were bitter recriminations, and at last Schliemann saw that nothing would be gained by further negotiations. He wrote to Virchow: "It was a terrible journey, with nothing gained."*

As old age came to him, he went back to his first love. That year he held the First International Congress on the Trojan Antiquities, inviting scholars from all over the world to view his finds, accompanying them through the ruins, telling them stories about those long-distant days before the mound was carved up in trenches and great galleries. He still spoke excitedly about further explorations, particularly in Crete, but he was aging rapidly. A photograph taken that year shows him with a strange pleading expression. He looks helpless and miserable, and there is something about him which suggests a bank clerk who is being retired from the office where he worked industriously all his life, a face empty of hope, and without strength. Photographs rarely flattered him. But there was strength in him still, and he still climbed among the ruins like a young chamois.

He was at Troy again the next year, holding his Second

---

* Schliemann never described the negotiations at length. I have based this account on the version given by Sir Arthur Evans, who eventually bought the property. Evans went to some pains to discover exactly what happened, and tells the story in his diary for March 22, 1894, printed in Joan Evans, *Time and Chance: The Story of Arthur Evans*. London, Longmans Green & Co., 1943, p. 313. (Payne's note).

International Congress. Scholars came, and he addressed them gracefully, no longer thundering against their obtuseness, their mediocrity, and their malice. One day he decided to make an excursion to Mount Ida, so that he could look once more on Troy, but the journey was abandoned when they came in the evening to a village in the foothills, and he complained of deafness and an excruciating pain in his ear. Virchow examined the ear, found a large swelling in the aural passage, and suggested an immediate return to Troy.

According to Virchow, there was one last attempt to scale Mount Ida. When the Congress came to an end, Schliemann decided to make a seven-day excursion in the valley. They rode on horseback. When they reached the foot of Mount Ida, Schliemann decided he could not let the opportunity pass. Once more he must sit on the throne of Zeus and gaze down on the beloved plain. They were near the top when a storm broke. It was such a storm as Schliemann had rarely encountered, with a magnificent display of thunder and lightning illuminating the four corners of the heavens. To escape the storm they took shelter under some rocks, but the rain was driven horizontally, and they were soaked to the skin. Then the storm cleared, and in the rain-washed light Schliemann looked down for the last time at the plain of Troy, the Hellespont, the islands of the Ægean, Samothrace, Lemnos, and Tenedos, and the long coastline reaching to Smyrna. Then like Moses, having seen the vision, he came down from the mountain.

The Congress was over, but the work went on, with Dörpfeld largely in control. As usual Dörpfeld was insisting that everything had to be photographed, labeled, ticketed, minutely examined, before it was thrown on the rubbish heap, and sometimes Schliemann would complain testily about the waste of time. But there were occasional rewards, like the fragments of gray Mycenaean pottery with characteristic stirrup-cup designs which were found during these last days. More fortress walls came to light, and soon they found a building formed of great boulders piled one on top of the other, and it was like Tiryns again. Once more Schliemann began to hope that the whole plan of Homeric Troy would be revealed to him before he died. To Virchow and Dörpfeld he spoke lightheartedly of how all of Homeric Troy would be laid bare by the following spring. Meanwhile the hot winds roared across the plain, and some of the workmen were struck with fever, and Schliemann continued to superintend the excavations, a small wizened man wearing a sun helmet who smiled easily and sadly.

Suddenly toward the end of July he decided to abandon the excavations until the next year. On August 1, 1890 he returned to Athens: the great stone house, the children growing up, the table piled high with notes on the year's work, and the ever-healing presence of Sophia to lighten his burdens. He did not know then that he would never see Troy again.

In Athens he was still restless, still pursuing dreams. He wrote to Virchow that he planned to visit the islands of Atlantis and to make a voyage to Mexico—perhaps somewhere there he would find the traces of Odysseus. He was sure he could find Atlantis in the Canary Islands, and had not Homer himself proclaimed that these islands enjoyed perpetual spring? Then, of course, the book on the recent excavations in Troy must be finished, and there would be another scientific congress and they would spend all spring and summer at Troy.

He no longer suffered from earache; the swelling had died down; perhaps there would be no need for an operation. Virchow advised postponing the operation as long as possible, and Schliemann was duly grateful for the advice. When Sophia went off to Vienna for a visit, he wandered round the house like a ghost, remembering one day toward the end of September that they had never celebrated their wedding anniversary together in Athens. So he wrote to her a long letter in classical Greek, chiding her for her absence:

I am proud of this day, and so I am inviting your relatives, and

I pray the gods will permit us to celebrate together next year, for we have lived together in health and happiness for twenty-one years. When I look back over those many years, I see that the fates have offered us much that is sweet and much that is bitter. I can never celebrate our marriage enough, for you have always been my beloved wife and at the same time my comrade, my guide in difficulties, and a friendly and faithful companion in arms, and always an exceptional mother. So I rejoice continually in your virtues, and by Zeus! I will marry you again in the next world!

About this time he decided to go to a clinic in Halle which had been recommended by Virchow. Sophia hurried back to Athens to help him pack. He seems to have had some premonition of his approaching death, for he was unusually solemn and quiet. He discussed his will with the directors of the bank. Once, when he was folding his clothes and putting them in a trunk, he was heard saying: "I wonder who will wear these clothes." The mood passed, but sometimes in the letters he wrote at this time we are aware of a strange apathy, a sense of brooding disquiet. Sophia wanted to accompany him on the journey, but he said he would be gone for only six weeks and there were the children to be looked after. At the last moment, when he was leaving for the train, Sophia held him back by the watch chain. She seemed to know she would never see him again.

He arrived in Halle early in November. It was a cold winter, the snow falling outside the windows of the clinic. The doctors examined his ears and pronounced that an operation on both ears was advisable. The next day they operated on him while he lay stretched out on a board covered with white oilcloth, which resembled, as he told a friend some days later, "one of those tables used for the dissection of the dead." The operation lasted one and three-quarter hours.

According to the doctors the operation was completely successful. Schliemann had some doubts. He felt miserable. He was not allowed to receive visitors. His head bandaged, surrounded by books, he kept up his vast correspondence. He wrote to Dörpfeld, begging forgiveness for all the sins he had committed and asking, if any shadow of discord ever rose between them, that they would declare themselves frankly face to face. On receiving a letter from his wife, he wrote: "To the wisest of all women, I read with wet eyes what you have written."

Though the doctors had declared that the operation was successful, the pain returned, more terrible than ever. It seemed that the periosteum was injured and inflammation was spreading through the inner ear. Against the advice of the doctors he decided to leave the hospital. He was given two little boxes containing the bones extracted from his ears, and then he went off to Leipzig to visit his publishers, and to Berlin to visit Virchow, who found him in good humor, though quite deaf. Schliemann reminded Virchow of his promise to come to the Canary Islands in the early spring, and then took the train for Paris.

He reached Paris on December 15, one of the coldest days of winter. He found six letters waiting for him from the faithful Sophia, who was almost beside herself with worry. He calculated that he would reach Athens by Christmas and still have time to visit the Museum at Naples, where the recent excavations at Pompeii were on display. To his wife he admitted it was his fault that the pain had returned—he had simply forgotten to put cotton wadding in his ears in the draughty railway carriage when he was immersed in reading the *Arabian Nights* in the original Arabic. He wrote his last letter to Virchow: "Long live Pallas Athene! At last I can hear again with the right ear, and the left will get better."

Pallas Athene and all the other Greek gods had protected him throughout his life, but now at last they withdrew into the clouds of Olympus. For the last time they permitted him to see treasure: but only for a brief moment, on a winter afternoon, suffering from high fever, in agony, with a doctor by his side.

He was already dying when he reached Naples. The pain was excruciating, and the two-day journey from Paris had weakened him. When the pains grew worse, he summoned first one doctor, then another. A ship was waiting for him, but he was too ill to make the sea journey and telegraphed to Athens, asking Sophia to delay the Christmas celebrations, and then went to visit another doctor, who recognized him and spoke gravely about archeology and suggested a drive to Pompeii.

Bundled up in his greatcoat, Schliemann sat back in the carriage during the long journey around the bay in the shadow of Vesuvius. He saw Pompeii. The colonnades, the roads rutted by ancient Roman carts, the *tabernae* where the wine sellers stood two thousand years before—they were all as he expected them to be. Then he returned to his hotel room, sent off more telegrams, announced that he would soon be making his way to Athens, and fought against the raging pain in his ears.

On Christmas Day he was crossing the Piazza della Santa Carità, perhaps on his way to the post office, when he suddenly collapsed on the cobblestones, conscious, his eyes wide open. A crowd gathered. People asked him questions, but he could only nod his head: he had lost the power of speech.

The police carried him to a hospital, but since he appeared to be perfectly well, only dazed and strangely mute, he was refused admittance. It was decided to take him to the police station. There he was searched for papers and money, but they found none. They did find the address of his doctor, who was summoned and immediately recognized his patient. The police were perplexed. Judging by his clothes, he was a poor man. Then why was the doctor so solicitous?

"No, he is a rich man," the doctor said. "I have seen him holding a wallet filled with gold coins!"

Then the doctor reached under the shirt and pulled out a heavy wallet full of gold.

Schliemann was carried back to his hotel, still conscious

and still in command of all his faculties except speech. At the hotel the ear was opened, but the malady had already attacked the brain, and there was little that could be done. He passed a quiet night. The next day it was discovered that the whole of his right side was paralyzed, and there was some talk of trepanning. Eight specialists were called in, and while they were in another room discussing what steps they would take, he died quietly in bed, conscious to the last.

Telegrams were sent off to Athens and Berlin, and soon Dörpfeld and Sophia's elder brother were on their way to Naples to escort the body back to Athens. On Sunday, January 4, 1891, nine days after his death, the coffin lay in the great hall of his palace in Athens, where the twenty-four marble gods towered against the sky. King George and the Crown Prince Constantine came to pay their respects and to lay wreaths beside the coffin, and messages of sympathy came from all over the world.

He had long ago chosen the place where he would be buried. He would be buried among the Greeks he loved in their own cemetery south of the Ilissus, in a tomb fit for a hero. From there his unquiet spirit could look out upon the Acropolis and the blue waters of the Saronic Gulf and the distant hills of Argolis. Beyond those hills the Kings of Mycenae and Tiryns had been buried. At the very end he was close to the heroes he worshiped, and the most adorable of the goddesses, clear-eyed Athena, gazed down at him from the ruined Parthenon on the cliffs.

With his death his new life began. The man who had conjured gold out of the earth had been a legend while he lived, but he was still more of a legend when he was dead. His rages, his arrogance, his embarrassing eccentricities were forgotten. They remembered his faith in Homer and the vastness of his determination to reveal the mysteries buried in the earth. His vices became virtues—his ruthless egoism no more than natural pride, his exaggerations the pardonable excesses of a man im-

patient for discovery. Men forgot that he retained to the end
of his life the habits which had made him a successful bank
clerk. Matthew Arnold[6] said that Homer was eminently rapid,
eminently plain and direct, and eminently noble, and Schliemann was the contrary of all these—a slow, cautious, complex,
devious man, often pompous and ill-tempered, with no natural
nobility in him.

Yet the legend which depicted him as a man of indomitable
spirit, standing upon the battlements of Troy and waging implacable war on his enemies, was sufficiently truthful to be
credible. When his coffin was laid on trestles in the hall of his
palace, a bust of Homer was placed at its head; there was
something wonderfully appropriate in the gesture, even
though in all his life Schliemann never discovered any object
dating from Homeric times.

So in the end he became one of the great forerunners, the
man who opened the way, the first of archeologists because
he was the enemy of classical archeology, the pure romantic
who threw the windows wide open and let the air in. Faith
and dreams led him on his journey, and he was not so very
far from the Homeric heroes whom he had adored ever since
he was a child. There was more greatness in him than he knew;
and it was not the greatness he thought he had achieved.
Homer paints the gods as all-seeing, strangely remote from
the earth, given to displays of ironical affection. A sense of
irony was the one god-like quality he lacked.

A few days after Schliemann's death Gladstone, who was
then eighty-one, wrote in a failing hand a letter of consolation
to Sophia. He described how deeply he had felt the force of
Schliemann's particular genius, and in a single paragraph he
described the nature of Schliemann's triumph. He wrote:

His enthusiasm called back into being the ancient spirit of
chivalry in a thoroughly pure and bloodless form. He had to

6. *Matthew Arnold:* English writer (1822–1888).

encounter in the early stages of his work both frowns and indifference, yet the one and the other alike had to give way, as
the force and value of his discoveries became clear, like mists
upon the sun. The history of his boyhood and youth were not
less remarkable than that of his later life. Indeed they cannot
be separated, for one aim and purpose moved them from first
to last. Either his generosity without his energy, or his energy
without his generosity might well have gained celebrity; in their
union they were no less than wonderful.

*The spirit of chivalry in a thoroughly pure and bloodless
form* . . . Schliemann would have disagreed. He would have
said he had given blood and flesh to the ancient heroes, for
had he not resurrected them from the grave? Like a magician
he had waved his wand over the buried cities and brought
them to life. We know those ancient people now because he
employed all his energy in coming to grips with them. Once
there were heroes who walked the earth, vast and magnificent
and mysterious, and now they were still vast and magnificent,
but less mysterious. Gaunt Achilles, cunning Odysseus,
Hector of the dancing helmet-crest—he had served them well
and never for a moment lost faith in them.

. . . 10 THE ENDURING FLAME

As HE sought shelter in the haunted house of his imagination,
an old man mad for gold, Schliemann sometimes gave the
impression of being a man for whom only the Homeric heroes
were real and all the rest of the world was anathema. During
the last five years of his life, he wrote and spoke in ancient
Greek and seemed strangely uninterested in anything that
was not touched by Homer's magic wand. He told a friend:
"Only Homer interests me: I am increasingly indifferent to
everything else." It was not only that Homer spoke to him
with the force of the tablets of the law. For him Homer was

a sign and a watchword, a way of life, a history of the earth, and the prophecy of a more vivid life in the future. Schliemann was not mad, but close to madness. His mania was to believe that a very bright and wonderfully pure civilization had once existed, and that it was worth while to enter that civilization even at the risk of lunacy.

Schliemann's mania was one he shared with many others. Keats,[1] too, had gazed upon a Greek vase and in a moment of illumination observed the ancient sacrifices being performed before his eyes. Goethe and Schiller[2] proclaimed their loyalty to a civilization which had long ago vanished from the earth. The young poet Friedrich Hölderlin[3] rejoiced in the Greek gods and celebrated them as though there still existed temples for their worship, himself a priest, an acolyte, a wanderer among the Greek islands, which he never saw except in the flaming light of his imagination.

In his greatest poem he made the imaginary journey across Greece to share the Last Supper with the disciples and then to take refuge on the island of Patmos with St. John. For Hölderlin, Christ was the greatest of gods, and all the Greek heroes were his sons:

> Calm is His sign
> In the thundering heavens. And One stands beneath
> His whole life long. For Christ lives still.
> For they, the heroes, His sons, and Holy Scripture
> Have all come from Him; and the lightning declares
> The deeds of the world till now,
> A conflict unceasing. But He is there.
> His works are known to Him from everlasting.

In the end, striving in the same breath after Christ and the gods of Greece, Hölderlin went mad, but not before he had

---

1. *Keats:* John Keats (1795-1821), English poet.
2. *Goethe and Schiller:* Johann Wolfgang von Goethe (1749-1832), and Johann Schiller (1759-1805), German poets.
3. *Hölderlin:* German poet (1770-1843).

composed poetry so rich in the music of the ancient Greeks and so passionately Christian that he became one of the greatest of Christian poets, while at the same time owing allegiance to Greece.

For Schliemann it was altogether simpler. Though he was brought up in a parsonage, he denied his Christian heritage, attended no church, and regarded the Bible as fiction. He was baffled by the New Testament: there were so many Greek words which had no equivalent in Homer. When Sophia's mother died, and he entered the death chamber where the priests were intoning the prayers for the dead, he was heard muttering: "Oh, it is all nonsense! There is no resurrection —there is only immortality!" The entire European tradition since the death of Homer meant nothing to him. Moses crossed the deserts of Sinai; Christ died; the Roman empire rose and fell; there came the flowering of the Renaissance, and then one by one the petals dropped from their stems; and it was all meaningless to him. To the end there was only Homer: the enduring flame.

After Schliemann's death the work he had begun so fruitfully continued. From all over Europe eager archeologists came to Greece and the Near East to dig among ruins and to take part in the process of resurrecting an ancient heroic society which had almost nothing in common with the society of their own age. Discoveries in Crete and Upper Egypt threw light on the Ægean civilization. In 1889, the year before Schliemann's death, Chrestos Tsountas discovered at Vaphio in Laconia two exquisite golden cups, one showing a bull enmeshed in a net, the other showing bulls wandering among olive trees in an idyllic landscape. These, too, must have belonged to a royal treasury. The next year he discovered in a tomb-chamber at Mycenae two amphorae bearing three strange signs on one of the handles; and the search for the Mycenaean script had begun.

Troy was not forgotten. Sophia set aside a sum of money

to enable the excavations to go on under the direction of Wilhelm Dörpfeld. The excavations ended in the summer of 1893, partly because of the heat and partly because Dörpfeld had exhausted his grant. That August he hurried to Potsdam, bearing photographs and plans of the ruins which he showed to the Kaiser Wilhelm II. When winter came he received the welcome news that the German Imperial Chancellor had been pleased to make a special grant of 30,000 marks for the excavations, and work was resumed in the spring of the following year.

Dörpfeld made a surprising discovery. By examining the plans and retracing Schliemann's earlier work, he found that Schliemann had completely missed Homeric Troy. At the point where Schliemann had been digging, Homeric Troy had been leveled to make room for the Roman city of Novum Ilium. All that remained of Priam's Troy was a house corner and a length of fortification wall, which Schliemann had assumed to be Macedonian because it was in an excellent state of preservation. He had touched Troy, but failed to recognize it, because he worked with such astonishing speed and because he was tempted to remove everything that was not Homeric from his path.

Dörpfeld later published an account of his excavations. With painstaking accuracy he went over the ground which Schliemann had uncovered, pointed to the errors which had been made, and listed the treasure. It is a long book, and very weighty in its Germanic way, but one of his conclusions would have been especially pleasing to Schliemann. After examining the traces of Homeric Troy and the earlier settlements, he wrote: "The Princes of Troy were in no way behind the Achaean Princes in their striving to build great citadels and magnificent palaces: they were a match for the rulers of Mycenae and Tiryns."

Meanwhile the French School at Athens was attempting to begin excavations at Crete. Nothing came of these efforts until 1898, when the Turks were expelled from the island. Then, not the French, but a rich Englishman, a former curator of the Ashmolean Museum at Oxford, succeeded in buying the land and uncovering the treasures which Schliemann had hoped to find as "the crown of my career." In a series of campaigns from 1900 to 1905, Sir Arthur Evans succeeded in winning a king's share of treasure from the ruined city of Cnossus. There was little gold, but he found magnificent frescoes and whole palaces and vast quantities of clay tablets inscribed with written signs. He unearthed a civilization which had existed in the sixth millenium B.C. and progressed continually until in some unexplained way, perhaps by fire and earthquake, the city was destroyed. When the dust had settled, it was possible to trace close affiliations between Cnossus and Mycenae.

About the time that Evans was uncovering written records from the abandoned library of Cnossus, more inscriptions dating back to the heroic age came to light in Greece. Keramopoullos discovered thirty inscribed vases in a storeroom of the "Palace of Cadmus" in Thebes. Here and there a few other inscriptions were discovered, but none could be deciphered. Evans continued his excavations without a break except during the war of 1914-1918, but he published his finds rarely and his monumental work, *The Palace of Minos*, gives only the sketchiest outline of the three scripts found in the ruins of the palace.

These scripts were of three kinds: one hieroglyphic or picture writing, another in a more sophisticated style called Minoan Linear A, and a third which was discovered in much greater quantities, called Minoan Linear B, which seemed to be derived from Linear A, as this in turn was derived from the hieroglyphics. To the end of his life Evans hoped to decipher these strange carved letters on the sunbaked bricks. He failed, and his failure was largely of his own choosing, for he hoarded his finds, rarely allowed other scholars to examine them, and regarded any attempt to decipher them as invasions on his own privacy. He had Schliemann's passion for keeping secrets.

Cnossus filled in the colors of the heroic age. The young cupbearers, the sloe-eyed girls, the delicate paintings of bulls tossing their youthful riders between their horns demonstrated the tenderness of the heroic age, as the graves of Mycenae described the lives of the warrior-kings. But when Cnossus had been unearthed—most of the work was finished by the summer of 1905—there followed a long period of frustration. It was as though the earth had given up all its secrets, and there were no more. A few unimportant finds were made. In 1926 Swedish scholars opened the unrifled tomb of a king, a queen, and a princess at Mideia near Mycenae; and learned little more than they knew before.

From 1932 to 1938 Carl Blegen of the University of Cincinnati worked at Hissarlik. He had the pure scholar's desire for accuracy, and a curious contempt for Schliemann. "It seems desirable, timely, and worth while," he wrote, "to return to Troy to undertake an exhaustive, painstaking re-examination of the whole site." He planned a work of sober research "with no compulsion to recover objects of startling or sensational character with high publicity value." His admirably detailed and documented volumes list innumerable pieces of gray pottery, and he was able to correct many of the mistakes of Schliemann and Dörpfeld, but he found no treasure. One gets the impression that he would have been a little annoyed if any treasure had fallen into his hands.

In 1938 the excavations at Hissarlik were abandoned, and Blegen turned his attention to a Mycenaean palace at Ano Englianos in western Messenia, the probable site of Nestor's Pylos. Here he discovered some objects which appeared at first sight to be even more valuable than treasure. In a narrow room of the palace he discovered a total of 618 sunbaked clay tablets, 20 of them intact, the others in fragments. All of them were in a slightly modified form of Minoan Linear B. The tablets appeared to form inventories, perhaps of slaves, soldiers, and objects of value belonging to the palace. But since the key to the script was still unknown, they defied translation. Then the war came, and all archeological work in Greece came to a stop.

The war supplied a breathing space. Men had time to ruminate over the finds, to move cautiously and fit the pieces of the jigsaw puzzle together. In particular it gave to young Michael Ventris, who had once listened with bated breath to Sir Arthur Evans discussing his discoveries at Cnossus, a clue to the decipherment of the mysterious illegible script which fascinated Blegen and Evans and all those who were brought in contact with it. Wartime cryptography provided the needed method.

Studying Blegen's finds at Pylos, Alice Kober, an American scholar, who did not live to see the final decipherment, had noted by an examination of the signs that they appeared to represent syllables of an inflectional language. The same groups of syllables would appear, but in each case they would be followed by a different final sign. So in Latin *dominus* becomes *dominum* in the accusative, *domini* in the genitive, and *domino* in the ablative.

There followed in quick succession a number of important discoveries. In 1950, while excavating a house outside the citadel at Mycenae, Alan Wace and George Mylonas discovered thirty-eight more tablets in Minoan Linear B. In November of the following year John Papademetriou discovered a new grave at Mycenae containing four skeletons, swords, daggers, vases, and gold ornaments. The most important find was a mask in electrum very close in form to the most archaic mask found by Schliemann. Gradually a whole new grave circle was being uncovered at Mycenae, but no more tablets were found there.

In February, 1952 the tablets discovered by Evans were at last published in a reasonably complete form by Myers in his book *Scripta Minoa II*, and with the evidence from Cnossus, Mycenae, and Pylos before him, Michael Ventris was able to go to work. Two months later the mystery was magnificently solved.

Ventris attacked the problem as an experiment in logic. He made no hypotheses about the nature of the language, though for some time he had held to the belief that it was akin to Etruscan. What he did was to assemble the signs and establish a complex pattern of their relationships, like the "grids" employed in cryptography. Toying with his grid, he did exactly what Champollion had done in attempting to decipher Egyptian hieroglyphics: he simply substituted for an often repeated syllable what seemed to be a likely sound. From the moment when he gave the value of *ko* to the first sign of one of the triplets, all the pieces in the jigsaw puzzle began to fall into place. To his astonishment he discovered that he was reading a language remarkably like ancient Greek, but strangely coarse and sometimes indistinct, as though spoken by a man with a cleft palate in a thunderstorm. It was recognizably Greek, in an ancient dialect, and though rough-edged and barbaric, would have been understood by Socrates. The Greek language was proved to be one of the oldest in existence, and words spoken at Cnossus in 1400 B.C. are still employed in the streets of Athens today.

While Michael Ventris was drafting his article on his discovery, Blegen found three hundred new tablets at Pylos. Among them there was one so striking and simple that he decided to publish it at once. It was quite evidently an inventory of one of the royal storerooms. On a single slab of baked clay, on nine registers, there was carved a series of syllables, nearly all of them followed by a picture of a vase with one, two, three, or four handles. The syllables evidently described the vases. Ventris substituted for the syllables the sounds he had previously deduced. Accordingly, before the picture of a four-handled vase, he read out the syllables *di-pas me-zo-he que-to-ro-wes.* In Homeric Greek *depas* is a "vase," *meizon* means "greater," *tessares* is "four." Ventris translated: "One larger cup with four handles." So he went on until he had deciphered all the remaining passages on the tablet, which read:

> Three wine jars
> Two tripods brought by Aigeus the Cretan
> One tripod defective in one leg
> One tripod brought by the Cretan charred around the legs
> Two larger cups with three handles
> One smaller cup with three handles
> One smaller cup with no handle
> One smaller cup with three handles
> One larger cup with four handles

Unfortunately, most of these documents consist of similar inventories. There are lists of slaves, sewing women, bath-pourers, soldiers. One document found at Pylos describes preparations for coastal defense and contains a long list of the military units and their commanders, among them a certain Orestes. Familiar names appear. We find Achilles and Hector on land records, and Æneas appears on a Mycenaean tablet as a man who was given a ration of oil. We find a reference to "a regiment of Tros," which may be Troy. On one tablet from Crete we can decipher the words: "To all the gods—a pot of honey," and "To the lady of our Labyrinth—a pot of honey." There are references to swords "with gold rivets around the hilt" and chariots "inlaid with ivory, fully rigged, fitted with reins, ivory head-stalls, and horn bits." No poems, no royal edicts, no letters have been found, though more clay tablets are continually turning up. Yet bit by bit archeologists are filling in the gaps of the Homeric story.

Significantly, Michael Ventris and John Chadwick dedicated their monumental *Documents in Mycenaean Greek* to the memory of Schliemann. The book, which reads like a detective story, was published in 1956, and in the same year

Ventris was killed in an automobile accident at the age of thirty-four.

In the roll call of those who have brought the Homeric age to life there are many names. Tsountas, Wace, Blegen, Mylonas, Papademetriou, Stamatakes, Ventris—there are many others; but all of them recognized the primacy of Schliemann. He stands above them all like a giant, because he was the boldest and saw farthest and never betrayed his faith in Homer.

> The long toll of the brave
> Is not lost in darkness:
> Neither hath counting the cost
> Fretted away the zeal of their hopes.
> Over the fruitful earth
> And athwart the seas
> Hath passed the light of noble deeds
> Unquenchable forever——

To Enrich Your Reading

The following questions are designed to help you think about four outstanding points of interest in the life of Heinrich Schliemann as portrayed by Robert Payne: the colorful events of Schliemann's career, Schliemann's interesting and complex personality, his archeological findings, and the significance of these findings to us.

CHAPTERS 1 AND 2

1. What was there about the environment of Heinrich's early childhood that fired his imagination?
2. Why did Heinrich in later life consider an engraving seen in childhood as the turning point of his life?
3. Why does the author include the incident of the stork and St. John's Land?
4. What effect did his father have on Heinrich's school career? On his friendship with Minna?
5. How did a drunken miller affect Heinrich's life?
6. After the shipwreck, what strong resolution did Heinrich make?
7. What was his main reason for studying languages? What unusual methods did he employ?

CHAPTERS 3 AND 4

8. What was strange about Schliemann's wooing of various young ladies in St. Petersburg?
9. What traits of character did Schliemann demonstrate in his search for gold in America? Cite examples.

10. What, in your opinion, was his most harrowing experience in America?
11. What special meaning did America have for Schliemann after his settlement and marriage in Russia?
12. In what ways did Schliemann escape his unhappiness in Russia?

CHAPTERS 5 AND 6

13. What connection does Robert Payne see in the death of Schliemann's cousin and Schliemann's trip to Greece?
14. Why did Schliemann choose Ithaca for his first excavations?
15. Payne writes that Schliemann's second wife, Sophia, "dominated him by appearing never to dominate him." Cite an example of this.
16. Describe Schliemann's feelings for Sophia.
17. What qualities of Homer's hero, Odysseus, did Schliemann possess? How did he demonstrate these qualities in his quest for the Trojan treasure?

CHAPTERS 7 AND 8

18. Why did Mycenae interest Schliemann as a site for excavation?
19. Give an example of an "unscientific" conclusion reached by Schliemann in the Mycenae excavations. What in Schliemann's nature led him to this type of error?
20. According to Payne, what is the real theme of the *Iliad?*
21. In what way does the Trojan War seem to Payne like a modern war?
22. What, according to Payne, gives Schliemann's discoveries their great significance?

CHAPTERS 9 AND 10

23. How did Schliemann finally dispose of his treasure? What is known about its location today?
24. What does Payne mean when he says that "a sense of irony was the one god-like quality Schliemann lacked"? Why would you agree or disagree with this judgment?
25. What surprising discovery by Dörpfeld added an irony to Schliemann's achievement?
26. How do you think Schliemann would have reacted to this if he were alive at the time?

Style and Vocabulary

WORD DERIVATIONS AND MEANINGS

Heinrich Schliemann discovered evidences of ancient civilizations in the dug-up fossil remains of old implements and buildings. By digging into the structure of many modern English words, we are able to discover fossil evidences of old languages. For example, the word *archeology*, whose dictionary definition is *study of antiquity*, is composed of two ancient Greek words, *archeo*, meaning *old*, and *logia*, meaning *words* or *study*.

Below in column 1 are ten words used in *The Gold of Troy* that are of ancient Greek or Latin origin. Match these words with their meanings in column 2. Then, using a good dictionary, check your work and add a third column in which you list the derivations and their meanings. Identify the language of origin by G. for Greek and L. for Latin placed before the derivations (e.g., G. *archeo*—old, *logia*—words or study).

Column 1	*Column 2*	*Column 3*
antediluvian	haughtiness	
clarity	cemetery	

antipodes	violator
diatribe	mysterious
philologist	announced
trespasser	verbal attack
inscrutable	opposite regions
revoked	language scholar
contumely	clearness
necropolis	canceled
	ancient

FOREIGN WORDS

Below are five modern foreign words used in the book. Those that are not explicitly defined by the author can be approximately understood from the sense of the whole context. The chapters in which the words occur are given so that you may skim for them (each word is italicized in the text). Write the word, its language of origin, and the meaning you are able to derive.

soirée	chapter 4
kabuki	chapter 4
frisson	chapter 4
firman	chapter 5
chutzpa	chapter 6

ARCHEOLOGICAL TERMS

The following words are of special archeological interest. After finishing *The Gold of Troy*, you should be able to pick out the best meanings from the various choices offered.

1. HIEROGLYPHICS a) upper classes, b) picture writing, c) extinct animals
2. CRYPTOGRAPHY a) study of codes, b) art of burial, c) forged inscription
3. EXCAVATION a) underground chamber, b) digging, c) collapse

4. OBSIDIAN a) volcanic rock, b) prehistoric, c) against the grain
5. RUBBLE a) mob, b) ancient coinage, c) broken stones
6. ARTIFACTS a) primitive art works and tools, b) facts about art, c) ancient artists
7. TERRA-COTTA a) hut made of earth, b) clay pottery, c) primitive bed
8. MORTUARY a) tomb, b) temple, c) palace
9. CITADEL a) big city, b) trench, c) fortress
10. AGORA a) figurine, b) market place, c) battlefield

Related Activities

1. A good biographer never presents the thoughts and spoken words of actual people unless they are based on documentary evidence. This may include letters, reliable reports of conversations, diaries and other records. However, many interesting works of the imagination, especially novels and plays, have grown out of biographical material. In these the writer may present dialogue and situations which might never have occurred but are consistent with an interpretation of the character. Read a play or novel based on a real person and then a biography of the same person. Report on both to the class, pointing out what the creative artist brought to the material that was not in the biography. Tell whether his interpretation seems justified to you. The following are titles of novels and plays from which you might choose: *Julius Caesar*, play by William Shakespeare; *Man of Destiny*, play about Napoleon by George Bernard Shaw; *Abe Lincoln in Illinois*, play by Robert Sherwood; *The Roaring Boys*, novel about Shakespeare by Robert Payne; *Lust For Life*, novel about Vincent Van Gogh by Irving Stone. Ask your librarian for further suggestions as well as titles of companion biographies.

2. Select a dramatic episode from *The Gold of Troy* and write a one-act play or short story based on it. You may imagine incidents that are not recorded in the book but which are consistent with the character and the chosen episode.
3. Make your own list of reasons why people enjoy reading biographies. Which of these reasons apply to novels also and which only to biographies?
4. Write an appraisal of the character of Heinrich Schliemann, covering his faults as well as his virtues. Indicate whether he is the sort of person you would care to know personally, and why.
5. Using a current edition of a good encyclopedia or other reliable source, report to the class on some recent archeological discoveries and their significance.

AMERICA, I LIKE YOU

P. G. Wodehouse

A PERSONAL COMMENTARY

P. G. WODEHOUSE

The Author and the Personal Commentary

P. G. Wodehouse once described the typical hero of his novels, Bertie Wooster, as having the "ability to keep the lip stiff and upper and make the best of things. Though crushed to earth, as the expression is, he rises again—not absolutely in mid-season form, perhaps, but perkier than you would expect and with an eye alert for silver linings." This characterization might be applied with equal justice to Wodehouse himself. The stiff and upper lip, the making the best of things, the perkiness, and the eye for the silver linings are all typical of the man as well as the man's hero.

Born on October 15, 1881 in the small town of Guildford, England, Pelham Glenville Wodehouse ("Plum" to his friends) attended a school originally founded by a friend of Shakespeare's. At the age of eighteen he became a clerk in a London bank. If one is to judge by the account of those days in *America, I Like You,* he was not very happy there. He sought escape by practicing writing at night and managed to get some paragraphs and verses accepted in a London newspaper column. These pieces were liked so well that he was offered the editorship of the column, which he promptly accepted. He quit his bank job and thus began a successful literary career.

From newspaper columns, Wodehouse branched out to free-lance magazine articles and stories. Later he followed with a host of full-length novels, lyrics for eighteen musical comedies (including *Anything Goes* to the music of Jerome Kern), personal commentaries, and an amusing collection of letters (*Author, Author*).

The novels, which won him his largest group of readers, all have a special set of characters that are stamped as unmistakably Wodehouse. In addition to the Bertie Wooster type of hero—spendthrift, not always bright, but resilient and thoroughly likable—there are usually a perfect butler, as likely as not named Jeeves, an irascible old father or uncle, referred to by Bertie as the "governor," a pretty girl or two, and an assortment of diverting characters from high, and sometimes low, British society. The titles of these books suggest their light-hearted spirit: *Love Among the Chickens, Uneasy Money, Leave It to Psmith, Laughing Gas, Young Men in Spats,* and *Thank You, Jeeves* are but a few.

One episode in Wodehouse's life was the subject of controversy. For several years prior to World War II he had been living in France and at the time of the Nazi invasion in 1940 was arrested. While interned, he unwisely made short-wave broadcasts from Berlin, in which his description of the internment experience, and of the German soldiers generally, struck British listeners as too frivolous. The "eye alert for silver linings" had found them in circumstances too tragic for a nation threatened by Nazism. As a result, there was a wave of denunciation of Wodehouse in his native country. Later he admitted "it was a crazy thing to do" and asked that allowances be made for writers, "all of them being more or less loony." His disclaimers of wrong intention were accepted by most of his countrymen, including Britain's Attorney-General, and such staunch anti-Nazis as Sir Anthony Eden and the writer George Orwell. The latter wrote an impressive essay in Wodehouse's defense. The episode perhaps illustrates that, in the un-Wodehousian world of war and suffering, bounce and cheer are sometimes not enough.

Wodehouse's career took him to America several times, and he finally settled in the United States. He became an American citizen in 1955. He now lives with his wife and animals in a house his wife bought on a whim in Remsenburg, Long Island,

New York. The name of his house is Blandings Castle, after one of his novels.

In his later years, Wodehouse continues to turn out typical Wodehouse novels. They are updated somewhat, and their settings, reflecting his new residence, are partly American (as in a 1964 publication, *Biffin's Millions*). Yet they continue to draw a sizable and appreciative audience. A tribute to Wodehouse's remarkable lasting quality is the comment by the British satirist Evelyn Waugh: "The first thing to remark about Mr. Wodehouse's art is its universality, unique in this century. Few forms of writing are as ephemeral as comedy. Three full generations have delighted in Mr. Wodehouse. He satisfies the most sophisticated taste and the simplest."

America, I Like You does indeed appeal to "the most sophisticated taste and the simplest." It is a perceptive comment on American life, sparkling with verbal wit, and at the same time a collection of personal reminiscences and outrageously funny stories.

Its excuse for being (as though a good book ever needs an excuse) appears to be Wodehouse's naturalization as an American citizen. In his own words, "What I am about to relate is just the simple story of my love affair with the United States of America." The statement has the deceptiveness of many Wodehouse statements. The story is not so simple—there are strands other than his American experience—and the love affair, like other love affairs, has its bumpy moments. Not everything about America meets with unqualified approval. Yet what results is a kind of prose love-song to his adoptive country.

One of the charms of the book is its apparently rambling manner. Each chapter is a separate essay only loosely connected to what follows. The connecting thread is a rough chronology of Wodehouse's American experiences. But there are numerous side excursions backwards and forwards in time, and to many places in and out of this world. It is sometimes hard to tell where literal fact ends and the special brand of Wodehousian truth begins. Was Wodehouse fired from his bank job for desecrating

a new ledger, or did he, as the above biographical sketch indicates, simply quit? The distinction is not important.

Each chapter, considered separately, is, like the book itself,
rather loose in form. Chatty, full of entertaining anecdotes (and
occasional humorous verses), the narrative seems to wander like
conversation from one topic to another. Yet there is much more
form and artfulness than meets the eye. The fun and games all
add up to something. There are pertinent things said about life
in general and the American scene in particular. The chapter
entitled *The Meteorite Racket,* for example, begins with a statement of satisfaction that the author chose writing as a career
instead of some other profession, such as selling second-hand
bridges, "snail-gathering and getting hit in the stomach by
meteorites." Some humorous remarks and stories later, all en-
larging on the "professions" mentioned, we get to the main point
of the chapter, a justification of Wodehouse's special field of
writing, humor, and a lament for the low estate humorous writing
has fallen to in the United States. We are given the reason for
the decline of humor: an increasing "touchiness now prevailing
in the American community." Agree or not, we are entertained
by the development of the idea, as well as by the stories, jokes,
and witty turns of phrase it provokes.

This is the method of the entire book: ideas suddenly surprise
us amidst the fireworks. While nothing in *America I Like You*
is likely to upset the universe or enlist its author in the ranks of
the great philosophers, it is an estimable contribution to the rich
English tradition of personal commentary.

1

WHEN I announce that I was born in England and reveal that I am an author, you will probably give a start of surprise and a puzzled look will come into your faces.

"But why," you will say, "are you writing this thing, whatever it is, in book form and not dishing it out on one of those lecture tours to which British authors are so addicted?"

You have touched on my secret sorrow. Nothing would please me better than to be out and about, rolling vast audiences in the aisles and having ladies' clubs tearing up the seats, but it is beyond my scope. I am not a convincing talker. Very few of the island race are, and this sometimes leads to unfortunate results. As witness the story of the two English explorers.

These two explorers—one from The Grange, Lower-Smattering-on-the-Wissel, Worcestershire, the other from Meadowsweet Hall, Higgleford-cum-Wortlebury-Beneath-the-Hill, Hants—were exploring in South America and chanced to meet one morning on a narrow mountain ledge high up in the Andes where there was not space for either of them to pass. It was a situation fraught with embarrassment, and for perhaps an hour they stood gazing at each other in silence. Then it occurred to one of them that by leaping outward and putting a bit of spin on himself he could jump around the other. This he proceeded to do, but by the worst of luck the same thought had occurred simultaneously to the second explorer, with the result that they collided in mid-air and perished in the fall from the precipice.

This would not have happened if they had been convincing talkers.

I have always had only the most rudimentary gift of speech. I was reading a book the other day entitled *How to Become a Charming Conversationalist*, and it took all the heart out of me.

"Are you audible?" it asked me. "Are you clear? Pleasant? Flexible? Vigorous? Well modulated? Acceptable in pronunciation? Agreeable in laughter?" And the answer was No. I was husky, hoarse, muffled, thin, indistinct, glottal, monotonous, jumbled, unacceptable in pronunciation and disagreeable in laughter—in short, the very opposite of Thomas Lomonaco, the courteous and popular Brooklyn taxi driver who was driving his taxi one afternoon not long ago at Jamaica Avenue and Seventy-fifth Street when he was hailed by Elmer Hinitz.

"Gimme about fifty cents' worth," said Elmer Hinitz.

At Eightieth Street he produced a switch knife and, leaning forward, tapped Thomas Lomonaco on the shoulder.

"This is a stick-up," he announced.

"No. Really?" said Mr. Lomonaco, interested.

"Yah. Slip me your money or I will expunge you."

"I see your point," said Mr. Lomonaco, "and I can fully appreciate your desire to add to your savings, with times as hard as they are in this disturbed postwar era. But your whole plan of campaign is rendered null and void by the fact that I have no money. Would it soften your disappointment if I offered you one of my cigarettes? They are mild. They satisfy."

Mr. Hinitz accepted a cigarette and the conversation proceeded along pleasant lines as far as 118th Street and Jamaica Avenue, when Mr. Lomonaco said, "Say, look. Do you know the police station?"

Mr. Hinitz said he did not.

"Most picturesque," said Mr. Lomonaco. "You'll like it. Let's drive there."

And his talk was so convincing that Mr. Hinitz immediately agreed. A good idea, he said, and he is now in custody, held in $1,000 bail.

To reporters Mr. Lomonaco stated that this was the second time he had been stuck up while pursuing his profession. The other time was in Williamsburg,[1] where a passenger threatened him with a pistol. Mr. Lomonaco, says the daily paper to which I subscribe, "talked him out of the pistol." Obviously a man who must have spent months, if not years, standing in front of a mirror, stretching his muscles, raising himself on tiptoe, rolling the head from side to side and repeating a hundred times the words "Give me a box of mixed biscuits, a mixed biscuit box, and sell me some short silk socks and shimmering satin sashes."

For this—in addition to lying on your back with a heavy weight on your stomach and shouting "Li-yah! Li-yah!"—is apparently what you have to do to become a convincing talker, and I can't manage it. It would cut into my time too much. So, as I said before, that is why I am writing this book and not delivering it verbally to lecture audiences.

As to what the book is, there will no doubt be fierce controversy. You can't call it an autobiography exactly; the word is too important. Another reason why its claim to be ranked as an autobiography falls to the ground and fails to hold water is that in order to write an autobiography that really is an autobiography you need a good memory, and mine is more like a sieve than anything human. On several occasions it has been suggested to me that I might take a pop at this sort of thing. "Yours has been a long life, Wodehouse," people say. "You look about a hundred and four. What memories you must have!" And it makes me feel silly to have to reply, "Memories? Ah, yes, to be sure. The only trouble is that I'm darned if I can remember them." I am absolutely incapable of filling a hundred pages with:

1. *Williamsburg:* section of Brooklyn.

CHAPTER ONE: The Infant
CHAPTER TWO: Childhood Days
CHAPTER THREE: Adolescence

and so forth. All I can recollect of my childhood days is
that I used to play with an orange, which is not good for
more than a paragraph, and that at the age of six I read the
whole of Pope's *Iliad*,[2] which naturally nobody is going to
believe. And as for adolescence, I recall nothing except that
I had a lot of pimples. (Today I have none. How often that
happens! We start out in life with more pimples than we
know what to do with and, in the careless arrogance of youth,
fancy that they are going to last forever; but one morning
we find that we are down to our last half dozen, and then
those go. There is a lesson in this for all of us, I think.)

I suppose what I ought to have done would have been to
take some sort of memory-training course. English literature
is full of tips on how to train the memory. Guiliemus Gro-
terolus Bergomatis (1565) advises washing the feet in warm
water. He also says, "The braynes of a henne doth helpe the
memorie," which is not much good for us, for when did
anyone ever meet a hen that had any brains, and warns us
against "garlyke, leekes, onyions, also peason and moyste
brothes." (Odd how this comic spelling has so completely
gone out nowadays. In 1565 it used to have them in stitches.)

William Vaughan (1600) recommends the bathing of the
head four times a year with hot lye made of ashes, followed
by a cold shower. "The sodaine powring down of cold water
. . ." No, please, William. If you mean "sudden pouring,"
say "sudden pouring." A man of your stature has no need
to descend to clowning for the sake of a cheap laugh. "The
sodaine powring down of cold water," he says, "is very
goode, for thereby the natural heate is stirred within the
bodie and the memorie is quickened."

But you remember the cold shower. That is the catch.

2. *Pope's Iliad:* the translation of Homer's epic by Alexander Pope (1688-
1744).

On the whole, the simplest memory-training methods are probably the best. A member of the British Parliament was once standing in the lobby of the House when a tall, distinguished-looking old gentleman came up and begged for a moment of his time.

"I have heard of you as one who takes up unpopular causes," he said, "and I should be extremely grateful if you would listen to my story."

It was a sad story. By industry and thrift he had amassed a large fortune, and now his relatives had robbed him of it and, not content with that, had placed him in a mental home. This was his day out.

"I have put the facts down in this document," he concluded. "Study it at your leisure. Communicate with me at your leisure. Thank you, sir, thank you. Good day."

Much moved by the other's exquisite courtesy, the M.P. took the paper, shook hands, promised that he would do everything in his power and turned to go back to the debate. As he did so, he received a kick in the seat of the pants which nearly sent his spine shooting through his hat.

"Don't forget!" said the old gentleman.

2

I don't think, though, that even if my memory were like a steel trap I would ever have the nerve to attempt a full-dress autobiography. To do that, you have to be somebody in the big league, one of those who have done the world's work, and I—let's face it—am a pretty insignificant sort of blister, not at all the type that leaves footprints on the sands of time, as the fellow said. Ask the first ten men you meet "Have you ever heard of P. G. Wodehouse?" and nine of them will answer No. The tenth, being hard of hearing, will say "Down the passage, first door on the right."

Not that I regret this obscurity. There are compensations

for being just one of the *canaille*.[3] People are always coming up to me in the street and saying "Hello there, Wodehouse. Don't you wish you were a celebrity?" And my invariable reply is "No, Smith or Stokes or Campanella" (if it happens to be Roy Campanella[4]), "I do not."

Nothing would induce me to be a celebrity. I would as soon be someone for whom the police are spreading one of those dragnets. If in a weak moment you let yourself become a prominent figure in the public eye these days, you are nothing but a straight man for all the comedians in the country. Joshing the eminent is now a national sport.

It was not always so. There was a time when celebrities lived the life of Riley. Everyone looked up to them and respected them. They had never had it so good. And then suddenly everything changed. Out like a cloud of mosquitoes came a horde of bright young men with fountain pens and notebooks, dogging their footsteps and recording their every unguarded speech, till today you can tell a celebrity at a glance by the nervous way he keeps looking over his shoulder and jumping at sudden noises. Many of them get the illusion that they are being followed about by little men with black beards.

It was *The New Yorker* that started it all with its profiles. It had the idea that if you tracked down your celebrity, lulled him into a false security with the respectfulness of your demeanor, got him talking and then went home and wrote a piece showing him up as a complete bird-brain, everybody—except the celebrity—would get a hearty laugh out of it. They "did" Ernest Hemingway[5] a year or two ago, sending a female reporter to spend the afternoon with him and write down every word he uttered, with of course the jolliest results. If you write down every word uttered by

3. *Canaille:* rabble (French).
4. *Roy Campanella:* baseball player.
5. *Ernest Hemingway:* American writer (1898-1961).

anyone over a period of several hours you are bound to hook an occasional fatuous remark.

It is getting so nowadays that celebrities are scared of opening their mouths. And perhaps I am wrong in saying that this harrying of the famous is a new thing, for I have been reading a book by Harold Nicolson[6] in which he tells how he felt as a young man when dining with Tennyson.[7]

An aching pause, and in a crisis of embarrassment one would pass into the dining room. The Laureate would begin to carve the boiled beef. A little fluttering conversation from Mrs. Tennyson about Yarmouth pier, a sudden growl from the Laureate—"I like my meat in wedges"—and the subject of Yarmouth pier would flutter down to another prolonged and awful silence.

One's sympathies are supposed, of course, to be with Harold. Mine are not. Tennyson is the one I am sorry for. The operative word in the passage I have quoted is the word "would." It shows us that the writer is not describing just one dinner at which he happened by bad luck to be present. He was always there. You couldn't keep him away. He oozed into the house like oil. Day after day the good gray poet—if he was a good gray poet, I can never remember which of them were—would be starting to dig in and get his, and he would look up and there would be Harold Nicolson, back again in the same old chair with the same popeyed expression on his face and his ears sticking up like a wire-haired terrier's. No wonder he went into a prolonged silence. It is a most unpleasant thing, when you want to be alone with your boiled beef, to look up from the carrots and gravy and see Harold Nicolson, knowing that he is just counting the minutes till you provide an amusing paragraph for his memoirs by saying something silly or choking on a hot potato.

6. *Harold Nicolson:* contemporary British biographer and historian.
7. *Tennyson:* Alfred, Lord Tennyson, outstanding English poet (1809-1892).

To you young men of today—you revolting goggle-eyed young snoopers—I would say this: Lay off those celebrities. Stop chivvying them. Give the poor slobs a break. You may be celebrities yourselves at any moment, so remember the story of the mother who was walking with her child on Hollywood Boulevard when a group of men in make-up came along.

The child pointed.

"Look, Mamma. Movie actors."

"Hush, dear," said the mother. "You don't know what *you* may come to some day."

And it is not as if the celebrities got anything out of it, though there have been indications recently that better times are coming. The name of John Harrington is probably not familiar to my readers, so I will explain that he is the director of sports at a Chicago broadcasting station, and the other day he received a stunning blow. He is still walking around in circles, kicking stones and muttering to himself, and the mildest of the things he mutters is "Bloodsuckers! Bloodsuckers!" If you care to describe him as cut to the quick, it will be all right with me.

What happened was that he wanted to interview some members of the Kansas City Athletics baseball club and was informed by them that they would be charmed if he would do so, provided he unbelted fifty dollars, cash in advance. No fifty fish, no interview. It was the first time anything like this had happened to him. One gets new experiences.

Hats off, I say, to those Kansas City athletes. For years there has been too much of this thing of notebooked young men sidling up to the celebrated and getting away with all sorts of good stuff without paying a cent for it. The celebs were supposed to be compensated by a few kind words chucked in at the beginning. "He looks like a debonair magician, quick and agile, in his fashionable suit of gray and elegant black patent-leather slippers." That was what the

London *Daily Express* said about Mr. Cecil Beaton[8] not long ago when he gave them an interview. A poor substitute for hard cash.

And it was an important interview, too, for in it Mr. Beaton revealed for the first time the sensational facts in connection with his recent visit to an amusing chateau in the wine country of France.

"Summer had come," he said (exclusive), "and I found the atmosphere most stimulating. We had an amusing dish—a delightful creamy mixture of something I can't quite remember, but I recall a mountain of truffles in it."

All that free! The circulation of the *Express* doubled. Lord Beaverbrook[9] was enabled to buy two more houses in Jamaica. But what did Mr. Beaton get out of it? Not a thing except the passing gratification of seeing himself described as a debonair magician in black patent-leather slippers. Does that pay the rent? It does not. You can wear black patent-leather slippers till your eyes bubble, but the landlord still wants his so much per each week. High time those Kansas City boys put their foot down.

Though they were not the first to do it. Apparently you have to be a baseball player to stand up for your rights. John Crosby was writing the other day about an exchange of views which took place some years ago between Bill Terry, at that time manager of the Giants, and a representative of *The New Yorker*, which wanted to do a profile of him. (A *New Yorker* profile takes up eighty-three pages in the middle of the magazine and goes on for months and months and months.)

"And where were you born, Mr. Terry?" inquired the profile hound, starting to get down to it.

A wary look came into Wm.'s face.

"Young fella," he said, "that information will cost you a lot of money."

8. *Cecil Beaton:* outstanding theater scene designer and photographer.
9. *Lord Beaverbrook:* British newspaper tycoon (1879-1964).

That ended the love feast. They had to fill up the eighty-three pages with one of those solid, thoughtful things of Edmund Wilson's.[10]

Hats off, therefore, also to Bill Terry. But though I approve of this resolve on the part of the celebrated to get in on the ground floor and make a bit, I am not blind to the fact that there is a danger of the whole thing becoming more than a little sordid. At first, till a regular scale of prices is set up and agreed to by both contracting parties, one foresees a good deal of unpleasant wrangling.

Let us say that you are a young fellow named Spelvin who in a recent golf tournament lost forty-three balls on eighteen holes, beating the record set up in 1951 by Otis G. Follansbee of Westhampton Beach, New York. It will not be long before there is a ring at the bell, followed by the appearance of a gentleman of the press.

"Good morning, Mr. Spelvin."

"Good morning."

"I am from *Time*. Three and forty balls on a round of golf last week we understand you lost and naturally anxious are our readers to hear——"

"How much?"

"Twenty dollars?"

"Make it thirty."

"Call it twenty-five. Okay?"

"Well, it depends. Are you going to refer to me as stumpy balding spectacled George Spelvin (28) no Hogan he?"

"Certainly not. I thought something on the lines of a debonair magician, quick and agile."

"Yes, I like that."

"Adding that not spoiled you has success."

"Excellent. I don't mind knocking off a couple of dollars for that."

"Make it five."

10. *Edmund Wilson:* literary critic.

"No, not worth five."

"Very well. Now tell me, Mr. Spelvin, can you describe your feelings when your forty-third ball disappeared over the horizon?"

"I felt fine."

"And may I say you did it all for the wife and kiddies?"

"Not for twenty-five bucks you mayn't. We'd better go back to the thirty we were talking about."

You see what I mean. Sordid. These negotiations are better left to one's agent. I have instructed mine to arrange for a flat payment of fifteen dollars, to be upped, of course, if they want to know what I had for dinner at that amusing chateau in the wine country.

The name of the *Time* man in the foregoing scene was not mentioned, but I presume he was one of those appearing in a little poem which I jotted down just now on the back of an old envelope after brooding, as I so often brood, on the list in *Time* of its editors, managing editors, assistant managing editors, deputy assistant managing editors, contributing editors, sympathetic encouraging editors, researchers and what not, which is my favorite reading. You will generally find me with my feet up on the mantelpiece, poring over this fascinating column, and it always inspires me to bigger and better things.

> I must confess that often I'm
> A prey to melancholy
> Because I do not work on *Time*.
> It must be jolly. Golly!
> No other human bliss but pales
> Beside the feeling that you're
> One of nine hundred—is it?—males
> And females of such stature.

> How very much I would enjoy
> To call Roy Alexander "Roy"
> And have him say "Hello, my boy!"

Not to mention being on terms of easy
camaraderie with

> Edward O. Cerf
> Richard Oulahan Jr.
> Bernadine Beerheide

Thanks for the Memory, Such As It Is

> Virginie Lindsley Bennett
> Rodney Campbell
> Estelle Dembeck
> Dorothea L. Grine
> Eldon Griffiths
> Hillis Mills
> Joseph Purtell
> Old Uncle Fuerbringer and all.

Alas, I never learned the knack
(And on *Time's* staff you need it)
Of writing English front to back
Till swims the mind to read it.
Tried often I've my darnedest, knows
Goodness, but with a shock I'd
Discover once again my prose
Had failed to go all cockeyed.

So though I wield a fluent pen,
There'll never be a moment when
I join that happy breed of men.

I allude to (among others)

> Douglas Auchincloss
> Lester Bernstein
> Gilbert Cant
> Edwin Copps
> Henry Bradford Darrach Jr.
> Barker T. Hartshorn
> Roger S. Hewlett
> Jonathan Norton Leonard

F. Sydnor Trapnell
Danuta Reszke-Birk
Deirdre Mead Ryan
Yi Ying Sung
Content Peckham
Quinera Sarita King
Old Uncle Fuerbringer and all,
Old Uncle Fuerbringer and all.

A pity, but too late to alter it now.

3

Another thing about an autobiography is that, to attract the
cash customers, it must be full of good stories about the
famous, and I never can think of any. If it were just a matter of dropping names, I could do that with the best of them,
but mere name-dropping is not enough. You have to have
the sparkling anecdote as well, and any I could provide
would be like the one Young Griffo, the boxer, told Hype
Igoe[11] about his meeting with Joe Gans, the then lightweight
champion. Having just been matched to fight Gans, he was
naturally anxious to get a look at him before the formal
proceedings began, and here is how he told the dramatic tale
of their encounter.

I was goin' over to Philadelphia to see a fight, Hype, and my
manager asks me would I like to meet Joe Gans. He asks me
would I like to meet Joe Gans, Hype, and I said I would. So
we arrive in Philadelphia and we start out for one of the big
sporting places where the gang all held out, and my manager
asks me again do I want to meet Joe Gans, and I say I do. So we
go to this big sporting place, Hype, and there's a big crowd
standing around one of the tables, and somebody asks me would
I like to meet Joe Gans, he's over at that table, and I say I
would. So he takes me to the table and says "Here's Young

11. *Hype Igoe:* sports writer.

Griffo, Joe," he says. "He wants to meet you," he says. And sure enough it was Gans all right. He gets up from the table. "Hello, Griff," he says, and I say, "Hello, Joe."

This was all. You might have thought more was coming, but no. He had met Gans, Gans had met him. It was the end of the story. My autobiography would be full of stuff like that.

I had long wished to make the acquaintance of Sir (then Mr.) Winston Churchill, but it was not till my third year in London that I was enabled to gratify this ambition. A friend took me to the House of Commons, and we were enjoying tea on the terrace when the object of my admiration came by.

"Oh, Winston," said my friend, "I want you to meet Mr. Wodehouse."

"How do you do?" said Mr. Churchill.

"How do you do?" I replied.

You can't charge people five dollars or whatever it is for that sort of thing.

This, then, is nothing so ambitious as an autobiography. What I am about to relate is just the simple story of my love affair with the United States of America, starting when we were both fifty years younger in a strange city where Thirty-fourth Street was uptown and there was no Marilyn Monroe, no Liberace, no Zsa Zsa Gabor and only a rough preliminary scenario of Billy Rose,[12] he being five years old at the time (and a sweet child, so they tell me). And we now approach the question of how—if at all—it is to be read, and I should like to make a suggestion with regard to the *modus operandi*, if that is the expression I want.

What I would wish the reader to do is to approach the thing in the indulgent spirit in which he listens to an after-

12. *Marilyn Monroe . . . Billy Rose:* popular theatrical personalities of late 1950's.

dinner speech. Let him try to imagine that he is leaning back in his chair flushed with heady wines and smoking a good cigar and that I, up at the top table, am in the process of being reminded by a remark of the last speaker of a little story about two Irishmen which may be new to some of you present here tonight. It will make all the difference.

It would, indeed, be a good idea if you actually had a square meal before starting to tackle the book. My publishers will support me in this. Simon tells me that when he and Schuster received my manuscript the mere sight of it gave them both a sort of sinking feeling. They spent the day shoving it across the table at each other, each trying to avoid the task of reading it. Two editors named Schwed and Goodman were called in and told to have a go, but after a couple of pages both resigned and are now coffee-planting in Kenya. The situation began to look like a deadlock, and then suddenly the idea struck Schuster—or it may have been Simon —that things might brighten after they had had dinner.

They dined as follows:

Le Dîner
Caviar Frais
Consommé Brunoise aux Quenelles
Darne de Saumon au Beurre de Montpellier
Blanchailles
Caille Demidoff
Sylphides à la Crême d'Ecrevisses
Mousse de Jambon à la Neva
Pointes d'Asperges à la Tallulah Bankhead
Fraises Melba
Diablotins
Corbeille de Fruits Exotiques

and the result was magical. Full to the eyebrows, with the coffee and old brandy at their side, they felt equal to anything now, and they pitched in and were past page 100 before they knew where they were.

So if you are hesitating about reading any further, say to yourself, "Courage! It can be done," and stoke up and go to it.

A word about the title. It is taken (by kind permission) from that grand old song by the Messrs. Kalmar and Ruby, which runs:

> America, I like you!
> You're like an uncle to me.
> From mountain to mountain
> To you my affection
> Is touching each hemisphere.
> Just like a little children
> Climbing his father's lap,
> America, how are you?
> And there's a hundred people feeling the same.
> The A stands for our Navy,
> The M for the soldiers we've got,
> The E for the heagle which flies up above us,
> The R for we can't go wrong,
> I for Independence,
> C stands for brave and bold,
> America, I like you,
> Don't bite the hand that's feeding you.

For years this stirring ballad has been a household word from one end of the country to the other. Harry Ruby often sings it at parties in Beverly Hills. And very unpleasant it sounds, I am told, for his voice is breaking.

. . . 2   AN OLD SWEETHEART WHO
                  HAS PUT ON WEIGHT

1

WHY AMERICA? I have often wondered about that. Why, I mean, from my earliest years, almost back to the time when I was playing with that orange, was it America that was always to me the land of romance? It is not as though I had been intoxicated by visions of cowboys and red Indians. Even as a child I never became really cowboy-conscious, and to red Indians I was definitely allergic. I wanted no piece of them.

I had no affiliations with the country. My father had spent most of his life in Hong Kong. So had my Uncle Hugh. And two other uncles had been known to the police of Calcutta and Singapore. You would have expected it to be the Orient that would have called to me. "Put me somewheres east of Suez," you would have pictured me saying to myself. But it didn't work out that way. People would see me walking around with a dreamy look in my eyes and my mouth hanging open as if I had adenoids and they would whisper to one another, "He's thinking of America." And they were right. I thought of America practically incessantly. I yearned for it with a fervor which equaled, if not surpassed, that of a Tin Pan Alley song writer longing to go back back back to his old Kentucky shack. But it was not till 1904— April 24, now a national holiday—that I was able at last to set foot on the sidewalks of New York.

On leaving school I had accepted employment in a London bank, and this restricted my freedom of movement. It was only after several years that I threw off the shackles and resigned.

Well, when I say "resigned . . ."

Let me tell you the story of the new ledger.

One of the things that sour authors, as every author knows, is being asked by people to write something clever in the front pages of their books. It was, I believe, George Eliot[1] who in a moment of despondency made this rather bitter entry in her diary:

Dear Diary: Am I a wreck tonight! I feel I never want to see another great admirer of my work again. It's not writing novels

1. *George Eliot:* pen name of Mary Ann Evans, author of *Silas Marner* and other novels (1819-1880).

that's hard. I can write novels till the cows come home. What slays you is this gosh-darned autographing. "Oh, *please!* Not just your *name.* Won't you write something *clever?*" To hell with it.

And Richard Powell, the whodunit author, was complaining along similar lines in a recent issue of the *American Writer*. "I begin sweating," he said, "as soon as someone approaches me with a copy of one of my books."

I feel the same. When I write a book, the golden words come pouring out like syrup, but let a smiling woman steal up to me with my latest and ask me to jot down something clever on the front page, and it is as though some hidden hand had removed my brain and substituted for it an order of cauliflower. There may be men capable of producing something clever on the spur of the moment, but I am not of their number. I like at least a month's notice, and even then I don't guarantee anything.

The only time I ever wrote anything really clever on the front page of a book was when I was a wage slave in this bank of which I was speaking. I was in the Cash Department at the time, and a new ledger came into the office and was placed in my charge. It had a white, gleaming front page, and suddenly, as I sat gazing at it, there floated into my mind like drifting thistledown the idea of writing on it a richly comic description of the celebrations and rejoicings marking the Formal Opening of the New Ledger.

It was great. But great. Though fifty-four years have passed since that day, I can still remember that. There was a bit about my being presented to His Gracious Majesty the King (who, of course, attended the function) which makes me laugh even now. ("From his tie he took a diamond tie-pin, and smiled at me, and then he put it back.") But the whole thing was terrific. I can't give the details. You will have to take my word for it that it was one of the most screamingly funny things ever written. I sat back on my stool and felt like Shakespeare. I was all in a glow.

Then came the reaction. The Head Cashier was rather an austere man who on several occasions had expressed dissatisfaction with the young Wodehouse, and something seemed to whisper to me that, good as the stuff was, it would not go any too well with him. Briefly, I got cold feet and started to turn stones and explore avenues in the hope of finding some way of making everything pleasant for all concerned. In the end I decided that the best thing to do was to cut the page out with a sharp knife.

A few mornings later the stillness of the bank was shattered by a sudden yell of triumph, not unlike the cry of a Brazilian wildcat leaping on its prey. It was the Head Cashier discovering the absence of the page, and the reason he yelled triumphantly was that he was feuding with the stationers and for weeks had been trying to get the goods on them in some way. He was at the telephone in two strides, asking them if they called themselves stationers. I suppose they replied that they did, for he then touched off his bombshell, accusing them of having delivered an imperfect ledger, a ledger with the front page missing.

This brought the head stationer around in person calling heaven to witness that when the book left his hands it had been all that a ledger should be, if not more so.

"Somebody must have cut out the page," he said.

"Absurd!" said the Head Cashier. "Nobody but an imbecile would cut out the front page of a ledger."

"Then," said the stationer, "you must have an imbecile in your department. Have you?"

The Head Cashier started. This opened up a new line of thought.

"Why, yes," he said, for he was a fair-minded man. "There is P. G. Wodehouse."

"Weak in the head is he, this Wodehouse?"

"Very, so I have always thought."

"Then have him on the carpet and question him narrowly," said the stationer.

This was done. They got me under the lights and grilled
me, and I had to come clean. It was immediately after this
that I found myself at liberty to embark on the life literary.

2

From my earliest years I had always wanted to be a writer.
I started to write at the age of five. (What I was doing before that, I don't know. Just loafing, I suppose.)

It was not that I had any particular message for humanity.
I am still plugging away and not a ghost of one so far, so it
begins to look as though, unless I suddenly hit mid-season
form, humanity will remain a message short. I just wanted to
write, and was prepared to write anything that had a chance
of getting into print.

Actually, I had made considerable progress while still
working in the bank. I had had my setbacks, of course—the
English Illustrated Magazine accepted a short story of mine
and were going to pay me fifteen shillings for it, but after
they had had it six months a new editor came in and returned
the thing to me with a rejection slip—but I had received
eleven shillings for an article in *Today* and half a crown for
some verses in *Scraps*, so when I turned pro I was off, as you
might say, to a running start. As I surveyed the literary scene,
everything looked pretty smooth to me. My lodgings cost
me a guinea a week, breakfast, lunch and dinner included,
and it seemed absurd to suppose that a man of my gifts would
not be able to earn a weekly twenty-one shillings, especially
in the London market of that time.

The early years of the twentieth century in London—it
was in 1902 that the Hong Kong and Shanghai Bank decided
(and a very sensible decision, too) that the only way to keep
solvent was to de-Wodehouse itself—were not too good for
writers at the top of the tree, the big prices being still in the
distant future, but they were fine for an industrious young
fellow who asked no more than to pick up the occasional

half-guinea. The dregs, of whom I was one, sat extremely pretty *circa* 1902. There were so many evening papers and weekly papers and monthly magazines that you were practically sure of landing your whimsical piece on The Language of Flowers or your parody of Omar Khayyám somewhere or other after about say thirty-five shots.

I left the bank at the beginning of September, and by the end of December I found that I had made £65 6.7, so for a beginner I was doing pretty well. But I was not saving enough for the visit to New York, on which my heart was set, and I saw where the trouble lay. I needed something in the way of a job with a regular salary.

There was an evening paper in London in those days called the *Globe*. It was a hundred and five years old and was printed—so help me—on pink paper. (One of the other evening papers was printed on green paper. Life was very full then, very rich.) It was a profitable source of income to all young writers because it ran on its front page what were called turnovers, thousand-word articles of almost unparalleled dullness which turned over onto the second page. A guinea was the guerdon for these. You dug them out of reference books.

In addition to the turnovers the *Globe* also carried on its front page a column, supposedly humorous, entitled "By the Way," and one day I learned that the man who wrote it had been a master at my old school. These things form a bond. I asked him to work me in as his understudy when he wanted a day off, and he very decently did so, and when he was offered a better job elsewhere, I was taken on permanently. Three guineas a week was the stipend—roughly fifteen dollars—and it was precisely what I needed. The work was over by noon, and I had all the rest of the day for freelancing. I began to save. By April 1904 I had sixty pounds stashed away and a trip to New York became a practical proposition.

The *Globe* gave its staff five weeks' holiday in the year.

Eight days crossing the Atlantic and eight days crossing it back again was going to abbreviate my visit, but I should at least have nineteen days in Manhattan, so I booked my passage second class on the *St. Louis* and sailed on April 16. And on April 24 there I was.

Right from the start I don't think I ever had any doubts as to this being the New York of which I had heard so much. "It looks like New York," I said to myself as I emerged from the customs sheds. "It smells like New York. Damme, it *is* New York." In which respect I differed completely from Signor Giuseppe Bertolo who, arriving there on the plane from Italy the other day, insisted against all argument that he was in San Francisco.

What he had overlooked was that to get from Italy to San Francisco you have to change at New York and take a westbound plane. All he knew was that his son in San Francisco had told him to come to Montgomery Street, where his—the son's—house was, so the moment the bus had deposited him at the terminus he hailed a taxi and gave the direction.

Now it so happens that there is a Montgomery Street in New York, down on the lower East Side, and the driver— José Navarro of 20 Avenue D, not that it matters—took him there. And this is where the plot begins to thicken. Nothing on Montgomery Street resembled the picture his son had sent him of the house for which he was headed, so Signor Bertolo decided to search on foot, and when he had not returned at the end of an hour Mr. Navarro drove to the Clinton Street police station and told his story. About 7 P.M. Signor Bertolo arrived at the police station, escorted by Patrolman Mario Pertini, and that was where things got complex and etched those deep lines which you can still see on the foreheads of the Clinton Street officials. For Signor Bertolo stoutly refused to believe that he was in New York. He insisted that he was in San Francisco. Hadn't he seen

Montgomery Street with his own eyes? The fact that some men of ill-will had spirited away his son's house had, he said, nothing to do with the case.

After about forty minutes of this Police Lieutenant Daly drew Patrolman Pertini aside. There was a worried look on his face, and he was breathing rather stertorously.

"Look, Mario," he said. "Are you absolutely sure this *is* New York?"

"It's how I always heard the story, Lieut," said Patrolman Pertini.

"Have you any doubts?"

"If you had asked me that question an hour ago—nay, forty minutes ago—Lieut, I'd have said, 'No, none,' but now I'm beginning to wonder."

"Me, too. Tell me in your own words, Mario, what makes —or shall we say used to make you think this is New York."

"Well, I live in the Bronx. That's in New York."

"There may be a Bronx in San Francisco."

"And here's my badge. Lookut. See what it says on it. 'New York City.' "

"You can't go by badges. How do we know that some international gang did not steal your San Francisco badge and substitute this one?"

"Would an international gang do that?"

"You never can tell. They're always up to something," said Lieutenant Daly with a weary sigh.

Well, it all ended happily, I am glad to say. Somebody called up the Signor's son and put the Signor on the wire, and the son told him that New York really was New York and that he was to get on the westbound plane at once. And there he is now, plumb spang in Montgomery Street, San Francisco, and having a wonderful time. (He specifies this in a picture postcard to a friend in Italy, adding that he wishes he—the friend—were here.) It is a great weight off everybody's mind.

The whole episode recalls a picture in *Punch* fifty years ago of an English visitor to Paris leaning out of the window of the train at the Gare du Nord and saying to a porter, *"Quel est le nom de cette place?"*[2]

Travelers to foreign parts should remember this. It is always safest to ask, *"Quel est le nom de cette place?"* before starting to explore.

3

To say that New York came up to its advance billing would be the baldest of understatements. Being there was like being in heaven without going to all the bother and expense of dying. And it is interesting—to me at any rate—to think that I saw more of New York in those nineteen days than in all the years I have spent there since. If you want to see a city, it is no good being a resident, you have to be a tourist. (Broadly speaking, a tourist is one who takes the sightseeing bus to Chinatown. I did this, and a friendly policeman showed me round. I tipped him a quarter. Well, how was I to know? In London its equivalent, a shilling, would have been lavish. I can still hear his indulgent laugh as he handed it back.)

What an amazingly attractive city New York was in those days! I still love it, of course, but today it is with the tempered affection which you feel for an old sweetheart who has put on a lot of weight. There is no concealing the fact that the dear old place has swollen visibly these last fifty years. In 1904, if I remember correctly, the tallest skyscraper was the New York *World* building. Handsome private houses lined Fifth Avenue. And the plays at the theaters were superb. *The Prince of Pilsen*, Rock and Fulton in *The Candy Shop*, Elizabeth Tyree in *Tit for Tat*, Lionel Barrymore as the boxer in Augustus Thomas' *The Other Girl* . . . gosh! I was taken to my first ball game, too, at the

2. *Quel . . . place:* "what is the name of this place?" (French).

Polo Grounds (Mathewson pitching) and am one of the few men now alive who saw Ping Bodie try to steal home.

And the food! It is odd, considering how intensely spiritual I am, that that was about all I could talk about when I got back to London.

I took to American food from the start like a starving Eskimo flinging himself on a portion of blubber. The poet Keats, describing his emotions on first reading Chapman's Homer, speaks of himself as feeling like some watcher of the skies when a new planet swims into his ken. Precisely so did I feel that afternoon at Sherry's when the waiter brought me my first slab of strawberry shortcake. And the same goes for my subsequent introduction to shad roe, corned beef hash (with egg), buckwheat cakes and soft-shell crabs. "No matter if it puts an inch on my waistline," I said to myself, "I must be in on this."

I have been criticized for these exotic tastes of mine. English friends have told me that at the mere sight of a soft-shell crab their stomachs winced like salted snails and turned three handsprings. I don't argue with them. It is never any good arguing about other people's food. We may not be able to understand why a cannibal chief should like to tuck into the broiled missionary, but he does. The thing simply has to be accepted, just as we accept the fact that Scotsmen like haggis and Frenchmen *bouillabaisse*, though in *bouillabaisse* you are apt to find almost anything, from a nautical gentleman's sea boots to a china mug engraved with the legend *"Un cadeau"* (a present) *"de"* (from) *"Deauville"* (Deauville), while as for haggis . . .

How extraordinary it is, is it not, to reflect that each year as St. Andrew's Day comes around Scotsmen all over the world are sitting at dinner tables waiting with gleaming eyes for the arrival of this peculiar dish. Incredible as it may seem, they are looking forward to eating it. I applaud their rugged courage.

The fact that I regard haggis with dark suspicion is probably due to my having read Shakespeare. In my formative years I came across that bit in *Macbeth* and it established a complex. You remember the passage to which I refer? Macbeth comes upon the three witches while they are preparing the evening meal. They are dropping things into a caldron and chanting "Eye of newt and toe of frog, wool of bat and tongue of dog" and so on, and he immediately recognizes the recipe. "How now, you secret, black and midnight haggis,"[3] he cries, shuddering.

This has caused misunderstanding and has done an injustice to haggis. Grim as it is, it is not as bad as that—or should not be. What the dish really consists of—or should consist of—is the more intimate parts of a sheep, chopped up fine and blended with salt, pepper, nutmeg, onions, oatmeal and beef suet. But it seems to me that there is a grave danger of the cook going all whimsy and deciding not to stop there. When you reflect that the haggis is served up with a sort of winding sheet around it, concealing its contents, you will readily see that the temptation to play a practical joke on the boys must be almost irresistible. Scotsmen have their merry moods like all of us, and the thought must occasionally cross the cook's mind that it would be a great joke to shove in a lot of newts and frogs and bats and dogs and watch the gang wading into them.

Nor could the imposture be easily detected. The Athol brose which accompanies the haggis is a beverage composed of equal parts of whisky, cream and honey. After a glass or two of this you simply don't notice anything. I must confess that if I were invited to a St. Andrew's Day dinner, I would insist on taking the Public Analyst with me and turning my plate over to him before I touched a mouthful. My caution might cast a damper over the party. Censorious looks might be directed at me. I would not care. "Safety

3. *Haggis:* Wodehouse's pun. The Shakespearean line refers to *hags*, not *haggis*.

first," I would say to the Public Analyst. "Just analyze this, old man, will you?" And only when he had blown the All Clear would I consent to join the revels.

4

Back in London, I found that I had done wisely in going to New York even for so brief a visit. The manner of editors changed toward me. Where before it had been "Throw this man out," they now said, "Come in, my dear fellow, come in and tell us all about America." It is hard to believe in these days, when after breakfasting at the Berkeley you nip across the ocean and dine at the Stork Club, but in 1904 anybody in the writing world who had been to America was regarded with awe and looked on as an authority on that terra incognita. Well, when I tell you that a few weeks after my return the *Daily Chronicle* was paying me £1.5 for a review of *The Prince of Pilsen* and *Pearson's Weekly* two guineas for "Baseball" and "New York Crowds," I think I have made my point sufficiently clear.

I was branching out in other directions, too. In 1906 I got a job at the Aldwych Theater writing encore verses for the numbers in a musical comedy called *The Beauty of Bath*, and it was there one night that I was introduced to a small child—at least, he looked like a small child and was, I believe, eighteen—who was trying to break in as a composer and, so they told me, showed promise. His name was Jerome Kern. We wrote a topical song together for *The Beauty of Bath* called "Mister Chamberlain," and it was a riot. Six or seven encores every night. I don't know if Jerry made anything out of it. My end of the thing was included in my two pounds a week salary.

So, on the whole, I was doing quite nicely in my chosen walk of life. I made £505.1.7 in 1906 and £527.17.1 in 1907 and was living, I suppose, on about £203.4.9. In fact,

if on November 17, 1907, I had not bought a Darracq car
for £450 (and smashed it up in the first week) I should soon
have been one of those economic royalists who get themselves so disliked. This unfortunate venture brought my
capital back to about where it had started in 1904, and a
long and dusty road had to be traveled before my finances
were in a state sufficiently sound to justify another visit to
America.

What took me there—in 1909—was Archie Fitzmaurice,
and as I write that name the years fall away, hair sprouts
on the vast bare steppes of my head, where never hair has
been within the memory of the oldest inhabitant, and I
am once more an eager young man going West in the hope
—what a hope!—of getting nine hundred bucks out of Archibald Fitzmaurice, the painstaking and enthusiastic literary
agent.

. . . 3   ARCHIE HAD MAGNETISM

NICHOLAS BOILEAU-DESPRÉAUX (1636-1711) once said, thereby getting himself into Bartlett's book of *Familiar Quotations*,
"Every age has its pleasures, its style of wit, and its own
ways." And, one might add, its own literary agents. It is
one of the compensations of advancing years that time seems
to bring with it bigger and better literary agents. When
you arrive at the stage where the question of Japanese second
serial rights crops up, you have generally got somebody
looking after you who is incapable of pocketing a yen.
But in one's early days, to get the cash from the outright
sale of a short story to a magazine was a wonderful adventure. Especially if your affairs were in the capable hands
of Archie Fitzmaurice.

My first dealings with Archie were through the medium
of the post. It was a medium to which, as I shall show later,
he did not always trust, but he did so on this occasion, and

very charming letters he wrote. I had sent the ms. of a novel of mine, *Love among the Chickens*, to a friend on the New York *World*. Pressure of work compelled him to hand it over to a regular agent. He gave it to Archie. That was the expression he used in writing to me—"I have given it to Archie Fitzmaurice"—and I think Archie must have taken the word "given" literally. Certainly, when the book was published in America, it had on its title page, "Copyright by Archibald Fletcher Fitzmaurice" and a few years later, when the story was sold for motion pictures, I was obliged to pay him two hundred and fifty dollars to release it.

For the book was published in America. I will say that for Archie—he sold not only the book rights but also the serial rights and at a price which seemed to me fantastic. A thousand dollars it was, and to one who, like myself, had never got above fifty pounds for a serial and whose record royalties were £18.11.4, a thousand dollars was more than merely good. It was great gravy. It made the whole world seem different. A wave of gratitude to my benefactor swept over me. I felt like a man who has suddenly discovered a rich uncle from Australia.

There was just one flaw in my happiness. The money seemed a long time coming. In the letter (a delightful letter) in which he informed me of the sale, Archie said that a draft would arrive on October first. By Christmas I was inclined to restlessness. In March I cabled, and received a reply: "Letter explaining. Check immediately." Late in April the old restlessness returned, for no explaining letter had arrived. Toward the middle of May I decided to go to New York. In several of his letters Archie had told me I was the coming man. I came.

Archie entered my life heralded by a cloud of smoke and the penetrating aroma of one of the most spirited young cigars I have ever encountered; a little vulturelike man with green eyes, yellow hands, a blue suit, a red tie and gray hair.

Quite a color scheme he presented that pleasant May morning.

"Say, listen," said Archie.

It was an interesting story that he had to tell. Where he had gone wrong, it seemed, was in trying to kill two birds with one stone. There was a charming girl of his acquaintance whom he had wanted me to meet, and he also wanted me to get my nine hundred dollars, and as this girl was leaving for England the happy idea struck him to give her the check to take to me. By doing this he would avoid all chance of having the letter get lost in the post and would enable his friend to meet me in circumstances where she would catch me at my best and sunniest—viz., while fingering a check for nine hundred dollars.

But what he had failed to take into account was that she would visit Monte Carlo on her way to England. . . .

There being no southern route in those days, this surprised me a little.

"Monte Carlo?" I said.

"Monte Carlo," said Archie.

"Monte *Carlo*?" I said.

"Monte Carlo," said Archie.

"But I didn't know . . ."

"Say, listen," said Archie.

He resumed his story. Yes, she had stopped over at Monte Carlo *en route*. But even then, mind you, it would have been all right if she had been by herself. She was a nice girl, who would never have dreamed of cashing a stranger's check. But her brother was with her, and he had fewer scruples. He gambled at the tables, and lost; borrowed his sister's jewelry, pawned it, and lost again. After that, there was nothing left for him to do but fall back on my check.

"But don't you worry," said Archie. "You shall be paid. I'll pay you myself. Yessir!"

And he gave me ten dollars and told me to get my hat and come along and see editors.

Archie had magnetism. There were moments before we

separated when I almost believed that story and thought it very decent of him to let me have ten dollars. Ten dollars, I meant to say . . . just like that . . . right out of his own pocket. Pretty square.

His generalship was, I admit, consummate. He never ceased to keep moving. All that day we were dashing into elevators, dashing out, plunging into editorial offices, plunging out, leaping onto street cars, leaping out, till anything like rational and coherent thought was impossible.

He made only one tactical error. That was when he introduced me to the man to whom he had given my check.

He was an author from Kentucky. His experience had been practically identical with mine. He had sent his stories from Kentucky to a friend in New York, and the friend had handed them on to Archie, and Archie had sold them with magical skill, and then there had occurred that painful stage-wait in the matter of the cashing up. Eventually, when he was about twelve hundred dollars in the hole, the author, breathing hot Southern maledictions, packed a pistol and started for New York.

I think Archie must have been a little out of sorts the morning they met. The best he could do in the way of a story was to say he had lost the money on Wall Street. Later, he handed the Kentuckian the check he had received from the magazine for my novel, saying that he had sent me another for the same amount.

I did not see that there was anything to be done. New York at that time was full of men who did not see that there was anything to be done about Archie. He was so friendly about it all. When unmasked, he betrayed none of the baffled fury of the stage villain. He listened to you and considered the matter with his head on one side, like a vulture accused of taking an eyeball to which it was not entitled.

"Why, say, yes," he would observe at length. "Say, listen, I want to have a talk with you about that sometime."

You intimated that there was no time like the present.

You pressed him. You were keen and resolute. And then somehow—for the life of you you could not say how—you found all of a sudden that the subject of your wrongs had been shelved and that you were accepting with every sign of good-fellowship a poisonous cigar from his vest pocket.

Yes, Archie had magnetism. Clients might come in upon him like lions, but they always went out like lambs. Not till they had been out from under his influence for a good hour or so did the realization of their imbecile weakness smite them, and then it was too late. His office, when they revisited it, was empty. He was off somewhere in the great open spaces, dashing into elevators, dashing out, plunging into editorial offices, plunging out, leaping into street cars, leaping out. And if by some miracle they did get hold of him, he just stuck his head on one side.

"Why, say, yes . . ."

And all the weary work started again.

I, have often thought that King Henry the Eighth would have got on well with Archie. They had much in common. It was the practice of Henry the Eighth to "extort gifts from his subjects," which was exactly what Archie was so good at doing. The only difference between the two was that Henry appears to have confined his extorting to New Year's Day, whereas Archie was an all-the-year-round man.

I got my information about Henry the Eighth from the New Year article in the Encyclopaedia Britannica, and while doing so noticed, not for the first time, a very annoying habit of that great work of reference. I allude to the way it has of leaving off just at the point where it has got the reader all agog and excited. Thus, having mentioned that on New Year's Day, 1553, the bluff monarch got into the ribs of Cardinal Wolsey to the tune of one hundred and seventeen pounds, seventeen shillings and sixpence, it signs off, leaving the reader completely mystified. Why one-seventeen, seventeen and six? Why the seventeen bob? Why the six-pence?

The generally accepted explanation, that the King met the Cardinal in a dark alley on his way back from the bank and stood him on his head and lifted the contents of his pockets—£117.17.6—does not satisfy me. If Cardinal Wolsey had drawn a check to Self, it would have been for some less eccentric figure, and, knowing that it was New Year's Day and Henry was about, he would certainly not have gone to the bank without an armed escort. It is far more likely that he got separated from the money at the conclusion of a gay party in the small hours of the morning of January 1. The waiter came along with the death knell, and King Henry, after the usual unconvincing fumbling, told him to give it to the clerical gentleman over there in the paper hat, the one blowing the squeaker.

This would explain everything. The check came to a hundred and seventeen pounds, sixteen shillings. A shilling for the waiter and sixpence for the hat-check girl, and there you are.

Only one man ever got the better of Archie, and he, oddly enough, was not one of the tough story writers who were or had been reporters, fellows like Joe O'Brien or Charlie Somerville, but a poet. Those were the days when New York magazines had rather a weakness for short, crisp, uplift poems calling on the youth of America to throw its chest out and be up and doing with a heart for any fate. They would print these on their List of Contents page, accompanied by pictures of semi-nude men with hammers or hoes, or whatever it might be, and a magician like Archie could get a hundred dollars out of them per poem. He had got a hundred for one of this man's poems, which ran, if I remember correctly:

> *Be!*
> *Be!*
> *The past is dead,*
> *Tomorrow is not born.*
>   *Be today!*

Today!
  Be with every nerve,
  With every fiber,
  With every drop of your red blood!
Be!
Be!

and he gave him his check for it, less the customary agent's ten per cent. The poet presented the check, and it bounced back at him.

You would have said that there was nothing to be done. Nor, in the case of a prose writer, would there have been. Undoubtedly I or Charles Neville Buck, my Kentucky friend, or any of the rest of Archie's stable would have treated the thing as a routine situation and handled it in the routine way, going around to see Archie—more as a matter of form than anything—and watching him put his head on one side and proceed through the "Why, say, yes" to the orthodox cigar.

But not the poet. Following his own advice, he decided that this was a moment to be with every nerve, with every fiber, with every drop of his red blood. He gave Archie's office boy fifty cents to nose about among Archie's papers and find out what his balance at the bank was. Having learned that it was $73.60, he paid in $16.40 to his account, presented the check again and cleaned him out. Archie never really got over that. He said it wasn't the money so much, it was the principle of the thing. It hurt him, the deceit-fulness on the part of one on whom he had always looked almost as a son.

There are moments, when I am feeling particularly char-itable, when I fancy that it was in that relationship that Archie regarded all of us bright young men. I tell myself that he meant well. He knew the temptations which New York holds for the young when they have money in their pockets, and he did all that in him lay to shield us from them. What he would really have liked would have been to hold a sort of patriarchal position to his clients. He owned a shack on Staten Island, and was always very urgent in inviting each new client to live there with him. His ideal, I believe, was to have the place full of eager youngsters, all working away at their stories and running to him when they wanted a little pocket money. He would have charge of all the cash accruing from their writings and would dole it out bit by bit as needed. He succeeded in inducing few young authors to see eye to eye with him in this matter.

. . . 4   HI, BARTLETT!

1

AT THE TIME of this second visit to New York I was still on the *Globe* doing the "By the Way" column, and had come over anticipating that after nineteen days I would have to tear myself away with many a longing lingering look behind and go back to the salt mines. But on the sixth day two strange things happened. I had brought with me a couple of short stories, and Archie sold one of them to *Cosmopolitan* for $200 and the other to *Collier's Weekly* for $300, both on the same morning. And—this is the second strange thing —he not only gave me the money, but waived his commission. Yes, that man, though there were a dozen ways in which he could have used it himself, let me have the whole five hundred. Pretty heart-warming, I thought.

Another thought that came to me as I fingered the rustling bills and tried not to look at Archie, whose eyes were wet with unshed tears, for he had already started to regret, was that this was a good thing and wanted pushing along. I realized, of course, that New York was more expensive than London, but even so one could surely live there practically forever on five hundred dollars. Especially as there were always the good old *Cosmopolitan* and jolly old *Collier's Weekly* standing by with their cornucopias, all ready to start pouring. To seize pen and paper and mail my resignation to the *Globe* was with me the work of an instant. Then, bubbling over with hope and ambition, I took a room at the Hotel Duke down in Greenwich Village and settled in with a second-hand typewriter, paper, pencils, envelopes and Bartlett's book of *Familiar Quotations*, that indispensable adjunct to literary success.

I wonder if Bartlett has been as good a friend to other authors as he has been to me. I don't know where I would have been all these years without him. It so happens that I am not very bright and find it hard to think up anything really clever without assistance, but give me my Bartlett and I will slay you. How many an erudite little article of mine could not have been written without his never failing sympathy, encouragement and advice.

It has always been a puzzle to me how Bartlett did it, how he managed to compile a volume of three million quotations or whatever it is. One can see, of course, how he started. In its early stages the thing must have been reasonably simple. I picture him at a loose end one morning, going about shuffling his feet and whistling and generally messing around, and his mother said, "John, dear, I wish you wouldn't fidget like that. Why don't you find something to *do?*"

"Such as——?" said John Bartlett (born at Plymouth, Mass., in 1820).

"Dig in the garden."

"Don't want to dig in the garden."

"Or spin your top."

"Don't *want* to spin my top."

"Well, why not compile a book of familiar quotations, a collection of passages, phrases and proverbs, traced to their sources in ancient and modern literature?"

John Bartlett's face lit up. He lost that sullen look.

"Mater," he said, "I believe you've got something there. I'll do just that little thing. I see what you mean. 'To be or not to be,' and all that guff. Paper!" said John Bartlett. "Lots of paper, and can anyone lend me a pencil? California, here I come!"

So far, so good. But after that, what? Where did he go from there? You aren't going to tell me that he had all literature at his fingers' ends and knew just what Aldus Manutius said in 1472 and George M. Cohan in 1904. I suppose he went about asking people.

"Know anything good?" says John Bartlett, buttonholing an acquaintance.

"Shakespeare?"

"No, I've got Shakespeare."

"How about Pliny the Younger?"

"Never heard of him, but shoot."

"Pliny the Younger said, 'Objects which are usually the motives of our travels by land and by sea are often overlooked and neglected if they lie under our eye.'"

"He called that hot, did he?" says John Bartlett with an ugly sneer.

The acquaintance stiffens.

"If it was good enough for Pliny the Younger it ought to be good enough for a popeyed young pipsqueak born at Plymouth, Mass., in 1820."

"All right, all right, no need to get worked up about it. How are you on Pliny the Elder?"

"Pliny the Elder said, 'Everything is soothed by oil.'"

"Everything is what by *what?*"

"Soothed. By oil."

"Well, I'll bung it down," said John Bartlett dubiously, "but I don't think much of it. Ask me, the man must have been pie-eyed. Pliny the Elder should have kept off the sauce."

And so the book got written. In its original form it contained only 295 pages, but the latest edition which Christopher Morley has edited runs to one thousand two hundred and fifty-four, not counting 577 pages of index. It just shows how this quotations collecting grips you. You say to yourself that one more—as it might be "Guard us from error in narration" (Abu Mohammed Kasim Ben Ali Hariri, 1054-1122)—won't hurt you, and then you'll quit, but can you? Have you the will power to stop with Abu Mohammed Kasim Ben Ali Hariri and not go off on a regular toot with Bernard of Cluny (twelfth century) and Meir Ben Isaac Neherai (*circa* 1050)? Ah!

One rather unpleasant result of this continual bulging process is that Bartlett today has become frightfully mixed. It is like a conservative old club that has had to let down the barriers and let in a whole lot of rowdy young new members who lower the tone. There was a time when you couldn't get elected to Bartlett unless you were somebody like Richard Bethell, Lord Westbury (1800-1873), but now you never know who is going to pop out at you from its pages. Gabriel Romanovitch Derzhavin (1743-1816) often says to Alexis Charles Henri Clérel de Tocqueville (1805-1859) that it makes him good and sore.

"Heaven knows I'm no snob," he says, "but really when it comes to being expected to hobnob with ghastly outsiders like P. G. Wodehouse and the man who wrote 'Ain't It Awful, Mabel,' well, dash it!"

And Alexis Charles Henri says he knows exactly how Gabriel Romanovitch feels, and he has often felt the same way himself. They confess themselves at a loss to imagine what the world is coming to.

2

I was down having a nostalgic look at the Hotel Duke the other day, and was shocked to find that in the forty-six years during which I had taken my eye off it it had blossomed out into no end of a high-class joint with a Champagne Room or a Diamond Horseshoe or something like that where you can dance nightly to the strains of somebody's marimba band. In 1909 it was a seedy rookery inhabited by a group of young writers as impecunious as myself, and all the dancing we ever did resembled that of the lawyer in Gilbert and Sullivan[1] who danced a dance in Westminster Court like a semidespondent fury, for he thought he never would hit on a chance of addressing a British jury. We did this when we found for the nth time that Archie Fitzmaurice was not going to part with that check of ours.

We paid weekly (meals included) about what you tip the waiter nowadays after a dinner for two, and it was lucky for me that the management did not charge more. If they had, I should have been in the red at the end of the first few months. For it was not long before I made the unpleasant discovery that my stuff, though bright and grammatical, was not everybody's dish. After that promising start both *Collier's* and the *Cosmopolitan* weakened and lost their grip. It was a year before I sold another one to *Collier's* and two before the *Cosmopolitan* got the right spirit again. If it had not been for the pulps—God bless them—I should soon have been looking like an Indian famine victim.

I have written elsewhere—in a book called *Heavy Weather*, if you don't mind my slipping in a quick plug—that the ideal toward which the city fathers of all English country towns strive is to provide a public house for each individual inhabitant. It was much the same in the New York of 1909 as regarded the pulp magazines. There was practically one per person. They flooded the newsstands . . . *Munsey's*, the *Argosy*, the *All-Story*, the *Blue Book*, the *Green Book*, the *Topnotch*, *Adventure*, *Ainslee's*, the *Popular*, and a

1. *Gilbert and Sullivan:* W. S. Gilbert (1836-1911) and Arthur Sullivan (1842-1900), composers of numerous operettas.

hundred others. They all published the most ghastly slush, and they were nearly all edited by Robert H. Davis, a man who found no difficulty in springing from pulp to pulp like the chamois of the Alps from crag to crag.

I have heard Bob Davis described as a hard-boiled editor, but he never struck me in that light. More like an angel in human shape he seemed to me. It was entirely owing to him that I was able to eat at all in the years when I first became a resident of New York.

Plots were my trouble. I was handicapped as a writer by the fact that I knew nothing about anything. All the other members of my circle had backgrounds on which they could draw. Charles Neville Buck had fraternized with Kentucky mountaineers since childhood, and could produce feud stories like rabbits out of a hat. Charlie Somerville was a reporter. Roy Norton had been with Rex Beach in the Klondike. I alone had nothing to write about except what I could dig out of a brain which has never amounted to much at the best of times. The typewriter clattering in the room on the right showed that Charles Neville Buck had got to the part where Big Hank Hawkins is saying to an acquaintance whom he had never much liked: "Gol durn yuh, Rupe Tolliver, for a sneakin', ornery, low-down, double-crossin', hornswog-glin' skunk. Git out of these hyah hills or I'll drill yuh like a dog." The one clattering in the room on the left indicated that Roy Norton was back again in the dance halls of Daw-son City. And where was Wodehouse? Just sitting there twiddling his fingers. I had a certain facility for dialogue and a nice light-comedy touch—at least, I thought it was nice—but what I needed was plots, and just as I was thinking I would never get another one, I met Bob Davis.

Bob was terrific. I would look in at his office on top of the Flatiron Building and find him at an enormous desk littered with paper, a smallish, almost circular man who seemed to be quivering like a dynamo all the time with sup-

Flatiron Building, New York City, early twentieth century.

pressed nervous force, of which he must have had plenty. Anyone who is editing fifty-seven or whatever it was simultaneous pulps has need of nervous force, especially if he has that legendary figure "Mr. Munsey"[2] getting in his hair from nine in the morning till six in the evening. After a few civil exchanges—I saying "Good morning, Mr. Davis" and he damning my eyes for interrupting his work—he would get down to business.

"What on earth have you been doing all these weeks? I haven't seen a line of yours. Why aren't you writing?"

"I can't get a plot."

"Can't get a plot? Can't get a *plot*? How do you mean, you can't get a plot?"

"There aren't any."

"What sort of plot do you want?"

"Any sort of plot."

"Wait!"

He springs from behind the desk and starts to pace the room. Two turns up and down and words begin to flutter from him like bats out of a barn. Five minutes later I have the plot complete. It is probably a frightful plot and I am going to blush all the time I am writing it up, but for the completed story I shall get at least fifty and possibly seventy-five dollars.

For I was lucky to meet Bob at a time when Mr. Munsey's ideas of payment had become more lavish than they had been in the nineties. Albert Payson Terhune in his *To the Best of My Memory* tells of selling a sixty-thousand-word serial to Bob and getting $125 for it. The only full-length novel I wrote for him brought me what *Variety* would call a hotsy $2,000 and enabled me to live like a prince for a year.

Bob needed handling. He tended at times to be fussy and a perfectionist. You had to take your stuff back quite often

2. *Mr. Munsey:* publisher Frank Munsey (1854-1925).

and fix it. But much could be done with tact. Terhune discovered this. He says:

I had sent him a yarn, and he had asked me to come to his office and talk it over with him. He told me there was something radically wrong with the upbuilding of the story; something he could not put his finger on but which was sharply apparent to him. He bade me take it home and pore over it and then rewrite it from a new angle.

I took it home and I left it unread and untouched, in its envelope, for ten days. Then, without changing so much as a comma, I sent it back to him. Promptly came an acceptance, together with a note from Davis saying that I had done clever work in smoothing out the story's kinks and readjusting its angle, and that now it was wholly satisfactory. His letter ended by saying this was a proof of the advantage of taking one's time and of rewriting a tale after putting it aside for a while.

3

I wrote every kind of story for Bob. I even wrote a series of whodunits, and got a nasty shock a month or two ago when one of them appeared in one of those reprint magazines, for I had hoped that my shame was buried in the mists of time.

Not that I have anything against whodunits. Very few of them are as bad as mine. But Bob always insisted on a love interest, and where he got the idea that anyone wants a girl messing about and getting in the way when the automatics are popping I could never understand. Nobody has a greater respect than myself for girls in their proper place—if I went to a night club and found no girls there, I should be the first to complain—but I maintain that they have no business in Lascar Joe's Underground Den in Limehouse on a busy evening. Apart from anything else, Woman seems to me to lose her queenly dignity when she is being shoved into closets with a bag over her head. And something of that sort is always happening to the heroine of a gooseflesher.

For, though beautiful, with large gray eyes and hair the color of ripe wheat, she is never a very intelligent girl. She may have escaped death a dozen times. She knows the Black-bird Gang is after her to get the papers. The police may have warned her on no account to stir outside her house. But when a messenger calls at half-past two in the morning with an unsigned note saying "Come at once," she just reaches for her hat and goes. The messenger is a one-eyed fellow with a pock-marked face and an evil grin, so she trusts him immediately and, having accompanied him into the closed car with steel shutters over the windows, bowls off in it to the ruined cottage in the swamp. And when the hero, at great risk and inconvenience to himself, comes to rescue her, she will have nothing to do with him because she has been told by a chap with half a nose that it was he who murdered her brother Jim.

This girl must go. What we all liked about Sherlock Holmes[3] was his correct attitude in this matter of girls in mystery stories. True, he would permit them to call at Baker Street and tell him about the odd behavior of their uncles and stepfathers—at a pinch he might even allow them to marry Watson—but once the story was under way they had to retire into the background and stay there.

The obvious person, of course, to rid us of these girls is the villain, but experience has taught us that we cannot rely on this man. He has let us down too often, and forfeited our confidence.

The trouble with the villain of what is now called the story of suspense is that he suffers from a fatal excess of ingenuity. When he was a boy, his parents must thought-lessly have told him that he was clever, and it has absolutely spoiled him for effective work.

3. *Sherlock Holmes:* fictional detective created by Sir Arthur Conan Doyle (1859-1930).

The ordinary man, when circumstances compel him to murder a female acquaintance, borrows a pistol and does the thing in some odd five minutes of the day when he is not at the office or the pictures. He does not bother about art or technique or scientific methods. He just goes and does it. But the villain cannot understand simplicity. It never occurs to him just to point a gun at the heroine and fire it. If you told him the thing could be done that way, he would suspect you of kidding him. The only method he can imagine is to tie her in a chair, erect a tripod, place the gun on it, tie a string to the trigger, pass the string along the walls till it rests on a hook, attach another string to it, pass this over a hook, tie a brick to the second string and light a candle under it. He has got the thing reasoned out. The candle will burn the second string, the brick will fall, and the weight will tighten the first string, thus pulling the trigger and completing a neat job.

Then somebody comes along and blows the candle out. I have known a villain to sit the heroine on a keg of gunpowder and expect it to be struck by lightning. You can't run a business that way.

Still, I suppose it is no use getting cross with the poor fellows. They are doing their best according to their lights. It is simply that they are trying to tackle a highly specialized job without the requisite training. What the villain needs to do is to forget all he thinks he knows and go right back to the beginning and start learning his ABC. He requires careful schooling.

The keynote of the curriculum of this school for villains would be the inculcation of simplicity and directness. For quite a while he would confine himself to swatting flies. The average villain's impulse, if called upon to kill a fly, would be to saw away the supports of the floor, tie a string across the doorway, and then send the fly an anonymous letter telling it to come at once in order to hear of something to its advantage. The idea being that it would hurry to the

room, trip over the string, fall on the floor, tumble into the
depths and break its neck.

That, to the villain's mind, is not merely the simplest, it
is the only way of killing flies. And the hardest task facing
the kindergarten authorities would be to persuade him that
excellent results may be obtained through the medium of a
rolled-up copy of the *Saturday Evening Post*. What these
men have got to learn is that the best way of disposing of a
girl with hair the color of ripe wheat is to hit that hair as
hard as possible with a section of gas pipe. Buying scorpions
to put in her bag or little-known Asiatic poisons with which
to smear her lipstick does no good whatever and only adds
to the overhead.

. . . 5   PUT ME AMONG THE EARLS

1

WELL, what with this and what with that, all right so far, I
felt, but the fact that I was able to pay my weekly bill at the
Duke and could sometimes—very occasionally—lunch at the
Brevoort did not satisfy me. I wanted something much more
in the nature of a Horatio Alger[1] success story, and I would
be deceiving my public if I were to say that I did not chafe.
I chafed very frequently. "What are you making of this life
of yours, Wodehouse?" I would often say to myself, and
it seemed to me that the time had come to analyze and evaluate
my position with a view to taking prompt steps through the
proper channels.

Quite suddenly I spotted what was wrong. It came to me
like a flash one morning when I was having a malted milk
shake at the drugstore around the corner. I had been labeling my stories "by P. G. Wodehouse" and this at a time

---

1. *Horatio Alger:* American author (1834-1899) who usually wrote stories
about poor boys becoming rich.

when a writer who went about without three names was practically going around naked. Those were the days of Richard Harding Davis, of Margaret Culkin Banning, of James Warner Bellah, of Earl Derr Biggers, of Charles Francis Coe, Norman Reilly Raine, Mary Roberts Rinehart, Clarence Budington Kelland and Orison Swett—yes, really, I'm not kidding—Marden. And here was I, poor misguided fool, trying to crash the gate with a couple of contemptible initials.

No wonder the slicks would not take my work. In anything like a decent magazine I would have stood out as conspicuously as a man in a seersucker suit at the first night of the Opera.

It frequently happens that when you get an inspiration, you don't stop there but go right ahead and get another. It was so with me now. Scarcely had the last remains of the milk shake gurgled up through the straw when I was telling myself that I had been all wrong in thinking that I knew nothing about anything. I knew quite a lot about English country-house life with its earls and butlers and younger sons, and it was quite possible—though I recognized this question as a very moot one—that the American magazine public would like to read about them. Worth trying, anyway.

Two days later I was typing on a clean white page

SOMETHING NEW
BY
Pelham Grenville Wodehouse

And I had a feeling that I was going to hit the jackpot. It seemed incredible to me that all this while I should have been chucking away an income-producing combination like Pelham Grenville Wodehouse. It put me right up there with Harry Leon Wilson, David Graham Phillips, Arthur Somers Roche and Hugh McNair Kahler.

If you ask me to tell you frankly if I like the name Pelham Grenville Wodehouse, I must confess that I do not. I have my dark moods when it seems to me about as low as you can get. I was named after a godfather, and not a thing to show for it but a small silver mug. But I was born at a time when children came to the font not knowing what might not happen to them before they were dried off and taken home. My three brothers were christened respectively Philip Peveril, Ernest Armine and Lancelot Deane, so I was probably lucky not to get something wished on me like Hyacinth Augustus or Albert Prince Consort. And say what you will of Pelham Grenville, shudder though you may at it, it changed the luck. *Something New* was bought as a serial by the *Saturday Evening Post,* and they paid me three thousand five hundred dollars for it, if you can believe there is that much money in the world. It was the first of the series which I may call the Blandings Castle Saga, featuring Clarence, ninth Earl of Emsworth, his son the Hon. Freddie Threepwood and his butler Beach, concerning whom I have since written so much.

Too much, carpers have said. So have cavilers, and they are probably correct. Except for the tendency to write articles about the Modern Girl and allow his side whiskers to grow, there is nothing an author today has to guard himself against more carefully than the Saga habit. He writes a story. Another story dealing with the same characters occurs to him, and he writes that. He feels that just one more won't hurt him, and he writes a third. And before he knows it, he is down with a Saga and no cure in sight.

This is what happened to me with Lord Emsworth and the Blandings Castle set and later on with Jeeves and Bertie Wooster. Beginning with *Something New,* I went on to *Leave It to Psmith,* then to *Fish Preferred,* after that to *Heavy Weather, Blandings Castle, The Crime Wave at Blandings, Uncle Fred in the Springtime, Full Moon* and *Pigs Have Wings.* And to show the habit-forming nature of the drug, while it was eight years after *Something New* before the *Leave It to Psmith* urge gripped me, only eighteen months elapsed between *Fish Preferred* and *Heavy Weather.*

In a word, once a man who could take it or leave it alone,
I had become an addict.

2

A critic, with whose name I will not sully my typewriter—
he has probably by now been eaten by bears like the children
who made mock of the prophet Elisha—was giving me the
sleeve across the windpipe the other day for this tendency
of mine to write so much about members of the British
peerage. Specifically, he accused me of an undue fondness
for earls.

Well, of course, now that I come to tot up the score, I
realize that in the course of my literary career I have fea-
tured quite a number of these fauna, but as I often say—well,
perhaps once a month—why not? I see no objection to earls.
A most respectable class of men they seem to me. And one
admires their spirit. I mean, while some, of course, have come
up the easy way, many have had the dickens of a struggle
starting at the bottom of the ladder as mere Hons., having
to go in to dinner after the Vice-Chancellor of the Duchy
of Lancaster and all that sort of thing.

Show me the Hon. who by pluck and determination has
raised himself from the depths, step by step, till he has become entitled to keep a coronet on the hat peg in the downstairs closet, and I will show you a man of whom any author
might be proud to write.

Earls on the whole have made a very good showing in
fiction. With baronets setting them a bad example by being
almost uniformly steeped in crime, they have preserved a
gratifying high standard of behavior. There is seldom anything wrong with the earl in fiction, if you don't mind a
touch of haughtiness and a tendency to have heavy eyebrows and draw them together in a formidable frown, like
the one in *Little Lord Fauntleroy*.[2] And in real life I can

2. *Little Lord Fauntleroy:* novel by Frances Hodgson Burnett (1849-1924).

think of almost no earls whose hearts were not as pure and fair as those of dwellers in the lowlier air of Seven Dials.

English literature, lacking earls, would have been a great deal poorer. Shakespeare would have been lost without them. Everyone who has written for the theater knows how difficult it is to get people off the stage unless you can think of a good exit speech. That is why, as you pass through Greenwich Village and other literary quarters, you see haggard men wandering about and sticking straws in their hair as they mutter:

> "Life, dear lady, is like . . ."
> "Life, dear lady . . ."
> "Dear lady, I have but two objections to life . . .
> One is that it . . ."

Than which nothing is sadder.

Shakespeare had no such problem. With more earls than he knew what to do with, he was on velvet. One need only quote those well-known lines from his Henry VII, Part One:

> My Lord of Sydenham, bear our royal word
> To Brixton's Earl, the Earl of Wormwood Scrubs,
> Our faithful liege, the Earl of Dulwich (East),
> And those of Beckenham, Penge and Peckham Rye,
> Together with the Earl of Hampton Wick;
> Bid them to haste like cats when struck with brick,
> For they are needed in our battle line,
> And stitch in time doth ever save full nine.
> (*Exeunt Omnes.*[3] *Trumpets and hautboys.*)

"Pie!" Shakespeare used to say to Burbage,[4] and Burbage would agree that Shakespeare earned his money easily.

A thing about earls I have never understood, and never liked to ask anyone for fear of betraying my ignorance, is

---

3. *Exeunt omnes:* Latin for *Exit all* (a stage direction).
4. *Burbage:* Richard Burbage (1567-1619), chief actor and manager of the theatrical company to which Shakespeare was attached.

why one earl is the Earl of Whoosis and another earl just
Earl Smith. I have an idea—I may be wrong—that the "of"
boys have a social edge on the others, like the aristocrats in
Germany who are able to call themselves "Von." One can
picture the Earl of Berkeley Square being introduced to
Earl Piccadilly at a cocktail party. The host says, "Oh, Percy,
I want you to meet Earl Piccadilly," and hurries away to
attend to his other guests. There is a brief interval during
which the two agree that this is the rottenest party they were
ever at and possibly exchange a remark or two about the
weather, then the Earl of Berkeley Square says, "I didn't
quite get the name. Earl of Piccadilly, did he say?"

"No, just Earl Piccadilly."

The Earl of Berkeley Square starts. A coldness creeps into
his manner.

"You mean *plain* Earl Piccadilly?"

"That's right."

"No 'of'?"

"No, no 'of.' "

There is a tense silence. You can see the Earl of Berkeley
Square's lip curling.

"Ah, well," he says at length, with a nasty little snigger,
"it takes all sorts to make a world, does it not?" and Earl
Piccadilly slinks off with his ears pinned back and drinks
far too many martinis in the hope of restoring his self-respect.
Practically all the earls who are thrown sobbing out of cocktail parties are non-*of*s. They can't take it, poor devils.

3

Twenty-one of my books were serialized in the *Saturday
Evening Post*. For the first one, as I say, I received $3,500,
for the second they raised me to $5,000, for the third to
$7,500, for the fourth to $10,000. That was when I felt safe
in going back to "P. G. Wodehouse."

It caused, of course, a good deal of consternation in the office. I am not sure whether there was a sharp drop in the circulation and advertisement figures, but the boys in Independence Square were badly shaken. Nevertheless, for the last twelve I got $40,000 per. Nice going, of course, and the stuff certainly came in handy, but I have always been alive to the fact that I am not one of the real big shots. I don't expect to go down in legend and song. I don't get nearly enough letters from admirers.

As everybody knows, an author's standing is estimated by the number of letters he receives from readers. It is the equivalent of the Hooper rating of television, and I have often felt sorry for men like Cicero and Diogenes Laertius,[5] who wrote in the days before the post office came into existence. They could never tell for certain when they had pushed their work across and made a solid hit with the public.

Diogenes Laertius, of course, had a few friends who thought he was great—or, at any rate, told him so when they had made quite sure he was picking up the tab for the round of Falernian wine, and sometimes a kindly senator would pat Cicero on the shoulder in the Campus Martius and say "I liked that last little thing of yours, Tullius; I can't remember what it was called. Are you writing anything now?" But getting right down to it, they were simply working in the dark, and it must have been discouraging for them.

There is no point on which your modern author is more touchy than this thing of testimonials from the public. You will see John P. Marquand saunter up to Erle Stanley Gardner and speak with an ill-assumed carelessness.

"You don't happen to know of a good secretary, do you, Stan?" he says. "I've been caught short, confound it. Mine has just got typist's cramp, answering letters from admirers of my books, and more pouring in daily."

"John," says Erle Stanley Gardner, "you know me. If I

5. *Cicero and Diogenes Laertius:* ancient Roman writers.

could help you out, I would do it like a shot. But I'm in just
the same jam myself. Both my secretaries collapsed this morning and are in the hospital with ice packs on their heads. I've
never known the fan mail heavier."

"Look here," says Marquand abruptly, "how many fan
letters did you get last week?"

"How many did you?" says Gardner.

"I asked you first," says Marquand, and they part on bad
terms.

And in another corner of the room Mickey Spillane rising
and walking away in a marked manner from Frances Parkin-
son Keyes.[6]

Going by this test, I should describe myself as a sort of
fair to medium, not on the one hand a socko and yet, on the
other, not laying a definite egg. The books I write seem to
appeal to a rather specialized public. Invalids read me. So
do convicts. And I am all right with the dog stealers. As
regards Obuasie I am not so sure.

From Obuasie (wherever that is) there reached me a short
while ago the following letter:

Dear Sir.
I have heard your name and address highly have been recommended to me by a certain friend of mine that you are the
best merchant in your city New York. So I want you to send
me one of your best catalogues and I am ready to deal with you
until I shall go into the grave. Soon as possible send me early.

Now it is difficult to know just what to make of a letter
like that. At first glance it would seem as if I had Obuasie
in my pocket. But there is always the possibility that some
confusion has arisen and that my correspondent is under
the impression that I deal in something quite different from
what I do deal in, whatever you may call it. Misunderstand-
ings so easily occur at a distance. One remembers the story

6. *Marquand . . . Gardner . . . Spillane . . . Keyes:* popular contemporary
writers.

of the drummer who traveled in cement docks and would often dash halfway across the world on hearing that there was a demand for his wares in Tierra del Fuego or Spitzbergen, only to discover, after he had dragged his bag of samples all that weary way, that what the natives wanted was not docks but socks.

Better, perhaps, then, for the moment not to get my publishers to flood Obuasie with my books, but to stick to the invalids and the convicts, who, with the dog stealers, surely make up a public quite large enough for any author who is not utterly obsessed by the lust for gold. Money isn't everything.

My popularity with invalids puts me in something of a quandary. Naturally I like my stories to be read as widely as possible, but, kindhearted by nature, I do not feel altogether happy when I gather that some form of wasting sickness is an essential preliminary to their perusal. And such seems to be the case.

I can understand it, of course. When you are fit and strong, you go about with your chin up and your chest out, without a single morbid tendency. "I feel great," you say, "so why should I deliberately take the sunshine out of life by reading Wodehouse?" And you don't. But comes a day when the temperature begins to mount, the tonsils to ache and dark spots to float before the eyes. Then somehow or other you find one of my books by your bedside, and the next thing you know you are reading it. And you go on reading it till health and sanity return.

It is not difficult to see what a dilemma this places me in. I need readers, and in order to have readers I must have invalids. And as soon as they become convalescent, I lose them. If you want to see a mind in a ferment of doubt and indecision, take a look at mine when the papers announce that another epidemic has broken out and hundreds are taking to their beds. One moment I am thinking how sad it all is, the next saying "My Public!" and wondering what the royalties will amount to.

But, you will say, why bother about the invalids if you have the dog stealers behind you? And here I am faced by a somewhat embarrassing confession. When I said I was read by dog stealers, I was swanking.[7] It is not a solid *bloc* of dog stealers who enjoy my work, but one solitary dog stealer and—a galling thought—a rotten dog stealer at that, for he specifically admits to having been arrested and imprisoned. And, further, I cannot help feeling that his motives in writing to me were mixed. It was not, I suspect, simply a gush of admiration for my artistry that led him to pen that letter but also the hope—expressed in his letter—that I would give him a sum of money sufficient to enable him to start a street bookmaker's business. And even if I am wronging him in this the outlook seems to me most unpromising. The more I think over his letter, the less confident do I feel that the man is going to be a steady source of income to me down the years.

It is no good kidding oneself. The way I figure it out is that in order to buy my books he will have to steal dogs, and he will certainly not steal dogs in anything like the necessary quantity unless he develops considerably more skill and know-how than he now possesses. He might have a good year, when the dogs came briskly in and he felt himself in a position not only to buy his own copy but to send others as birthday presents to his friends, but the chances are far greater that his crude and bungling methods will lead to another arrest, and what use will he be to me, shut off from the bookstores just when my new novel needs support to make it go? As a commercial proposition I can only write him down as shaky, and it would probably be sounder bookkeeping to take him out of the dog-stealer column and lump him in with the convicts.

7. *Swanking:* boasting excessively.

I have had so many letters over the years from convicts that I have begun to think that the American criminal must look on one or more of my works as an essential part of his kit. I seem to see the burglar's mother sending him off for the night shift.

"Another glass of hot milk, Clarence?"

"No, thank you, Mother. I must be going."

"Yes, it is getting late. Are you well wrapped up?"

"Yes, Mother."

"Wearing your warm underclothing?"

"Yes, Mother."

"Have you everything you need? Gat?[8] Brass knucks? Wodehouse novel? Oxyacetylene blowpipe? Trinitrotoluol? Mask?"

"Yes, Mother."

"Then heaven speed you, boy, and always remember what your dear father used to say: 'Tread lightly, read your Wodehouse, save your pennies and the dollars will take care of themselves.' "

There was a bank robber in Chicago not long ago who in a fit of preoccupation caused by business worries imprudently took with him by mistake a book of light essays by Frank Sullivan. The shock of discovering his blunder, when he opened the volume to go on with Chapter Eleven, so unnerved him that he missed the policeman at three yards and was expelled from his gang in disgrace. You cannot be too careful if you wish to succeed in a difficult and overcrowded profession.

. . . 6   THE METEORITE RACKET

1

But though my public is, as I have said, a limited one, I have never been sorry that I became a writer. Taking it by and

8. *Gat:* gun.

large, I have not done so badly. Certainly a good deal better than I would have done in some of the other professions. I am thinking at the moment of the secondhand bridge business, snail-gathering and getting hit in the stomach by meteorites.

The secondhand bridge racket attracts many because at first sight it looks like finding money in the street. You get anything from $125,000 for a used bridge, but—and here is the catch—it is by no means everybody who wants a used bridge. They were trying to sell the one on Third Avenue over the Harlem River the other day, and despite all the efforts of the auctioneers to sales-talk the customers into scaring the moths out of their pocketbooks no one would bid a nickel for it.

It was a good bridge, too. It had four trusses and between the trusses three lanes for vehicular traffic, and was capable of carrying a hundred thousand vehicles and five hundred thousand pedestrians daily. "Give it to your girl for Christmas and watch her face light up," said the advertisements, but nothing doing. It went begging.

Snail-gathering, which flourishes mostly in Austria, if you can call it flourishing, is another profession into which I doubt if I would put any son of mine. I was shocked to learn the other day that the Austrian boys who track the creatures down get only a shilling a pound for them. (It should be schilling, but I can't do the dialect.)

I don't know how many snails go to the pound, for it must vary a good deal according to their size and robustness. You get great, big, hulking snails, the sort of snails whose friends call them Butch and Fatso, and conversely you get wan, wizened little snails which have stunted their growth with early cigarette smoking. But, be that as it may, two or three hundred pounds of them must take quite a bit of assembling, and I think that what the Austrians call schnirkel-schnecke gatherers come under the head of sweated labor. Yet Austrian fathers are rather pleased when their sons tell them that that is the walk in life which they have chosen.

"Pop," say the Austrian son, "I want to be a schnirkel-schnecke gatherer."

"Capital, capital (*Das Kapital, Das Kapital*)," says the Austrian father, and tells him to start right in.

A misguided policy, it seems to me, because when the schnirkel-schneckes are sold to a French restaurant, the French restaurant gets about $280.01 for the same amount of schnirkel-schneckes for which the schnirkel-schnecke gatherers got about $27.45, leaving the latter down a matter of $252.56. (Check these figures.) Obviously what the boy ought to do is get a job in a French restaurant, marry the boss's daughter and become a part proprietor.

I don't see there is much future, either, in the getting-hit-in-the-stomach-by-meteorites racket.

Yes, I know what you are going to say. You are going to tell me that down in Sylacauga, Alabama, last year, Mrs. Ann Elizabeth Hodges, as she lay on the sofa in her living room, was hit in the stomach by a meteorite which came in via the roof, and sold it—the meteorite—for $2,700 to a Montana museum.

"Reason it out," I can hear you saying. "Two thousand seven hundred smackers, and all that from one meteorite, mark you. A meteorite a day—"

"—keeps the doctor away. True. So far I am with you. But——"

"At $2,700 per meteorite per person per day, that would be $985,500 a year—or in Leap Year $988,200. That's nice money."

"Ah," I reply, "but have you considered that whole days might pass without your getting hit in the stomach by a meteorite? They are most unreliable things. Capricious. You can't count on them. There must be dozens of people in America who have not been hit in the stomach by a meteorite and quite likely will not be."

"I never thought of that," you say, and you go off and become an average adjuster and do well.

And meanwhile Mrs. Ann Elizabeth Hodges, in the suit of chain mail which she now habitually wears, is lying on her sofa in Sylacauga, Alabama, looking up at the ceiling and hoping for the best. Good luck, Mrs. Hodges. I think you are living in a fool's paradise, but nevertheless good luck.

2

Yes, I am glad I stuck to writing, even though I have never succeeded in reaching the heights. I suppose, if you come right down to it, that I am to literature about what Pinky Lee[1] is to television. I go in for what is known in the trade as "light writing," and those who do that—humorists they are sometimes called—are looked down upon by the intelligentsia and sneered at. One of them of my acquaintance was referred to in a weekly paper not long ago as "that burbling pixie." Well, you can't go calling a man a burbling pixie without lowering his morale. He frets. He refuses to eat his cereal. He goes about with his hands in his pockets, kicking stones. The next thing you know, he is writing thoughtful novels analyzing social conditions, and you are short another humorist. With things going the way they are, it won't be long before the species dies out. Already what was once a full-throated chorus has faded into a few scattered chirps. Now and then you can still hear from the thicket the gay note of the Perelman,[2] piping as the linnets do, but Perelman can't go on forever, and then what?

I recently edited an anthology of the writings of American humorists, and was glad to do so, for I felt that such publications ought to be encouraged. Publish an anthology of their writings, and you revive the poor drooping souls like watered flowers. The pleasant surprise of finding that somebody loves

1. *Pinky Lee:* television master-of-ceremonies for children's programs in the 1950's.
2. *Perelman:* S. J. Perelman, humorous essayist; author of *The Road to Miltown* and other works.

them makes them feel that it is not such a bad little world after all, and they pour their dose of strychnine back into the bottle and go out into the sunlit street through the door instead of, as they had planned, through the seventh-story window. Being asked for contributions to the book I have mentioned was probably the only nice thing that had happened to these lepers since 1937.

Three suggestions as to why "light writing" has almost ceased to be have been made—one by myself, one by the late Russell Maloney and one by Wolcott Gibbs. Here is mine for what it is worth.

Humorists, as I see it, have always been looked askance at, if not actually viewed with concern. At English schools in my boyhood they were divided into two classes, both unpopular. If you merely talked amusingly, you were a "silly jackass." ("You *are* a silly jackass!" was the formula.) If your conversation took a mordant and satirical turn, you were a "funny swine." And whichever you were, you were scorned and despised and lucky not to get kicked. It is to this early discouragement that I attribute the fact that no Englishman, grown to man's estate, ever says anything brighter than "Eh, what?" and "Most extraordinary."

Russell Maloney's theory is that a humorist has to be a sort of dwarf. In the Middle Ages, he points out, the well-bred and well-to-do considered nothing so funny as a man who was considerably shorter than they were, or at least cultivated a deceptive stoop. Today the humors of maladjustment have succeeded the humors of deformity, and they want you to be neurotic. If you aren't neurotic, you simply don't rate. And the reason why there are so few humorists nowadays is that it is virtually impossible to be neurotic when you have only to smoke any one of a dozen brands of cigarettes or eat any one of a dozen brands of breakfast food to be in glowing health both physically and mentally. If I have tried once to be neurotic, I have tried a hundred times, but no luck. Just when I thought I was beginning to get somewhere, I would smoke a Fortunate or take a spoonful of Cute Crispies, and back to where I had started.

What Wolcott Gibbs thinks—and what Wolcott Gibbs thinks today Manchester thinks tomorrow—is that the shortage is due to the fact that the modern tendency is to greet the humorist, when he dares to let out a bleat, with a double whammy from a baseball bat. In the past ten years, he says, the humorist has become increasingly harried and defensive, increasingly certain that the minute he raises his foolish head the hot-eyed crew will be after him, denouncing him as a fiddler while Rome burns. Naturally after one or two experiences of this kind he learns sense.

Gibbs, I think, is right. Humorists have been scared out of the business by the touchiness now prevailing in every section of the community.

"Never," said Robert C. Ruark in the *World-Telegram* not long ago, "have I heard so much complaining as I have heard this year. My last month's mail has contained outraged yelps on pieces I have written concerning dogs, diets, ulcers, cats and kings. I wrote a piece laughing at the modern tendency of singers to cry, and you would have thought I had assaulted womanhood."

A few days before the heavyweight championship fight between Rocky Marciano and Roland La Starza, an Australian journalist who interviewed the latter was greatly struck by his lucid replies to questions.

"Roland," he wrote, "is a very intelligent young man. He has brains. Though it may be," he added, "that I merely think he has because I have been talking so much of late to tennis players. Tennis players are just one cut mentally above the wallaby."[3]

I have never met a wallaby, so cannot say from personal knowledge how abundantly—or poorly—equipped such animals are with the little gray cells, but of one thing I am

3. *Wallaby:* small kangaroo.

sure and that is that letters poured in on the writer from Friends of the Wallaby, the International League for Promoting Fair Play for Wallabies and so on, protesting against the injustice of classing them lower in the intellectual scale than tennis players. Pointing out, no doubt, that while the average run-of-the-mill wallaby was perhaps not an Einstein, it would never dream of bounding about the place shouting "forty love" and similar ill-balanced observations.

I don't know what is to be done about it. It is what the French would call an impasse. Only they say amh-parrse. Silly, of course, but you know what Frenchmen are. (And now to await the flood of stinkers from Faure, Pinay, Maurice Chevalier, Mendès-France, Oo-La-La and Indignant Parisienne.)

They say it is possible even today to be funny about porcupines and remain unscathed, but I doubt it. Just try it and see how quickly you get a stream of letters beginning:

"Sir:
    With reference to your recent tasteless and uncalled-for comments on the porcupine . . ."

A writer in one of the daily papers was satirical the other day about oysters, and did he get jumped on! A column-long letter next morning from Oyster Lover, full of the bitterest invective. And the same thing probably happened to the man who jocularly rebuked a trainer of performing fleas for his rashness in putting them through their paces while wearing a beard. Don't tell me there is not some league or society for the protection of bearded flea trainers watching over their interests and defending them from ridicule.

In short, I do not think I am putting it too strongly when I say that things have come to a pretty pass.

"What we need in this country," said Robert Benchley[4]

4. *Robert Benchley:* American humorist, author, and movie personality (1889-1945).

in one of his thoughtful essays, "is fewer bridges and more fun." And how right he was, as always. We have the Triborough Bridge, the George Washington Bridge, the Fifty-ninth Street Bridge, auction bridge, contract bridge, Senator Bridges and Bridgehampton, Long Island, but where's the fun?

When I first came to America, everyone was gay and lighthearted. Each morning and evening paper had its team of humorists turning out daily masterpieces in prose and verse. Magazines printed a couple of funny short stories and a comic article in every number. Publishers published humorous books. It was the golden age, and I think it ought to be brought back. I want to see an S. J. Perelman on every street corner, a Bob Benchley in every drugstore. It needs only a little resolution on the part of the young writers and a touch of the old broad-mindedness among editors.

And if any young writer with a gift for being funny has got the idea that there is something undignified and antisocial about making people laugh, let him read this from the Talmud,[5] a book which, one may remind him, was written in an age just as grim as this one.

. . . And Elijah said to Berokah "These two will also share in the world to come." Berokah then asked them "What is your occupation?" They replied "We are merrymakers. When we see a person who is downcast, we cheer him up." These two were among the very select few who would inherit the Kingdom of Heaven.

. . . 7   TO THE CRITICS, THESE PEARLS

1

I HAD SCARCELY typed that passage referring to the critic who complained of my writing too much about earls when I opened a weekly paper and darned if another critic hadn't

5. *Talmud:* ancient Hebrew commentaries.

started a second front and was complaining of my writing too much about butlers. "It is time that Mr. Wodehouse realized," he said, "that Jeeves has become a bore." (Not that Jeeves is a butler. He is a gentleman's personal gentleman.) I shall, of course, reply to this hellhound the moment I can get around to it, and I shall not mince my words.

Having now reached the stage—one foot in the grave and the other not far off it—where I can legitimately get pompous and start giving advice to the youngsters, I would urge what are sometimes called commencing authors to make up their minds as soon as possible as to what is to be their attitude toward the critics.

Many people would counsel the young author to ignore hostile criticism, but to my thinking this is cowardly and he will be missing a lot of fun. An unfavorable review should be answered promptly with a carefully composed letter, which can be either (a) conciliatory or (b) belligerent.

Specimen A. The Conciliatory

Dear Mr. Worthington,

Not "Sir." "Sir" is abrupt. And, of course, don't say "Mr. Worthington" if the fellow's name is Schwartz or Heffelfinger. Use your intelligence, Junior. I am only sketching the thing out on broad lines.

Dear Mr. Worthington,

I was greatly impressed by your review in the *Booksy Weekly* of my novel *Whither If Anywhere* in which you say that my construction is lamentable, my dialogue leaden and my characters stuffed with sawdust, and advise me to give up writing and get a job in a putty-knife factory.

Oddly enough, I do have a job in a putty-knife factory. I write in the evenings, and I should hate to give it up, and I feel sure that, now that I have read your most erudite and helpful criticisms, I can correct the faults you mention and gradually improve my output until it meets with your approval. (And I need scarcely say that I would rather have the approval of

Eustace Worthington than that of any other man in the world, for I have long been a sincere admirer of your brilliant work.)

I wonder if you would care to have lunch with me sometime and go further into the matter of my book and its many defects. Shall we say the Colony some day next week?

Yours faithfully,

G. G. Simmons

P. S. What an excellent article that was of yours in the *Police Gazette* some weeks ago on "The Disintegration of Reality in the Interest of the Syncretic Principle." I could hardly wait to see how it all came out.

P.P.S. Are you fond of caviar?

P.P.P.S. I will see if I can get the Duke of Windsor to come along. I know how much he would like to meet you.

This is good and nearly always makes friends and influences people, but I confess that I prefer the other kind, the belligerent. This is possibly because the Wodehouses are notoriously hot-blooded. (It was a Wodehouse who in the year 1911 did seven days in the county jail—rather than pay a fine—for failing to abate a smoky chimney.)

Specimen B. The Belligerent

Sir:

Not "Dear Sir." Weak. And not "You louse," which is strong but a little undignified. Myself, I have sometimes used "You fatheaded fool," but I prefer "Sir."

Sir:

So you think my novel *Storm over Flatbush* would disgrace a child of three with water on the brain, do you? Who are you to start shooting off your head, you contemptible hack? If you were any good, you wouldn't be writing book reviews for a rag like the one you befoul with your idiotic contributions, the circulation of which, I happen to know, is confined exclusively to inmates of Bloomingdale[1] and members of the proprietor's family.

---

1. *Bloomingdale:* mental hospital in upper New York State.

Your opinion, may I add, would carry greater authority with me, did I not know, having met people who (with difficulty) tolerate your society, that you still owe your tailor for that pair of trousers he made for you in the spring of 1946 and that the lady who presides over the boarding house which you infest is threatening, if you don't pay six weeks' back rent soon, to throw you out on the seat of them.

Yours faithfully,

CLYDE WEATHERBEE

P.S. *Where were you on the night of June the fifteenth?*

Now that's good. That cleanses the bosom of the perilous stuff that weighs upon the heart. But don't send this kind of letter to the editor of the paper, because editors always allow the critic to shove in a reply in brackets at the end of it, thus giving him the last word.

2

As a matter of fact, though, I was quite pleased to come across that slam at Jeeves, for I have felt for some time that something should be done to restore vigor and vitality to literary criticism, and this seemed to show that here and there traces of the old rugged spirit still lingered. Too many critics today are gentle souls who would not harm so much as a minor poet. But when I was a young man they lived on raw meat, and an author who published a book did so at his own risk. If he got by without severe contusions of his self-respect, he knew that he must be pretty good. And if the reception of his first novel left him feeling as if he had been drawn through a wringer or forcibly unclothed in public, that was an excellent thing for his art. It put him on his toes. If he had the right stuff in him, he persevered. If he hadn't, he gave it up.

But nowadays reviewers are all sweetness and light, and the question "Have you read any good books lately?" is one which it is impossible to answer, for there are no good books now—only superb books, astounding books, richly rewarding books, vitally significant books and books which we are not ashamed to say brought tears to our eyes.

Some people (who ought to blush for themselves) say that the reason for this tidal wave of amiability is the fact that reviewers today are all novelists themselves, and this tempers their acerbity. Old Bill, they argue, who does the literary page of *The Scrutineer*, is not going to jump on Old Joe's *Sundered Souls* when he knows that his own *Through a Mist Darkly* is coming out next week and that Joe does the book column in *The Spokesman*.

This, of course, is not so. Nobody who really knows reviewers and their flaming integrity would believe it for a moment. It is with genuine surprise that William, having added *Sundered Souls* to the list of the world's masterpieces, finds that Joseph, a week later, has done the same to *Through a Mist Darkly*. An odd coincidence, he feels.

No, the whole trouble is that critics today, with the exception of a few of the younger set who have an unpleasant downy growth alongside the ears, are all clean-shaven, whereas those of a more virile age let the jungle in. The Edinburgh reviewers were beavers to a man, and everybody knows how bitter they were.

Whether they were bitter because they had beards or grew beards because they were bitter is beside the point. The fact remains that all the great literary rows you read about were between men who looked like English sheep dogs. They used to get into fights in clubs, and roll about on the floor, clawing at each other's beards, thereby increasing the gaiety of nations more than somewhat.

The connection between superfluous hair and caustic criticism is not hard to understand. There is probably nothing which so soothes a man and puts him in a frame of mind to see only good in everything as a nice clean shave. He

feels his smooth, pink cheeks, and the milk of human kindness begins to gurgle within him. "What a day!" he says, as
he looks out of window. "What eggs! What bacon!" he says,
as he starts his breakfast. And, if he is a literary critic, "What
a book!" he feels as he leafs through the pages of the latest
ghastly effort of some author who ought to be selling coals
instead of writing novels. And with tears dripping from the
end of his nose he records this opinion in his column.

But let a man omit to shave, even for a single day, and
mark the result. He feels hot and scrubby. Within twelve
hours his outlook has become jaundiced and captious. If
his interests lie in the direction of politics, he goes out and
throws a bomb at someone. If he is an employer of labor,
he starts a lockout. If he is a critic, he sits down to write his
criticism with the determination that by the time he has finished the author will know he has been in a fight.

You have only to look about you to appreciate the truth
of this. All whiskered things are testy and short-tempered—
pumas, wildcats, the late Karl Marx[2] and, in the mating season,
shrimps. Would Ben Jonson[3] have knifed a man on account
of some literary disagreement if he had not been bearded to
the eyebrows? Can you imagine a nation of spruce, clean-
shaven Bolsheviks, smelling of Mennen's skin lotion? There
is only one thing to be done. We must go back to whiskers.
And there must be no half-measures.

It is not enough to have a beard like Rex Stout's,[4] which,
though technically a beard, is not bushy enough to sour the
natural kindliness of his disposition. We must have the old
Assyrian grogans, the great, cascading, spade-shaped things
the old Victorians grew—whether under glass or not has
never been ascertained. Then we shall begin to get somewhere.

I realize that I shall suffer from the change. Thre will be
no more of those eulogies of my work like "8 by 10½, 315

2. *Karl Marx:* founder of modern communism (1818-1883).
3. *Ben Jonson:* English poet, playwright, and critic (1573-1637).
4. *Rex Stout:* contemporary mystery writer.

pp.," which I have been pasting into my scrapbook for so many years. But I am prepared to sacrifice myself for the sake of literature, and I know that a general outcropping of spinach among critics would raise the whole standard of writing.

A young author would think twice before starting his introspective novel of adolescence if he knew that it would be handed over for review to somebody who looked like Wilkie Collins[5] at the age of sixteen. Nervous women would stop writing altogether, and what a break that would be for the reading public. The only novelists who would carry on would be the small, select group of tough eggs who had what it takes.

And it is useless for the critics to protest their inability to fall in with the idea. It is perfectly easy to grow whiskers. There used to be a whiskered all-in wrestler called Man Mountain Dean. He did it. Are our reviewers going to tell me that they are inferior in will power and determination to an all-in wrestler?

Tush!

If I have seemed to speak warmly on this subject, it is because it is one on which I hold very strong views. I have embodied these in a lyric which I am sure you will all want to hear. It is supposed to be sung by a small bearded man who goes to a party and they ask him to sing, and he says Oh, I can't, and they say Oh, do, and he says the only thing he can sing is a song about whiskers, so they say All right, sing a song about whiskers. And he clears his throat and says "Mi-mi-mi" a couple of times in an undertone, and begins:

> The world is in a mess today,
> Damn sight worse than yesterday,
> And getting a whole lot worser right along.

5. *Wilkie Collins:* English novelist (1824-1889).

It's time that some clear-thinking guy
Got up and told the reason why
America has started going wrong.
If laws are broke and homes are wrecked,
It's only what you might expect
With all the fellows shaving all the time.
Yes, sir, the moment you begin
To crop the fungus from the chin
You're headed for a life of sin
And crime.

What this country needs is men with whiskers
Like the men of an earlier date.
They were never heels and loafers
And they looked like busted sofas
Or excelsior in a crate.
Don't forget it was men with whiskers
Who founded our New Yorks, Detroits and San Franciskers.
What this country needs is men with whiskers
Like the men who made her great.

The pioneers were hairy men,
Reckless devil-may-care-y men,
Who wouldn't have used a razor on a bet.
For each had sworn a solemn oath
He'd never prune the undergrowth;
Their motto was "To hell with King Gillette!"
And when they met on country walks
Wild Cherokees with tomahawks,
I'll say those boys were glad they hadn't shaved.
When cornered by a redskin band,
With things not going quite as planned,
They hid inside their whiskers and
Were saved.

What this country needs is men with whiskers,
For the whisker always wins.
Be it war or golf or tennis
We shall fear no foeman's menace

With alfalfa on our chins.
Whitman's verse,[6] there is none to match it,
But you couldn't see his face unless you used a hatchet.
What this country needs is men with whiskers
Out where the best begins.

What this country needs is men with whiskers
Like the men of Lincoln's day.
At the Wilderness and Shiloh
They laid many a doughty guy low,
They were heroes in the fray.
Theirs is fame that can never die out,
And if you touched their beards, a couple of birds would fly
    out,
So let's raise the slogan of "Back to whiskers!"
And three cheers for the U.S.A.

3

As regards my stressing the butler note too determinedly in my writing, the critics are probably correct.

"Why is it," asks one of them in a thoughtful passage, "that Wodehouse writes so much about butlers? There must be an explanation. This squareshooter would not do it without some excellent reason."

Well, I'll tell you. Butlers have always fascinated me. As a child, I was raised on the fringe of a butler belt; as a young man I was a prominent pest at houses where butlers were maintained; and later I employed butlers; so it might be said that I have never really gone off the butler standard. And all through the years these men have piqued my curiosity. Mystery hangs about them like a nimbus. How do they get that way? What do they think about? Where do they go on their evenings off? Why do they always wear

6. *Whitman's verse:* reference to work of Walt Whitman, American poet (1819-1892).

derby hats? And why are they called butlers? If the word
is a corruption of bottlers, it is surely a misnomer. A butler
does not bottle. He unbottles.

Though not today. Very little unbottling has taken place
since the social revolution set in in England. For forty years
and more I have omitted no word or act to keep butlers
in the forefront of public thought, and now they have ceased
to be. I have been goggled at by my last butler. Makes
one sort of sad, that.

It is possible that at this point you will try to bring the
roses back to my cheeks by mentioning a recent case in the
London courts where a young peer was charged with biting
a lady friend in the leg and much of the evidence was supplied by "the butler." I read about that too, and it cheered
me up for a moment. But only for a moment. I told myself
cynically that this "butler" was probably just another of
those modern makeshifts. No doubt in many English homes
there is still buttling of a sort going on, but it is done by
ex-batmen, promoted odd-job boys and so forth, callow
youngsters not to be ranked as butlers by one who, like
myself, was around and about in London in 1903 and saw
the real thing. Butlers? These chinless children? Faugh, if
you will permit me the expression.

I have an English friend who has a butler, and I was
congratulating him on this the last time we met. He listened
to me, I thought, rather moodily. "Yes," he said when I had
finished, "Murgatroyd is all right, I suppose. Does his work
well and all that sort of thing. But," he added with a sigh,
"I wish I could break him of that habit of his of sliding
down the banisters."

The real, crusted, vintage butler passed away with Edward the Seventh. One tried one's best to pretend that the
Georgian Age had changed nothing, but it had. The post-
First-World-War butler was a mere synthetic substitute for
the ones we used to know. When we old dodderers speak

of butlers, we are thinking of what used to lurk behind the front doors of Mayfair[7] at the turn of the century.

Those were the days of what—because they took place late in the afternoon—were known as "morning calls." Somewhere around five o'clock one would put on the old frock coat (with the white piping inside the vest), polish up the old top hat (a drop of stout helped the gloss), slide a glove over one's left hand (you carried the other one) and go out and pay morning calls. You mounted the steps of some stately home, you pulled the bell, and suddenly the door opened and there stood an august figure, weighing two hundred and thirty pounds or so on the hoof, with mauve cheeks, three chins, supercilious lips, and popping, gooseberry eyes that raked you with a forbidding stare, as if you were something the carrion crow had deposited on the doorstep. "Not at all what we have been accustomed to," those bulging eyes seemed to say.

That, at least, was the message I always read in them, due no doubt to my extreme youth and the fact, of which I never ceased to be vividly aware, that my brother's frock coat and my Cousin George's trousers did not begin to fit me. A certain anemia of the exchequer caused me in those days to go about in the discarded clothes of relatives, and it was this that once enabled me to see that rarest of all sights, a laughing butler. By the laws of their guild butlers of the Edwardian epoch were sometimes permitted a quick, short smile, provided it was sardonic, but never a guffaw. I will come back to this later. Wait for the story of the laughing butler.

My acquaintance with butlers and my awe of them started at a very early age. My father being a judge in Hong Kong, my parents were abroad most of the time when I was in the knickerbocker stage, and during my school vacations I was

7. *Mayfair:* fashionable district of London.

passed from aunt to aunt. A certain number of these aunts were the wives of clergymen, which meant official calls at the local great house, and when they paid these calls they took me along. Why, I have never been able to understand. Even at the age of ten I was a social bust, contributing little or nothing to the conversation. The thing generally ended in my hostess smiling one of those painful smiles and suggesting that it would be nice for your little nephew to go and have tea in the servants' hall.

And she was right. I loved it. My mind today is fragrant with memories of kindly footmen and vivacious parlormaids. In their society I ceased to be shy and kidded back and forth with the best of them. The life and soul of the party they will probably describe me as, when they write their autobiographies. But these good times never lasted. Sooner or later in would come the butler, like the monstrous crow in *Through the Looking Glass*,[8] and the quips would die on our lips. "The young gentleman is wanted," he would say morosely, and the young gentleman would shamble out, feeling like $.30.

Eventually I reached the age when the hair whitens, the waistline expands and the terrors of youth leave us. The turning point came when I realized one morning that, while I was on the verge of fifty, my butler was a mere kid of forty-six. It altered the whole situation. One likes to unbend with one's juniors, and I unbent with this slip of a boy. From tentative discussions of the weather we progressed until I was telling him what hell it was to get stuck halfway through a novel, and he was telling me of former employers of his and how the butler's cross is that he has to stand behind Mr. Big's chair night after night and listen to the funny noise he makes over his soup. You serve the soup and stand back and clench your hands. "Now comes the funny

8. *Through the Looking Glass:* satire by Lewis Caroll, author of *Alice in Wonderland*.

noise," you say to yourself. Night after night after night.
This explains what in my youth had always puzzled me, the
universal gloom of butlers.

Only once—here comes that story I was speaking of—have
I heard a butler laugh. On a certain night in the year 1903,
when I had been invited to dinner at a rather more stately
home than usual and, owing to the friend who has appeared
in some of my stories under the name of Ukridge having
borrowed my dress clothes without telling me, I had to
attend the function in a primitive suit of soup-and-fish bequeathed to me by my Uncle Hugh, a man who stood six
feet four and weighed in the neighborhood of three hundred
pounds.

Even as I dressed, the things seemed roomy. It was not,
however, until the fish course that I realized how roomy
they were, when, glancing down, I suddenly observed the
trousers mounting like a rising tide over my shirt front. I
pushed them back, but I knew I was fighting a losing battle.
I was up against the same trouble that bothered King Canute.[9]
Eventually, when I was helping myself to potatoes and was
off my guard, the tide swept up as far as my white tie, and
it was then that Yates or Bates or Fotheringay or whatever
his name was uttered a sound like a bursting paper bag and
hurried from the room with his hand over his mouth, squaring himself with his guild later, I believe, by saying that
he had had some kind of fit. It was an unpleasant experience
and one that clouded my life through most of the period
1903-4-5, but it is something to be able to tell my grand-
children that I once saw a butler laugh.

Among other things which contributed to make butlers
gloomy was the fact that so many of their employers were
sparkling raconteurs. Only a butler, my butler said, can realize what it means to a butler to be wedged against the side-

9. *King Canute:* futilely commanded the sea to recede.

board and unable to escape and to watch his employer working the conversation around to the point where he will be able to tell that good story of his which he, the butler, has heard so often before. It was when my butler mentioned this, with a kindly word of commendation to me for never having said anything even remotely clever or entertaining since he had entered my service, that I at last found myself understanding the inwardness of a rather peculiar episode of my early manhood.

A mutual friend had taken me to lunch at the house of W. S. (Savoy Operas) Gilbert just outside London, and midway through the meal the great man began to tell a story. It was one of those very long, deceptively dull stories where you make the build-up as tedious as you can and pause before you reach the point, so as to stun the audience with the unexpected snaperoo. In other words, a story which is pretty awful till the last line, when everything becomes joy and jollity.

Well, sir, there was Sir William Schwenck Gilbert telling this long story, and there was I, a pie-faced lad of twenty-two in my brother's frock coat and my Cousin George's trousers, drinking it respectfully in. It did not seem to me very funny, but I knew it must be because this was W. S. Gilbert telling it, so when the pause before the punch line came, I laughed.

I had rather an individual laugh in those days, something like the explosion of a gas main. Infectious, I suppose you would call it, for the other guests, seeming a little puzzled, as if they had expected something with rather more point from the author of *The Mikado*,[10] also laughed politely, and conversation became general. And it was at this juncture that I caught mine host's eye.

I shall always remember the glare of pure hatred which

10. *The Mikado:* operetta by Gilbert and Sullivan.

Sir William S. Gilbert.

I saw in it. If you have seen photographs of Gilbert, you will be aware that even when in repose his face was inclined to be formidable and his eye not the sort of eye you would willingly catch. And now his face was far from being in repose. His eyes, beneath their beetling brows, seared my very soul. In order to get away from them, I averted my gaze and found myself encountering that of the butler. His eyes were shining with a doglike devotion. For some reason which I was unable to understand, I appeared to have made his day. I know now what that reason was. I suppose he had heard that story build up like a glacier and rumble to its conclusion at least twenty times, probably more, and I had killed it.

And now Gilbert has gone to his rest, and his butler has gone to his rest, and all the other butlers of those great days have gone to their rests. Time, like an ever-rolling stream, bears all its sons away, and even the English butler has not been immune. He has joined the Great Auk, the passenger pigeon and the snows of yesterday in limbo.

But I like to think that we shall meet beyond the river. I cannot believe that this separation will endure forever. I tell myself that when the ninth Earl of Emsworth, who is now, I suppose, rubbing along at Blandings Castle with the assistance of a charwoman, finally hands in his dinner pail after his long and pleasant life, the first thing he will hear as he settles himself on his cloud will be the fruity voice of Beach, his faithful butler, saying "Nectar or ambrosia, m'lord?"

"Eh? Oh, hullo, Beach. I say, Beach, what's this dashed thing?"

"A harp, m'lord."

"What am I supposed to do with it?"

"Play on it, m'lord."

"Eh? Play on it? Oh, you mean *play* on it. Like Harpo Marx,[11] you mean?"

"Precisely, m'lord."

"Most extraordinary."

"Yes, m'lord."

"Is everybody doing it?"

11. *Harpo Marx:* comedian whose act included playing the harp.

"Yes, m'lord."

"My sister Constance? My brother Galahad? Sir Gregory Parsloe? Everybody?"

"Yes, m'lord."

"Oh? Sounds odd to me. Still, if you say so. Give me your A, Beach."

"Very good, m'lord."

. . . 8   MY IRON RESOLVE TO TAKE ISH

1

I HAVE TOLD the story of my early struggles, showing how by the simple process of calling myself Pelham Grenville Wodehouse I was enabled to rise on stepping stones of my dead self to higher things and get into the chips, and here, I suppose, if I really knew how to write an autobiography, I would describe in pitiless detail what I did after that. But though it will probably mean my getting drummed out of the Autobiographers' Guild and having my buttons—coat buttons only, let us hope—snipped off in a hollow square, I shall refrain. To my mind there is nothing so soporific as an author's account of his career after he has become established. As one of the good gray poets once said: Of all sad words by plane or boat, the saddest are these—"And then I wrote . . ."[1]

I have known novelists, when relating the story of their lives, to give not only a complete list of their novels but the plots of many of them. Brutal, I call it. Far better, when one feels an autobiography coming on, to remember the splendid words of Mr. Glen Johns of Fort Erie, Ontario, on the occasion of his winning the raw-egg-eating champion-

1. *Of . . . wrote:* Wodehouse is punning John Greenleaf Whittier's lines from "Maud Muller"—". . . of all sad words of tongue or pen, The saddest are these: 'It might have been!' "

ship of Canada last spring—ah, Fort Erie, Ontario, in the springtime!—by eating twenty-four raw eggs in fourteen minutes.

A thing I never understand, when I read an item like that in the paper, is how these fellows do it. I mean, you take me. I have built up a nice little conservative business over the years, and there is no mystery about my beginnings. You can trace my progress step by step. But how does a man so shape himself that he becomes able to eat twenty-four raw eggs in fourteen minutes?

One feels the same thing about performers at the circus. How did the man who dives through a hole in the roof into a small tank first get the impulse? One pictures him studying peacefully for the Church, without a thought in his mind of any other walk in life, when suddenly, as he sits poring over his theological books, a voice whispers in his ear. "This is all very well," says the voice, "but what you were really intended to do was to dive through holes in the roof into tanks. Do not stifle your individuality. Remember the parable of the talents." And he throws away his books and goes out to see an agent. Some sort of spiritual revelation like this no doubt happened to Mr. Johns.

But I was going to tell you about those splendid words he spoke. Interviewed after the twenty-fourth egg and asked how he did it, he replied: "I ate twenty-one eggs in twelve minutes, and then I ate another three, making twenty-four in all."

"No, no, I mean how did you *start*?"

"With the first egg . . . Call it Egg A or (1). I ate that egg, then I ate another egg, then I ate another egg, then I ate another egg, then I ate another egg, then I ate another egg, then I ate another egg, then . . ."

Substitute "wrote" for "ate" and "book" for "egg," and an author has said everything that needs to be said.

For the benefit of the small minority who are interested

in statistics I will state briefly that since 1902 I have produced ten books for boys, one book for children, forty-three
novels, three hundred and fifteen short stories and have
been author or part author of sixteen plays and have written
the lyrics for twenty-two musical comedies. Then there is
the matter of light verse. I have written more light verse
than you would think possible. In the six years that I was
doing the "By the Way" column on the *Globe* I had to write
a set of verses every morning between 10:00 and 11:30 in
addition to the paragraphs, and I suppose there is no man
alive more qualified to turn out one of those You Too Can
Croon in June pieces which you see in literary papers. But
it was only recently that I became a serious poet.

They do ask the darnedest questions on television. There
is a thing on Sunday nights called "Elder Wise Men," and
the elderly sage they got hold of the other evening was John
Hall Wheelock, the man who wrote a poem about having
a black panther caged within his breast (than which I can
imagine nothing more disturbing for anyone of settled habits
and a liking for the quiet life).

"Tell me, Mr. Wheelock," said the interviewer—who was
something special in the way of TV interviewers, few of
whom have any peers when it comes to asking the fatuous
question—"could you have helped being a poet?"

The implication being, one presumes, that he felt that
Mr. Wheelock hadn't *tried*. He could have pulled up in time
if he had had the right stuff in him, but he adopted a weak
policy of drift and *laissez-faire*, and the next thing he knew
he was writing about panthers caged within his breast.

"I don't believe I could," said Mr. Wheelock, and one
pictures the interviewer clicking his tongue censoriously.

But I doubt that the thing is always deliberate. Many who
become poets are more to be pitied than censured. What
happens is that they are lured on the downward path by the
fatal fascination of the limerick form. It is so terribly easy

to compose the first two lines of a limerick and, that done, the subject finds it impossible to stop. (Compare the case of the tiger cub which, at first satisfied with a bowl of milk, goes in strictly for blood after tasting its initial coolie.) And the difficulty of finding a last line discourages these men from sticking to limericks, which would be fairly harmless. So they take the easier way and write serious poetry. It was after they had scribbled down on the back of a bill of fare at the Mermaid Tavern[2]

> *There was a young lady (Egyptian)*
> *Who merits a word of description*

that Shakespeare, Bacon, Marlowe and the Earl of Oxford realized that the rhyme scheme was too tough.

"Bipshion?" suggested Bacon. (He would.)

"What do you mean, bipshion?" said Marlowe irritably. "There isn't such a word."

"Hips on?"

"Doesn't rhyme."

"I seem to have heard people talking of having conniption fits," said Shakespeare diffidently. "How about 'And she suffered from fits (viz., conniption)'? Just a suggestion."

"And as rotten a one as I ever heard," snapped Marlowe.

"Oh, hell," said the Earl of Oxford. (These peers express themselves strongly.) "Let's turn it into a play."

And they wrote *Antony and Cleopatra*.

A similar thing happened with Tennyson's

> *There was a young fellow named Artie*
> *Who was always the life of the party.*

This subsequently became *Idylls of the King*.

My own case is rather interesting. As I say, I had never written anything but light, frivolous verse, but I happened one Sunday morning to be skimming through my *New*

---

2. *Mermaid Tavern:* meeting place of Shakespeare and other men of letters mentioned.

York Times—for though well stricken in years, I can still lift my Sunday *New York Times*—and as I turned to the correspondence page of the book section I suddenly quivered in every limb. It was as though I had been slapped between the eyes with a wet fish.

I don't know if you know the correspondence page of the book section of the Sunday *New York Times*. It consists of heated letters denouncing opinions expressed in letters of the previous week, and what had attracted my attention was one that began:

Sir:
    I take issue with Percy G. Swisher . . .

I would like my readers to try repeating those words to themselves. I think they will find that after a few minutes their haunting beauty grips them as it gripped me. I felt, and I have no doubt they will feel, that only poetry—and the finest poetry—could do justice to the theme. In a trice I was at my desk with the old pipe drawing well and a pot of black coffee at my elbow, and in another trice—if not sooner—I was well into my first serious poem. (The stuff seemed just to pour out.)

It would be a dirty trick, after getting you all worked up like this, to withhold it from you, and I do not propose to do so. It ran:

> *The day, I recall, was a spring one,*
>   *Not hot and oppressive, though warm,*
> *The sort of a day apt to bring one*
>   *Right up to the top of one's form.*
> *So when a kind friend and well-wisher*
>   *Said "Don't just sit dreaming there, kid.*
> *Take issue with Percy G. Swisher,"*
>   *I replied "Yes, I will." And I did.*
>
> *I felt rather sorry for Percy.*
>   *I hated to crush the poor fish.*

But no inclination to mercy
*   Could shake my resolve to take ish.*
You can't be a competent isher,
*   If from thoughts of the rough stuff you wince.*
I took issue with Percy G. Swisher.
*   He's never been quite the same since.*

So though low in the world's estimation,
*   A bit of a washout, in short,*
I have always this one consolation:
*   I tell myself, "Courage, old sport!*
There are others more gifted and risher
*   And plenty more beautiful,* BUT
You took issue with Percy G. Swisher,
*   So you might be much more of a mutt."*

From there to writing "Excelsior" and "The Boy Stood
on the Burning Deck"[3] was but a step.

2

There was a millionaire in one of George Ade's[4] *Fables,* who
having devoted a long life to an unceasing struggle to amass
his millions, looked up from his deathbed and said plain-
tively, "And now, perhaps, somebody will kindly tell me
what it has all been about." I get that feeling sometimes.
Couldn't I, I ask myself, have skipped one or two of those
works of mine and gone off and played golf without hurting
English literature or jeopardizing my financial position? Take,
for instance, a book I wrote in 1909 called *The Swoop,* a
skit on the invasion-of-England stories which were so prevalent then. I wrote the whole twenty-five thousand words
of it in five days and nearly expired, and, selling at a shilling,
it brought me in royalties of £9.14.6. Was it worth the
trouble and anguish?

I'm glad I asked myself that. Yes, it was, for I had a great

3. *Excelsior . . . Deck:* "Excelsior" is a poem by Longfellow; "The Boy
Stood on the Burning Deck" was written by Felicia Hemans.
4. *George Ade:* American humorist (1866-1944).

deal of fun writing it. I have had a great deal of fun—one-sided, possibly—writing all my books. Doctor Johnson[5] once said that nobody but a blockhead ever wrote except for money. I should think it extremely improbable that anyone ever wrote anything simply for money. What makes a writer write is that he likes writing. How about the people who write letters to the papers saying they have heard the cuckoo, Doc? Are you telling me they do it for money? You're crazy, Johnson. They do it because they have something to say which they must get out of their systems. They are the people Walter Pater[6] had in mind when he spoke of "burning with a hard gemlike flame."

Although it is many years since I myself gave up writing letters to the papers, I still keep in close touch with the correspondence columns of the English journals, and it is a source of considerable pain to me to note today what appears to be a conspiracy of silence with regard to the cuckoo, better known possibly to some of my readers as the *Cuculus canorus*. I allude to the feathered friend which puzzled the poet Wordsworth so much. "O Cuckoo! shall I call thee Bird, Or but a wandering Voice?" he used to say, and I don't believe he ever did get straight about it.

In my young days in England the cuckoo was big stuff. Thousands hung upon its lightest word. The great thing, of course, was to be the first to hear it, for there was no surer way of getting your letter printed.

Virtually all the men at the top of the profession—Verb Sap, Pro Bono Publico, Fiat Justitia,[7] and the like—had started their careers by hearing the first cuckoo and getting the story off to the paper while it was hot. It was the recognized *point d'appui*[8] for the young writer.

5. *Doctor Johnson:* Samuel Johnson (1709-1784), the most influential literary figure of his day and author of the first comprehensive English dictionary.
6. *Walter Pater:* English author (1839-1894).
7. *Verb Sap, Pro Bono Publico, Fiat Justitia:* Latin for "Word to the Wise," "For the Public Good," "Let There Be Justice."
8. *Point d'appui:* starting point (French).

"My boy," I remember Fiat Justitia saying to me once after he had been kind enough to read some of my unpublished material, "don't let editorial rejections discourage you. Where you have gone wrong is in writing about social trends and the political situation. You must not try to run before you can walk. Begin, like all the great masters, with the cuckoo. And be careful that it is a cuckoo. I knew a man who wrote to his daily paper saying that he had heard the first reed-warbler, and the letter was suppressed because it would have given offense to certain powerful vested interests."

But how changed are conditions today. My attention has been drawn to a letter in one of the London Sunday papers:

Sir:

If the hypothesis be accepted without undue dogmatism in the present rudimentary state of our knowledge that brain is merely the instrument of mind and not its source, the terms soul and spirit could plausibly be regarded as redundant.

Pretty poor stuff. Not a word about hearing the cuckoo, which could have been brought in perfectly neatly in a hundred ways.

Before I broke into the game I used to think of the men who had their attention drawn as unworldly dreamers living in some ivory tower, busy perhaps on a monumental history of the Ming dynasty or something of that sort and never seeing the papers. But when I became a correspondent myself and joined the well-known Fleet Street club, The Twelve Jolly Letter-Writers, I found I had been mistaken. Far from being dreamers, the "My-attention-has-been-drawn" fellows were the big men of the profession, the topnotchers.

You started at the bottom of the ladder with:

Sir:

I heard the cuckoo yesterday . . .

then after some years to a position where you said:

Sir:

The cuckoo is with us once again, its liquid notes ringing through the countryside. Yesterday . . .

and finally, when the moment had come, you had your attention drawn.

There was, as I recollect it, no formal promotion from the ranks, no ceremony of initiation or anything like that. One just sensed when the time was ripe for one to become an A.D., like an English barrister, who has built up a large practice as what is known in legal circles as a Junior, when he decides that the time is ripe for him to become a Queen's Counsel, or, as the expression is, to "take silk."

I inadvertently caused something of a flutter in the club, I remember, soon after I had taken silk, and got hauled over the coals by that splendid old veteran Mother of Six (Oswaldtwistle).

"Gussie," he said to me one morning—I was writing under the name of Disgusted Taxpayer in those days, "I have a bone to pick with you. My attention has been drawn to a letter of yours in the *Daily Telegraph* in which you say that your attention has been called to something."

"What's wrong with called?" I said. I was young and headstrong then.

"It is not done," he replied coldly. "Attentions are not called, they are drawn. Otherwise, why would Tennyson in his well-known poem have written:

Tomorrow'll be the happiest time of all the glad new year.
Of all the glad new year, Mother, the maddest merriest day,
For my attention has been drawn to a statement in the
press that I'm to be Queen of the May, Mother, I'm to be
Queen of the May."

I never made that mistake again.

3

Returning to Doctor Johnson, I am sorry I had to put him in his place like that and make such a monkey of him. I ought to have remembered that when he said that silly thing about writing for money he was not feeling quite himself. He was all hot and cross because of the Lord Chesterfield business. You probably remember the circumstances. He had wanted Lord Chesterfield to be his patron, and had been turned down like a bedspread. No wonder he was in an ugly mood.

In the days when I was hammering out stories for the pulps and trying not to listen to the soft whining of the wolf outside the door I often used to think how wonderful it would be if the patron system of the eighteenth century could be revived. None of that nonsense then of submitting your novel to a cold-eyed publisher and having to listen to him moaning about the growing cost of paper and regretting the impossibility under existing conditions of springing anything in the nature of an advance. All you had to do was to run over the roster of the peerage and select your patron. You wanted somebody fairly weak in the head, but practically all members of the peerage in those happy days were weak in the head and, there being no income tax or surtax then, they could fling you purses of gold without feeling it. Probably some kindly friend put you on to the right man. "Try young Sangazure,"[9] he said. "I know the nurse who dropped him on his head when a baby. Give him the old oil and it's a cinch. Don't forget to say 'My lord' and 'Your lordship' all the time. They love it."

I have never been able quite to understand what were the actual preliminaries. I imagine that you waited till your prospect had written a poem—and this was bound to happen sooner or later—and then you hung around in his anteroom till you were eventually admitted to the presence. You found your man lying on a sofa reading the eighteenth-century equivalent of *Captain Billy's Whizz Bang*, and when he

9. *Sangazure:* Wodehouse is playing on the fact that much of English aristocracy is descended from the Norman French. The French words *sang* and *azure* mean "blood" and "blue," respectively.

Sam Johnson, from a portrait by Joshua Reynolds.

said "Yes?" or "Well?" or "Who on earth let *you* in?" you explained that you had merely come to look at him. "No, don't move, my lord," you said. "And don't speak for a moment. Let me just gaze at your lordship." You wanted, you said, to feast your eyes on the noble brow from which had proceeded that "Ode to Spring."

The effect was instantaneous.

"Oh, I say, really?" said the member of the peerage, softening visibly and drawing a pattern on the carpet with his left toe.

"You really like the little thing, what?"

"*Liked* it, my lord! It knocked me flatter than a griddle

cake, my lord. That bit at the beginning, 'Er, Spring, you perfectly priceless old thing.' Some spin on the ball there, my lord. However did your lordship do it?"

"Oh, just thought of it, you know, and sloshed it down as it were. Just thought of it and sloshed it down, if you see what I mean."

"Genius! Genius! Do you work regular hours, my lord, or does your lordship wait for inspiration?"

"W. for i. mostly. But tell me. You seem a knowledgeable sort of bloke. Do you write yourself by any chance? I mean write and all that sort of rot, what?"

"Why, yes, my lord, I am a writer, my lord. Not in your lordship's class, of course, but I do scribble a bit."

"Make a good thing out of it?"

"So far no, my lord. You see, to get anywhere these days, my lord, you have to have a patron, and patrons don't grow on every bush, my lord. How did that thing of your lordship's go? Ah, yes. 'Oh Spring, oh Spring, oh glorious Spring, when cuckoos sing like anything.' Your lordship certainly gave that one the works."

"Yes, not baddish, was it? Rather goodish, what, what? I say, look here, here's a thought. How about me being your patron?"

"Your lordship's condescension overwhelms me."

"Right ho, then, that's all fixed up. Tell my major-domo as you go out to fling you a purse of gold."

4

Recently I have seemed to detect welcome signs indicating that the patron is coming back. I wrote a piece the other day about being in the telephone book, in which I gave my telephone number.

"In the life of every man living in New York and subscribing to the New York telephone service" (I wrote) "there comes a moment when he has to face a problem squarely and make a decision. Shall he—or, alternatively, shall he not —have his name in the book? There is no middle course. Either you are in the book or you aren't. I am in myself. I suppose it was wanting to have something good to read in the long winter evenings that made me do it. For unquestionably it reads well.

"Wodehouse P G 1000 PkAv . . . BUtrfld 8-7598. Much better, it seems to me—zippier is perhaps the word I want— than Wodczaika Theo 279 Riv Dr . . . ACdmy 2-6098, which comes immediately before it, and Wodilly Selma 577 Grand . . . CAnl 6-0099, which comes immediately after. Both are good enough in their way, but they are not Wodehouse P G 1000 PkAv . . . BUtrfld 8-7598. In moods of depression I often turn to the well-thumbed page, and it always puts new heart in me. 'Wodehouse P G,' I say to myself. '1000PkAv,' I say to myself. 'BUtrfld 8-7598,' I say to myself. 'Pretty good, pretty good.' "

Well, for weeks after the article had appeared no day passed without two or three people calling up to ask if that really was my telephone number. One of them called all the way from Pasadena, California. He said—this seems almost inconceivable, but I am quoting him verbatim—he said he thought my books were God-awful and he couldn't read another of them if you paid him, but he did enjoy my articles and would I like a Russell Flint print of a nude sitting on the banks of the Loire. I said I would—you can't have too many nudes about the home—and it now hangs over my desk. And the point I am making is this: Whatever we may think of a man who does not appreciate my books, we must applaud what is unquestionably the right spirit. We authors live, of course, solely for our Art, but we can always do with a little something on the side, and here, unless I am mistaken, we have the old patron system coming into its own again. It should, in my opinion, be encouraged.

If any other members of my public feel like subsidizing me, what I need particularly at the moment are:

> Golf Balls
> Tobacco
> A Cadillac
> Dog Food Suitable for
> > (a) A Foxhound
> > (b) A Pekinese
> Cat Food Suitable for
> > A Cat
> and
> Diamond Necklace Suitable for
> > A Wife

I could also do with a case of champagne and some warm winter woollies. And a few shares of United States Steel would not hurt.

Contributions should be addressed to me at Blandings Castle, Basket Neck Lane, Remsenburg, Long Island, New York.

. . . 9   THE SLAVE OF A BAD HABIT

1

FOR I AM LIVING in the country now. Call me up at BU 8-7598 as of even date, and you will be answered by Mignon G. Eberhart, the mystery writer, who has taken on the old duplex pnthse apt., unless she's changed the number.

I loved that duplex pnthse apt, but—or, as we fellows in the book say, BUt—I am not sorry to have moved. Being in the book, I got publicity of the right sort and my winter evening reading was all arranged for, but the trouble was that when people, curled up in the old armchair with the New York Telephone Directory, saw

> Wodehouse P G 1000 Pk Ave.......BUterfld 8-7598

it put ideas into their heads. Briefly, I had become, especially

around Christmas time, a sitting duck for every toucher on
the island of Manhattan, and it was rarely that a morning
passed without my hearing a breezy voice on the telephone.

"Mr. Wodehouse?"

"Speaking."

"Is that Mr. Wodehouse?"

"In person."

"Well, well, well! Well, well, well, well, *well!* How are

P. G. Wodehouse at Blandings Castle.

William Cole

you, P. G., how *are* you? Fine? Fine! No colds, coughs or rheumatic ailments? Splendid. That's wonderful. This is the Rev. Cyril Twombley. You won't know my name, but I am one of your greatest fans and I simply couldn't resist the urge to call you up and tell you how much I love your books. I think I've read every line you've written. Great stuff, P. G., great stuff. Jeeves, eh? Ha ha ha ha ha!"

Well, by my halidom,[1] I would be saying to myself by this time, this is extremely gratifying. One is above any petty caring for praise or blame, of course, but still it is nice to feel that one's efforts are appreciated. Furthermore—though one is too spiritual to give much thought to that—a man as enthusiastic as this will surely buy a copy of that book of ours that is coming out next month, which means fifty-two and a half cents in royalties in our kick, and may quite possibly give copies to his friends. (Five friends? Ten friends? Better be on the safe side and call it five. Well, that is $2.62 or thereabouts, and you can buy a lot of tobacco for $2.62.)

But hark, he is proceeding.

"That was why I had to call you, P. G., old top. I just wanted to tell you what pleasure you have given me, and I am sure a great number of other people . . . and—oh, yes—there was one other thing. Our church is getting up a Christmas bazaar and we are hoping you will . . ."

In theory the unlisted subscriber avoids all this. If you try to get a number that is not in the book, Information pins your ears back good and proper.

"Sorrrrrr-eeeeeee, we are not allowed to give out that numbah," says Information.

But the catch is, the unlisted boys tell me, that you keep giving it out yourself to casual acquaintances who write it down and give it to their casual acquaintances who write it down and . . . but you get the idea. Pretty soon it is public

---

1. *Halidom:* holiness.

property. Russell Maloney, dealing with this subject, mentions an unlisted friend of his who, totting up the score after a certain period of time, found that his number was in the possession of eleven girls he no longer liked any more, fifty-six he had never liked, a former business associate who was suing him at the moment, a discarded masseur, three upholsterers who had made estimates for covering a sofa, and an unidentified alcoholic who called up at regular intervals and always between the hours of three and four in the morning.

To another point which Mr. Maloney brought up I never paid much attention. He thought that by being in the book you became a social outcast, scorned and sneered at by the swells who had unlisted numbers, the inference being that you couldn't be very hot if you weren't important enough to keep your number a secret confined to a small private circle.

It may be so. Nevertheless, during the seven years I was at the duplex pnthse apt I continued to instruct the brass hats of the system to publish my telephone number. A fig, I felt, for the snobs who would look down on me. What was good enough for the AAAAAAAABBEE Moving & Storage Co and for the Zzyzzy Ztamp Ztudioz Co was good enough for me.

Still, it is probably just as well that I bought this Long Island estate and became Squire Wodehouse and got away from it all.

2

There are things, of course, that one misses when one has ceased to be part of the New York scene. One is no longer, for instance, in a position to play straight for the New York taxi driver and help him get a few well-spotted laughs. I always enjoyed doing that, though there are quite a number of people who do not. Many resent the resolute Bob Hopefulness of these public servants and listen sourly as the wise-cracks come pouring back at them. They think hard thoughts of the newspapermen who for years have fostered the legend of the witty taxi driver.

"They have been exalted as a group and called brilliant conversationalists so long," says one disgruntled commentator, "that they have come to believe the stories they have read about themselves and so ham it up and babble nonsense over their shoulders whenever they have a passenger who will listen."

I am not sure that it is the newspapermen who are to blame. I think the whole thing dates back to the time when one of them, a man who liked his joke of a morning, chanced to drive Eddie Cantor[2] one day and on the strength of his *bon mots*[3] got enrolled on the latter's staff of gag writers. The word went around that fame and fortune awaited the hackie with a good comedy routine, and the boys buckled down to it seriously, with the result that if you take a taxi now you find yourself in the position of one of those Hollywood magnates who get acted at all the time.

You know how it is if you are a Hollywood studio boss with jobs in the pictures to give away. Never a peaceful moment. Your butler recites "Gunga Din" at you as he brings you your breakfast. Your chauffeur, learning from the grapevine that a big musical is coming along, sings "*O Sole Mio*" as he helps you into your car. You get to your office and think the worst is over, and your secretary, as she hands you your mail, goes into a quick monologue whimsically humorous for the most part but always with the tear behind the smile. And when you return home in the evening, you get the butler again, this time in imitations of popular screen favorites.

It is much the same when you take a New York cab. A taxi

2. *Eddie Cantor:* radio humorist (1892-1964).
3. *bon mots:* French for *clever remarks*.

ride in New York is not so much a taxi ride as an audition.

"Say, mister."

"Hullo?"

"English, ain't you?"

"That's right."

"I see by the papers there's a lot of talk over there about this hydrogen bomb."

"Quite a good deal, I believe."

"Same here. Fission. That's all they talk about. Just fission. Now that's a funny thing. I can remember the time when fission was what you did in the creek with a hook and line. Hey, hey, hey."

If the newspapermen are really responsible for this sort of thing, they have much to answer for. The only poor consolation one has is the reflection that if this had been taking place on the burlesque stage one would by now have been hit over the head with a rolled-up umbrella. Still, as I say, I miss it.

Only once were my cordial relations with New York taxi drivers marred. My charioteer had opened brightly and confidently, getting some nice yaks at the expense of the police force and the street-cleaning system, and then he said:

"English, ain't you?"

"That's right."

"I see by the papers there's a lot of talk over there about this hydrogen bomb."

"Quite a good deal, I believe."

"Don't talk about much else, do they?"

"Not much."

"Now that's a funny thing. I can remember——"

"Yes," I said. "You know how it is in England. All that interests them is huntin', shootin' and fission."

He gave a startled gasp, and silence fell, lasting till we arrived at my destination. My better self had woken by now, and I gave him a fifty-cent tip, but there was no light

in his somber eyes as he trousered it. The unforgivable sin
had been committed. He was feeling as Danny Kaye might
feel if his supporting cast started hogging the comedy. As
he drove away, his head was bowed and his air that of a
man who has been wounded in his finest feelings.

3

But I suppose the thing one misses most in the country is
the crime wave. One got a lot of crime in New York. It
seemed to be all the go. Practically everyone you met was
either coming away from sticking up a bank or just setting
out to stick up a bank, for these institutions have a fascination for the criminal classes, attracting them much as catnip
attracts cats. A young man went into a bank the other day
and asked to see the manager. Conducted into his office, he
said he wanted a loan.

"Ah, yes," said the manager. "A loan, eh? Yes, yes, to be
sure. And what is your occupation?"

"I stick up banks," said the young man, producing a gun.

The manager handed over $204 without collateral or ar-
gument.

But the underworld is not hidebound. It prefers banks,
but it is always ready to try a sideline, realizing that a change
of routine keeps a man fresh and alert. A short while before
I withdrew to the country I had a visit from the police. No,
nothing I had done. I was as pure as the driven snow. What
these policemen wanted was to sell me a gadget designed
to baffle the criminal classes when they called at the back
door and knocked on it and said they were from the grocer's,
delivering groceries, and then, when you let them in, stuck
you up.

The cagey thing, of course, was not to let them in, and
that was where you got your eight dollars' worth out of this
gadget. It was a round affair with a hole and a flap and you

fixed it to your back door, and when the criminal classes arrived and said they were from the grocer's, you lifted the flap and looked through the hole and said, "Oh, you are, are you? Then where are the groceries, and why are you wearing a black mask and toting around a whacking great sawn-off shotgun?" Upon which, they slunk off with horrid imprecations.

I bought the gadget, and as I attached it to the door I found myself wondering why it is worth these crime wavers' while to take so much trouble for such small results.

I am not, of course, speaking of the aristocracy of the profession who rob banks and loot the apartments of Texas millionaires. They make a nice living, their earnings being substantial and free of income tax. I mean the young fellows who waylay passers-by on dark nights. Start waylaying passers-by on dark nights, and nobody you meet ever seems to have more than $1.50 on him. Nine times out of ten he has left his wallet on the dressing table at home or turns out to be a policeman in plain clothes. I would not advise any youngster I was fond of to adopt this profession.

And apart from the meager gains the whole thing must be so embarrassing. You know how you feel when you have to accost a perfect stranger. You cough and shuffle your feet and say, "Er, excuse me." I don't see how you can begin with "This is a stick-up." It sounds so abrupt. I suppose the thing to do would be to lead up to it, sort of.

"Oh—er—excuse me, could you oblige me with a match? What a nuisance it is to run short of matches, is it not? The evenings seem to be drawing in now, don't they? Christmas will be here before we know it, will it not? Good night, sir, good night, and many thanks. Oh, by the way, before I forget. Might I trouble you to hand over your money and valuables?"

That might ease the strain a little, but nothing could ever make it pleasant for a shy man to do this sort of thing. Suppose you happen to run across somebody whose hearing is not as keen as it might be.

You say, "This is a stick-up."

He says, "Huh?"

You say, "A stick-up."

He says, "Huh?"

You say, "A stick-up. A STICK-up. S for Samuel, T for Thomas——"

He says, "I'm afraid I couldn't tell you. I'm a stranger in these parts myself."

Then what?

But the gravest peril in the path of the young stick-up man, to my mind, is the fatal tendency to get into a rut. Consider the case of one whom for convenience's sake we will call The Phantom. I quote from my daily paper:

Lazarus Koplowitz and his wife Bella live at 60 Sixth Avenue, Brooklyn, where they operate a candy store. Three times in the last month they have been robbed by the same man, who appears at the same time of day—3:15 P.M.—and threatens them with the same knife. The first time, on February 10, the unwelcome caller took $10 from Mr. Koplowitz. He returned on February 17 and took $10 from Mrs. Koplowitz.

Police planted a detective in the store for some days at the calling hour, then took him away. On February 24, the man came back and took $10.

I see no future for this Phantom. He has become the slave of a habit.

. . . 10 LIFE AMONG THE ARMADILLOS

1

WE GET NONE of that sort of thing down here at Remsenburg, but life is never dull. There is always something doing.

One morning not long ago the telephone-answering executive of the New York *Herald Tribune* answered the telephone, and the caller said that his name was Sidney A. Schwartz. He lived at Riverhead, Long Island, where he kept bees.

"Ah, yes, bees," said the *Herald Tribune* man. "And how are they all?"

"They're fine," said Mr. Schwartz, "but what I called up for was to ask if you would like to have ten armadillos."

It was a strange and interesting story that he had to relate. What put the idea into his head he could not say, but one afternoon as he was looking at his bees the thought flashed into his mind—Why bees? Why not armadillos?

He knew nothing of armadillos at this time except that nobody had ever claimed that they wrote the plays of Shakespeare, but he went out and bought a couple, and it so happened that they were of opposite sexes.

Well, you know what that means in armadillo circles. All that Kinsey stuff. And when the union of two armadillos is blessed, the result is eight armadillos, sometimes more but never less. Pretty soon armadillos began to sprout in every nook and cranny of the Schwartz home. Some houses have beetles, some have mice. His had armadillos, and he soon became apprised of the drawbacks to this state of affairs. In addition to requiring large quantities of dog food, frozen horse meat, cod-liver-oil and cream cheese, which dented the household budget considerably, armadillos—for reasons best known to themselves—sleep all day and come to life, like dramatic critics, only after dark. And unfortunately they are noisy and rowdy.

It was not long before *chez*[1] Schwartz had become to all intents and purposes a night club, one of the more raffish kind, with armadillos, flushed with cream cheese, staggering about and shouting and yelling and generally ending up

1. *chez:* "house of" (French).

with a couple of ugly brawls before they turned in for the day. Pandemonium is the word that springs to the lips. It does not require much imagination to picture what it must be like with ten armadillos always around, two of them singing duets, the others forming quartets and rendering "Sweet Adeline" in close harmony. Far into the small hours, mind you.

Mr. Schwartz approached the Bronx Zoo. Would they like ten armadillos? No, said the Bronx Zoo, they wouldn't. He tried to dispose of them at sacrifice prices to a New York dealer, but again there was nothing doing. He was stuck.

And this is where I think that Mr. Schwartz shows up in a very creditable light. Where a weaker man would have gone off into a corner and sat there with his head between his hands, he acted. He had always wanted a Ph.D.[2] degree, and here, he suddenly saw, was where he could get one. He would write a thesis on the nine-banded armadillo (*Dasypus novemcinctus*) and clean up. He divided the young armadillos into two groups, it was no good trying to do anything with the father and mother, they were too soppy to register, and—I quote the *Herald Tribune*:

One group he made to walk incessantly upon a treadmill to the extent of three miles a day. The other he allowed to lead completely sedentary lives, undisturbed by anything except the thoughts that normally disturb armadillos in the springtime. And at the end of some weeks he found that the armadillos which had led the strenuous life were happier than the armadillos which had lain slothful and passive.

And he got his Ph.D., showing that out of evil cometh good, and that has cheered him up quite a bit, but I must confess that I find the reasoning of his thesis shaky. How does he know that the athletic armadillos were happier than the other lot? They may have been just putting a brave face

2. *Ph.D.*: Doctor of Philosophy.

on things and keeping a stiff upper lip. You can't go by an
armadillo's surface manner. Many an apparently cheery armadillo without, you would say, a care in the world is really
nursing a secret sorrow, sobbing into its pillow and asking
itself what is the good of it all and how can it shake off this
awful depression. I should require a lot more evidence than
Mr. Schwartz has submitted to convince me that the ones
he thinks so chirpy are really sitting on top of the world
with their hats on the side of their heads.

But what interests me chiefly in the story is not the *joie
de vivre*[3] or lack of *joie de vivre* of the armadillos but the
Schwartz angle. If I say that my heart bleeds for him, that
is not putting it at all too strongly. He has got his Ph.D.,
yes, and that in a way, I suppose, is a happy ending, but he
has also got all those armadillos and more probably coming
along every hour on the hour. The place must be a shambles.

Riverhead is only seven miles from where I live. I must
drop over there when I can spare time and study the situation
at first hand. Taking care to go in the daytime, before the
cod-liver-oil corks have started to pop and the night revels
have begun. One does not want unpleasantness.

2

The coming of autumn always brings a touch of sadness to
the sportsman who lives in the country in America, for he
finds himself at a loose end. Wasping is over. Tick-stalking
is over. Worst of all, the mosquito season is a thing of the
past. Nothing remains but the flies, and a big-game hunter
who has looked his mosquito in the eye and made it wilt
can scarcely be expected to take more than a tepid interest in
flies. One likes a tang of peril with one's sport.

Compared with the mosquito, what a miserable, coddled
creature a fly is. It takes three weeks to breed a new gener-

3. *Joie de vivre:* "joy in living" (French).

ation of flies, and even then the temperature has to be seventy degrees. A spell of cold weather, and the fly simply turns its face to the wall and packs up. How different with the mosquito. Two million dollars are spent yearly in efforts to keep mosquito eggs from hatching. Lamps, sprays and drenches without number are brought into action, and oil in tons poured on the breeding grounds. And what happens? Do they quail? Do they falter? Not by a jugful. They come out in clouds, slapping their chests and whistling through their noses, many of them with stingers at both ends.

Science has now established that the only mosquitoes that sting are the females. The boy friends like to stay at home curled up with a good book. One pictures the male mosquito as a good-natured, easy-going sort of character, not unlike Arthur Godfrey,[4] and one can imagine him protesting feebly when the little woman starts out on a business trip.

"Oh, *no*! Not again? Are you really going out at this time of night, old girl?"

"I work better at night."

"Where are you off to now?"

"New York."

"You mean Newark?"

(The scene of the conversation is the Jersey marshes.)

"No, I don't mean Newark. I mean New York."

"You can't possibly go all the way to New York."

"Pooh."

"It's all very well to say pooh. You know as well as I do that a mosquito can only fly two hundred yards."

"I can take the Holland Tunnel."

"Costs fifty cents."

"Oh, you think of nothing but money," says the female mosquito petulantly.

And she strops her stinger on the doorstep and goes off,

4. *Arthur Godfrey:* jovial television personality.

and probably gets squashed. Rather sad, that. Somebody's mother, you know. Still, we cannot allow ourselves to become sentimental about mosquitoes.

As an old hunter, I like the story of the general who, captured by the Chinese in Korea, relieved the monotony of imprisonment by killing mosquitoes. His record was a 522-mosquito day in 1953, but his best all-over year was 1952, when he bagged twenty-five thousand four hundred and seventy-five. The secret of success, he says, is to wait till the quarry flattens itself against the wall. The simple creature does not realize that the wall is whitewashed, and falls a ready prey to the man who, not letting a twig snap beneath his feet, sneaks up behind it with a handsomely bound copy of *The History of the Communist Party in the Soviet Union.*

They say 1956 is going to be a good mosquito year. Let us hope so, for there are few more stirring sights than a mosquito hunt with the men in their red coats and the hounds baying and all that sort of thing.

Meet you in the Jersey marshes.

... II THIN BLESSINGS IN DISGUISE

"WELL, from what you have been telling us, Mr. Wodehouse, it would seem that you have quite a high opinion of this America of ours."

"Extremely high. The land of the free and the home of the brave, I sometimes call it."

"Any criticisms?"

"One or two, perhaps."

"Let's have them."

"You won't be offended?"

"No, no. Go right ahead."

"Well, take, for instance, income tax."

"You view it with concern?"

"Of the deepest description."

"How well I know that feeling. There was no income tax when you first came over here, was there?"

"No. They started it in 1913. No doubt it seemed to the authorities a good idea at the time, but I think they have overdone it. It was a mistake to allow it to develop into such a popular craze. And the whole spirit has changed since those early days."

"In what way?"

"Well, take the case of a friend of mine back in 1914. He found, on going over his income tax return, that he had overpaid the Internal Revenue the sum of $1.50. He wrote a civil letter, asking for a refund, and received an equally civil reply, in which the Internal Revenue regretted the error and begged to enclose, as requested, check for $15. My friend returned the check, saying that there had been a mistake, and the authorities, more apologetic than ever sent him another for $150. When he returned this check, they almost groveled and enclosed one for $1,500. My friend was content at this point to take his profit and retire from the game, but I still think that if he had had the vision and enterprise to carry on he could have cleaned them out. You wouldn't get anything like that happening nowadays."

"You certainly wouldn't. Of all the hard-boiled, stony-eyed, protruding-chinned lineal descendants of Jesse James who ever took the widow and the orphan by the scruff of the neck and rubbed their noses in the mud, these modern Internal Revenue thugs are the . . . But I must not allow myself to become bitter. After all, there is a bright side to the income tax."

"I have not detected it myself."

"Well, look. Say what you will, the filling up of the forms has given us all a delightful indoor game in which young and old can take part with equal enjoyment. See the family clustered around the table. There is Father, with his spectacles on, jotting down some notes on Amortization. There is Mother, leaning over his shoulder and pointing out that by taking Sec. 6248 H and putting it on top of Sub-sec. 9730 G he can claim immunity from the tax mentioned in Sec. 4537 M. And gathered about them are the children, sucking pencils and working out ways of doing down the supertax. You get the picture?"

"It rises before my eyes. 'See, Papa,' cries little Cyril gleefully, 'I note that gifts (not made as a consideration for services rendered) and money and property acquired under a will or inheritance (but the income derived from money or property received by gift, will or inheritance) are, according to Sub-sec. 2427, not subject to tax, and the way it looks to me is that you can knock off the price of the budgeregah's birdseed.' And so it goes on, each helping the other, all working together in that perfect harmony which goes to make the happy home. Nor is this all."

"I know what you are going to say. Filling in the income tax forms has kindled again all the old spirit of love and family affection. How differently nowadays the head of the house regards his wife and children. Many a man who has spent years wondering why on earth he ever linked his lot with a woman whom he has disliked from the moment they entered the Niagara Falls Hotel and a gang of boys and girls who seemed to grow more repulsive every day gratefully revises his views as he scans Schedule C. His wife may be a nuisance about the home, but she enables him to split the income. And the children. As the father looks at their hideous faces and reflects that he is entitled to knock off a nice little sum per gargoyle, the austerity of his demeanor softens and he pats them on the head and talks vaguely about ice cream for supper."

"Profoundly true, I think I must withdraw my criticism of the income tax."

"I thought you would."

"But on the subject of the New York pigeon I will speak out fearlessly, let the chips fall where they may. There are far too many pigeons in New York. Why all these pigeons? That is what I ask myself. Why?"

"Oh, well . . . You understand the facts of life, don't you? You start with a certain number of pigeons of—er—opposite sexes, and when springtime comes the male pigeon and the female pigeon, in whose bosoms there has burgeoned a feeling deeper and warmer than that of ordinary friendship . . . It's all a little delicate, of course . . . Well, to put it in a nutshell, time marches on and you get more pigeons."

" 'More' is right. I see no need for this monstrous regiment of pigeons and would like to run them all out of town . . . except Walter Pidgeon,[1] whom I admire. But don't get me wrong. I am not a pigeonophobe. Down at Remsenburg many of my best friends are pigeons. I keep open garden for them, and you will often find half a dozen moaning if not in the immemorial elms, at least in the maple tree I bought last week from the nursery garden in Patchogue."

"I see. What you deprecate is the drift to the towns."

"Exactly. A pigeon in the country, fine. But in New York it just takes up space which could be utilized for other purposes. When I had my duplex pnthse apt at 1000 PkAv (BUtrfld 8-5029), there used to be about a thousand of them who hung around the Eighty-fifth Street entrance to the Park, sneering at passers-by and talking offensively out of the corners of their mouths. And you had to give them bread. I tried not giving them bread, but I couldn't keep it up. My nerve failed me. I knew they would fix me somehow. There are a hundred things a gang of pigeons can do to get back at those who have incurred their displeasure—gargling on the window sill at five in the morning, scaring the daylights out of you by tapping on the pane with their beaks, swooping at

---

1. *Walter Pidgeon:* English actor.

your face, pecking at your ankles—I couldn't risk it. It wasn't good enough."

"Appeasement, you felt, was the only course?"

"There was nothing else for it. The situation, then, until I moved to the country, was, briefly, this. Each year by the sweat of my brow I won a certain amount of bread, and this bread I would naturally have liked to reserve for the use of what for convenience' sake may be grouped under the head of 'my loved ones'—myself, my wife, my foxhound, my Pekinese and, of course, any guests who might happen to drop in. But much of it had to go to support a mob of pigeons who had never done a stroke of honest work in their lives. Playboys—every one of them. And they weren't even grateful. Slip a squirrel a bit of bread, and you get value for money. It sits up like a dog. It climbs on your arm. It does everything but give three rousing cheers. Stake a pigeon to a similar bit of bread, and what happens? Not so much as a nod of thanks. The bird just pecks at it in a condescending sort of way.

" 'Bread!' it says to the other pigeons, with a short laugh, and not a nice laugh, either. 'Stale bread! He wouldn't spring a nickel for a bag of peanuts, would he? Oh, no, not Wodehouse. Who does the man think he is? Gaspard the Miser? We'll have to fix Wodehouse.'

" 'Shall we commence on him now?' says a second pigeon.

" 'No, we must wait,' says the first pigeon. 'We can't do nothing till Martin gets here.'

"I have no doubt that if I had not fled the city and gone into hiding in Remsenburg, I should have been rubbed out by this time."

"They're tough babies."

"You're right, they're tough babies."

"Up in Washington, I see by my paper, they are hoping to chase the pigeons away from the Treasury Department building by stringing electric wires where the birds roost. William W. Parsons, Assistant Secretary of the Treasury for Admin-

istration, told a House Appropriations Subcommittee he
thought it would work."

"Not a hope. It's no good, Parsons, old man. You're just a
dreamer chasing rainbows, Bill, old chap. New York pigeons
would scoff at such a childish device. Their feet hardened
by years of mooching around Central Park, they would simply feel a pleasant tickling sensation if you touched off electric shocks under them."

"But these are Washington pigeons. They probably have
not the same morale and will to win."

"No. The Treasury Department might just as well save its
money. If there is one thing life has taught me, it is that there
is nothing you can do about pigeons. You either have them
or you don't. It is as simple as that."

"You are probably right. And is there anything else in this
land of ours that you feel you wish to criticize?"

"The hurricanes."

"Ah, yes, the hurricanes. Carol and Edna and Ione and all
that bunch."

"Not Ione. Ione is a nice girl. She went out to sea."

"But Carol, I believe, gave you south-shore-of-Long-Island-
ers all she had got?"

"Edna also. But when she looked in, eleven days after
Carol, she did not have the same scope for self-expression.
Carol had caught us unprepared, but we were ready for Edna.
Baths had been filled with water, candles laid in. Conditions
under Carol would have brought a startled 'Gee whiz!' to the
lips of King Lear,[2] but Edna was a flop. A dramatic critic
who was staying in Nantucket at the time of her arrival gave
her a bad notice, being rather severe about her lack of significant form and uncertain direction of interest. Apparently,
when she got to Nantucket, she split in two."

"One of those road shows that turn into turkeys."

2. *King Lear:* Shakespearean character who braves a storm.

"You said it."

"A thing about hurricanes that puzzles me is why Cape Hatteras affects them so emotionally."

"I know what you mean. Everything is fine up to there—wind at five miles an hour, practically a dead calm—but the moment a hurricane sees Cape Hatteras it quivers in every limb and starts blowing 125 m.p.h."

"Hysteria?"

"Possibly. But why?"

"It's odd, is it not? And here is another odd thing. Everything in America that you have criticized turns out to have its bright side."

"Not pigeons."

"No, not pigeons, but everything else. The income tax gives solidarity to the American home. The mosquito provides unforgettable days on shikar. And the hurricane proves to be a blessing in disguise."

"I don't follow you there."

"I read in the paper that Carol put two hundred and sixty thousand telephones out of action. Surely this was an excellent thing. Is it not a pleasant thought that for three days Vera (aged sixteen) was not able to call up Clarice (fifteen and a half) and tell her what Jane had said about Alice? The father of many a family of growing girls, reveling in the unaccustomed peace, must have wondered why people made such a fuss about hurricanes. And, of course, during those three days there was no television."

"A-a-a-a-a-a-ah! Now you're talking!"

. . . 12   GAUGHAN THE DELIVERER

1

I SOMETIMES THINK I could endure television with more fortitude if they didn't laugh so much all the time.

Turning on the television set after reading the morning papers is like coming out of the shadows into a world of sunshine.

American papers today go in exclusively for gloom. I never saw so many people viewing with concern and contemplating with the gravest apprehension as are writing now for the daily press of the country. Talk about looking on the dark side. The only ones who do not prophesy the collapse of civilization at 3:30 sharp (Eastern Standard Time) a week from Wednesday are those who make it Tuesday afternoon at 2:45. But twiddle that knob and everything is joy and happiness and the laughter of little children.

At least, one assumes that they are little children. On the evidence submitted I would say their mental age was about six. Everybody is laughing on television these days. The studio audiences have, of course, been laughing themselves sick for years on the most flimsy provocation, but now the contagion has spread to the performers.

The other day John Crosby—not to be confused with Bing, Bing sings—John is the fellow who watches television for the New York *Herald Tribune*, than which I can imagine no more appalling job—just think of *having* to watch television—you don't catch John Crosby singing—he groans a good deal probably, so that you may think he is singing, but . . . Where was I? I seem to have lost the thread. Ah, yes, John Crosby. My reason for bringing him up was that he was complaining the other day about the time when Senator Margaret Chase Smith interviewed the Burmese Premier U Nu, on television and U Nu was so doubled up with laughter throughout that you could scarcely follow what he was saying. It came out something like this:

"If aggression—ha, ha, ha,—comes up from a foe—ha, ha, ha—the United Nations are quite ready to pass resolutions condemning that foe, but—wait, folks, you ain't heard nothin' yet—when aggression comes from friends, they like—this is going to slay you—they like to keep a little quiet—ha, ha, ha

—or even if they are not quiet, they don't do full justice, ho, ho, ho."

The whole punctuated with roars of merriment from the studio audience. No wonder John Crosby screams thinly and jumps six feet straight up in the air if you tap him unexpectedly on the shoulder. Just a bundle of nerves, our John.

The gruesome thing, to my mind—and mine is not a mind to be sneezed at—is that this is not always the laughter of a real studio audience. Frequently, it is canned or bottled. They preserve it on sound tracks, often dating back for years, so that what you are getting is the mummified mirth of people who, in many cases, died way back in about 1946, and if that is not an eerie thought, what is? "The voice I hear this passing night was heard In ancient days by emperor and clown," as Keats[1] put it, switching off the comedy program.

Furthermore, somebody has invented what is known as a laugh machine which can produce completely artificial laughter. The man in charge of it keeps pressing a button at intervals during the cross-talk act, and the comedians love it.

Living-laughter studio audiences, as opposed to laugh machines and those indomitable wraiths who, in spite of having passed beyond the veil, are still in the highest spirits and always ready to do their bit, seem to be governed by some code of rules, probably unwritten and conveyed by word of mouth, for it is surely straining the probabilities a good deal to assume that a studio audience can read. It is a code subject to alteration without notice, and a certain amount of confusion sometimes results. Thus, it used to be obligatory to laugh whenever anyone on the television screen mentioned Brooklyn. If there was one credo rooted in the minds of the citizenry it was that the word Brooklyn was cachinnogenic. And now there has been a shift in the party line, and today you have to laugh at Texas.

Nobody knows why. It is just an order that has come down

1. *Keats:* John Keats, English poet (1795-1821). The quotation is from his "Ode to a Nightingale."

from the men higher up. It is perfectly permissible under the new rules to keep a straight face when somebody speaks of Oshkosh, Kalamazoo or the Gowanus Canal, but a studio audience which fails to laugh at the story of the Texan who refused steak *aux champignons*[2] because he did not like champagne poured over his steak soon finds itself purged. The secret police are knocking at its door before it knows where it is.

But there is a fine spirit stirring in America these days, I am glad to say, as fine as that of '76. The people are on the march. The other day someone whipped out a revolver and shot his television set, and a week or so ago there was a still more impressive demonstration. Folks, let me lead by the hand into the Hall of Fame, Richard Gaughan.

At one-thirty in the afternoon of what will no doubt be known as Gaughan's Day and celebrated as a national festival, Richard Gaughan (29), of 75 Sherman Avenue, entered the studio of the Columbia Broadcasting Company during the rehearsal of a television show, armed with an eight-inch carving knife.

"I hate all television!" he announced. "I hate commentators. I hate the whole lousy bunch. There ought to be a law against television. I want to kill a TV operator."

Having spoken these words, which must have touched a responsive chord in many a bosom, this splendid fellow proceeded to stab a cameraman and to hit the producer on the frontal bone with a carafe. And lest you purse your lips at the latter statement, saying to yourselves "Hullo! What's this? Did Gaughan weaken?" I must explain that a carafe, picked up on the set, was all he had to work with. After he stabbed the cameraman, the knife broke. He had paid only fifty-nine cents for it, not reflecting that you cannot get a really good carving knife as cheap as that. If you are going to stab cameramen, it is always wisest to go as high as a dollar.

2. *Aux champignons:* "with mushrooms" (French).

It was as he was about to attack the director that the police came in and scooped him up, a sad disappointment to the better element. It appears that there is some law against wiping out television directors with carafes, one of those strange laws that get passed occasionally, nobody knows why.

Where Richard Gaughan—Gaughan the Deliverer most of us are calling him now—went wrong in my opinion, was in confining his activities to a rehearsal, for by doing so he missed the studio audience. He should have bided his time till one of these gangs had been assembled.

Where everything about television is so frightful, it is difficult to say which is its most repulsive feature, but the majority of connoisseurs would, I think, pick the studio audience. If it would only stay quiet, nobody would have any complaint, but it won't. It laughs like a congregation of hyenas at everything. The other night on what was for some reason described as a comedy program a girl said to a man, "You are selfish."

To which he replied: "How dare you call me a shellfish?"

The studio audience let out a bellow of mirth which was audible as far downtown as the Battery, and all over America strong men gritted their teeth and muttered, "Gaughan, thou shouldst be living at this hour!"[3]

But a time will come. In ninety days or whatever it is he will be with us once more. Good hunting, Richard Gaughan. And don't make that mistake again of trying to do it on the cheap. Avoid bargain prices. Even if it costs as much as two dollars, get a good knife.

2

From the foregoing remarks you may have formed the impression that I dislike television. I would not go so far as to say that. Apart from thinking it the foulest, ghastliest, loath-

---

3. *Gaughan . . . hour!:* The line, from the poem *London, 1802* by William Wordsworth, actually reads, "Milton, thou shouldst be living at this hour!"

somest nightmare ever inflicted by science on a suffering human race and the programs, except for the Wednesday and Friday night fights, the most driveling half-witted productions ever seen outside Guest Night at a home for the feeble-minded, I do not particularly object to it. As far as I am concerned, it can carry on, provided—I say provided—I have not to excite the derision of the mob by appearing on the screen myself.

But how often this happens. Every time I have a new book out, it comes again . . . the Finger. The telephone rings, and it is my publishers' publicity man informing me briskly that I am to appear on television next week—Monday, 8:30, Sonny Booch's "Strictly for Morons" half-hour; Tuesday, 9:15, Alonzo Todd's "Park Your Brains in the Cloakroom"; and Thursday, 7:35, Genevieve Goole Pobsleigh's "Life Among the Halfwits."

You might suppose from all this that there is a great popular demand for me, that America wants Wodehouse and refuses to be put off with President Eisenhower, Mary Martin[4] and similar cheap substitutes, but this is not so. There may be men in the United States more insignificant than myself, men whose names mean even less to the far-flung citizenry, but they would take a bit of finding. Bloodhounds would be needed and private eyes with magnifying glasses. No, the explanation is that this publicity man thinks it will boost the sales of my book if I am seen by millions on the television screen, not realizing, poor deluded soul, that the one way of slaying a book is to let the people get a look at the author.

Authors as a class are no oil paintings. You have only to go to one of those literary dinners to test the truth of this. At such a binge you will see tall authors, short authors, stout authors, thin authors and authors of medium height and girth, but all of these authors without exception look like something

4. *Mary Martin:* popular musical comedy star.

that would be passed over with a disdainful jerk of the beak
by the least fastidious buzzard in the Gobi Desert. Only very
rarely do we find one who has even the most rudimentary
resemblance to anything part-human.

If they wanted to interview me on the radio, that would
be different. I might do myself a bit of good by saying a few
graceful words on the radio. I have an attractive voice, rich,
mellow, with certain deep organ tones in it calculated to make
quite a number of the cash customers dig up the $3.50. But
it is fatal to let them see me.

Owing to my having become mentally arrested at an early
age, I write the sort of books which people, not knowing the
facts, assume to be the work of a cheerful, if backward, young
fellow of about twenty-five. "Well, well," they tell one another, "we might do worse than hear what this youngster has
to say. Get the rising generation point of view, and all that."
And what happens? "We have with us tonight, Mr. P. G.
Wodehouse" . . . and on totters a spavined septuagenarian, his
bald head coated with pancake flour to keep it from shining
and his palsied limbs twitching feebly like those of a galvanized frog. Little wonder that when the half-yearly score sheet
reaches me some months later I find that sales have been what
publishers call "slow" again. America's book-buyers have decided as one book-buyer to keep the money in the old oak
chest, and I don't blame them. I wouldn't risk a nickel on
anyone who looks as I do on the television screen.

I have never understood this theory that you don't get the
full flavor of a writer's work unless you see him. On every
newspaper staff in America there are half a dozen columnists,
and every day each of these columnists has his photograph at
the head of his column. All wrong it seems to me. I mean, after
you have seen Westbrook Pegler or Hy Gardner three or four
hundred days in succession you have had practically all you
require and their spell wanes. It is a significant thing, I think,
that the greatest of all columnists, Walter Winchell, who has

led the field for a matter of twenty-five years, has never allowed his photograph to appear. And Walter is a good-looking man, too, not unlike what I was in my prime.

That is the maddening thing about this television business, that they are catching me too late. "Oh, God, put back Thy universe and give me yesterday," as the fellow said. Well, no, not yesterday perhaps, but say 1906 or thereabouts. I really was an eyeful then. Trim athletic figure, finely chiseled features and more hair on the top of my head than you could shake a stick at. I would have been more than willing to exhibit myself to America's millions then. But now I have definitely gone off quite a bit, and that is why, when this publicity man calls up and starts persecuting me with his loathsome addresses, I have my answer ready, quick as a flash.

"Terribly sorry," I say. "I'm just off to the Coast."

Heaven bless the Coast. It is the one safe refuge. Even press representatives or public relations lizards or whatever they call themselves know they can't get at you there. And these constant visits to the Coast are improving my prestige. "Wodehouse always seems to be going to Hollywood," people say. "Yes," reply the people these people are addressing, "the demand for him in the studios is tremendous." "Odd one never sees his name on screen credits," say the first people. "Oh, no." (Second people speaking.) "He writes under a number of pseudonyms. Makes a fortune, I understand."

. . . 13 THE GIRL IN THE PINK BATHING SUIT

1

As a matter of fact, I have been to Hollywood, though not recently. I went there in 1930. I had a year's contract, and was required to do so little work in return for the money I received that I was able in the twelve months before I became a fugitive from the chain gang to write a novel and fourteen short stories, besides brushing up my golf, getting an attractive suntan and perfecting my Australian crawl in the swimming pool.

It is all sadly changed now, they tell me. Once a combination of Santa Claus and Good-Time Charlie, Hollywood has become a Scrooge.[1] The dear old days are dead and the spirit of cheerful giving a thing of the past. But in 1930 the talkies had just started, and the slogan was come one, come all, and the more the merrier. It was an era when only a man of exceptional ability and determination could keep from getting signed up by a studio in some capacity or other. I happened to be engaged as a writer, but I might quite as easily have been scooped in as a technical adviser or a vocal instructor. (At least I had a roof to my mouth, which many vocal instructors in Hollywood at that time had not.) The heartiness and hospitality reminded one of the Jolly Innkeeper (with entrance number in Act One) of the old-style comic opera.

One can understand it, of course. The advent of sound had made the manufacture of motion pictures an infinitely more complex affair than it had been up till then. In the silent days everything had been informal and casual, just a lot of great big happy schoolboys getting together for a bit of fun. Ike would have a strip of celluloid, Spike a camera his uncle had given him for Christmas, Mike would know a friend or two who liked dressing up and having their photographs taken, and with these modest assets they would club together their pocket money and start the Finer and Supremer Films Corporation. And as for bothering about getting anyone to write them a story, it never occurred to them. They made it up themselves as they went along.

The talkies changed all that. It was no longer possible just to put on a toga, have someone press a button and call the

1. *Scrooge:* miser in Charles Dickens' *Christmas Carol* (1843).

result *The Grandeur That Was Rome* or *In the Days of Nero*.
A whole elaborate new organization was required. You had to
have a studio Boss to boss the Producer, a Producer to produce
the Supervisor, a Supervisor to supervise the sub-Supervisor,
a sub-Supervisor to sub-supervise the Director, a Director to
direct the Camera Man and an Assistant Director to assist the
Director. And, above all, you had to get hold of someone to
supply the words.

The result was a terrible shortage of authors in all the
world's literary centers. New York till then had been full of
them. You would see them frisking in perfect masses in any
editorial office you happened to enter. Their sharp, excited
yapping was one of the features of the first or second-act
intermission of every new play that was produced. And in
places like Greenwich Village you had to watch your step
very carefully to avoid treading on them.

And then all of a sudden all you saw was an occasional
isolated one being shooed out of a publisher's sanctum or
sitting in a speakeasy sniffing at his press clippings. Time after
time fanciers would come up to you with hard-luck stories.

"You know that novelist of mine with the flapping ears
and the spots on his coat? Well, he's gone."

"Gone?"

"Absolutely vanished. I left him on the steps of the club,
and when I came out there were no signs of him."

"Same here," says another fancier. "I had a brace of playwrights to whom I was greatly attached, and they've disappeared without a word."

Well, of course, people took it for granted that the little
fellows had strayed and had got run over, for authors are
notoriously dreamy in traffic and, however carefully you
train them, will persist in stopping in the middle of the street
to jot down strong bits of dialogue. It was only gradually
that the truth came out. They had all been decoyed away to
Hollywood.

What generally happened was this. A couple of the big film executives—say Mr. Louis B. Mayer and Mr. Adolf Zukor—would sight their quarry in the street and track him down to some bohemian eating resort. Having watched him settle, they seat themselves at a table immediately behind him, and for a few moments there is silence, broken only by the sound of the author eating corned beef hash. Then Mr. Mayer addresses Mr. Zukor, raising his voice slightly.

"Whatever was the name of that girl?" he says.

"What girl?" asks Mr. Zukor, cleverly taking his cue.

"That tall, blonde girl with the large blue eyes."

"The one in the pink bathing suit?"

"That's right. With the freckle in the small of her back."

"A freckle? A mole, I always understood."

"No, it was a freckle, eyewitnesses tell me. Just over the base of the spinal cord. Well, anyway, what was her name?"

"Now what was it? Eulalie something? Clarice something? No, it's gone. But I'll find out for you when we get home. I know her intimately."

Here they pause, but not for long. There is a sound of quick, emotional breathing. The author is standing beside them, a rapt expression on his face.

"Pardon me, gentlemen," he says, "for interrupting a private conversation, but I chanced to overhear you saying that you were intimately acquainted with a tall, blonde girl with large blue eyes, in the habit of wearing bathing suits of just the type I like best. It is for a girl of that description that I have been scouring the country for years. Where may she be found?"

"In God's Back Garden—Hollywood," says Mr. Zukor.

"Pity you can't meet her," says Mr. Mayer. "You're just her type."

"If you were by any chance an author," says Mr. Zukor, "we could take you back with us tomorrow. Too bad you're not."

"Prepare yourselves for a surprise, gentlemen," says the victim. "I *am* an author. George Montague Breamworthy. 'Powerfully devised situations'—*New York Times.* 'Sheer, stark realism'—New York *Herald Tribune.* 'Whoops!'—*Women's Wear.*'"

"In that case," says Mr. Mayer, producing a contract, "sign here."

"Where my thumb is," says Mr. Zukor.

The trap has snapped.

2

That was how they got me, and it was, I understand, the usual method of approach. But sometimes this plan failed, and then sterner methods were employed. The demand for authors in those early talkie days was so great that it led to the revival of the old press-gang. Nobody was safe even if he merely looked like an author.

While having a Malted Milk Greta Garbo with some of the old lags in the commissary one morning about halfway through my term of sentence, I was told of one very interesting case. It appeared that there was a man who had gone out West hoping to locate oil. One of those men without a thought in the world outside of oil; the last thing he had ever dreamed of doing was being an author. With the exception of letters and an occasional telegram of greeting to some relative at Christmas, he had never written anything in his life.

But, by some curious chance, it happened that his appearance was that of one capable of the highest feats in the way of literary expression. He had a domelike head, piercing eyes, and that cynical twist of the upper lip which generally means an epigram on the way. Still, as I say, he was not a writer, and no one could have been more surprised than he was when, walking along a deserted street in Los Angeles, thinking of oil, he was suddenly set upon by masked men, chloroformed, and whisked away in a closed car. When he came to himself he was in a cell on the Perfecto-Zizzbaum lot with paper and a sharpened pencil before him, and stern-featured men in felt hats and raincoats were waggling rubber hoses at him and telling him to get busy and turn out something with lots of sex in it, but not too much, because of Will Hays.[2]

The story has a curious sequel. A philosopher at heart, he accepted the situation. He wrenched his mind away from oil and scribbled a few sentences that happened to occur to him. He found, as so many have found, that an author's is the easiest job in existence, and soon he was scratching away as briskly as you could wish. And that is how Noel Coward[3] got his start.

But not every kidnaped author accepted his fate so equably. The majority endeavored to escape. But it was useless. Even if the rigors of the pitiless California climate did not drive them back to shelter, capture was inevitable. When I was in Hollywood there was much indignation among the better element of the community over the pursuit of an unfortunate woman writer whom the harshness of her supervisor, a man of the name of Legree, had driven to desperation. As I got the story, they chased her across the ice with bloodhounds.

The whole affair was very unpleasant and shocked the softhearted greatly. So much so that a Mrs. Harriet Beecher Stowe[4] told me that if M.G.M. would meet her terms for the movie, she intended to write a book about it which would stir the world.

"Boy," she said to me, "it will be a scorcher!"

I don't know if anything ever came of it.

---

2. *Will Hays:* movie censor of the 1930's.
3. *Noel Coward:* modern British playwright.
4. *Harriet Beecher Stowe:* author of *Uncle Tom's Cabin* (1811-1896).

3

I got away from Hollywood at the end of the year because
the jailer's daughter smuggled me in a file in a meat pie, but
I was there long enough to realize what a terribly demoraliz-
ing place it is. The whole atmosphere there is one of insidious
deceit and subterfuge. Nothing is what it affects to be. What
looks like a tree is really a slab of wood backed with barrels.
What appears on the screen as the towering palace of
Haroun-al-Raschid is actually a cardboard model occupying
four feet by three of space. The languorous lagoon is simply
a smelly tank with a stagehand named Ed wading about in
it in bathing trunks.

It is surely not difficult to imagine the effect of all this on
a sensitive-minded author. Taught at his mother's knee to
love the truth, he finds himself surrounded by people making
fortunes by what can only be called chicanery. After a month
or two in such an environment could you trust that author
to count his golf shots correctly or to give his right sales
figures?

And then there was—I am speaking of the old days. It is
possible that modern enlightened thought has brought improvements—the inevitable sapping of his self-respect. At
the time of which I am writing authors in Hollywood were
kept in little hutches. In every studio there were rows and
rows of these, each containing an author on a long contract
at a weekly salary. You could see their anxious little faces
peering out through the bars and hear them whining pite-
ously to be taken for a walk. One had to be very callous
not to be touched by such a spectacle.

I do not say that these authors were actually badly treated.
In the best studios in those early talkie days kindness was
the rule. Often you would see some high executive stop
and give one of them a lettuce. And it was the same with
the humaner type of director. In fact, between the directors

and their authors there frequently existed a rather touching friendship. I remember one director telling a story which illustrates this.

One morning, he said, he was on his way to his office, pre-occupied, as was his habit when planning out the day's work, when he felt a sudden tug at his coattails. He looked down and there was his pet author, Edgar Montrose (Book Society Recommendation) Delamere. The little fellow had got him in a firm grip and was gazing up at him, in his eyes an almost human expression of warning.

Well, the director, not unnaturally, mistook this at first for mere playfulness, for it was often his kindly habit to romp with his little charges. Then something seemed to whisper to him that he was being withheld from some great peril. He remembered stories he had read as a boy—one of which he was even then directing for Rin-Tin-Tin[5]—where faithful dogs dragged their masters back from the brink of precipices on dark nights, and, scarcely knowing why, he turned and went off to the commissary and had a Strawberry and Vanilla Nut Sundae Mary Pickford.

It was well that he did. In his office, waiting to spring, there was lurking a foreign star with a bad case of tempera-ment, whose bite might have been fatal. You may be sure that Edgar Montrose had a good meal that night.

But that was an isolated case. Not all directors were like this one. Too many of them crushed the spirit of the captives by incessant blue-penciling of their dialogue, causing them to become listless and lose appetite. Destructive criticism is what kills an author. Cut his material too much, make him feel that he is not a Voice, give him the impression that his big scene is all wet, and you will soon see the sparkle die out of his eyes.

I don't know how conditions are today, but at that time

5. *Rin-Tin-Tin:* dog movie performer.

there were authors who had been on salary for years in Hollywood without ever having a line of their work used. All they did was attend story conferences. There were other authors whom nobody had seen for years. It was like the Bastille.[6] They just sat in some hutch away in a corner somewhere and grew white beards and languished. From time to time somebody would renew their contract, and then they were forgotten again.

As I say, it may be different now. After all, I am speaking of twenty-five years ago. But I do think it would be wise if author-fanciers exercised vigilance. You never know. The press-gang may still be in our midst.

So when you take your pet for a walk, keep an eye on him. If he goes sniffing after strange men, whistle him back.

And remember that the spring is the dangerous time. Around the beginning of May, authors get restless and start dreaming about girls in abbreviated swim suits. It is easy to detect the symptoms. The moment you hear yours muttering about the Golden West and God's Sunshine and Out There Beyond the Stifling City put sulphur in his absinthe and lock him up in the kitchenette.

. . . 14 FRANCIS BACON AND THE PLAY DOCTOR

1

AND NOW Ho for a chapter on the theater and what I have done to put it on the map.

A dramatist friend of mine was telling me the other day that he had written his last play. He was embittered because the star for whom he had been waiting for two years backed out on obtaining a big television contract and another star for whom he had been waiting two years before that suddenly went off to Hollywood. And this after he had worked

6. *Bastille:* French prison.

like a beaver rewriting his play to suit the views of the manager, the manager's wife, the principal backer and the principal backer's son, a boy of some fourteen summers named Harold, on whose judgment the principal backer placed great reliance.

Furthermore, he said, he could no longer face those out-of-town preliminary tours, with their "Nobody comes to the theater on Monday in these small towns. Wait till Tuesday," "Well, Tuesday, everyone knows, is a bad night everywhere. Wait till Wednesday," and "You can't get 'em into the theater on a Wednesday. Wait till Thursday. Thursday will tell the story." And always the manager at his elbow, chewing two inches of an unlighted cigar and muttering, "Well, boy, there ain't no doubt but what it's going to need a lot of work."

Myself, I have never regretted my flirtations with the drama. They cost me a lot of blood, sweat and tears, not to mention making me lose so much hair that nowadays I am often mistaken in a dim light for a Hallowe'en pumpkin, but one met such interesting people. I have encountered in the coulisses enough unforgettable characters to fix up the *Reader's Digest* for years and years. Most of these are enshrined in the pages of a book called *Bring on the Girls* which Guy Bolton and I wrote not long ago.

My first play was written in collaboration with a boy named Henry Cullimore when I was pushing seven. I don't quite know what made us decide to do it, but we did so decide, and Henry said we would have to have a plot. "What's a plot?" I asked. He didn't know. He had read or heard somewhere that a plot was a good thing to have, but as to what it was he confessed himself fogged. This naturally made us both feel a little stymied, but we agreed that there was nothing to do but carry on and hope that everything would pan out all right. (Chekhov[1] used to do this.)

He—Henry Cullimore, not Chekhov—was the senior part-

1. *Chekhov*: Anton Chekhov (1860-1904), Russian dramatist.

ner in the project. He was two or three years older than I
was, which gave him an edge, and he had a fountain pen. I
mostly contributed moral support, pursuing the same method
which I later found to answer so well when I teamed up
with Guy Bolton. When Guy and I pitched in on a play,
he would do the rough spadework—the writing—and I used
to look in on him from time to time and say "How are you
getting on?" He would say, "All right," and I would say,
"Fine," and go off and read Agatha Christie.[2] Giving it the
Wodehouse Touch, I used to call it. And so little by little
and bit by bit the thing would get done.

This system worked capitally with all the Bolton-Wode-
house productions, and I believe it was the way Beaumont
and Fletcher[3] used to hammer out their combined efforts.
("How goeth it, my heart of gold?" "Yarely, old mole. Well,
fairly yarely." "Stick at it, boy. Hard work never hurt anyone.") But Henry Cullimore let me down. A broken reed,
if ever there was one. He got as far as

ACT ONE

(Enter Henry)

HENRY: What's for breakfast? Ham and oatmeal? Very nice.

but there he stopped. He had shot his bolt.

How he was planning to go on if the divine afflatus had
not blown a fuse, I never discovered. I should imagine that
the oatmeal proved to be poisoned—("One of the barbiturate
group, Inspector, unless I am greatly mistaken")—or a dead
body dropped out of the closet where they kept the sugar.

The thing was never produced. A pity, for I think it
would have been a great audience show.

Since then I have been mixed up in sixteen straight plays
and twenty-two musical comedies as author, part author or

2. *Agatha Christie:* contemporary mystery writer.
3. *Beaumont and Fletcher:* Francis Beaumont (1584-1616) and John
Fletcher (1579-1625), English writing team.

just hanging onto the author in the capacity of Charles his friend. In virtually every theatrical enterprise there is a Charles his friend, drawing his weekly royalties. Nobody ever quite knows how he wriggled in, but there he is. Affability of manner has a good deal to do with it.

But though I attached myself to these straight plays, some of them the most outstanding flops in the history of the stage, my heart was never really in them. Musical comedy was my dish, the musical comedy theater my spiritual home. I would rather have written *Oklahoma!* than *Hamlet.*[4] (Actually, as the records show, I wrote neither, but you get the idea.)

It was in 1904 that I burst on the theatrical scene with a lyric in a thing called *Sergeant Brue* at the Prince of Wales Theater in London. In 1906 I got a job at two pounds a week as a sort of utility lyricist at the Aldwych Theater in the same town. This, as I have already recorded, involved writing some numbers with a young American composer named Jerome Kern, and when, a good many years later, I ran into him and Guy Bolton in New York, we got together and did what were known as the Princess shows, hot stuff in their day. After that I worked with Victor Herbert, George Gershwin, Rudolf Friml, Vincent Youmans, Emmerich Kalman, Ivan Caryll, Franz Lehar and what seems to me now about a hundred other composers. For years scarcely a day passed whose low descending sun did not see me at my desk trying to find some rhyme for "June" that would not be "soon," "moon," "tune" or "spoon." (Billy Rose at the outset of his career suddenly thought of "macaroon" and from that moment never looked back.)

It is not to be wondered at, then, that when I can spare a moment of my valuable time, I find myself brooding on the musical comedy theater of today. The subject is one of com-

---

4. *Oklahoma!* . . . *Hamlet: Oklahoma!* is a musical by Rodgers and Hammerstein; *Hamlet* is the great tragedy by William Shakespeare.

pelling interest. What is going to happen to it? Can it last? If so, how much longer? Will there come a day when we reach out for it and find it isn't there? Are the rising costs of production ever going to stop rising? And if they don't stop rising, what will the harvest be? It is difficult enough to prise the required two hundred and fifty thousand dollars out of the investing public now. What of tomorrow, when it will probably be half a million?

Have you ever tried to touch anyone for two hundred and fifty thousand dollars? It is by no means the same thing as asking for a five till Wednesday, old man. It takes doing. Howard Dietz, on whom be peace, once wrote an opening chorus for a revue which Max Gordon produced. It ran:

> What's all that cheering in the streets?
> What's all that cheering you're
>   hearing in the streets?
> Max Gordon's raised the money,
> Max Gordon's raised the money . . .

and while joining in the cheering, one cannot help dropping a silent tear as one thinks of what Max must have gone through. And in his capacity of prominent Broadway manager, he presumably had to do it again and again and again.

How anyone who has once raised the money for a New York musical can bring himself to do it a second time is more than I can imagine. A few years ago a management decided that the moment had come to revive a show with which I had been connected somewhere around 1920 and asked me to come to a "backers' audition." I was there through the grim proceedings, and came away feeling like one of those can-you-spare-a-nickel-for-a-cup-of-coffee gentlemen of leisure who pop up through the sidewalk in front of you as you take your walks abroad down Washington Square way. My hat, quite a good one, seemed battered and shapeless, there were cracks in the uppers of my shoes, and an unwholesome growth of hair had sprouted on my cheeks, accompanied by a redness and swelling of the nose. I felt soiled. (There were headlines in all the papers—WODEHOUSE FEELS SOILED.)

A backers' audition is composed of cringing mendicants— the management, a pianist, some hired singers and some friends and supporters who are there to laugh and applaud —and a little group of fat, rich men with tight lips and faces carved out of granite, whom you have assembled somehow and herded into a hotel suite. These are the backers, or it might be better to say you hope they are the backers, for while there is unquestionably gold in them thar heels, the problem is how to extract it.

Cigars, drinks, and caviar have been provided, and the management proceeds to read the script, pausing at intervals to allow the hired singers to render the songs. The fat, rich men sit there with their eyes bulging, in a silence broken only by the champing of jaws and a musical gurgle as another highball goes down the gullet, and then, loaded to the Plimsoll mark[5] with caviar, they file out, not having uttered a word.

And this goes on and on. In order to collect the money to produce *Oklahoma!* eighty-nine of these auditions had to be given. I imagine that it was not till about the sixty-third that somebody stirred in his chair and brought out a checkbook. Perhaps one of the songs had touched his heart, reminding him of something his mother used to sing when he clustered about her knee, or possibly conscience whispered to him that as he was all that caviar ahead of the game, he ought to do something about it. So he wrote his check.

But for how much? Ten thousand? Twenty thousand? Even if it was fifty thousand it merely scratched the surface. It is a matter of record that *Oklahoma!* was still twenty thou-

5. *Plimsoll mark:* indicates when a ship is fully loaded.

sand short when it opened out of town, and would never
have been brought into New York if S. N. Behrman[6] had
not come to the rescue.

However, let us suppose that somehow you have contrived
to wheedle two hundred and fifty thousand dollars out of
the money classes. What then? You are then faced with the
prospect of having to play to thirty-three thousand a week
simply to break even. I was shown the weekly balance sheet
of an apparently very prosperous musical comedy the other
day. The gross box-office receipts were $36,442.90, which
sounds fine, but after all expenses had been paid the profit
on the week was $3,697.83. I am no mathematician, but it
looked to me as if they would have to go on doing about
$37,000 a week for about a year and a half before the
backers drew a cent. No wonder these prudent men are often
inclined to settle for free cigars and caviar and not get mixed
up in all that sordid business of paying out money.

That is why if you ever catch me in pensive mood, sitting
with the chin supported in the hand and the elbow on the
knee, like Rodin's "Thinker," you can be pretty sure that I
am saying to myself, "Whither the New York musical-comedy theater?" or possibly, "The New York musical-comedy
theater . . . whither?" It is a question that constantly exercises me. I can't see what, as the years roll by and costs
continue to rise, is going to happen to the darn thing.

Financing a straight play is, of course, simpler, but even
this is not easy. Perhaps the best plan is to follow the example
of a recent manager who induced a rich acquaintance to part
with the necessary cash by reading him Eugene O'Neill's
The Hairy Ape.

"Good, don't you think?" he said.

"Terrific," said the rich acquaintance. The manager then
used the money to put on a bedroom farce which he had

6. *S. N. Behrman:* modern American playwright.

written, and when the backer saw it on the opening night in Philadelphia, he was a little puzzled.

"But this isn't the play you read me," he said.

"Oh, well," said the manager, "you know how these things always get changed around a bit at rehearsals."

2

It is the stagehand situation that causes a good deal of the present unrest. This situation—I am speaking of the stage-hand situation—is quite a situation. The trouble—briefly—is this. Stagehands cost money, and theatrical managers hate parting with money. The scene-shifters' union, on the other hand, is all for it. Blow the expense, says the scene-shifters' union. It likes to see money scattered in handfuls, always provided it is someone else's (or someone's else, as the case may be). This leads to strained relations, pique on both sides and the calling of some most unpleasant names. I have heard managers refer to the union as vampires, while the union, speaking of the managers, is far too prone to make nasty cracks about people who are so tight they could carry an armful of eels up six flights of stairs and never drop one of them.

Most plays nowadays are in one set, and a manager who puts on a one-set play feels that once this one set is in posi-tion he ought to be able to pay the scene-shifters off and kiss them good-by. He sees no reason why he should have to pay a weekly wage to a gang of scene-shifters just for not shifting scenes. All he wants is an operative who will go over the set from time to time with a feather duster, to keep the moths from getting into it.

The union does not take this view. It holds that if the manager hasn't any scenes to shift he darned well ought to have, and it insists on him employing the number of scene-shifters who would have been required to shift the scenes if there had been any scenes to shift, if you follow me. And as any attempt to brook the will of the union leads to a strike of stagehands, which leads to a strike of electricians, which leads to a strike of actors, box-office officials, gentlemanly ushers and the theater cat, it gets its way. Thus we find Ruth Draper,[7] who does her stuff with no scenery at all, obliged during her latest engagement to employ seven stagehands. Victor Borge, giving a two-hour solo performance on the piano at the Booth, had eight. (Why this discrimination?) And a recent one-set comedy with three characters in it was attended nightly by no fewer than fifteen admirers and well-wishers. Some plays these last seasons have suffered from audience thinness, but no manager has ever run short of stagehands. They are there from the moment the curtain goes up, with their hair in a braid.

At the risk of becoming too technical, I must explain briefly how a troupe of stagehands with nothing to do is organized. There is, I need scarcely say, nothing haphazard about it. First—chosen by show of hands (stagehands)—comes the head man or Giant Sloth. His job is to hang upside down from a rafter. Next we have the Senior Lounger and the Junior Lounger, who lie on couches—Roman fashion—with chaplets of roses around their foreheads. Last comes the rank and file, the twelve Lilies of the Field. It was because I was uncertain as to the duties of these that I looked in the other night at one of the theaters to get myself straight on the point, and was courteously received by the Junior Lounger, a Mr. B. J. Wilberforce, who showed no annoyance at being interrupted while working on his crossword puzzle.

"I was wondering, Mr. Wilberforce," I said, when greetings and compliments had been exchanged, "if you could tell me something about this situation."

"What situation would that be?" he asked.

---

7. *Ruth Draper:* monologist.

"The scene-shifter situation," I said, and he frowned.

"We prefer not to be called scene-shifters," he explained. "There seems to us something a little vulgar about shifting scenes. It smacks too much of those elaborate musical productions, where, I am told, the boys often get quite hot and dusty. We of the elite like to think of ourselves as America's leisure class. Of course, when there is work to be done, we do it. Only the other night, for instance, the director thought that it would brighten things up if an upstage chair were moved to a downstage position. We were called into conference, and long before the curtain rose for the evening's performance the thing was done. Superintended by the Giant Sloth, we Loungers—myself and my immediate superior, Cyril Muspratt—each grasped one side of the seat and that chair was moved, and it would have been the same if it had been two chairs. I am not saying it did not take it out of us. It did. But we do not spare ourselves when the call comes."

"Still, it does not come often, I suppose? As a general rule, you have your leisure?"

"Ah, yes. We have lots of time to fool around in."

"Never end a sentence with a preposition, Wilberforce," I said warningly, and he blushed. I had spoken kindly, but you could see it stung.

At this moment somebody on the stage said in a loud voice: "My God! My wife!"—they were playing one of those Victorian farce revivals designed to catch the nostalgia trade —and he winced.

"All this noise!" he said. "One realizes that actors have to make a living, but there is no need for a lot of racket and disturbance. It is most disagreeable for a man doing his crossword puzzle and trying to concentrate on a word in three letters beginning with E and signifying 'large Australian bird' to be distracted by sudden sharp cries. Still, it might be worse. At the Bijou, where they are doing one of those gangster things, the Giant Sloth was often woken three or four times in an evening by pistol shots. He had to complain about it, and now, I believe, the actors just say, 'Bang, bang!' in an undertone. Three letters beginning with E," he mused.

I knew it could not be the sun god Ra. Then suddenly I got it.

"Emu!"

"I beg your pardon?"

"That large Australian bird you were speaking of."

"Of which you were speaking. Never end a sentence with a preposition, Wodehouse."

Sensing that tempers were rising, I bade him good night and went on my way. So I still don't know how those Lilies of the Field fill in their time. Perhaps they just catch up with their reading.

They tell a tale in Shubert Alley[8] of a manager who walked one day on Forty-Fifth Street west of Broadway and paused to watch workmen razing the Avon Theater.

"Gosh!" he said, much moved. "They're using fewer men to tear down the building than we used to have to hire to strike a one-set show."

And there, gentle reader, let us leave him.

3

One enormous improvement in the theater of today is the almost total disappearance of the play doctor or play fixer or whatever he liked to call himself. The best description of this pest is the one given by George S. Kaufman in his 1925 comedy, *The Butter and Egg Man*. In Act Two, while the after-the-opening-at-Syracuse conference is in progress, there is a knock at the door, and Bernie Sampson comes in.

"Bernie Sampson," says Mr. Kaufman, "is a young man with that air of sophistication about him that can be acquired

8. *Shubert Alley:* lane in New York's theater district.

only through long service on Broadway. Once, many years
before, he had made a suggestion for the improvement of a
play that had just opened out of town. The suggestion was
misunderstood by the producer, and the mistaken suggestion
saved the play. Ever since then Bernie Sampson has been a
recognized play fixer."

Shakespeare, the Baconians[9] maintain, was nothing but a
Bernie Sampson. All the work he did, they say, was to practice spelling his signature on the covers of the prompt copy,
and in support of this contention a Baconian of my acquaintance tells a story which he claims is thoroughly documented
—only unfortunately in a cipher which nobody but he can
read.

It seems, according to this man, that Bacon, best known
to the reading public of his day as the author of two bright
little works entitled *Novum Organum* and *De Interpretatione
Naturae*, had always had the firm conviction that he could
write a play. He was, in short, a dreamer. (Aren't we all?)
So in the intervals of looking after the Exchequer, of which,
it will be remembered, he was the genial and popular Chancellor, he sat down with the old quill and inkhorn and dashed
off a tragedy called *Hamlet*.

He then began sending it around to the managers.

The first manager kept it six months, and, when Bacon
wrote enquiring after it, sent him back a farcical comedy by
Marlowe, Ben Jonson and Peele, regretting that it was not
in his power, much as he admired it personally, to produce
the same.

Bacon sighed, and sent another copy to another manager.

When a year had elapsed, he wrote, apologizing for what
might seem impatience on his part but asking if any decision
on his drama *Hamlet* had been arrived at. Five weeks later,

9. *Baconians:* people who believe that Sir Francis Bacon, essayist, philosopher, lawyer and politician of Shakespeare's time, is the author of the plays
attributed to Shakespeare.

he received by the same post his manuscript and a letter from the manager saying that there had evidently been some mistake, for no such manuscript had come to his office.

By this time Bacon had begun to realize, as so many have realized since, that things theatrical are inseparable from a sort of brisk delirium usually associated only with the interiors of homes for those who have found the strain too much for them. And he had just decided to give the thing up and start on another book of essays when quite unexpectedly a manager who had had the script three years and had quite gone out of his mind (Bacon's mind), wrote asking him to call. And after waiting for four hours in the outer office with a crowd of blue-chinned men who were telling each other how they had jumped in and saved the show when they were with the Earl of Worcester's company, he was shown in.

"Now, this what's-it-name-of-yours," said the manager, "this *Hamlet*—of course, we'll have to change the title—I think it's got a chance. But it needs fixing. You're new to this game, I imagine?"

Bacon muttered something about having done a bit of writing.

"Plays?"

"Essays."

"Essays!" said the manager with a short laugh. "Well, as I was saying, we'll have to get the thing fixed. And the man to do it is young Shakespeare. Clever boy. In my company. He'll know what to do with it. Now about terms. You get one per cent of the gross."

Bacon, who as Chancellor of the Exchequer was pretty good at figures, protested that one per cent of the gross was not enough.

"Now, sweetheart," said the manager—all right, I'll come right out with it. It was Burbage—"Don't you begin opening your mouth too wide, like the rest of them. When you came into my office, I said to myself 'There's a sensible, level-headed young chap,' I said to myself. 'You won't find him wanting the earth.' You aren't going to make me alter my opinion? Of course you aren't. Why, if we do fifteen ducats, four pieces of eight and a rose noble on the Saturday night, you'll make a pile out of one per cent. Sign here."

A shrewd man, Bacon realized that there was nothing else for him to do. The superstition current in theatrical circles that there was a kind of magic in play-writing, and that nobody could fathom the mysteries of the craft unless he was one of the small coterie who spent their time in the Mermaid Tavern buying sack for managers, was too strong for him. He knew his *Hamlet* was good, but he had gathered by this time that he would never get it produced unless he consented to hand it over to the man who had been "twenty years in the business" to pull to pieces. So he signed the contract, and Burbage sent the office boy round to the Mermaid for Shakespeare.

A week later they all lunched together at that hostelry. Shakespeare had the script with him, and when the meal was over he took from his doublet a fat sheaf of notes.

"Well, kid," he said, "I've read that soap opera of yours. Of course there ain't no doubt but what it needs a lot of work. For one thing, your finish is weak. What you want at the final curtain is to have the whole crowd jump on one another and everybody kill everybody else. Lookut. The King poisons the wine and Laertes poisons the sword and then Laertes plugs Hamlet with the sword and drops it and Hamlet picks it up in mistake for his own and plugs Laertes, and then the Queen drinks the poisoned wine and Hamlet sticks the King with the poisoned sword. Is that good, or is it good?"

"It's swell, Bill," said Burbage.

"But surely," said Bacon, "isn't all that a little improbable?"

"It's what the public wants," said Shakespeare coldly. "Or maybe you think I don't know?"

"Sure he knows you know, Bill," interposed Burbage soothingly. "Don't get your shirt out. We're all working for the good of the show. Is there anything else?"

"Is there anything else! Why, there's nothing else but something else. The whole thing's a mess."

"Is that so?" said Bacon.

Bacon.

Shakespeare.

"Yeah, this *is* so," said Shakespeare. "Why, you've made your hero a looney."

"His sufferings drove him mad," said Bacon.

"Not in any charade I'm going to have anything to do with his sufferings didn't," retorted Shakespeare. "Listen! I've been in this business twenty years——"

"And can't even spell your own name."

"I can too spell my own name."

"Well, what is it? Shakespeare, Shakspere, Shikspur or Shakspur? It comes out different every time."

"It does, does it?"

"Yes, it does."

"Well, be that as it may, you can't ask an audience to root for a looney."

Burbage intervened again.

" 'S all right, Bill," he said, patting Shakespeare's arm, " 's all right. Frankie knows that as well as we do. He gets the angle. You see, Frankie, we gotta think of the Wednesday matinee audiences. Wednesday matinee audiences don't like loonies. So you'll make him not crazy, Bill?"

"I'll do better than that. I'll make him *pretend* he's crazy. See? Everybody fooled but the audience."

"I told you this boy was clever," said Burbage to Bacon, who had turned rather pale and was beginning to pluck at the tablecloth.

"I still think he ought to be mad," he said.

"Well, I'll tell you what I'm sure Bill here will do to meet you, Frankie. He'll make the girl, Ophelia, mad. The customers don't mind a girl being crackers."

"All girls are crackers, anyway," said Shakespeare, speaking in rather a peevish tone, as if he had been reminded of some private grievances. He paused, and frowned thoughtfully as he turned his notes. " 'To be or not to be . . .' " he murmured, "I'm wondering about that 'To be or not to be' speech. They don't like soliloquies."

Bacon was now thoroughly aroused.

"Says you!"

"Yeah, says me."

"How about Elmer Rice[10] and *Dream Girl*?"

"That's all right about Elmer Rice. Those Yanks'll do anything."

---

10. *Elmer Rice:* modern American playwright.

"Now, now, boys," said Burbage. "Hello, you leaving, Frankie?"

"Yes," said Bacon. "I am going to take a couple of aspirins and try to forget."

That is the story my Baconian acquaintance tells. And when I asked him how it came about that no mention of Bacon's share in the authorship has come down to us, he had his answer to that.

Shakespeare, he says, did offer to have the program read as follows:

HAMLET
BY
WILLIAM SHAKESPEARE
(Based on a suggestion by F. Bacon)

But Bacon, after sitting through a rehearsal or two and reading the revised script, decided to take his name off the bills.

. . . 15 SAY IT WITH RATTLESNAKES

"AND NOW tell me, Mr. Wodehouse. You knew America when. What strikes you as the principal changes in the American scene—or, if you prefer it, the New York scene—since you first visited the country as a pie-faced lad in your early twenties fifty-one years ago? Come on, Grandpop. Last chapter. Say a few words."

"Well . . . New York scene, you said?"

"That's right."

"You don't want a lot of guff about Rockefeller Center and the Triborough Bridge?"

"No, no. Human interest stuff."

"Well, lemme think. Jussa minute. Changes? Principal changes?"

"Are there things, for instance, from the old days that you miss in these modern times?"

"Now you're talking. I miss those sacred concerts."

"Those—what was that once again?"

"Sacred concerts. On Sundays. When I first came to New York, they were the only form of Sunday entertainment the authorities would allow. They took place at the Palace or the Winter Garden, and began with some devotional exercises by Professor Wilkinson's Almost Human Seals, followed by the Hoopla Troupe, Acrobats Extraordinary, and Vokes and Dooley, the Somewhat Different Cross-Talk Comics. Then came Mick, Mac and Mabel in their Merry Mélange of Hoofing and Hilarity. Freddie Fitzgibbon, the Personality Kid, and so on through Vosper, the Ventriloquist and the Brothers Alonzo with their Jaunty Juggling to Sid Sterling and Company in the dramatic sketch 'She Was Only a Fireman's Daughter.' "

"Ah, yes, I see. Vaudeville shows."

"Nothing of the kind. Vaudeville shows, indeed! Do you think the City Fathers would have allowed vaudeville shows on Sunday? These were sacred concerts. The celebrants wore their ordinary clothes. That, in the view of the City Fathers, was the acid test. If you did your stuff in a green wig, purple dress clothes and a scarlet top hat, you were a vaudeville act. Stick to mufti, and you became a sacred concert. When Vokes enquired of Dooley the identity of the lady with whom he had seen him walking down the street, he was clad in blue serge. And when Dooley replied that his female companion was not a lady but his wife, he did it in a dotted herringbone suit with satin-lined sleeves and scallops on the pocket flaps. It was all very devout."

"No doubt you attribute your present depth of character to those sacred concerts?"

"A good deal of it. Call it two-thirds."

"I'm sorry I was too young to join the congregation myself. It must have been most inspirational. An amusing little misunderstanding, that, between Vokes and Dooley."

"Oh, very."

"And what other changes have you noticed, Mr. Wodehouse?"

"Well, there's the American Christmas. It's not the simple festival it used to be. It seems to have got elephantiasis or something."

"We celebrate it, you mean, in a big way nowadays?"

"Too big, in my opinion. I don't want to do anyone an injustice, but the thought has sometimes crossed my mind that some of these department stores are trying to make money out of Christmas."

"Oh, surely not?"

"The idea horrifies you?"

"Intensely."

"It horrified Mr. Macy and Mr. Gimbel when I put it up to them. 'Absurd,' said Mr. Macy. 'Good heavens, no, dear old chap,' said Mr. Gimbel.[1] But I still have my doubts. All these Santa Clauses pulling in the customers."

"Now there's a job I shouldn't care to have. Children crawling all over you."

"Yes, I was talking to one of them the other day in a drugstore where he had gone in his brief time off to refresh himself with a small wassail bowl. I asked him if he didn't ever falter. He gave me a look. He said that a Santa Claus who faltered would receive short shrift from his brother Santa Clauses. Before you could say 'Saks Fifth Avenue' he would find himself in a hollow square, being formally stripped of his whiskers and stomach padding."

"They are a very proud guild, I believe."

"He told me one thing that shocked me a good deal. For years I have been worrying myself sick, wondering why yaks' tails were imported into the United States from Tibet. I could not understand there being any popular demand for them. I know that if someone came up to me and said 'Mr. Wodehouse, I have long been a great admirer of your work and

---

1. *Mr. Macy and Mr. Gimbel:* founders of rival department-store chains.

would like to make some small return for the many happy
hours you have given me. Take this yak's tail, and make of it
a constant companion,' I would thank him and giggle a little
and say how frightfully good of him and it was just what I
had been wanting, but I should most certainly leave the thing
in the subway on my way home. I now have the facts. Yaks'
tails are used for making beards for department-store Santa
Clauses. You wince, I notice."

"Yes, I do. I find a picture rising before my eyes of some
unfortunate yak wandering around Tibet without a tail. You
don't have to know much about the sensitive nature of the
yak to realize what this must mean."

"It bathes the bereaved animal in confusion?"

"He doesn't know which way to look. But enough of a
distasteful subject. Tell me more about these changes that
you have observed. In what other respect does the New York
of today differ from the New York of 1904?"

"One notices an extraordinary improvement in the manners
of the populace."

"You find them polished these days?"

"They are all as polite as pallbearers. It may be Emily Post's[2]
daily advice on deportment that has brought about the change.
Or perhaps it is because I have been over here, setting them a
good example."

"Possibly."

"Probably. When I first came to the country, New Yorkers
were all splendid fellows, but inclined to be a little on the
brusque side. They snarled at you. They shoved you and
asked curtly who you were shoving. At baseball games it was
customary to advocate the assassination of the umpire and to
start the good work off by hurling pop bottles at him. One of
my earliest recollections of the city is of watching a mob of
travelers trying to enter a subway train and getting jammed in
the doorway. Two subway officials were standing on the

2. *Emily Post:* authority on etiquette.

platform, and the first subway official said to the second subway official, 'Pile 'em in, George, pile 'em in.' Whereupon the two put their heads down and took a running dive at the mass like members of a football team bucking the line. It was effective, it was as though those passengers had been shot out of a gun, but it could not happen today."

"I get what you mean. George and his colleague would at least say 'Pardon us, gentlemen.' "

"Exactly. You see it everywhere, this new courtesy. Billy Rose recalls the occasion when he was driving his car and stalled the engine at a street intersection. The lights changed from green to red and from red back to green again, but Billy continued to maintain his status quo. A policeman came over. 'What's the matter, son?' he asked sympathetically. 'Haven't we any colors you like?' "

"He could scarcely have been nicer, could he?"

"Boxers, too, not so long ago a somewhat uncouth section of the community who were seldom if ever mistaken for members of the Vere de Vere family, have now a polish which makes their society a pleasure. There was a boxer at the St. Nicholas Rink not long ago who came up against an antagonist with a disagreeably forceful left hook which he kept applying to the jaw and the lower ribs. The victim's manager watched pallidly from outside the ropes, and when his tiger came back to his corner at the end of the round he was all concern and compassion.

" 'Joey,' he asked anxiously, 'how do you feel?'

" 'Fine, thank you,' said the boxer. 'And you?' One can almost hear Emily Post cheering in the background."

"Quite."

"Even the criminal classes have caught the spirit. From Passaic, New Jersey, comes the news that an unidentified assailant plunged a knife into the shoulder of James F. Dobson, spun him around and then, seeing his face, uttered a sharp exclamation. 'Oh, I beg your pardon,' he said. 'I got the wrong guy.'

"Frank and manly. It was what Emily Post has always insisted on. If you find yourself in the wrong, admit it and apologize."

"What you say is very gratifying, Mr. Wodehouse. Then America is all right, you think?"

"With one grave exception. I allude to the matter of divorce."

"Too much of it, you feel?"

"Too little, my good sir. It's heartbreaking. When Australia regained the Davis Cup, there was not unnaturally chagrin and disappointment and a tendency on the part of the citizenry to let the upper lip unstiffen a bit, but the downhearted were able to console themselves with the reflection that, whatever might happen on the tennis court, in one field America still led the world. Her supremacy in the matter of divorce remained unchallenged. Patriots pointed with pride at the figures, which showed that while thirteen—I think it was thirteen—in every thousand American ever-loving couples decided each year to call it a day, the best the nearest competitor, Switzerland, could do was three. 'As long as we have Arline Judge, Hollywood film stars and Tommy Manville,'[3] people told one another, 'we're all right. Come the three corners of the world in arms, and we shall shock them.' And, of course, at times they did, considerably.

"But now there has been a rude awakening. We learn from the New York *Daily Mirror* that 'an amazing thing has been happening, little noticed, in our national life. Since 1946 there has been a forty-per-cent decline in the number of divorces.' Just like that. No preparation, no leading up to it, no attempt to break the thing gently. It is as if the *Mirror* had crept up behind America and struck her on the back of the head with a sock full of wet sand.

"The paper omits to mention what is happening in Switz-

3. *Arline Judge . . . Tommy Manville:* actress and millionaire playboy, each of whom was married several times.

erland, but one assumes that the Swiss are still plugging along in the old dogged way and maybe by this time have got up to five or even six per thousand. For don't run away with the idea that the Swiss do nothing but yodel and make milk chocolate. They have plenty of leisure, be well assured, for divorce actions. Probably at this very moment some citizen of the inland republic is on the witness stand showing the judge the lump on his head where the little woman hit him with a cuckoo clock."

"And where do you place the blame?"

"Certainly not on Hollywood. The spirit of the men there is splendid. Every day one reads in the gossip columns another of those heart-warming announcements to the effect that Lotta Svelte and George Marsupial are holding hands and plan to merge as soon as the former can disentangle herself from Marcus Manleigh and the latter from Belinda Button, and one knows that George and Lotta are not going to let the side down. In due season she will be in court telling the judge that for a week the marriage was a very happy one, but then George started reading the paper at breakfast and refusing to listen when she told him of the dream she had had last night, thus causing her deep mental distress. No, the heart of Hollywood is sound."

"It may be that it is the judges who are lacking in team spirit. A great deal must always depend on the judges."

"Some of them are all right. Not a word of complaint about the one in Hackensack, who recently granted Mrs. Carmella Porretta a divorce because her husband, Salvatore, struck her with a buttered muffin. We applaud also his learned brother in Indianapolis who allowed Mrs. Dorothy Whitehouse to sever the knot because her husband, Donald, insisted on buying the groceries and always brought home ham, to which she was allergic. But what are we to say of Domestic Relations Judge Richard Douglass of Knoxville, who, when Mrs. Edna Hunt Tankersley applied to him for her twelfth divorce, callously informed her that as far as he was concerned she had got her 'final final decree'? In other words, when this devoted woman, all eagerness to see America first, comes up for the thirteenth time, her industry and determination will be un-rewarded. No baker's dozen for Edna, unless, of course, she is shrewd enough to take her custom elsewhere.

"Has Judge Douglass never reflected that it is just this sort of thing that discourages ambition and is going to hand the world's leadership to the Swiss on a plate with watercress round it?

"Nor are all the states pulling their weight. Some are above reproach. In Washington, for instance, there are eleven sep-arate and distinct grounds for divorce. But in South Carolina divorce is actually not permitted. Can one be surprised that the Swiss, who pull together as one man in every patriotic movement, are steadily creeping up and likely to forge ahead at any moment?"

"Of course, we may be in just a temporary slump. You know how these strange lapses from form happen from time to time. Willie Mays[4] couldn't hit a thing at the beginning of last season. Maybe we have become overconfident. Or do you think that the modern American husband, instead of get-ting a divorce, finds it cheaper to dissect his bride with the meat ax and deposit the debris in a sack in the back yard?"

"I doubt it. One has heard, of course, of the man in Chicago named Young who once, when his nerves were unstrung, put his wife, Josephine, in the chopping machine and canned her and labeled her 'Tongue,' but as a rule the American wife does not murder easy."

"You have some special case in mind?"

"I was thinking of the young husband and wife in Cali-fornia. For three or four days, it seems, theirs was a happy marriage, but then, and as so often happens, the husband be-

4. *Willie Mays:* baseball player.

came restless and anxious for a change. At first he thought of divorce, and then he thought again and remembered the Californian community law which gives the sundered wife half her husband's property. And he was just reconciling himself to putting a new coat of paint on her and trying to make her do for another year, when an idea struck him. Why not say it with rattlesnakes?"

"Odd how one has these inspirations."

"So he got a rattlesnake and put it in the pocket of his trousers and hung the trousers over a chair in the bedroom, and when his wife asked him for some money, he told her she would find his wallet in his trousers pocket,

" 'In the bedroom,' he said, and she went into the bedroom, whence her voice presently emerged.

" 'Which trousers?'

" 'The gray ones.'

" 'The ones hanging on the chair?'

" 'That's right.'

" 'Which pocket?'

" 'The hip pocket.'

" 'But I've looked there,' said his wife discontentedly, 'and all I could find was a rattlesnake.' "

2

"So you see it is not so simple."

"Still, if we pull shoulder to shoulder . . . What is needed is something in the nature of a crusade."

"I intend to start one."

"Ah yes, you have recently become an American citizen, have you not?"

"I have, and a red-blooded one, at that. I had always been a sort of honorary American, but it seemed to me that the time had come when I ought to start running things. There will be a lot of changes around here, now I've got the vote.

I shall take a firm line with juvenile delinquency, for instance. It is getting so nowadays that you can't go for a stroll without having some teen-ager hold you up with a gun and stick lighted matches between your toes. I shall vote against this."

"What are your views on referendum and the initiative?"

"Yes."

"And housing conditions?"

"I am in favor of them."

"Will you vote Democrat or Republican?"

"Probably."

"Thank you, Mr. Wodehouse."

To Enrich Your Reading

If P. G. Wodehouse were preparing this section of the book, he might entitle it *Spoiling the Fun*. There is nothing like careful analysis to take the joy out of humor, especially humor so light and frothy as *America, I Like You*. And yet (watch that *yet*, Mr. Wodehouse would admonish us), there are ideas behind each chapter's store of humor. To focus on some of the ideas, as well as to savor the humor itself, the following questions—with apologies—are presented.

CHAPTER 1

1. What human ability is praised in the anecdotes of the two explorers and the taxi driver? To what extent does Wodehouse have this ability?
2. What reasons does Wodehouse give for not writing an autobiography?
3. What is the point of the story about the poet Tennyson and Harold Nicolson?

CHAPTER 2

4. In telling how he was fired from his bank job, Wodehouse may have exaggerated a bit. What parts of the account, however, strike you as probably truthful?
5. What does Wodehouse mean by the chapter title, *An Old Sweetheart Who Has Put on Weight?* How appropriate do you think it is?

CHAPTER 3

6. How would you describe Wodehouse's attitude toward Archie's "magnetism"?

CHAPTER 4

7. How has Bartlett been a "friend to authors"? What does Wodehouse imply about authors, including himself, who make liberal use of him?
8. What criticisms are made of girls and villains in suspense stories? From suspense books you have read (and movies you have seen), how justified do these criticisms seem to you?

CHAPTER 5

9. What does Wodehouse imply about his books when he notes their popularity among invalids?

CHAPTER 6

10. What moral is there to the story of Mrs. Hodges and the meteorite?
11. How does Wodehouse document his statement that "humorists have been scared out of the business by the touchiness now prevailing in many sections of the community"? To what extent would you agree or disagree with the statement?

CHAPTER 7

12. In his novels, two of Wodehouse's chief character types are English earls and butlers. In chapter 5 there is a discussion of earls; in this chapter, of butlers. Which of the

two types do you think Wodehouse admired more, and for what reasons?

Chapter 8

13. A good example of Wodehouse's ability to find both amusement and significance in everyday things is his treatment of readers' letters to newspapers. What particular amusement and significance does he find in these letters?

Chapter 9

14. Wodehouse has been occasionally criticized for being too flippant about serious things. Do you feel this criticism is applicable to his remarks on crime in New York City? Defend your opinion.

Chapter 10

15. What are Wodehouse's objections to the Schwartz thesis on armadillos? How valid do these objections seem to you? What application might they have to other "scientific" studies?

Chapter 11

16. What aspects of American life is Wodehouse able to spoof through his discussion of the income tax and hurricanes?

Chapter 12

17. What does Wodehouse find especially "gruesome" about television laugh machines?

18. Why does he find the laughter of a studio audience even more objectionable? What is your opinion?

CHAPTER 13

19. Why was Hollywood a bad place for authors, according to Wodehouse?

CHAPTER 14

20. How might a member of the stagehands' union react to Wodehouse's diagnosis of the ills of the American theater?
21. Modern theater practices and the controversy over the authorship of Shakespeare's plays are ridiculed in the fantasy on the writing of *Hamlet*. What points made about each topic amuse you most?

CHAPTER 15

22. Wodehouse expresses views on such miscellaneous aspects of American life as vaudeville, the celebration of Christmas, manners, and marriage. Describe these views, and tell which he seems *least* in earnest about.

Style and Vocabulary

HYPERBOLE, UNDERSTATEMENT, AND EUPHEMISM

Much of the charm and humor in *America, I Like You* lie in the clever turns of phrase. These most often take the forms of *hyperbole, understatement,* and *euphemism. Hyperbole* works through exaggeration, by making a thing seem bigger, better or worse than it is. The description of persons after a big dinner as "full to the eyebrows" is an example.

Understatement, on the other hand, achieves its effect by making a thing seem smaller than it is. To characterize the astonishing growth of New York City by the mild remark that "the dear old place has swollen visibly" is understatement. *Euphemism* scores by making the insignificant sound significant, or an unpleasant thing appear quite normal or pleasant. The reference to thieves as the "criminal classes" is a typical Wodehouse euphemism. Below are ten quotations from *America, I Like You* that are examples of hyperbole, understatement, or euphemism. Some quotations may be examples of two at the same time. See if you can properly label each quotation. (Difficult words whose meanings are necessary to full understanding are italicized. If you do not know their meanings, look them up before you attempt the labeling.)

1. . . . the years fall away, (and) hair sprouts on the vast bare *steppes* of my head. . . .

2. charioteers (for taxi drivers)

3. A certain *anemia* of the *exchequer.* . . .

4. . . . a big-game hunter who has looked his mosquito in the eye and made it wilt can scarcely be expected to take more than a tepid interest in flies. One likes a tang of peril with one's sport.

5. As the father looks at their hideous faces and reflects that he is entitled to knock off a nice little sum per *gargoyle* (as income tax exemptions). . . .

6. . . . even when in repose his face was inclined to be formidable and his eye not the sort of eye you would willingly catch.

7. Most of these (theater people) are *enshrined* in the pages of a book.

8. . . . (he) dashed off a tragedy called *Hamlet.*

9. At baseball games it was customary to advocate the assassination of the umpire and to start off the good work by hurling pop bottles at him.

10. (The boxer) . . . came up against an antagonist with a disagreeably forceful left hook which he kept applying to the jaw and lower ribs.

Slang and Colloquialisms

As a writer with a keen ear for spoken language, Wodehouse brightens his pages with a choice use of slang and colloquialisms. Some of his expressions are distinctly British; others have a definite American flavor. Although now quite common, all of them, if heard for the first time, are vivid and special in a way that more formal language often is not. Below, in italics, are a few samplings. See if you can translate them into conventional English.

1. No fifty *fish*, no interview.
2. . . . when it comes to being expected to *hobnob* with ghastly outsiders . . . .
3. I even wrote a series of *whodunits*.
4. When we old *dodderers* speak of butlers . . . .
5. I was enabled to . . . *get into the chips*.
6. . . . his supporting cast started *hogging* the comedy.
7. . . . mine is not a mind *to be sneezed at*.
8. (pigeons') feet hardened by years of *mooching* around Central Park.
9. . . . as to what it was, he confessed himself *fogged*.
10. You don't want a lot of *guff* about Rockefeller Center.

Literary and Foreign Words

Another characteristic of Wodehouse's style is his deliberate use of literary and foreign words. Where a simple, everyday expression might do, Wodehouse will often choose an uncommon or non-English word for comical effect. It is as though he were making fun of the use of such words while using them himself. The result is a disarming self-mockery.

His description of himself as a "spavined septuagenarian" (a lame seventy-year old) is a typical example. Below in column 1 are some of the literary and foreign words in *America, I Like You*. See if you can match them with their meanings in column 2. If you are puzzled by a foreign word, do not hesitate to use an English dictionary, as all of these words also appear in English writings other than Wodehouse's.

Column 1	*Column 2*
1. impecunious	a. bottle
2. mendicants	b. clothing store
3. shikar	c. ghosts
4. acerbity	d. warrior
5. canaille	e. penniless
6. wraiths	f. beggars
7. guerdon	g. praises
8. imprecations	h. angers
9. coterie	i. hunt
10. carafe	j. waterway
	k. land-measurement
	l. reward
	m. drunkard
	n. lowest class of people
	o. repairers
	p. exclusive group
	q. sharpness
	r. ugly
	s. curses
	t. restaurant

Related Activities

1. In the last chapter of *America, I Like You*, Wodehouse imagines himself interviewed on his impressions of American life. Suppose that you are the reporter conducting

the interview. Write your own account of it, touching on the following subjects not covered in the original interview but discussed in the book: American television and movies, life in the country, scientific method, the income tax, writing letters to editors, and people who interview a celebrity.

2. Write a letter to a newspaper editor expressing your own views on one of the topics in question 1.

3. In *America, I Like You* there are many passing references to figures from history and culture. Below are a few of them. Write a sentence identifying each, using an encyclopedia where necessary: Henry VIII, Ben Jonson, Dr. Samuel Johnson, Cicero, Wilkie Collins, Chekhov, and Greta Garbo.

4. Read a novel by P. G. Wodehouse and report on it to the class. Tell what you think of the characters, setting, humor, and plot.

5. Organize a classroom debate on the topic raised in the chapter, "Francis Bacon and the Play Doctor": *Resolved,* that William Shakespeare is the author of the plays generally attributed to him. (Prepare by doing research on the various theories and their refutations.)

6. In *America, I Like You* there are amusing imaginary accounts of how *Hamlet* and Bartlett's *Familiar Quotations* got written. Write such an account of the origins of *Webster's Dictionary*, the *Encyclopedia*, or any of the works in this textbook.

7. There are a number of comic verses in *America, I Like You.* In keeping with their spirit, write a review of *America, I Like You* in verse.

QUESTIONS FOR COMPARATIVE STUDY

1. "Men at some time are masters of their fates," wrote Shakespeare. Compare the extent to which Michael Henchard, Heinrich Schliemann, Henry Higgins, and P. G. Wodehouse appear to be masters or victims of their fates.
2. Compare Schliemann's and Wodehouse's reasons for making their first trips to America. How are these reasons justified by events?
3. America also has a symbolic meaning for each of the men. Tell what it is, and whether it seems supported by the facts of American life.
4. What similarities of character do you note in Henchard, Schliemann, and Higgins? What important differences are there?
5. Compare the attitudes toward women of each of these men. Which do you think shows the most consideration for women? Justify your choice.
6. How are Eliza Doolittle and Elizabeth-Jane Newson different persons at the end of their stories from what they are at the beginning?
7. In your opinion, are these changes more the result of their education (i.e., Eliza's lessons from Higgins and Elizabeth-Jane's course of independent reading) or their other experiences? Justify your answer.
8. Which character arouses in you the greater sympathy and admiration, Higgins or Henchard? Explain your reaction.
9. The plots of *The Mayor of Casterbridge* and *Pygmalion* each flow from an unusual upset in human relationships.

What changes in society have taken place since the mid-nineteenth century for *The Mayor of Casterbridge* and the early twentieth century for *Pygmalion* that make those events less likely to occur today?

10. Poverty plays an important role in the lives of Henchard, Eliza, and Schliemann. How does each of these persons react to it?

11. What in the emotional relationship of Schliemann and his second wife, Sophia, resembles the relationship of Higgins and Eliza? What differences are there?

12. What qualities do Archie of *America, I Like You* and Alfred Doolittle of *Pygmalion* have in common? Which character is the more interesting and amusing, and for what reasons?

13. Compare Wodehouse's attitudes and ideas about class relationships, as evidenced by his discussions of earls and butlers as well as various random remarks, with those of Shaw.

14. Which "lower-class" characters are made to seem more appealing to you, Hardy's Peter's Finger crowd or Shaw's slum cockneys, and for what reasons?

15. In a novel the characters and events are largely imaginary; in a biography they are based on what has actually happened. Yet a novelist is bound to some extent by the facts of history and reality, and a biographer may use creative imagination in providing background and interpretation. Cite specifically important factual elements furnished by Hardy in *The Mayor of Casterbridge*, and creative contributions made by Payne in *The Gold of Troy*.

16. The spell of ancient Greece permeates three works in this volume. In *The Mayor of Casterbridge* it is the concept of tragedy; in *The Gold of Troy* it is the Homeric world; in *Pygmalion* it is an old myth given new application. After becoming better acquainted with our Greek heritage through readings in Aristotle's *Poetics* (for his definition

of tragedy), Homer's *Iliad* and *Odyssey*, and Bulfinch's *Mythology* (for the Pygmalion and other myths), show what Greek influences figure in the works, and in what ways.

17. The authors of *Pygmalion*, *The Mayor of Casterbridge*, and *America, I Like You* all have keen ears for regional and class differences in speech. Draw up a chart with headings for each of these works, and under the headings list as many examples of different types of speech as you can. For example, under *America, I Like You* you might note: "I was goin' over to Philadelphia to see a fight, Hype, and my manager asks me would I like to meet Joe Gans."—lower-class urban American.

18. If a playwright like Shaw were to write a play about Heinrich Schliemann, viewing him more as a comic than as a heroic figure, on what phases of his career might he concentrate? What aspects of his character do you think he would stress?

19. Among its many values, literature deepens our knowledge of human nature. What would you say are the chief insights into the nature of man to be drawn from each of the books in this volume?

20. If you were given the choice of one of the books in this volume for re-reading five years from now, which would you choose and why?